For Clare

Published by Big Finish Productions Ltd
PO Box 1127
Maidenhead
Berkshire
SL6 3LW

www.bigfinish.com

The Big Finish Companion – Volume 1 © Richard Dinnick 2011

Managing Editor: Jason Haigh-Ellery

ISBN: 978-1-84435-524-2
Cover and interior design by Alex Mallinson
Layout by Anthony Lamb
Editor: Mark Wright

First published November 2011

The Big Finish Companion – Volume 1 © Richard Dinnick

Printed and bound in Great Britain by Biddles Ltd
www.biddles.co.uk

THE BIG FINISH COMPANION

VOLUME I

FOREWORD BY
COLIN BAKER

RICHARD DINNICK

AFTERWORD BY
DAVID WARNER

CONTENTS

FOREWORD BY COLIN BAKER

When my 'Abrupt Finish' terminated my tenure as the Doctor in 1986, I thought that was it. But the old adage 'Never Say Never' proved true. In 1989, I was asked to reprise my role for *The Ultimate Adventure* on stage. And even this 'Second Finish' proved to be far from 'ultimate'. Exactly ten years later, Big Finish hove into view and Peter, Sylvester and I recorded **The Sirens of Time** written and directed by Nick Briggs.

That began what was certainly to be a renaissance and reformation combined for old Sixie. The vision, enterprise and commercial courage of Jason Haigh-Ellery, Gary Russell and Nick Briggs originally, and latterly David Richardson too, have allowed me (and I am sure all the other willing refugees from the TV series) to develop and extend our Doctors, companions and other characters beyond the restricting confines of a visual medium into the even wider realms of imagination that an audio-only medium allows. As a result, I still look the same as I did in 1986, so do Peter and Sylvester (actually they do pretty much, darn it) – but I think you know what I mean.

If ever a subject were ideal for audio then it must be **Doctor Who**. Writers can be completely free to create landscapes and scenarios exponentially wider and more diverse than certainly could have been conveyed on TV back in the 80's, although undoubtedly video technology has now moved on. And when a character says 'That is the most beautiful man/woman/ flower/alien artefact' I have ever seen, none of our expectations are confounded or disappointed as we, the listeners are the set designers and visualisers.

I know I speak for all my colleagues when I say that a diary that does not have a future engagement to record a Big Finish story in it is a barren one. They are wonderfully made, lovingly and lavishly post-produced and so far have not exhausted the seemingly limitless creativity and imagination of an ever-growing pool of writers.

Of course, Big Finish now produces so much more than **Doctor Who**. But it began with us… And long may it continue.

Colin Baker

August 2011

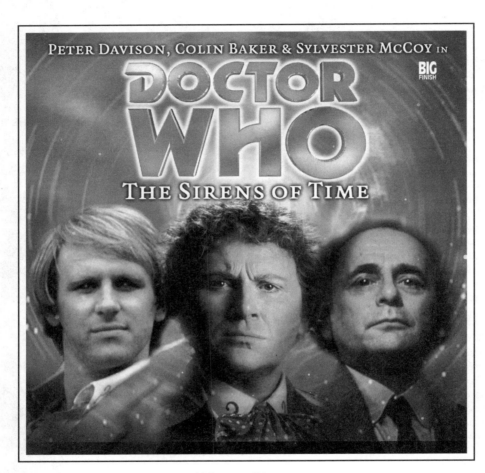

Where it all began…

INTRODUCTION

This book can trace its origins back to a meeting I had with Jason Haigh-Ellery in March of 2009. Amongst other things, I floated the idea of using the Big Finish magazine, *Vortex*, as a place to continue the work begun by Benjamin Cook in his seminal *Doctor Who: The New Audio Adventures: The Inside Story*. It then developed into an email conversation with David Richardson and I started work on the 51st **Doctor Who** release, **The Wormery**, which was due to see publication in May 2009.

While I was busy taking up Gary Russell's time in Cardiff and pestering poor Paul Magrs and Steve Cole, a halt was called to proceedings. Jason, Nick and David didn't think *Vortex* was the right outlet for that sort of content. So, we began discussing the possibility of a new book instead. At this stage, the subject matter was going to be purely **Doctor Who** related and – given the experience of clearing rights for Simon Guerrier's *Bernice Summerfield: the Inside Story* book – Jason emails me on 4 August to say that Big Finish were going to drop the idea.

Meanwhile things ticked over with John Dorney asking me to co-write a *Bernice Summerfield* play and Paul Spragg asking me to attend a writers' meeting for a third season of *Stargate* audios. In January 2010, as I was preparing to head out to LA to attend the Gallifrey One convention, I received an email from Jason saying that he and Nick wanted to discuss a behind-the-scenes episode guide type thing with me.

So that is what we did. To begin with, the new book was simply called the Big Finish Episode Guide. I came up with the name Companion in my initial breakdown of what was going into each volume during March 2010. We also agreed a delivery date of July.

Then I started work on it.

I don't think I will ever be able to convey the amount of work one of these books involves. Simon Guerrier very kindly offered some sage advice on putting such a tome together (and *The Big Finish Companion* is not as complex as his Benny book). I do not think any of us quite envisaged how much time would be needed to do justice to the 214 plays this volume contains.

It has been a joy and a captivating journey of discovery, and re-listening to the output of Big Finish cannot be described as a chore! However, what it comes back to is time – I estimate somewhere in the region of 2,000 hours all told spread between April and November 2010 writing what amounts to about 300,000 words. So my sincere apologies for the tardiness of this book, but we all wanted to ensure that it was as good as it could possibly be.

For each section is a mini Inside Story in its own right. Each play had to be listened to and synopsised. Facts had to be unearthed; a great many writers, actors, directors, producers and other artists had to be approached and, in some cases, interviewed. I hope you think it has been worth the extra months' wait.

It has been a privilege to spend so much time in the company of Big Finish and its people. I hope you will find your time equally well spent and that the Big Finish Companion proves as fascinating a book to read as I have found it to write.

Richard Dinnick

SECTION 1

DOCTOR WHO – MAIN MONTHLY RANGE

February 1999: Mike Tyson, the former heavyweight boxing champion is sentenced to a year's imprisonment for assault, US President Bill Clinton is acquitted in his impeachment trial and Pluto – now classed as a 'dwarf planet' – moved past Neptune to resume its more usual position as the outermost planet. Along with these events, it was in the stars that the BBC's largely ignored property, **Doctor Who**, was about to get a much-needed shot in the arm. But the story of Big Finish Productions actually begins three years earlier…

In 1996, Gary Russell had just written the novelisation of the **Doctor Who** TV movie for BBC Books and was discussing the possibility of doing official *Doctor Who* audio dramas with Nicholas Briggs. They both thought it was a great idea, so an approach was made to the BBC about obtaining a licence for a series of new **Doctor Who** audio adventures starring Eighth Doctor Paul McGann. 'They very quickly came back to us and said "Yeah… No. Goodbye",' explains Gary. 'At the time they thought the movie would spearhead a whole new series, so that died a death.'

Gary decided that audio adventures were still worth pursuing and he went on to secure the rights to produce the **Bernice Summerfield** range. That story is covered in section 8 of this volume and more comprehensively in **Bernice Summerfield: The Inside Story**.

'It was actually the BBC that approached us to do *Doctor Who*,' says Gary. Stephen Cole, at the time in charge of merchandising **Doctor Who** at BBC Worldwide, had heard the **Bernice Summerfield** plays produced by Big Finish and was very impressed. So impressed that he played them to his superiors at the BBC. Cole convinced BBC Radio Collection that they should stick to releasing broadcast **Doctor Who** stories as audio CDs, which were quite successful, and let Big Finish take the risk of producing original, full-cast plays. 'It was the most flattering thing in the world,' says Gary.

'Gary knew I was a businessman but with a love of science fiction,' says Jason Haigh-Ellery, Managing Director of Big Finish. 'He wanted me to run the business side of things as he was completely capable of running the production side.' As it happens the business side of things was not that big a concern in the planning stages… 'The original plan was for us to do six **Doctor Who** releases a year…' Only six? 'Yep. That was the plan. We didn't perceive that there would be a big enough demand to do more.'

At the time, Gary Russell was freelance, having just given up the editorship of *Doctor Who Magazine*. 'The audios were going to be part of his freelance income – not a full-time job!' says Jason.

In January 1999, Gary organised a meeting of potential writers to which he invited Peter Anghelides, Nick Briggs, Paul Cornell, Steve Cole (who would act as executive producer for BBC Worldwide), Mark Gatiss, Andy Lane, Alistair Lock, Steven Moffat, Marc Platt, Jacqueline Rayner, Justin Richards and Mike Tucker. Peter Anghelides could not attend, while Steven Moffat left early. 'I think he was only interested in being involved if we were creating a new Doctor,' says Gary. 'I do wonder if we'd had McGann from the off, whether Steven would have written for us.'

From this meeting, the initial run of plays was sketched out and writers, plotlines and directing duties allocated. Then in February 1999, Jason and Gary made the news public at the Gallifrey One convention in Los Angeles. The news was also announced in issue 275 of *Doctor Who Magazine* with an official press release following in April.

Big Finish then approached the four surviving actors who had portrayed the Doctor on television – Tom Baker, Peter Davison, Colin Baker and Sylvester McCoy. At this stage, they did not approach Paul McGann. Of the four, only Tom Baker was – at the time – not interested in recreating the part on audio.

Nick Briggs was chosen to write the first **Doctor Who** play. 'My first thought was that if we're doing a **Doctor Who** story, it's got to have Daleks in it,' he says. 'But Jason was still negotiating for the rights to use them, so I thought, well, it's got to be a multi-Doctor story to lay our wares out for the audience. I instantly had the idea that we would give each of those Doctors an adventure, and then bring them all together for the multi-Doctor element in the final episode.'

After settling on the format of the play, Nick initially considered a rematch between the Doctor and the War Lord (from the 1969 TV story **The War Games**), but Gary Russell pointed out that Terrance Dicks had already done something similar in the Virgin New Adventures novel *Timewyrm: Exodus*. Briggs explains: 'I never really read the books… I didn't want to create an alien that just twiddled its moustache and said "I is evil". So I came up with **The Sirens of Time**.'

The Sirens of Time #1 was released in July 1999. 'When we launched the range, we did it properly,' says Jason. 'It was the first time a CD had been on the cover of *Doctor Who Magazine* and everyone really bought into the idea of old Doctors in studio recording new stories. It was new and exciting! DWM got behind it. At the time this was really useful for them because they could write pages and pages about Big Finish and in one issue I think there were 20 pages all about us! That

RELEASES #1 - #75

wasn't every issue, but it was a good relationship that worked for both of us.'

Two months later, the second **Main Monthly Range** release, **Phantasmagoria #2** by Mark Gatiss, was released, and from the start of 2000, the releases went monthly. 'I can't remember who broached it first, but it was obvious to Gary and me that the sales we were having meant we could afford to record at a faster rate,' says Jason. 'It was a very important moment for Big Finish because if we hadn't had that successful launch we would probably have continued in a semi-fan sort of way doing one every two months and then it may have died after two years.'

Big Finish Productions has gone on to release at least one **Doctor Who** story every month for over 10 years asserts Jason. 'I never dreamt we'd have done that! If we'd come out of it having done 30 releases over five years, I would have been very happy!'

The fact Big Finish continues to develop is a testament to both the company and **Doctor Who** itself. Jason Haigh-Ellery is keen to point out the importance of subscribers to Big Finish. 'It was the subscription money that allowed us to do it professionally,' he says. 'I have always been very, very grateful to the subscribers – especially those who have been with us for years – because they helped invest in new **Doctor Who**. That's why we're always very happy to give away subscriber freebies!'

In addition to the three returning Doctors, Big Finish approached and contracted the various

actors who had played their companions on television: Mark Strickson (Turlough), Nicola Bryant (Peri), Sarah Sutton (Nyssa) and Sophie Aldred (Ace). Though they would later create new companions to accompany the Doctors, this was not something that had been planned from the start, as Gary Russell explains: 'I don't think we'd ever seriously thought about creating new companions for any of the TV Doctors. We were either going to have Doctors on their own or Doctors with their TV companions.

Nevertheless, the team eventually decided to create a new character to accompany Colin Baker as the Sixth Doctor: Dr Evelyn Smythe. The creation of Evelyn's character is examined alongside her first story – **The Marian Conspiracy #6** – later in this section.

Just before Gary conceived Evelyn in a swimming pool (more on which later), Jason Haigh-Ellery had received notice from Roger Hancock Limited (the company that handles the Terry Nation estate) that Big Finish could use the Daleks. Indeed, within the first year, Big Finish had brought back the Daleks, the Ice Warriors and Brigadier Lethbridge-Stewart. 'Old aspects of the show are great,' says Gary, 'as long as they are used intelligently.'

The following year saw Lalla Ward and Bonnie Langford reprise their roles as Romana II and Mel

Above:
Early days – the assembled cast of
Phantasmagoria, Big Finish's second **Doctor**
Who audio release, during recording in June 1999.

SECTION 1

respectively, while new stories were written for series classics, the Master and the Silurians. Perhaps the most unlikely companion to see his debut in an audio drama was one from the *Doctor Who Magazine* comic trip… Frobisher.

'I'll tell you why we did Frobisher,' says Gary Russell. 'Because we thought it'd be a laugh! We thought it would be a funny thing and Rob (Shearman) had done this brilliant script and I said, 'let's stick a penguin in there'!' How did Rob take the inclusion of the talking penguin in November 2000's **The Holy Terror #14**? 'I think he looked at me like I'd just weed all over his favourite cushion. Then he went away and put Frobisher in it,' says Gary. 'And Robert Jezek was the only person I ever thought of to play Frobisher.'

2001 was notable as the year Big Finish secured the talents of Paul McGann and started to release complete seasons of new adventures for the Eighth Doctor. Because Hollywood studio Universal owned the rights to the characters in the 1996 TV movie – other than the Doctor – Big Finish could not use the character of Grace Holloway. 'That said,' adds Gary, 'having created Evelyn it was easy to say we wanted to create someone new for Paul…'

Gary Russell was set on the idea of having a holiday rep as the Doctor's new companion. Jason was not as keen, wanting someone that was out of her time in a similar vein to the Second Doctor's companion, Victoria Waterfield. When Alan Barnes hit upon the idea of setting the first story aboard the doomed airship R101, Gary and Jason had their compromise – the 1930s – and Charlotte Pollard was born (played by India Fisher).

That same year, Erimem was introduced as a new companion for the Fifth Doctor. Again, this companion would be out of her own time, but even more so as she was an Egyptian Princess from 1419 BC. The character first appeared in **The Eye of the Scorpion #24** by Iain McLaughlin, commissioned as part of the open submissions window the previous year.

2002 opened with a second season of Eighth Doctor stories and saw the return of the Nimon, the Daleks (the first time the Eighth Doctor would meet them), Romana and Rassilon. The latter two appeared in the stunning season finale by Alan Barnes called **Neverland #33**, which saw the Doctor possessed by the evil anti-time entity, Zagreus.

Below:
Keeping it in the family – Georgia Moffett joins her father, Peter Davison, for the recording of **Red Dawn** in November 1999.

Opposite page:
The Sixth Doctor (Colin Baker) and President Romana (Lalla Ward) were reunited on Gallifrey in **The Apocalypse Element.**

2002 also saw the release of Marc Platt's much admired **Spare Parts #34**, a story that (along with Rob Shearman's **The Holy Terror #14**) would go on to be described by Russell T Davies as 'some of the finest drama ever written for any genre, in any medium, anywhere' and form the inspiration behind the 2006 TV stories **Rise of the Cybermen** and **The Age of Steel**.

The year culminated with a trilogy of villainous tales for Omega, Davros and the Master reaching a crescendo with Big Finish's 50th *Doctor Who* story, **Zagreus**, which picked up where **Neverland #33** had left off, taking the Eighth Doctor in a totally new direction. This direction required another new companion and so the first alien from another universe came aboard the TARDIS in the form of C'rizz (played by Conrad Westmaas).

Explains Gary: 'We initially talked it over – Jason and [assistant producer] Ian Farrington and me – and what we wanted to do was take the Doctor out of his comfort zone and take the audience out of its comfort zone, too. No Daleks, no Cybermen, no Gallifrey. And I thought that was daring!'

'The thing I never got to grips with – and I discussed this with Alan Barnes – was the different physics of a new universe.' Instead, this new universe was to have no linear time. 'That became a concept that writers found very difficult. If you want one thing from me in this book where I say, "that was a mistake", then this is it! I shouldn't have done it because I didn't think it through. I was too headstrong and arrogant.'

The original plan was to have the Eighth Doctor trapped in the Divergent Universe for three years. Gary thinks he should probably have retired Charley at that stage, too. 'What Russell T Davies would have done at the end of **Scherzo #52** is he would have written Charley out and said 'your story has come to an end',' Gary explains. 'I, being less sensible and less practical says, "I love working with India; I don't want to get rid of her"'.

In September 2003 the BBC announced that a new series of *Doctor Who* was in the pipeline with writer Russell T Davies at the helm. It would not be on television screens for another two years, but the Big Finish team knew it was coming and had to make – and alter – plans accordingly.

For example, although the Doctor and Charley had only just entered the Divergent Universe and teamed up with C'rizz, it was felt that they should return to our universe at the end of the following Eighth Doctor season. That season was pulled forward in the schedule so that new listeners could join the Eighth Doctor on his adventures any time after the broadcast of the first new TV story, **Rose**, in March 2005.

One aspect of the original plan that stayed was the idea of C'rizz committing suicide. 'It was always the intention that right at the end – and I said this to Conrad – that C'rizz was going to commit suicide. At that time it was going to be at the end of the Divergent arc, rather than 20 years later!'

Gary also had a clear idea of how that would have happened. 'I wanted this story where the Doctor is lost inside the TARDIS and the walls are covered in blood and chains – like in the horror movie *Hellraiser* – in which C'rizz would have sacrificed himself to reunite the Doctor and Charley while providing the gateway back into the normal universe.'

The curtailment of the arc meant that certain stories had their universal setting changed. **Scaredy Cat #75**, **Time Works #80** and **Something Inside #83** would have formed part of the third Divergent season. As such, **Terror Firma #72** and **Other Lives #77** were commissions drafted in at a late stage.

'It was always leading to **Absolution #101**, which was always going to be by Scott Alan Woodard,' says Gary. 'That would have led into **The Next Life #64** by Alan Barnes and myself, which would have finished off Rassilon and sealed the Divergent Universe.'

THE LAND OF THE DEAD

#4

SYNOPSIS

Tracking strange power readings to Alaska, the Doctor and Nyssa find a curious house built into a cliff face. They are attacked by an unseen monster and take refuge inside the building, where they meet Monica, Tulung, Gaborik and Brett, all involved in the creation of a 'house' that celebrates the life of Brett's father. He died some 30 years ago when a local archaeological dig was destroyed in mysterious circumstances. Each room in the house is constructed from an individual earth 'element' (timber, bone, ice, etc) and Nyssa is attacked by 'hybrid' monsters in the Ocean room. Gaborik saves her and tells her that the composite creatures are figures form the Inuit legend of Sedna, the sea spirit that was betrayed by her father and now rules over Adlivum – the land of the dead. They have been angered and want revenge… However the Doctor theorises that the animals are regenerating themselves, creating the hybrids. He sends Nyssa to the old archaeological camp where she can examine the samples. She discovers that the bone fragment is over 260 million years old – part of the Permian era – a period of pre-history during which 96 per cent of all life on Earth was wiped out. The Doctor then concludes that these creatures, which he calls Permians, are native to Earth and evolved a bioelectric field that weakens their prey. He says they must have wiped out most other life forms and then turned on each other, leaving a remnant to fall dormant and become fossilised. All the Earth elements in Brett's house have awakened the Permians, whose numbers are now large enough to form a pack and breed. Deducing that the archaeological dig of 30 years ago was destroyed by his father using dynamite, Brett tries something similar, killing himself and all but two Permians. The Doctor lures the surviving creatures back to the house where he burns it to the ground, destroying the last Permians.

PLACEMENT

Between the TV story **Time-Flight** and Big Finish audio adventure **Winter for the Adept #10**.

TRIVIA

- **The Land of the Dead** was Stephen Cole's first script for Big Finish.
- The CD release included a floor plan of the building. This was a bit of fun on Gary's part. "I was ripping off Malcolm Hulke's Target novelisation of *The Cave Monsters* which does the same thing" he says. "It was part homage and part 'what can we put in the CD booklet?', rather than actually being intended as a guide for listeners!"
- Steve Cole was writing children's books based on the BBC series *Walking with Dinosaurs* at the time: hence the use of fossils in this story.
- The script picks up on Nyssa's psychic abilities first seen in 1982's **Time-Flight**, a character arc that Gary Russell was keen to develop for the audio range.
- Cole included many iconic lines from the Fifth Doctor's era on TV such as "I should have known" (from **Earthshock**)!
- The cover features an image of the skull belonging to Jon Merrick, also known as 'The Elephant Man', which was tweaked slightly so that it looked alien and unusual.

PRODUCTION SUMMARY

"The script was written in about a week by Steve Cole because Sylvester wasn't available to record **The Fearmonger #5**, and I didn't want another Colin story so soon after **Whispers**. The only one I trusted other than Justin to deliver in time was Steve. We also only had Peter Davison for part of the time, so it was a bit of a mixed bag production-wise."
Gary Russell

WORKING TITLE(S)

The story had the working titles of both 'Adlivum' and its translation: 'Land of the Dead' (minus the definite article).

RETURNING MONSTERS/CHARACTERS

None.

CREW

Writer	**Stephen Cole**
Director	**Gary Russell**
Producers	**Jason Haigh-Ellery**
	Gary Russell
Executive Producer (BBC)	**Stephen Cole**
Music and Sound Design	**Nicholas Briggs**
Cover Art	**Peri Godbold**
Theme	**Delia Derbyshire**

CAST

The Doctor	**Peter Davison**
Nyssa	**Sarah Sutton**
Monica Lewis	**Lucy Campbell**
Supplier	**Alistair Lock**
Shaun Brett	**Christopher Scott**
Tulung	**Neil Roberts**
Gaborik	**Andrew Fettes**

TECHNICAL

Story Code	**6C/A**
Recorded Date	**24 and 25 July 1999**
Release Date	**January 2000**
Place of Recording	**The Nu Groove Studios, London**
Number of CDs	**2 (also released on double cassette)**
Total Duration	**144' 43"**
Number of Episodes	**4**
Duration of Episodes	**1 (31' 10")**
	2 (30' 06")
	3 (25' 35")
	4 (27' 52")
ISBN	**1-84435-064-9**

#5 | THE FEARMONGER

CREW

Writer	**Jonathan Blum**
Director	**Gary Russell**
Producers	**Jason Haigh-Ellery**
	Gary Russell
Executive Producers (BBC)	**Stephen Cole**
	Jacqueline Rayner
Music and Sound Design	**Alistair Lock**
Cover Art	**Clayton Hickman**
Theme	**Delia Derbyshire**

CAST

The Doctor	**Sylvester McCoy**
Ace	**Sophie Aldred**
Sherilyn Harper	**Jacqueline Pearce**
Stephen Keyser	**Mark Wright**
Walter Jacobs	**Mark McDonnell**
Mick Thompson	**Vince Henderson**
Paul Tanner	**Jonathan Clarkson**
Roderick Allingham	**Hugh Walters**
Alexsandr Karadjic	**Jack Galagher**
Hospital Tannoy Voice	**John Ainsworth**
Hospital Doctor, Heckler	**Alistair Lock**

TECHNICAL

Story Code	**7R**
Recorded Date	**4 and 5 September 1999**
Release Date	**February 2000**
Place of Recording	**The Nu Groove Studios, London**
Number of CDs	**2 (also released on double cassette)**
Total Duration	**100' 25"**
Number of Episodes	**4**
Duration of Episodes	**1 (25' 53")**
	2 (26' 06")
	3 (25' 08")
	4 (23' 18")
ISBN	**1-84435-044-4**

SYNOPSIS

In a future Britain, Sherilyn Harper is the leader of the New Britannia Party. She is attracting a growing number of people to her extremist right-wing views through broadcasts and rallies. The TARDIS brings the Doctor and Ace to London on the trail of an energy creature that can disguise itself using others. This 'Fearmonger' feeds on fear and terror and it seems that Walter Jacobs may have found it because he can hear a monstrous voice whenever Harper speaks. He tries to kill Harper, but this makes her more popular and creates an even deeper schism in society. The Doctor, too, thinks that the Fearmonger has taken Harper as a host, but before he can act several terrorist attacks carried out by the newly formed United Front devastate the city of London. They claim to be anti the New Britannia Party and its policies. The Doctor constructs a device that can destroy the monster but leave its host untouched, which he plans to use while radio DJ Mick Thompson interviews Harper on his show. However, when the Doctor

uses the device, he finds that the Fearmonger is not in Harper. Ace then starts to hear the monstrous voice when the Doctor speaks. She believes he has been possessed. Acting alone, the Doctor then tricks Harper's aide Roderick Allingham into a secret meeting with the United Front. Thompson has the meeting bugged and broadcasts it, revealing that New Britannia set up the United Front to purposefully terrorise the people so they would sweep to power on a wave of paranoia. The riots break up and the remaining protestors go to Harper's home to make her pay for the deception. Ace then confronts the Doctor and accuses him of being the Fearmonger. The Doctor points out that the creature must have been in Walter all along and then it switched hosts, but not to him. Ace realizes that she has become increasingly suspicious and paranoid and she must therefore be the new host. She uses the Doctor's device on herself, killing the creature and allowing her to leave with the Time Lord once more.

PLACEMENT

Between the television adventure, **Survival** and Big Finish audio adventure **The Genocide Machine #7**.

TRIVIA

- Jacqueline Pearce, who played Sherilyn Harper, appeared in the 1985 TV story **The Two Doctors** as Chessene, but is also well known for her role as Servalan in *Blake's 7*.
- Hugh Walters (Roderick Allingham) had appeared in three TV stories: as William Shakespeare in **The Chase**; Runcible in **The Deadly Assassin**; and as Vogel in **Revelation of the Daleks**.
- This play replaced a Paul Cornell story, The Summoning (later **The Shadow of the Scourge #13**) when that script was delayed due to a delicate political situation between the BBC and Virgin Books.
- The idea for the story came from an episode of The X-Files and had originally been conceived as a pitch to Bill Baggs's BBV series, *The Professor and Ace*.
- Mark Wright, playing the role of Stephen Keyser, was in studio as a reporter for *SFX* magazine, with the part written specially to give an angle for a feature on Big Finish. This would not be Mark's last appearance in the studio.
- The character of Sherilyn Harper is based on the Australian politician Pauline Hanson and New Britannia on One Nation, the far-right, nationalist political party that Hanson set up.
- Sylvester McCoy almost didn't make it to the studio because (due to a miscommunication) he was working in Scotland. He drove overnight to be in studio in time to make the recording!
- Vince Henderson (Mick Thompson) is the husband of Sophie Aldred.
- This was the first Big Finish release to feature a cover by Clayton Hickman.

PRODUCTION SUMMARY

"I think I wanted a sort of *New Adventures*-style story for the initial Seventh Doctor release and when Paul couldn't deliver, I thought of Jon Blum and Kate Orman as the logical replacements. As it happens, Kate was too busy but Jon already had an idea he was developing so we ran with that. The first draft needed a lot of work and it was all a bit of a rush in the end. I'm not sure we achieved everything we wanted to with the story, but you can't have everything, can you?"
Gary Russell

WORKING TITLE(S)

None.

RETURNING MONSTERS/CHARACTERS

None.

Check box - Cassette ☐ CD ☐ MP3 ☐

THE MARIAN CONSPIRACY

#6

SYNOPSIS

The Doctor tracks down Evelyn Smythe, a history lecturer, and tells her she is a nexus point in Earth's history. She tells him that her Tudor ancestor, John Whiteside-Smith, was important and that Queen Mary had his father executed. As the Doctor examines her family records, they begin to change, erasing Evelyn from the timeline. The pair travel to the Elizabethan era where the Doctor heads off to see the queen while Evelyn visits a local tavern. The Doctor finds Mary, not Elizabeth, on the throne, deduces that the TARDIS arrived too early and manages to ingratiate himself into Mary's court. At the tavern, Evelyn makes the mistake of toasting "Queen Elizabeth" but she is saved by Protestant supporters and taken to the Rev Thomas Smith. However, he thinks the new arrival is a spy. After telling them Mary will never have any children, Evelyn leaves to make sure the Doctor knows it is Mary's reign. Her handbag contains painkillers and the Catholic Bishop of Aix accuses her of being an assassin. The Doctor convinces Mary otherwise and when the queen takes one of Evelyn's pills the pain she has been suffering is relieved. As a reward Mary insists on the Doctor marrying her lady in waiting, Sarah Whiteside. Evelyn thinks that, because he has assumed the name John Smith, the Doctor must be her ancestor's father! When Thomas really does try to poison the queen, the Doctor and Evelyn are arrested as co-conspirators and taken to the Tower of London. There they realise that Sarah is actually secretly married to Rev Thomas Smith. Mary does execute Thomas but spares Sarah because she is pregnant. With history put right, Evelyn insists on staying with the Doctor so she can study history first hand.

PLACEMENT

Between the television adventure, **The Trial of a Time Lord** and **The Spectre of Lanyon Moor #9**.

TRIVIA

- This was Stephen Cole's last story as an Executive Producer for the BBC.
- The initial proposal from Jacqueline Rayner featured Peri, not Evelyn, because the latter's character hadn't been invented at that stage!
- The sixth release was originally pencilled in as a Dalek story to be written by Colin Brake, while Jac was down to provide the eighth story, initially conceived to be a Roman historical.
- The idea that the Doctor would rescue Leaf and Crow's families as well as the men themselves came from Colin Baker and Maggie Stables during recording.
- Jac's family wondered if Evelyn was named after her grandmother, Dorothy Evelyn. She wasn't – the name was thought up by Gary Russell – but still is a nice coincidence.
- Mel Giedroyc and Sue Perkins were originally mentioned in connection with the roles of Lady Sarah and Queen Mary.

PRODUCTION SUMMARY

"I gave the idea of Evelyn to Jac Rayner and she said she could do something with it. And kudos to Jac because she fleshed it all out. She wanted to do a Mary Queen of Scots story and that fitted well with the character. Jac is a wonderful writer and she did such a good job of bringing Evelyn to life. It was a brilliant script, great fun."
Gary Russell

WORKING TITLE(S)

The Maryan Conspiracy (changed due to the 'I' spelling being the more accepted form of the word).

RETURNING MONSTERS/CHARACTERS

None.

CREW

Writer	**Jacqueline Rayner**
Director	**Gary Russell**
Producers	**Jason Haigh-Ellery**
	Gary Russell
Executive Producer (BBC)	**Stephen Cole**
	Jacqueline Rayner
Music and Sound Design	**Alistair Lock**
Cover Art	**Clayton Hickman**
Theme	**Delia Derbyshire**

CAST

The Doctor	**Colin Baker**
Evelyn	**Maggie Stables**
George Crow	**Sean Jackson**
John Wilson	**Gary Russell**
William Leaf	**Jez Fielder**
Lady Sarah	**Jo Castleton**
The Queen	**Anah Ruddin**
Reverend Thomas	**Nicholas Pegg**
Francois De Noailles	**Barnaby Edwards**
Royal Guard	**Alistair Lock**

TECHNICAL

Story Code	**7C/A**
Recorded Date	**23 October 1999**
Release Date	**March 2000**
Place of Recording	**The Nu Groove Studios, London**
Number of CDs	**2 (also released on double cassette)**
Total Duration	**107' 04"**
Number of Episodes	**4**
Duration of Episodes	**1 (24' 29")**
	2 (28' 21")
	3 (25' 07")
	4 (29' 07")
ISBN	**1-903654-17-3**

PROFILE 1

EVELYN SMYTHE

Evelyn Smythe was born in a swimming pool. At least, her character was. 'I was sitting round a hotel swimming pool in the summer of '99 with a load of friends at an American convention, Convergence,' says Gary Russell. 'I asked for a piece of paper and wrote: 'Evelyn Smythe, 60s, history teacher'. And everyone started throwing ideas in: she was into cats; she was into chocolate, blah, blah, blah. Some of these things we kept; some we didn't.'

Originally conceived as being ten years older (65 became 55), Gary only ever had one person in mind to play her. 'The only reason I created Evelyn was purely for Maggie Stables because I love her and she had got on very well with Colin during recording for **The Sirens of Time #1**,' says Gary. 'If I had ever been producer of the TV series, I would have created Evelyn Smythe as the companion. It would be the stupidest thing in the world to do on TV, but it worked on audio.'

Why did she work so well? 'Maggie. Evelyn is Maggie. A smart, intelligent woman who can hold her own with Colin Baker.'

On his return to the UK, Gary sent the basic character outline to Jason Haigh-Ellery, which read: 'Think Amelia Rumford meets Angela Lansbury meets Margaret Rutherford meets Cameca meets Maggie Stables (i.e. that's who's going to play her!)'. He also had to let Jacqueline Rayner know that her proposed historical (March 2000s **The Marian Conspiracy #6**) would not now feature Peri. 'Huge kudos to Jac,' says Gary. 'She fleshed it all out and wrote such a great script.'

In **The Marian Conspiracy**, Evelyn's first trip in the TARDIS would see her meeting Queens Mary and Elizabeth I. Being a doctor of history, she could not resist travelling on with the Doctor to see her subject brought to life by the Time Lord.

Soon she was meeting the Brigadier, facing Daleks on Gallifrey and in the Tower of London (again), as well as battling Silurians with Charles Darwin. 'There's a line from **The Spectre of Lanyon Moor #9** where she uses the word 'yomping',' remembers Gary. 'And that is Evelyn Smythe! That line sums the

Below:
Evelyn's second adventure, **The Spectre of Lanyon Moor,** reunited the Doctor with Brigadier Lethbridge-Stewart.

character up beautifully! Nick Pegg deserves credit for her as well because he gave her so much spunk and guts and intelligence and smarts.'

Although a meeting of great minds, the Doctor and Evelyn's relationship was not always a smooth one. She kept secrets from him – such as her heart condition – and he could often upset her. The most extreme example of this came in **Project: Lazarus #45** in which she blamed the Doctor for the death of Cassie, a young woman she believed the Doctor could have saved. In real life, the opposite was true. 'It was a really good relationship,' says Gary. 'So much of what Colin and Maggie did fed back into what the Doctor and Evelyn did over the next couple of years. It was like *On Golden Pond*. Those two were the Doctor and Evelyn!'

While visiting the planet Világ, Evelyn met and fell in love with Governor Rossiter during an attempted invasion by the Killorans (**Arrangements for War #57**). Not surprisingly, when the Doctor and Evelyn returned to the planet a year later she elected to stay with Rossiter. She became involved in the planet's politics and underwent surgery on her heart.

Later, in **Thicker Than Water #73**, the Sixth Doctor brought his new companion Mel to meet her. During this adventure, Evelyn was kidnapped and fell seriously ill. Fortunately Rossiter's daughter, Sofia, was a doctor and managed to cure her. While recovering she received a visit form the Seventh Doctor. He told her that he was now travelling with Cassie's son (Hex – see his character profile alongside **The Harvest #58**).

The character of Evelyn continued to appear in the **Doctor Who Main Monthly Range** with plays set before her departure on Világ. Evelyn tragically meets her demise in **A Death in the Family #140**. Having found an artifact from a crashed time ship on Világ, she is transported back in time to the year 1871 AC on the planet Pelechan. The details and people from the time ship become the origin of civilization and religion on Pelechan.

There she meets Hex, who is dropped off by the Seventh Doctor so that she can tell him all about his mother, Cassie. Trying to reveal the planet's origins, Evelyn has a heart attack and is attended to by Hex. She then dies, but not in vain. The Seventh Doctor asks Evelyn to trap the Word Lord in her mind as she perishes, fighting to the end as she always had throughout her many adventures.

NB. Evelyn Smyth also accompanied the Sixth Doctor in **Real Time**, a play commissioned as an animated webcast for the BBC **Doctor Who** site (and subsequently released by Big Finish as an audio-only CD).

Above:
The part of Dr Evelyn Smythe was written especially for actress Maggie Stables.

Left:
Living History – Evelyn was able to see the past she loved so much coming alive during her travels with the Doctor.

STORM WARNING

#16

SYNOPSIS

Trying to rid the TARDIS of scavenging vortisaurs, the Doctor materialises aboard the R-101, the doomed airship that crashed and burned on its maiden voyage. Here he meets a plucky young stowaway, Charlotte "Charley" Pollard. Together they discover that one of the passengers, Lord Tamworth (Britain's Minister of the Air), is taking the airship to the extremely dangerous altitude of 5000 feet. The Doctor realises that Tamworth is using the R101 to rendezvous with an alien ship. When he finds that Tamworth is returning a telepathic alien called a Triskele, the Doctor accompanies it back to its ship. Here he discovers that the race is split into three castes: the peaceful Engineers, the violent Uncreators and the one with power over both: the Lawgiver. As neither an Engineer nor an Uncreator can become the next Lawgiver, the Triskelion came to Earth to seek a replacement. However, the Uncreators instigate a riot by telepathically controlling the men aboard the R101. In the melee, British agent Rathbone shoots the Lawgiver dead. The Uncreators are free of the Lawgiver's control and immediately declare war on humanity. As the humans retreat, the Uncreator Prime tries to get Rathbone to kill Tamworth, but the human resists and instead kills the Uncreator Prime. Tamworth agrees to go with the Triskelion as an adviser to help them develop a new way of life. However, once they are gone, Rathbone reveals he has taken an Uncreator weapon – an action that will upset the timelines. He and the Doctor struggle and in the fight, Rathbone ruptures one of the airship's hydrogen tanks before falling to his death. The Doctor rescues Charley by riding a vortisaur to safety as the airship explodes. The Doctor then recalls that there were 54 bodies recovered from the R101. With Tamworth gone the body count will be one person short. Although horrified by the potential paradox, the Doctor decides to let Charley travel with him due to her boundless enthusiasm.

PLACEMENT

Between The TV Movie and **Sword of Orion #17**.

TRIVIA

- Mark Gatiss was a friend of composer David Arnold (famous for composing music for the *James Bond* film series) and suggested that he could provide a new arrangement of the theme. Gary jokingly asked Mark to ask David, never suspecting that he would. "Shortly afterwards, a cassette arrived from David with the theme on," Gary says. "For no fee! I later interviewed David for *Mojo* magazine. He talked about doing it and I revealed that was for me and finally had the chance to thank him personally!"
- When he was writing the story, Alan Barnes imagined the speech patterns of Robert Hardy when scripting Lord Tamworth's dialogue.
- India Fisher had previously appeared in **Winter for the Adept #10** as Peril Bellamy.
- Episode 1 (featuring a different version of the theme) was also included on a free CD, which was cover-mounted on issue 300 of *Doctor Who Magazine*.
- The story was broadcast on BBC 7 in four parts from 6th August 2005 and then again from 27th August 2006.
- This play and the subsequent three feature the **Doctor Who** logo in copper. They are the only ones to do so because the BBC contacted Gary to say they would prefer the logo to be used in blue. "I said I'd prefer not to tweak mid-season but promised it'd go back to blue for the second McGann run," Gary recalls. "And they agreed."
- Alan Barnes came up with the idea for the story after seeing a poster for an unmade Hammer film called 'Zeppelin vs Pterodactyls'.

PRODUCTION SUMMARY

"Alan did a lot of work on Charley but it was me who came up with the R101 stuff. Alan then had to go away and research it. Originally there was some sub-plot in which a clairvoyant was flying the airship but we ditched that. Of course, this was part of the block we recorded at Christchurch studios in Bristol and we actually recorded this story third, I think, after **Sword of Orion** but I remember thinking that we'd got a really good team with Paul and India because they hit it off so well."
Gary Russell

WORKING TITLES(S)

Dirigible of Doom (a joke!), Blood and Thunder.

RETURNING MONSTERS/CHARACTERS

None.

CREW

Writer	**Alan Barnes**
Director	**Gary Russell**
Producers	**Jason Haigh-Ellery**
	Gary Russell
Executive Producer (BBC)	**Jacqueline Rayner**
Music and Sound Design	**Alistair Lock**
Cover Art	**Clayton Hickman**
Theme	**David Arnold**

CAST

The Doctor	**Paul McGann**
Charley	**India Fisher**
Lord Tamworth	**Gareth Thomas**
Lt-Col Frayling	**Nicholas Pegg**
Rathbone	**Barnaby Edwards**
Chief Steward Weeks	**Hylton Collins**
Triskelion	**Helen Goldwyn**
Announcer	**Mark Gatiss**

TECHNICAL

Story Code	**8B**
Recorded Date	**18 May 2000**
Release Date	**January 2001**
Place of Recording	**Christchurch Studios, Bristol**
Number of CDs	**2**
Total Duration	**116' 00"**
Number of Episodes	**4**
Duration of Episodes	**1 (25' 03")**
	2 (25' 29")
	3 (36' 11")
	4 (29' 17")
ISBN	**1-903654-24-6**

PROFILE 2 CHARLOTTE ELSPETH POLLARD

Charley Pollard made her debut in the first of Big Finish's Eighth Doctor releases, **Storm Warning #16**. The character's journey to 1930 was an interesting one that started back in the Victorian era. Her name was always going to be Charley, but Jason Haigh-Ellery wanted someone out of their own time.

'We were thinking that she should be an Edwardian maid – sort of *Upstairs, Downstairs*,' explains Gary Russell. However, the team soon realised that this was too similar to Victoria Waterfield, the Second Doctor's companion played by Deborah Watling.

At the time, Gary had been watching many TV shows about holiday reps so next up, he and Jason discussed a 1950s air stewardess. 'We wanted someone who had a sense of adventure to her,' says Gary. 'And we wanted something of [pioneering British aviator] Amy Johnson about her because when I'd been doing Audio Visuals, if we'd had a fifth season of those we would have introduced her as the companion for Nick's Doctor.'

This rather nebulous character brief was given to writer Alan Barnes who came back with Charlotte Elspeth Pollard and her voyage aboard the doomed airship, the R101.

'Whereas I would stake a claim to Evelyn or Hex, Charley was not mine,' admits Gary. 'What Alan brought to the table with Charley gives him a huge ownership of the character.' The other person that could claim ownership to the character is India Fisher, but it might not have been her playing the role...

At the storyline stage, the age of the character changed and Sarah Mowat, who was being considered for the role (and who played the eponymous Sirens in Big Finish's first ever **Doctor Who** play **The Sirens of Time #1**), had to be replaced by a younger actress. Gary Russell immediately suggested India Fisher, with whom he had worked with on the Fifth Doctor and Nyssa story, **Winter for the Adept #10** only a few weeks previously.

Gary liked Alan's idea for the air disaster and they discussed what should happen in relation to the crash. 'If Evelyn started out with a time paradox, then Charley is the ultimate time paradox...' says Gary. 'It was a nice conceit. It worked well.' Of course, there were other survivors of the R101 disaster in real life (seven in total), but not in the Big Finish **Doctor Who** continuity! 'I remember saying to Alan at the time: "don't worry, you'll never have to resolve this"!'

The character of Charley would go on to have many adventures with the Eighth Doctor, her desire to reach Singapore to meet a mystery man being explored in **Seasons of Fear #30** and the paradox that Gary assured Alan would not be his problem being addressed two years later in the stories **Neverland #33** and **Zagreus #50**. By Alan Barnes.

Other members of Charley's family appeared on audio. Her mother, Lady Louisa Pollard (played by Anneke Wills) appeared in **Zagreus #50**, **The Next Life #64**, and **Memory Lane #88**. India played one of her own sisters, Cecilia, in the **Gallifrey** release **A Blind Eye #1.4**, while another, Margaret, can be found in the Short Trips anthology, *The Centenarian*.

After adventures in the Divergent Universe, Charley's story with the Eighth Doctor came to an end in **The Girl Who Never Was #103** after 27 main range adventures. However, uniquely at that stage, the character would return to the **Doctor Who** fold not only with a different Doctor, but with an earlier incarnation, adding yet another paradox to Charley's life. A few months' later she met up with the Sixth Doctor in **The Condemned #105** and started traveling with him.

Charley's adventures continued with the Sixth Doctor for eight further stories until 2009 and her final departure in **Blue Forgotten Planet #126**. In that story, it is revealed that after the Sixth Doctor picked her up, Charley was replaced by an entity called Mila who was hidden in the TARDIS. Mila had been experimented upon by the Daleks and had taken refuge in the TARDIS during the Doctor's first incarnation.

It is the Viyrans that restore Charley to her corporeal being and when she meets up with the Sixth Doctor once more, she finds that Mila is still travelling with him, pretending to be Charley. When Mila sacrifices herself to save the Doctor, Charley persuades the Viyrans to put everything right. The aliens replace the Doctor's memories of travelling with "Charley" with those of travelling with the real Mila, thus preventing him from remembering her when his future self meets her aboard the R101.

There are plans in motion for a possible series of spin-off adventures featuring the character of Charley Pollard, but at the time of writing there is no producer assigned, no scripts written and no release date set. With Charley it seems it must always be a case of wait and see...

Above:
*Former **Doctor Who** companion Anneke Wills played Charley's mother, Lady Louisa Pollard.*

PROFILE 2

Left:
Charlotte Elspeth Pollard was played for 37 Big Finish **Doctor Who** adventures by India Fisher.

Below:
The Edwardian Adventuress, the Time Lord and the Eutermesan – India Fisher, Paul McGann and Conrad Westmaas enjoyed adventures in the Divergent Universe.

PROFILE 2

CHARLOTTE ELSPETH POLLARD

ACTRESS INTERVIEW: INDIA FISHER

What led to your casting as Charley Pollard?

I was in a show up in Edinburgh that Jason Haigh-Ellery came to see and he asked me if I'd like to audition for Big Finish. I had no idea that they were only just starting out at that point. I met Gary Russell and Nick Briggs in a room above a pub on the Gray's Inn Road, although Nick remained behind a mixing desk with headphones on, so I don't think a nod of the head actually counts as meeting someone! They gave me a disconcertingly large pile of papers with various monologues on and said I had 5-10 minutes to look through them and if I could come up with as many different voices as possible; so no pressure. I was desperate to impress and racked my brains for as many voices and accents as I could possibly manage, even sinking to the lows of a bad Margaret Thatcher impersonation, which Gary – from time to time at conventions – tries to get me to repeat. Believe me, nobody wants that. I didn't hear from them for months, so presumed the Margaret Thatcher was a step too far, but then I got a call asking me to play Peril Bellamy in **Winter for the Adept**. Apparently it was that performance that led to my being cast as Charley. Luckily the character wasn't a butcher's daughter from Grantham.

What was the process of Charley's character development?

Charley is Alan's baby. I was told that I'd be playing Paul McGann's companion but not much more, so I read **Storm Warning** with massive excitement, although I will admit to flicking to the end to see whether I survived and breathing a huge sigh of relief to discover I did! Alan gave me Charley fully formed; she just jumped out from the page. I had to do very little in the way of character discovery, or deciding what type of person she was. From the moment I read her lines I knew who she was. It was such a wonderful piece of writing. The relationship between her and the Doctor was instantly cemented on board the R101; the banter is there from the start. I'm an inherently lazy actor, I'm ashamed to admit, and so it was a dream come true for me. No acting involved – just say Alan's lines and all the work's been done for you. In the initial season I had no idea what they had planned for Charley, and I'm not entirely sure Gary or Alan did either. She was just on the ride of her life, and so was I. I hadn't really done much audio work before Big Finish so it was a very steep learning curve. But the scripts were marvellous, the people I was getting to act with amazed me and I just listened and learnt as much as I could. And I made a lot of tea!

How did those thoughts change over the next nine years?

It still amazes me that I've been playing Charley for so long. I do find it hard to talk about her as a character, or an acting exercise, as she's become such a part of me. I don't have to get into character; she's just there. I don't have to ask, "how would Charley react in this situation?" – I just know. It's not that we are similar, but she does have characteristics that are a side of my personality that's easy to bring out. I have been extremely lucky with the stories I've been given, the writers over the years have all been wonderful at picking up on her voice. Rarely have I read a script and thought, "ooh that doesn't seem like Charley". Sometimes there has been a colloquialism that Charley wouldn't know being from the 1930s, that's needed to be changed, but in terms of her personality everyone has got her exactly right. She's such fun to play; enthusiastic, gung-ho, brave, caring. I think I've played every possible emotion over the years, but I especially love the fact that she always comes out fighting whatever is thrown at her.

And now Charley's travels with the Doctor seem to be over...?

Yup, that's very sad. But the beauty of time travel is that you never know...

Charley is a much-loved character. Why do you think that was?

I was, and always will be, astonished by the reaction to Charley. I have no idea why people have taken her to their hearts so much. But I can only guess that it's because she's someone who adores travelling with the Doctor, and I think that's important; we can relate to her enthusiasm, her excitement at each new adventure. Also the banter with the Doctor is a crucial element. She's not a pushover, she speaks her mind and has an opinion, she's not afraid to stand up for what she believes in.

Right:
What does the future hold for Charley Pollard?

Which of Charley's stories are your favourites?

I'll always have a soft spot for **Storm Warning** and **Blue Forgotten Planet** as they were my first and last. **Chimes of Midnight** is a cracker, but then I think Rob Shearman can do no wrong. I loved recording **Other Lives,** as my sister was in it, although we didn't actually get to act together. **The Condemned** for being my first play with Colin, but it's also a brilliant story. **Patient Zero** – anything with a Dalek and the wonderful Michael Maloney gets my vote.

What was it like to work with Paul McGann?

As I said I had done very little audio when I first started working with Paul, so watching him work taught me a huge amount. He's an extremely talented actor, with an instantly recognisable and wonderful voice. I'm sure he won't mind my saying that there were times when he hadn't read the script prior to recording, and I was in awe of his ability to sight read long complicated passages and make perfect sense of them, without actually knowing where the sentence was heading. A skill I sadly didn't pick up!

How did that differ to working with Colin Baker?

Working with Colin was a joy. We are quite similar in the way we approach things and I felt we instantly clicked. From the very start it felt as if we'd been working together for years. I loved the fact that a new Doctor opened up such different opportunities for Charley. She was much more grown up; she felt she was protecting the Doctor from her knowledge of his future. She blossomed in her time with the Sixth Doctor, from a young girl in awe of life and this man, to someone who took control of her own destiny and ultimately decided to wipe herself from his memory in order to protect him. I adored playing this new side to her and it was made all the more enjoyable being alongside Colin for the journey. I was extremely sad to leave him, and the tears at the end of **Blue Forgotten Planet** are genuine and mine, not Charley's.

How was your relationship with Gary Russell?

I had a brilliant relationship with Gary, which became stronger and stronger over the years of working together. In the early days we recorded several plays at once over a week in Bristol, as Paul was living there at the time, so the rest of the cast would all stay in a hotel. This led to many a night spent laughing in the bar and meant I became really close to Gary, far closer than you would normally to a director. I'll always remember him sitting on the floor of the studio, script in front of him, scoring a line across the page when

we'd finished a scene. The sound of pen on paper always meant he was happy with the performance and we were moving on. Sadly I now don't see as much of him as I'd like as he's up in Cardiff in pastures new, but we keep in touch.

What changed when Nick Briggs took over?

I have to preface anything I say about Nick by admitting that he is one of my closest friends, so take whatever I say with a pinch of salt! I was thrilled for him when he said that he'd be taking over from Gary, and I think he's done a brilliant job, so far. There's always time for him to mess things up though! But I can't say anything too derogatory as my journey with Big Finish has now become intertwined with Nick. I'm pretty sure, I may be wrong, that he was responsible for the decision to put Charley with the Sixth Doctor, for which I am eternally grateful. He wrote what we referred to as "The Charley Finale", giving me a better ending than I could ever have hoped for. He is the one mooting – and I may be wrong – that he write a few spin off stories for Charley. So, God love him for never quite managing to kill me off. Although after he reads this he may change his mind!

If you could start again with Charley, would you want to change anything?

I realise this is rather a dull answer, but I'm not sure I'd change anything about Charley. If you changed anything then she wouldn't be Charley. In terms of story arc, I loved where she ended up, how she grew and matured over the years. I might not have done the Divergent Universe bit, but hey, you've got to try everything once, even a time traveller travelling to a place with no time!

How satisfied were you with your character's departure?

I adored Charley's departure. **Blue Forgotten Planet** is one of my favourite stories. I can't thank Nick enough for his handling of it all. The scene where she tells the Doctor that she's going to ask the Viyrans to erase her from his memories was one of the most moving I've ever done. Both Nick and I were in tears. I realise it's up for debate whether that was 'Mila Charley' or Charley at that point, but in my mind it's clear. Only the real Charley would be magnanimous enough to erase herself and be replaced with Mila. I just loved it. And the stories running up to the end were brilliant too, being given a chance to play 'Mila Charley' being another subtle variation. And it meant I had scenes where I had to argue with myself, which is always brilliant fun.

What's next for India Fisher and for Charlotte Elspeth Pollard?!

Ah that's the $64,000 question isn't it?

#17 SWORD OF ORION

CREW

Writer	**Nicholas Briggs**
Director	**Nicholas Briggs**
Producers	**Jason Haigh-Ellery**
	Gary Russell
Executive Producer (BBC)	**Jacqueline Rayner**
Music & Sound Design	**Nicholas Briggs**
Cover Art	**Clayton Hickman**
Theme	**David Arnold**

CAST

The Doctor	**Paul McGann**
Charley	**India Fisher**
Grash	**Bruce Montague**
Deeva Jansen	**Michelle Livingstone**
Chev	**Helen Goldwyn**
Ike	**Ian Marr**
Vol	**Hylton Collins**
Kelsey	**Toby Longworth**
Digly	**Barnaby Edwards**
Thinnes	**Mark Gatiss**
Cybermen	**Nicholas Briggs**
	Alistair Lock

TECHNICAL

Story Code	**8C**
Recorded Date	**16 and 17 May 2000**
Release Date	**February 2001**
Place of Recording	**Christchurch Studios, Bristol**
Number of CDs	**2**
Total Duration	**123' 22"**
Number of Episodes	**4**
Duration of Episodes	**1 (34' 44")**
	2 (26' 24")
	3 (29' 02")
	4 (33' 12")
ISBN	**1-903654-15-7**

SYNOPSIS

The Doctor takes Charley to the bazaar on Garazone Central. Here they become involved in what they think is a smuggling operation. Following a shopkeeper called Ike, they find that the TARDIS has been taken aboard a ship called the *Vanguard*. Its new Captain, Deeva Jansen, takes the ship to a derelict star destroyer. The Doctor and Charley are questioned by the crew, but as systems begin to fail on the ship, it is obvious they are not responsible. They then discover the star destroyer belongs to the Cybermen who are waking from hibernation. While the crew try to prevent the Cybermen from boarding, Charley and the Doctor find out about the Orion War, which has been fought between humans and their artificially intelligent androids over the artificial beings' rights. The Doctor then discovers Jansen is an agent of Earth Security sent to determine the military worth of Cyber technology. To escape the Cybermen on the Vanguard, the Doctor, Charley, Jansen and Ike spacewalk back to the star destroyer – spotting an ion storm approaching them. This will interfere with the Cyber systems and force the Cybermen to return to hibernation. Before that happens, however, the Cybermen capture them and Jensen tries to make a deal. The Leader rejects the offer and instead orders them to be taken for conversion. However the Doctor argues that the ion storm will destroy the Cyber ship unless he uses the TARDIS to construct a shield. Jansen then attacks the Cybermen and the Doctor and Charley escape with her. It is then revealed that Jansen is an android double agent and her real mission was to learn about the conversion process so it could be used to create cybernetic troops in the Orion War. Jansen then sacrifices herself to save Charley and the Doctor when the Cybermen attack. The ion storm hits and destroys the ship and the Cybermen. The Doctor and Charley leave in the TARDIS.

PLACEMENT

Between **Storm Warning #16** and **The Stones of Venice #18.**

TRIVIA

- This is the first Big Finish play to feature the Cybermen.
- **Sword of Orion** is based on an *Audio Visuals* story of the same name.
- The story was broadcast on BBC 7 in four parts from 3 September 2005, and was repeated in 2006.
- The original CD release contains an error. There is a scene in which a character returning to the control room speaks before the door has opened to allow him entry. This error was only corrected in the version broadcast on BBC 7 (and available on **The Eighth Doctor Collection** box set).
- The Orion War is used as the backdrop to the **Cyberman** series.
- Clayton Hickman's original version of the cover featured a Cyberman from the 1968 TV story **The Wheel in Space** and Gary Russell originally thought that **Earthshock**-style Cybermen might be suitable before opting for **Invasion**-style ones.
- There is also a planet on the cover of the release despite the fact that none appears in the story!

PRODUCTION SUMMARY

"Right from the off I wanted to team Paul's Doctor with classic enemies. And I knew that Nick's script for **Sword of Orion** would need very little work to be ready in a short time period. I showed Nick some of the other scripts and he tweaked the *Audio Visuals* version to fit with our vision of the Eighth Doctor."
Gary Russell

WORKING TITLES(S)

None.

RETURNING MONSTERS/CHARACTERS

Cybermen.

THE STONES OF VENICE

#18

SYNOPSIS

The Doctor takes Charley to Venice, but arrives in the city's final days during the 23rd century. Here they meet Eleanor Lavish who tells them Venice is sinking because of the curse of Estella and her lover, Count Orsino, who betrayed her. While Charley chats to a gondolier called Pietro, the Doctor meets a man called Churchwell who looks after Orsino's art collection. Pietro tells Charley that Orsino is looking for Estella's remains so that he might bring her back to life and lift the curse. However, the gondoliers do not want him to because they have become amphibians and want to take over the city. They want Venice to die. In order to fool Orsino they dress Charley in Estella's wedding dress and drug her. Elsewhere, the Doctor and Churchwell are captured by a cult who worship Estella. The pair are forced to break into the Duke's palace and steal a portrait of Estella (something that Churchwell says does not exist). However, gondoliers attack them and the leader of the cult, Vincenzo, before Orsino's guards rescue them and bring them before the Count. Vincenzo tells Orsino that he has Estella's remains and will swap them for the portrait he knows to exist. Leaving Ms Lavish on the throne, they all travel to the cult's lair where they and open the casket supposedly containing Estella's body – to find it empty. As Venice sinks, Orsino, Vincezo, Pietro, the Doctor and Charley make it onto the Duke's barge and return to the palace, which is miraculously still standing. Here Ms Lavish tells everyone that she is actually Estella. The Doctor reveals that Estella is an alien who has been forcing Venice to decay while she and Orsino live on using her people's technology. Orsino then begs Estella to join him as he sacrifices himself to save the City. She does so and Venice is returned to normal.

PLACEMENT

Between **Sword of Orion #17** and **Minuet in Hell #19**.

TRIVIA

- This was the first Eighth Doctor audio drama to be recorded by Big Finish. It is therefore Paul McGann's first appearance since the 1996 TV Movie and India Fisher's first performance as Charley Pollard.
- The story was broadcast on BBC 7 in four parts from 1 October 2005, and was repeated from 22 October 2006 and 19 September 2007.
- The story was re-released as part of **The Eighth Doctor Collection** box set in August 2008 along with **Sword of Orion #17**, **The Stones of Venice** and the "season 2" story **Invaders from Mars #28** along with a 12-page booklet and an audio documentary looking at the making of the four stories.
- The storyline was always intended for Paul McGann but Gary suggested it might make a good Fifth Doctor and Nyssa story if they didn't secure Paul's services.
- The original synopsis was one of the three (along with **The Spectre of Lanyon Moor #9** and **The Holy Terror #14**) that were sent to Tom Baker in 2001.
- The role of Vincenzo was Mark Gatiss's favourite for Big Finish. "I did **Stones of Venice** as Christopher Lee and Paul McGann laughed a lot so I carried on!" he says. "I love doing accents and voices and find it very helpful as a way into a character."
- The first draft of the script used "Kirsty" as the new companion's name because this was what it was before Gary changed it to Charley…

PRODUCTION SUMMARY

"I love Paul Magrs but I had to remove quite a lot of double-entendres from this script and chisel the edges off a few other choice phrases. I think at one stage Paul wanted the Duchess to be Iris Wildthyme, but I vetoed that as being too much!"
Gary Russell

WORKING TITLES(S)

My Last Duchess.

RETURNING MONSTERS/CHARACTERS

None.

CREW

Writer	**Paul Magrs**
Director	**Gary Russell**
Producers	**Jason Haigh-Ellery** **Gary Russell**
Executive Producer (BBC)	**Jacqueline Rayner**
Music	**Russell Stone**
Sound Design	**Andy Hardwick @ ERS**
Cover Art	**Clayton Hickman**
Theme	**David Arnold**

CAST

The Doctor	**Paul McGann**
Charley	**India Fisher**
Count Orsino	**Michael Sheard**
Ms. Lavish, Estella	**Elaine Ives-Cameron**
Churchwell	**Nick Scovell**
Pietro	**Barnaby Edwards**
Vincenzo	**Mark Gatiss**

TECHNICAL

Story Code	**8D**
Recorded Date	**15 and 16 May 2000**
Release Date	**March 2001**
Place of Recording	**Christchurch Studios, Bristol**
Number of CDs	**2**
Total Duration	**111' 07"**
Number of Episodes	**4**
Duration of Episodes	**1 (32' 04") 2 (27' 09") 3 (24' 56") 4 (26' 58")**
ISBN	**1-903654-25-4**

PROFILE
3

"they don't know this yet but she's going to stick around", so I would occasionally say to Caroline, "can you do it like *this*" or "make it a bit more inquisitive". We were sewing those seeds right from the word go so that we had an intelligent, sparky, spunky character.'

Gary then asked Iain McLaughlin's permission to take the character forward. He was very pleased, as he told Benjamin Cook in 1993: 'I was really chuffed that Big Finish thought Erimem was interesting to keep around.'

In McLaughlin's fictional Egypt the Doctor realises that Erimem's name was not in the history books and that Amenhotep was succeeded by Thutmose IV. He thought she would be killed but, of course, she actually just disappeared in a time machine.

Erimem had been raised not only as an Egyptian princess – and thus had a certain haughtiness to her – but also as a fearsome warrior – so was a little bloodthirsty, too. 'My biggest fear was that she sounded too similar to Leela,' confides Gary, but the consensus seems to be that the writers managed to avoid turning the Egyptian warrior princess into the noble savage of the Sevateem.

Despite being assigned a good balance of historical and SF settings, Erimem seemed to flourish in more historical adventures – whether it was Paris in 1626 (**The Church and the Crown #38**), Tibet in 1917 (**The Roof of the World #59**), Nicaea in 325 AD (**The Council of Nicaea #71**) or running around with Vlad the Impaler in the Romania of 1462 (**Son of the Dragon #99**).

After many adventures Erimem eventually fulfilled her royal destiny on the planet Peladon, becoming queen in Barnaby Edwards's **The Bride of Peladon #104**. Of course, with Big Finish now producing linked 'seasons' of plays it is perfectly possible Erimem will return to the **Main Monthly Range** or indeed be seen gracing the cover of a **Companion Chronicle**. Time will tell.

Erimem also appeared in *The Coming of the Queen* by Ian McLaughlin and Claire Bartlett, which was set before the events of **The Eye of the Scorpion #24**. It was published by Big Finish in 2005 as part of the *New Worlds* novel range.

Below:
Three's company – Nicola Bryant, Peter Davison and Caroline Morris at the recording of **The Eye of the Scorpion**, July 2001.

PROFILE 3 ERIMEM

**WRITER INTERVIEW:
IAIN MCLAUGHLIN (CREATOR)**

The original storyline for The Eye of the Scorpion **included the real Pharaoh Hatchepsut and was set a century before Erimem's time. How did you come up with the name and character of Erimem – and why move it forward 100 years?**

I moved it forward 100 years, because in my head that original era was the time of Hatchepsut. There had been strong efforts to write her out of history by the pharaohs who followed Hatchepsut – having her name destroyed on temples, stonework and so on and it didn't feel right to have another female pharaoh at the same time. On the other hand, a hundred years on, history seems a bit woozy anyway – the stories say one pharaoh got the gig because the gods helped him find and uncover the Sphinx after it had been buried in the sand. That seemed a more fitting era for the Doctor to become involved.

Erimem's character was initially a reaction to Hatchepsut, who had really wanted the throne. Erimem didn't. That made her a different character altogether, it made her reactions to the situation and the people around her different. It gave the chance for her to be quite a tragic figure, and one who had a lot in common with the Doctor. That's why they had that little campfire scene when they discussed having to do their duty in an old civilisation dominated by rules. They recognised something kindred in each other.

The name Erimemushinteperem doesn't actually mean anything. I spent ages trying to piece together a name that would suit her and wound up with a choice of Ann-Ankh-Amun, which would have been fine, or Erimem. I eventually picked Erimem because it wasn't like any of the real pharaohs of the time and set her apart. So, if her name were ever uncovered by historians, she would be a total mystery.

What was it about the character that made her so well defined?

A large part of it comes down to the amount of time she had in the story. She was central in every episode and had the chance to act as a companion to both the Doctor and to Peri when the Doctor was on his Hartnell-holiday in episode 2. Putting her at the heart of the episodes and letting her have that time gave me the chance to explore her world a bit and let her talk for herself with the Doctor and Peri. We got to see her building friendships, we got to see her nobility and courage, and we also had time to see that inside she was still a scared 17-year-old kid who was horribly lonely. We got to see a lot of her personality in just 2 hours. And I have to say that a lot of that personality came through the performances Gary Russell got from the cast. Not just Caroline Morris, who was absolutely perfect, but also from Peter Davison and Nicola Bryant, and also from Jonathan Owen who played Antranak.

Was the character based on anyone? If so, who, why and what traits did you take?

There are obviously a few bits of Hatchepsut still in Erimem's make-up – leading the army into battle

Right:
The cast of **The Eye of the Scorpion**, Erimem's first adventure (l-r back): writer Iain McLaughlin, Jack Galagher, Harry Myers, Stephen Perring, Jonathan Owen, Mark Wright; (front): Peter Davison, Nicola Bryant, Caroline Morris

being the most obvious. Her willingness to torture is something that suited the time in question, though had it remained as Hatchepsut, there would probably have been a bit more torture. I think I took on board a bit of the legend of Queen Elizabeth I as well. One woman ready to fight and die for her country. Whether that was true of Queen Bess or not I don't know – but it was the way she was often portrayed. I'm thinking of Flora Robson's ultra-patriotic turn in *The Sea Hawk*. I know that was a jingoistic propaganda performance to raise patriotic spirits in WW2 but it stuck with me.

In terms of look, I always imagined Erimem to look like Naima Belkhiati, one of the Honeyz and I've always written her that way.

When did it become apparent that Big Finish wanted to use Erimem as a companion?

I knew Gary liked the character – he'd said so in a couple of emails. That got me thinking that maybe I could use her again sometime, and I had a story in mind for the Sixth Doctor to meet her later. Valley of the Dying Sun it was called, I think. It never went past a short synopsis on my computer, though. On the Saturday of the recording, Gary asked if he could keep Erimem around for a while. And I was more than delighted with that. The contract was clear that Big Finish could have used her anyway but I always thought it was very generous of Gary to ask.

What did you think of Caroline Morris's performance?

Caroline's performance is the reason Erimem was kept on, I'm sure of that. She was outstanding. She got absolutely everything I wanted for Erimem and added huge amounts of depth to her. Some lines in a script are functional. They're never meant to be but sometimes you just need to get across a piece of information. She took those lines and gave them more than I'd put in. She was brilliant.

How soon were you asked to write *No Place Like Home* for Erimem?

The email must have pinged into my inbox sometime in mid-2002. It took about a nanosecond to say I was up for it. Writing something short and with a very small cast was a challenge I really liked the sound of.

How happy were you with the journey the character went on?

A mixture of happy and not-so-happy. I liked the way she relished the travel, the way she grew into her relationships with Peri and the Doctor, but some bits of her personality got a bit lost or side-lined along the way. Her eagerness to learn and her atheism were really important in forming the character. She had to lose her faith in the Gods or would never have been able to doubt herself when she was to become

Pharaoh. That came and went a bit. Different writers see her in different ways so it's unavoidable – it's not something I'm going to have a strop about.

What did you think of Erimem ending up as a Queen on Peladon when she has never been that keen on regal positions?

I'm afraid that really jarred with me. I didn't like it at all. Part of the reason she and the Doctor had got on so well was that they were both rebelling against their staid, rules-obsessed civilisations. Erimem accepting that her destiny was to rule was like the Doctor quietly going back to live on Gallifrey. It certainly wasn't the way I would have liked her to go. On the other hand, I know a lot of people liked it and thought it was a satisfying end for her story, so what do I know? I'm not going to throw a hissy fit over it. If you ask ten writers to write out a character you're going to get ten different endings. Just because I would have done it differently doesn't make me right and everyone else wrong. We all just look at it differently.

Your original idea was to write a story set in Poldark's Cornwall. Do you think there would have been a potential companion in that story?

More than likely. I can't remember too much about what I'd jotted down but I think I had the local squire's daughter and a miner's daughter involved somewhere. The miner's daughter idea was probably influenced by Demelza in the Poldark saga. I had a huge crush on Angharad Rees when I was a lad. The other two stories I sent at roughly the same time as **Eye of the Scorpion** also had stand-in companions. 'The Lone Warrior' had a skint Victorian seamstress who'd just been chucked out of her lodgings and 'A Stitch in Time' had a Stone Age girl who was given a mental leg-up. The seamstress might have been a fun companion but the cave-girl would have been superficially too similar to Leela. Besides, her story was told inside that script.

Would you like to see Erimem in the Companion Chronicles range?

Definitely – if I get to write it! Actually, we've pitched an idea for one. Whether anyone likes it or not we'll have to wait and see.

Is there anything else you would like to say about Erimem?

I have a very paternal view of Erimem. I'm glad she had the chance to develop as a character and I love the way some of the writers handled her. **The Church and The Crown** is my favourite Erimem story and I thought **The Kingmaker** was terrific as well. **Son of the Dragon,** too. I hope we haven't seen the last of Erimem. I'd love the chance to write for her again and I'm immensely grateful to Gary Russell for giving me the chance to write her in the first place.

#25 COLDITZ

CREW

Writer	**Steve Lyons**
Director	**Gary Russell**
Producers	**Jason Haigh-Ellery**
	Gary Russell
Executive Producer (BBC)	**Jacqueline Rayner**
Music and Sound Design	**Toby Richards and Emily Baker at Cressida**
Cover Art	**Clayton Hickman**
Theme	**Delia Derbyshire**

CAST

The Doctor	**Sylvester McCoy**
Ace	**Sophie Aldred**
Klein	**Tracey Childs**
Feldwebel Kurtz	**David Tennant**
Hauptmann Julius Schäfer	**Toby Longworth**
Flying Officer Bill Gower	**Nicholas Young**
Timothy Wilkins	**Peter Rae**
Prisoner, Guard	**Neil Corry**

TECHNICAL

Story Code	**7U**
Recorded Date	**26 and 27 May 2001**
Release Date	**October 2001**
Place of Recording	**The Moat Studios, London**
Number of CDs	**2**
Total Duration	**106' 55"**
Number of Episodes	**4**
Duration of Episodes	**1 (25' 47")**
	2 (26' 29")
	3 (26' 32")
	4 (28' 07")
ISBN	**1-903654-47-5**

SYNOPSIS

Colliding with something in the vortex, the TARDIS materialises in Colditz Castle in 1944. They are immediately caught and Ace's CD Walkman is taken away by brutal German officer Kurtz, while a Gestapo officer is summoned to examine the TARDIS. Ace, calling herself McShane, meets fellow prisoner Gower, and the Doctor is tortured by Kurtz. A female Gestapo officer called Klein arrives and dismisses Kurtz. She tells the Doctor she knows the blue box is a TARDIS and threatens to shoot Ace. So the Doctor and Klein enter the ship, where she tells him that she has not come for the TARDIS but for the Doctor himself. Klein takes the Doctor into the nearby wood and there they find an imprint of the Doctor's TARDIS on the ground. Somehow Klein travelled to 1944 from the future using a version of the Doctor's TARDIS. Frustrated, Klein is forced to return to Colditz Castle with the Doctor so that she may take the TARDIS sitting in the courtyard. The Doctor works out that Klein is from a future in which the Nazis won the war; a future created by the Doctor's very arrival at Colditz. Klein reveals she was helped by an assistant called Schmidt who programmed the TARDIS for her. To ensure history takes its proper course, the Doctor and Ace retrieve her CD Walkman and the Doctor realises that the thing they collided with in the vortex was his own TARDIS that Schmidt – an alternative future incarnation – sent back so that he would arrive in the first place. As Klein flees Colditz, the Doctor and Ace manage to get back to the TARDIS. However, Kurtz tries to prevent them leaving, becoming trapped in the doors as the ship leaves. This rips his body apart. Ace has done a lot of growing up in Colditz and from now on tells the Doctor to call her McShane.

PLACEMENT

Between **Dust Breeding #21** and **The Rapture #36**.

TRIVIA

- The story features David Tennant – who would later go on to play the Tenth Doctor – in his first **Doctor Who** role – as the Nazi, Feldwebel Kurtz.
- Steve Lyons originally wanted to use the Master as the time traveller but this idea was nixed because he was already being included in **Dust Breeding #21**.
- Steve then came up with another Time Lord character from the Celestial Intervention Agency (CIA) before abandoning that idea, too.
- Finally, he came up with the character of Klein, the time-travelling Nazi, played by Tracey Childs, although the character had initially been male.
- Klein would return to Big Finish in **A Thousand Tiny Wings #130** after a gap of 105 stories and nine years. As Gary Russell noted in 1993's *The New Audio Adventures: The Inside Story* "There's more of Klein's story to tell"…
- The idea for the story came from Steve and his brother playing the Parker Brothers' board game 'Escape from Colditz' (which was devised by actual escapee Pat Reid in 1973).
- Steve also read two of Reid's books about his time at and escape from Colditz in *Colditz: The Colditz Story* (published by Hodder & Stoughton in 1952) and *The Latter Days at Colditz* (also published by Hodder & Stoughton the following year).

PRODUCTION SUMMARY

"We wanted to make Ace more grown up so we came up with the idea that she shouldn't have the 'Ace' nickname any more. So I came up with the whole 'McShane' thing. Although Steve had written the first draft by then so we had to change it to accommodate the new direction. We also had a few problems with the post-production."
Gary Russell

WORKING TITLES(S)

None.

RETURNING MONSTERS/CHARACTERS

None.

PRIMEVAL

SYNOPSIS

In order to find medical help for Nyssa – who has suffered a psychic collapse – the Doctor takes her to her home planet of Traken, 3000 years before it was destroyed. Here he seeks out a scientist called Shayla, who takes them to the Consuls of Traken. She tells them that Nyssa has been tainted by evil. The Doctor is surprised by the Trakenites' apparent superstitious nature and Nyssa confirms that her people were like this when the Source – actually a sentient sun – was self-governing: before the advent of the first Keeper of Traken. The Consuls then decide to banish the Doctor and Nyssa, claiming that their paradise must not be infected. Knowing that Nyssa will die without help, Shayla secretly takes the Doctor to meet with Kwundaar, an omniscient being who is lurking at the edge of the Union's space, waiting with an invasion force. After attacking the Doctor psychically, Kwundaar agrees to help on the condition that the Doctor brings him an item from the Source chamber on Traken. However, the Doctor escapes and returns to Traken,

finding Nyssa recovered. It is revealed that Kwundaar is responsible for Nyssa's illness and he is manipulating the Doctor. On Traken, the Doctor and Nyssa head for the Source. There he opens its protective shielding, but finding nothing of note, the Doctor resets it, boosting the power to prevent Kwundaar controlling it. This is exactly what Kwundaar wanted him to do because the additional shielding keeps the light of the Source from getting out. Realising what has happened, the Doctor tells Nyssa the Source override code. It transpires that Kwundaar was once the god of Traken and that he gave the natives the science that helped them build the Source and banish him. All seems lost but when Kwundaar takes the code from Nyssa's mind and inputs it, the Source transfers its powers to whoever is inside. As the Source opens, the Doctor is sitting in the Keeper's chair – he has become the first Keeper of Traken and Kwundaar burns in the Source's pure light. The Doctor then abdicates the power to Shayla before leaving with Nyssa, who decides not to stay.

PLACEMENT

Between **The Mutant Phase #15** and **Spare Parts #34**.

TRIVIA

- This story is a prequel to the 1981 TV story, **The Keeper of Traken**.
- As such, Russell Stone added xylophone music to the score in a nod to the music heard at Cassia's wedding in that TV story.
- Susan Penhaligon, who here plays Shayla, appeared in the 1972 TV story **The Time Monster** as Lakis.
- Gary Russell initially asked Alan W Lear (writer of **Minuet in Hell #19**) to come up with ideas for ancient Traken but they weren't what Gary was after.
- The names of all the characters have their origins in theology.
- Lance Parkin has said he prefers his original scripts for **Primeval** over his original scripts for **Davros #48**.
- Lance's initial pitches to Big Finish included 'The First Keeper', which formed the basis for this story), 'Iron Empire' (a sequel to the *Doctor Who Weekly* comic strip story *The Iron Legion* by Pat Mills and John Wagner) and 'Sovereignty' (which was set on the Falkland Islands during the conflict of 1982).
- Gary changed the title because it gave away the ending of the play.
- The fact that the play was set on Traken was kept secret right up until release. The planet isn't even mentioned in the blurb!

PRODUCTION SUMMARY

"John Ainsworth suggested to me that it might be an idea to set some stories in the history of other planets that'd been visited in **Doctor Who** and not just Earth. I asked him which one he thought might be suitable and he said 'Traken' so we could include Nyssa, and so Traken it was! Again, I wanted the psychic powers thing for Nyssa and so gave these strands to Lance who I knew wanted to write a **Doctor Who** play. The first draft wasn't as good as I'd hoped, but Lance did a good job with the second one."
Gary Russell

WORKING TITLES(S)

The First Keeper.

RETURNING MONSTERS/CHARACTERS

The Keeper of Traken.

CREW

Writer	**Lance Parkin**
Director	**Gary Russell**
Producers	**Jason Haigh-Ellery** **Gary Russell**
Executive Producer (BBC)	**Jacqueline Rayner**
Music	**Russell Stone**
Sound Design	**Gareth Jenkins @ ERS**
Cover Art	**Clayton Hickman**
Theme	**Delia Derbyshire**

CAST

The Doctor	**Peter Davison**
Nyssa	**Sarah Sutton**
Shayla	**Susan Penhaligon**
Kwundaar	**Stephen Greif**
Sabian	**Ian Hallard**
Anona	**Romy Tennant**
Janneus	**Rita Davies**
Hyrca	**Mark Woolgar**
Narthex, Captain Kabe	**Billy Miller**
Etrayk	**Alistair Lock**

TECHNICAL

Story Code	**6C/D**
Recorded Date	**24 and 25 August 2001**
Release Date	**November 2001**
Place of Recording	**The Moat Studios, London**
Number of CDs	**2**
Total Duration	**107' 11"**
Number of Episodes	**4**
Duration of Episodes	1 (28' 08") 2 (24' 39") 3 (22' 24") 4 (32' 00")
ISBN	**1-903654-51-3**

#27  THE ONE DOCTOR

CREW

Writers	**Gareth Roberts**
	Clayton Hickman
Director	**Gary Russell**
Producers	**Jason Haigh-Ellery**
	Gary Russell
Executive Producer (BBC)	**Jacqueline Rayner**
Music and Sound Design	**Alistair Lock**
Cover Art	**Clayton Hickman**
Theme	**Delia Derbyshire**
	Brian Hodgson &
	Paddy Kingsland
	(Part 3)

CAST

The Doctor	**Colin Baker**
Mel	**Bonnie Langford**
Banto Zame	**Christopher Biggins**
Sally-Anne Stubbins	**Clare Buckfield**
Cylinder, The Jelloid	**Matt Lucas**
Councillor Potikol, Assembler 2	**Stephen Fewell**
Citizen Sokkery, Mentos	**Nicholas Pegg**
The Questioner, Queen Elizabeth	**Jane Goddard**
Assembler 1	**Adam Buxton**
Guards	**Mark Wright**
	Alistair Lock

TECHNICAL

Story Code	**7C/R**
Recorded Date	**28 and 29 April 2001**
Release Date	**December 2001**
Place of Recording	**The Moat Studios, London**
Number of CDs	**2**
Total Duration	**109' 00"**
Number of Episodes	**4**
Duration of Episodes	1 (22' 08")
	2 (26' 40")
	3 (22' 24")
	4 (26' 27")
ISBN	**1-903654-56-4**

SYNOPSIS

Far into the future, the Doctor and Mel answer a distress signal from the Generios system. However, they emerge into a celebration. It appears the famous Time Lord known as the Doctor has saved them from the evil Skelloids! The Doctor is sceptical. Meanwhile, two con artists, Banto Zame and Sally-Anne Stubbins are posing as the Doctor and his companion. They are awaiting a large bank transfer of their reward money, but the planet's leader, Potikol, says that a piece of space debris is interfering with the computer networks. The Doctor confronts Zame who, thinking that the real Doctor is another con man, reveals that they have tricked many worlds into paying rewards for saving them from fake alien invasions. When the space debris turns out to be a huge alien ship demanding the system's three greatest treasures, Zame assumes the Doctor is playing the same con he is. However, when the ship destroys one of the outer planets, Zame decides to leave in the 'STARDIS' a teleportation capsule shaped like a blue 'portaloo'. The Doctor and Mel go with them and manage to steer it to the real TARDIS. Zame realises the truth and asks to be let go but the Doctor is intent on finding the treasures and Zame will join him. While Zame and Mel look for the first treasure, 'Unit ZX419', the Doctor and Sally Anne leave to search for the second, 'Mentos'. Unit ZX419 turns out to be an infinite piece of self-assembly furniture and Mentos is a trans-dimensional quiz machine that can answer any question. The four team up to find the last treasure: a huge diamond in the possession of the mournful Jelloid. Successful in their missions, they return to Potikol, but the aliens take Zame captive, saying the quest has been a ploy to deliver the Doctor into their hands so that he may answer for his crimes against their race. The Doctor and Mel leave Sally-Anne to claim her reward.

PLACEMENT

Between the 1986 TV story **The Trial of a Time Lord** and the Big Finish adventure **The Juggernauts #65**.

TRIVIA

- The final track contains a bonus Easter egg of the questions posed by Mentos in the play, and a mini story set at Christmas (aping a similar, well-known scene in **The Daleks' Master Plan**, and mocked again many years later in **The Eighth Doctor Adventures** story **Relative Dimensions #4.07**.
- This was Gareth Roberts and Clayton Hickman's first script for Big Finish. Roberts went on to write for the revived **Doctor Who** TV series while Hickman has written for *The Sarah Jane Adventures*.
- The story uses the electronic, 1972 'Delaware' theme for part three. It was composed by Brian Hodgson and Paddy Kingsland but was never broadcast on UK TV.
- Gary originally considered Liza Tarbuck for the role of Sally-Anne, but the actress was unavailable and the part went to Clare Buckfield, well known for her roles as Natasha Stevens in *Grange Hill* and Jenny Porter in *2point4 Children*. She has also appeared in two **Eighth Doctor Adventures**: as Trisha Tomorrow in **Horror of Glam Rock #1.3** and Spring-Heeled Sophie in **Dead London #2.1**.
- Gareth and Clay's first proposal to Gary was for a Fifth Doctor story called 'A Song for Death', which would go on to form the basis for their subsequent play, **Bang-Bang-a-Boom #39** and their second was called 'Crossroads in Time', featuring a motel…

PRODUCTION SUMMARY

"A brilliant script by Gareth and Clay although I did ask that they remove the name 'Doctor Who' from their list of aliases the Doctor was known as. They asked me if I could reschedule the play because it was originally slated for an August release but they thought Christmas would be more appropriate. I agreed wholeheartedly and it won the *DWM* poll for that year! Yes, I was very happy with this one."
Gary Russell

WORKING TITLES(S)

None.

RETURNING MONSTERS/CHARACTERS

None.

Check box - CD ■ MP3 ■

INVADERS FROM MARS

#28

SYNOPSIS

The Doctor and Charley arrive in New York, 1938, and find the charred body of a private detective who has been killed by an alien weapon. At the man's office, the Doctor pretends to be the detective and meets Glory Bee, who needs help looking for her missing uncle, an atomic scientist called Stepashin. Elsewhere, rehearsals are under way for Orson Welles's famous War of the Worlds radio broadcast, but network chairman, Bix Biro, is nervous. His lover has been kidnapped by Cosmo Devine, a Nazi sympathiser, and threatened with death unless Biro tells him where the alien technology is. Charley is also kidnapped and at Devine's house she meets Biro's lover, Jimmy Winkler. He tells her that the Mob has found alien technology and Devine is intending to help the Nazis invade America with it. In the Mob's lair Stepashin is examining a tank full of aliens. Mob boss Don Chaney explains that he intends to sell the alien technology

to the highest bidder – but not the Nazis. The Doctor and Glory are also taken to the lair where the woman reveals she is a Soviet agent here to bring Stepashin back to Russia before he can defect. However, two aliens turn up looking for their lost brethren just as Welles's broadcast takes place. They find Charley who has escaped from Devine just as panic begins to spread. Devine arrives at Don Chaney's lair with a squad of Nazi soldiers but when they open the tank, the soldiers are killed. The aliens turn up at the lair and are revealed to be not powerful warlords at all, but criminals operating a protection racket. The Doctor tells them that real alien warlords have arrived in the shape of the Martians and then escapes to the studio where he convinces Orson Welles to help him. When the broadcast goes wrong, Stepashin saves the day by blowing up the ship in the world's first nuclear explosion.

PLACEMENT

Between **Minuet in Hell #19** and **The Chimes of Midnight #29**.

TRIVIA

- Episode 1 of this play was included on the **Ratings War** CD that was given away with issue 313 of *Doctor Who Magazine*, although it did not have David Arnold's arrangement of the theme and had India Fisher playing the reception guest, which was later re-recorded by Katy Manning.
- This story was broadcast on BBC 7 in four parts from 29 October 2005, and was repeated from 17 November 2006.
- Mark Benton, who here plays Ellis, would go on to play Clive in the 2005 TV story, **Rose**, while Jessica Stevenson played Joan Redfern in 2007's **Human Nature** and **The Family of Blood** as well as Verity Newman in 2009's **The End of Time**, while Simon Pegg took the role of the Editor in 2005's **The Long Game**.
- David Benson (John Houseman), would appear in other Big Finish productions, but is best known to audio fans as Panda in the company's **Iris Wildthyme** series.
- Mark Gatiss only had the initial idea of what if Orson Welles's broadcast had masked a real invasion when he came to the Eighth Doctor story meeting. "Everyone else had these incredibly detailed outlines," he recalls. "I remember Alan Barnes giving us a précis of **Neverland** and I thought: 'Christ, I don't know as much about **Doctor Who** as I thought I did'! It was very jolly, though."

PRODUCTION SUMMARY

"It was hard work juggling everything but my cast was brilliant and everyone was having such a good time they didn't seem to mind if they had to hang around. I think the only way you can be truly happy with the production of something you've written is to direct it yourself. Then there's no-one else to blame if it doesn't come off!"
Mark Gatiss

WORKING TITLES(S)

None.

RETURNING MONSTERS/CHARACTERS

None.

CREW

Writer	**Mark Gatiss**
Director	**Mark Gatiss**
Producers	**Jason Haigh-Ellery** **Gary Russell**
Executive Producer (BBC)	**Jacqueline Rayner**
Music and Sound Design	**Alistair Lock**
Cover Art	**Clayton Hickman**
Theme	**David Arnold**

CAST

The Doctor	**Paul McGann**
Charley	**India Fisher**
Mouse, Winkler, Luigi, Heavy	**Ian Hallard**
Ellis	**Mark Benton**
John Houseman, Thug, Streath	**Jonathan Rigby**
Orson Welles, Professor Stepashin, Halliday	**David Benson**
Bix Biro, Noriam, Man	**Paul Putner**
Don Chaney, Actor	**Simon Pegg**
Glory Bee, Carla, Women	**Jessica Stevenson**
Cosmo Devine, Hotel Clerk	**John Arthur**
Mrs Van Buren	**Katy Manning**
Radio Announcer	**Mark Gatiss**
Thug/Toastmaster	**Alistair Lock**

TECHNICAL

Story Code	**8F**
Recorded Date	**16 and 17 January 2001**
Release Date	**January 2002**
Place of Recording	**Christchurch Studios, Bristol**
Number of CDs	**2**
Total Duration	**96' 01"**
Number of Episodes	**4**
Duration of Episodes	**1 (23' 34")** **2 (20' 18")** **3 (22' 16")** **4 (29' 53")**
ISBN	**1-903654-57-2**

#29

THE CHIMES OF MIDNIGHT

CREW

Writer	**Robert Shearman**
Director	**Barnaby Edwards**
Producers	**Jason Haigh-Ellery**
	Gary Russell
Executive Producer (BBC)	**Jacqueline Rayner**
Music	**Russell Stone**
Sound Design	**Andy Hardwick @ ERS**
Cover Art	**Clayton Hickman**
Theme	**David Arnold**

CAST

The Doctor	**Paul McGann**
Charley	**India Fisher**
Edith	**Louise Rolfe**
Mr. Shaughnessy	**Lennox Greaves**
Mrs. Baddeley	**Sue Wallace**
Frederick	**Robert Curbishley**
Mary	**Juliet Warner**

TECHNICAL

Story Code	**8G**
Recorded Date	**17 and 18 January 2001**
Release Date	**February 2002**
Place of Recording	**Christchurch Studios, Bristol**
Number of CDs	**2**
Total Duration	**115' 51"**
Number of Episodes	**4**
Duration of Episodes	1 (27' 01")
	2 (26' 50")
	3 (28' 57")
	4 (33' 03")
ISBN	**1-903654-58-0**

SYNOPSIS

The Doctor and Charley arrive in a dark and deserted Edwardian house on Christmas Eve. In a lit version of the house, the staff are preparing for Christmas and berating hapless scullery maid Edith Thompson for being 'nothing and nobody'. The Doctor and Charley hear the ticking of a clock and as it strikes ten they find themselves in the lit version of the house, where Edith has been drowned in the kitchen sink. The Doctor questions the staff but each suspects the others because they have shifty eyes. Charley is returned to the dark house where Edith tells her that she is tired of being killed and that she must remember the name Edward Grove. As the clock strikes eleven, Mrs Baddeley the cook is found dead and the Doctor works out that the servants are being killed in a manner representative of their jobs. The clock then strikes midnight and the Doctor and Charley find themselves playing out the same scenario with slight variations. As Charley becomes part of the scenario with no memory of the Doctor, the Time Lord discovers that Edward Grove is the address of the house. As midnight strikes again, the scene resets and Charley's memories are restored but she is taken back to the dark house where she meets Edith, who she now remembers as one of the servants from the Pollard household. Edith explains that the household all went into mourning when they found her diary in the wreck of the R101 and Edith committed suicide. Charley now knows that she died in the crash. The house takes possession of the butler and explains that it came into existence because of the temporal anomaly caused by the Doctor's rescue of Charley, who is about to kill herself. The Doctor intervenes and then Charley stops Edith doing the same, promising to always remember her. Edward Grove dies as the paradox is broken and the TARDIS departs.

PLACEMENT

Between **Invaders From Mars #28** and **Seasons of Fear #30**.

TRIVIA

- This story was broadcast on BBC 7 in four parts from 17 December 2005 and repeated from 17 December 2006 – the last of the **Main Monthly Range** releases, before **The Eighth Doctor Adventures** took over.
- Rob pitched this to Gary Russell as a mix between *Upstairs, Downstairs* and *Sapphire & Steel*.
- To underline the point, the names of the characters Shaughnessy and Mrs Baddeley are derived from Alfred Shaughnessy, the script editor, and the actress who played the cook Mrs Bridges in *Upstairs, Downstairs*. Frederick was also the name of a footman in the series, played by Gareth Hunt.
- One idea for the play that didn't quite happen was for it to take place in real-time. This came from a film Rob had seen called *Nick of Time*, which did the same.
- Rob says that he didn't enjoy writing the story and it isn't his favourite, although he is very proud of it!
- The clock on the cover is actually one of the faces of Big Ben and is the first release to feature an image of India Fisher as Charlotte Pollard.
- This was the first Big Finish play that Barnaby Edwards directed. He has gone on to direct many, many more!

PRODUCTION SUMMARY

"This one scared me half to death when I first read it and I really wanted to direct it, too! But I gave this one to Barney and he did a great job. It was meant to be the first story in the second McGann season because I wanted something light to kick off the season. Then we had to pull the recording dates forward, and when Rob delivered the script, it became clear that Mark Gatiss's script was far better as a season opener."
Gary Russell

WORKING TITLES(S)

None.

RETURNING MONSTERS/CHARACTERS

None.

SEASONS OF FEAR

SYNOPSIS

The Doctor finally succeeds in bringing Charley to the Singapore Hilton in 1930. While Charley meets her man, the Doctor is approached by Sebastian Grayle, an immortal human who explains that he killed the Time Lord some time ago and has come to gloat. This version of 1930 Singapore is an illusion created by his masters, who rule over all space and time. The Doctor and Charley depart and track Grayle to Britain, 305 AD, where he is a Roman Decurion. However, he is already in contact with the aliens and is about to sacrifice the other Romans. The Doctor and Charley manage to save the men in the fort but Grayle is given his immortality and leaves as the fort is destroyed. Analysing the alien signal, the Doctor realises that they won't be able to communicate with Grayle again for 750 years. So they travel forward to the court of Edward the Confessor, where they prevent Grayle from unloading a huge pile of plutonium to power a transmat for bringing his masters to Earth. The TARDIS then travels to Buckinghamshire in 1806 where they find an outpost of the original Hellfire Club in Wickham Caves. Here the Doctor and Charley encounter Grayle who this time manages to operate the transmat and the Doctor is horrified to see old enemies the Nimon emerge. The Doctor and Charley escape and pilot the TARDIS into the vortex but the Nimon and Grayle follow. The Doctor expels the Nimon but is himself swept out into the time vortex. However, the Doctor has set up a time tunnel and arrives back in the Roman fort. When Grayle arrives, he meets his earlier self. The Decurion is appalled by the older man's willingness to destroy the Earth and stabs him to death. The Doctor takes Charley back to Singapore again but this time there is no Grayle. However, something evil has entered the universe of which the Doctor is unaware…

PLACEMENT

Between **The Chimes of Midnight #29** (as well as *DWM* giveaway **Living Legend**) and **Embrace the Darkness #31**.

TRIVIA

- Gary Russell originally wanted a *New Adventures*-style story in this slot called 'Time's Champion', which he thought would suit Paul Cornell.
- A Dalek falls through time and space towards the end of episode one. This is explained in **The Time of the Daleks #32**.
- The opening of the play has an opening voice over, which is an homage to the *Doctor Who* TV Movie. "I thought we could get through large chunks of set-up more quickly via a voiceover," Paul says. "I didn't feel I had to avoid doing that, because the form had already set it up."
- Stephen Fewell, who here plays Marcus/Richard Martin, also played the parts of Paul Webster in **Red Dawn #8**, Potikol in **The One Doctor #27** and, of course, Benny's husband Jason Kane in the **Bernice Summerfield** range.
- Paul Cornell was not happy with the original draft. "At the end, modern Grayle killed ancient Grayle, as opposed to the other way round, before ancient Grayle had gained the power from his masters," he explains. "Which led to time paradoxes, and multiple copies of the Doctor and Charley. It was horrible!"
- According to Paul, Caroline Symcox was the reason the play worked. "She turned it round, added the Sword of Mithras to wrap things up," he says. "Hence the duel. She sorted out the plot in one draft. I just then added a few cute lines of dialogue. It's really about half and half original work."
- "The final script was pretty different from the first draft," Caroline recalls. "The characters were the same, but the turning points of their development had changed… In addition the basic story behind the Nimon on Earth had also changed."

PRODUCTION SUMMARY

"I gave Paul the idea of the Nimon at a convention. They have such great voices! Then their original idea was to have four separate time zones, with the same cast playing different people in each. But this is one of my pet hates. I don't like asking actors to perform multiple roles as a 'favour'. So I insisted that we find different actors for each segment."
Gary Russell

WORKING TITLES(S)

Time's Champion.

RETURNING MONSTERS/CHARACTERS

The Nimon, Rassilon, a Dalek (in cameo).

CREW

Writer	**Paul Cornell**
	Caroline Symcox
Director	**Gary Russell**
Producers	**Jason Haigh-Ellery**
	Gary Russell
Executive Producer (BBC)	**Jacqueline Rayner**
Music	**Jane Elphinstone**
Sound Design	**Gareth Jenkins @ ERS**
Cover Art	**Clayton Hickman**
Theme	**David Arnold**

CAST

The Doctor	**Paul McGann**
Charley	**India Fisher**
Sebastian Grayle	**Stephen Perring**
Marcus, Richard Martin	**Stephen Fewell**
Lucillius, Nimon Voice	**Robert Curbishley**
Edward the Confessor	**Lennox Greaves**
Edith	**Sue Wallace**
Lucy Martin	**Justine Mitchell**
Rassilon	**Don Warrington**
Waiter, Prisoner	**Gareth Jenkins**

TECHNICAL

Story Code	**8H**
Recorded Date	**19, 20 and 27 January 2001**
Release Date	**March 2002**
Place of Recording	**Christchurch Studios, Bristol**
Number of CDs	**2**
Total Duration	**119' 28"**
Number of Episodes	**4**
Duration of Episodes	**1 (30' 42")**
	2 (27' 21")
	3 (29' 02")
	4 (32' 33")
ISBN	**1-903654-59-9**

#31

EMBRACE THE DARKNESS

CREW

Writer	**Nicholas Briggs**
Director	**Nicholas Briggs**
Producers	**Jason Haigh-Ellery**
	Gary Russell
Executive Producer (BBC)	**Jacqueline Rayner**
Music and Sound Design	**Jim Mortimore**
Cover Art	**Clayton Hickman**
Theme	**David Arnold**

CAST

The Doctor	**Paul McGann**
Charley	**India Fisher**
Orllensa	**Nicola Boyce**
Ferras	**Lee Moone**
Haliard	**Mark McDonnell**
ROSM, Solarian, Cimmerian	**Ian Brooker**
Cimmerian Voice	**Nicholas Briggs**

TECHNICAL

Story Code	**8J**
Recorded Date	**22, 25 and 26 January 2001**
Release Date	**April 2002**
Place of Recording	**Christchurch Studios, Bristol**
Number of CDs	**2**
Total Duration	**124' 28"**
Number of Episodes	**4**
Duration of Episodes	1 (30' 17") 2 (35' 05") 3 (27' 18") 4 (32' 18")
ISBN	**1-903654-60-2**

SYNOPSIS

Avoiding a fleet of Type 70 TARDISes, the Doctor and Charley arrive in the Cimmerian system, where they are captured by a computerised rescue vehicle, ROSM G273. It is there to investigate a distress signal from a survey team on the fourth planet. Finding Charley to be giving off unusual readings, ROSM decides to terminate her, but she flees the ship in an escape pod which takes her to the survey team's base on Cimmeria IV. There, the base has suffered a power failure and the three members of the team – Orllensa, Ferras and Haliard – are being assaulted by aliens who are using a particle beam to remove their eyes, whispering 'embrace the darkness'. ROSM docks with the base where the Doctor and an assault unit start investigating. Charley encounters one of the aliens – a Cimmerian – who tells her that light is bad. The ROSM assault unit stuns the alien and it is taken aboard the rescue ship for examination. The Cimmerian restores eyesight while the Doctor finds the controls for the artificial suns that are awaiting activation around the planet and switches them on. This is a terrible mistake. The Cimmerians explain that the Solarians came to Cimmeria because they were dying from a plague and that the Cimmerians are healers. However, the sheer number of Solarians meant that the Cimmerians were dying from the effort of curing them and to save themselves they darkened the sun. As the suns illuminate the planet, a fleet of ships enter the system. The crew, along with the Doctor and Charley, leave in the rescue ship, but ROSM has shut down weapons and they are forced to surrender. However, the Solarians turn out to be of the same species as the Cimmerians – archaeologists investigating the mistreatment of the Cimmerians. The Doctor and Charley depart as the two races are reunited.

PLACEMENT

Between **Seasons of Fear #30** and the **Companion Chronicles** story **Solitaire #4.12**, and before **The Time of the Daleks #32**.

TRIVIA

- The fleet of type 70 TARDISes at the beginning of the story are explained in **Neverland #33**.
- The name ROSM is based on the lead character of Rossum in *RUR*, the play by Karel Čapek, which first used the word 'robot', derived from the Czech word for 'forced labour'.
- The story was originally conceived for the Seventh Doctor and Ace and featured a character called Kalendorf – a name Nick Briggs eventually used in his **Dalek Empire** series.
- The story includes a Solarian which the Doctor identifies as sounding familiar. This is because Nick himself thought it rang a bell, completely overlooking the similarity with the name 'Silurian'!
- Nick describes the week in which the recording of this play took place as one of the worst in his life. He'd been involved in a car accident while he was in Bristol, had terrible flu and was suffering from an overbearing girlfriend.

PRODUCTION SUMMARY

"The title is an example of my belief that titles should contrast something nice ('embrace') with something horrible ('darkness'). I remember that Jim Mortimore and I disagreed about the post-production on this story. He wanted to cut most of episode one because he didn't think the acting was as strong as it should be but I pointed out that it would make no sense if we did that! I'm also very proud of the script and my episode one cliff-hanger, where Charley says: 'You've lost your eyes!'."
Nicholas Briggs

WORKING TITLES(S)

Return of the Swarm.

RETURNING MONSTERS/CHARACTERS

None.

Check box - CD ■ MP3 ■

THE TIME OF THE DALEKS

#32

SYNOPSIS

Realising that William Shakespeare is being erased from history, The Doctor takes Charley to a future version of Britain in which its leader, General Mariah Learman, is in charge of a dictatorship and insanely obsessed with Shakespeare. She has been experimenting with time travel using mirrors with the help of a pair of Daleks. They claim to venerate the Bard, but the Doctor doubts this. Indeed, when he and kitchen boy Will examine a Shakespeare play, they find it blank. When an army of Daleks arrives, they take Learman's niece, Viola, Charley and the kitchen boy hostage, forcing the Doctor to work on the master clock mechanism that controls the mirror portals. It is revealed that Learman wants the Daleks to kill Shakespeare so that she alone will know of his genius. The Doctor then learns that there is a fleet of Dalek time ships trapped in the vortex and that when it was endangered by the temporal device

they were using, the pilot and three strategists were sent to engineer this rescue attempt. One of the strategists was killed and the pilot was destroyed by a temporal discharge when Learman touched it upon its arrival. But why? And what was the 'device'? The Dalek Emperor then reveals that his plan to unleash a temporal extinction device are almost complete but they need another pilot, so Learman is mutated and placed in a Dalek casing. The Doctor realises that the Daleks have trapped themselves in a paradox. As they operate the master clock device aboard their ship, everything goes wrong and they send three strategists and the pilot to organise a rescue – as they always have done. The Doctor works out that the kitchen boy is in fact a young Will Shakespeare, rescued by Viola, and returns him to his own time, deeply worried that Charley is the cause of all the paradoxes he has been encountering…

PLACEMENT

Between the **Companion Chronicles** story **Solitaire #4.12** and **Neverland #33**.

TRIVIA

- This story concludes Big Finish's initial Dalek Empire arc (preceded by **The Genocide Machine #7**, **The Apocalypse Element #11** and **The Mutant Phase #15**) and ties in with the stand-alone **Dalek Empire** series.
- Justin had developed the idea and brought along a synopsis to the meeting that took place at the Fitzroy Tavern in London for the Eighth Doctor writers.
- Justin wanted "something that was a striking audio juxtaposition; something that the Daleks would do or say in aural terms that seemed completely out of character, yet could be justified and become a lynchpin of the plot."
- Paul Cornell asked Justin to give him a Dalek falling through time for his 'Roman story' (which turned into **Seasons of Fear #30**).
- There was a special Dalek convention, Day of the Daleks, held at the Adelphi Hotel in Liverpool in 2000 that Justin attended. He couldn't be on the Big Finish panel because his story hadn't been announced, so he had to sit in the audience listening to Nick Briggs talking about the company's plans for the Daleks while he had the script for episode two in his hotel room!
- Justin was very happy with the finished article. "The production was, as ever, absolutely spot on," he says. "Nick's direction and music really enhanced it, and Ian's post-production is a joy. Bit of a baptism of fire for him, I think, but he and Nick – and the cast – made me sound really good!"

PRODUCTION SUMMARY

"Justin's script was fine although I had to add some stuff in. I loved all the Shakespearean dialogue the Daleks had to do. The major problem was that each episode was over 45 minutes long. Back in those days, Big Finish wasn't too concerned if a story overran, but this was immense and it completely knackered Paul McGann. He had come back from a gruelling filming stint so he was tired anyway. I remember that he was almost physically incapable of doing the other plays in the run he was so exhausted. But he's such a professional and has such charisma that we managed it!"
Nicholas Briggs

WORKING TITLES(S)

Time of the Daleks.

RETURNING MONSTERS/CHARACTERS

Daleks.

CREW

Writer	**Justin Richards**
Director	**Nicholas Briggs**
Producers	**Jason Haigh-Ellery**
	Gary Russell
Executive Producer (BBC)	**Jacqueline Rayner**
Music	**Nicholas Briggs**
Sound Design	**Ian Potter**
Cover Art	**Clayton Hickman**
Theme	**David Arnold**

CAST

The Doctor	**Paul McGann**
Charley	**India Fisher**
General Mariah Learman	**Dot Smith**
Major Ferdinand	**Julian Harries**
Viola	**Nicola Boyce**
Kitchen Boy	**Jem Bassett**
Priestly	**Mark McDonnell**
Hart	**Lee Moone**
Professor Osric	**Ian Brooker**
Dalek voice	**Nicholas Briggs**
Dalek voice, Yokel	**Clayton Hickman**
Marcus	**Robert Curbishley**
Mark Anthony, Army Officer, Tannoy	**Ian Potter**
Rassilon	**Don Warrington**

TECHNICAL

Story Code	**8K**
Recorded Date	**22 - 23 January 2001 and 27 February 2002**
Release Date	**May 2002**
Place of Recording	**Christchurch Studios, Bristol**
Number of CDs	**2**
Total Duration	**122' 08"**
Number of Episodes	**4**
Duration of Episodes	**1 (31' 24")**
	2 (31' 02")
	3 (28' 05")
	4 (31' 48")
ISBN	**1-903654-61-0**

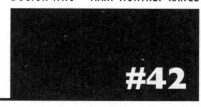

THE DARK FLAME

#42

SYNOPSIS

The Doctor and Ace arrive on Marran Alpha, a planet where Benny is helping the scientists with their experiments in Black Light energy drawn from fluctuations within the space-time continuum. Benny's friend, Victor, has been coerced into digging up the mass grave of a group of fanatics so that his captor, Broke – a devotee of the Dark Flame cult – can find the remains of the cult's leader, Vilus Kull. When Remnex, one of the scientists, is killed, Benny realises that the visions she sees are of black flames and must be linked to the old cult. But another scientist, Slyde, kidnaps Benny and takes her to the planet's subterranean caves where it is revealed he is working with Broke. They then use Remnex's body as a new host for their Emissary. Victor manages to escape and although mortally wounded takes the skull back to the Doctor at the research base and dies as he gives it to the Time Lord. The Doctor gives the skull

to Ace and leaves for the caves. Here he meets the Emissary who resurrects all its dead fanatics. The Doctor explains that the Time Lords believe the Dark Flame evolved at the end of the universe, so comes from the very distant future. Meanwhile, Slyde has been unsuccessful in obtaining the skull from Ace so the Emissary orders the Doctor to retrieve it or his undead followers will kill Benny. With the skull back in his possession, the Emissary intends to use it with the Black Light converter to bring the Dark Flame to this universe. However, the Doctor works out that the Dark Flame is just a force of nature, not sentient. It is being controlled by Kull and that if the Doctor had control, things would be different. So he challenges Kull to a mental duel and while this is happening Benny and Ace deactivate the Black Light converter, sending the Dark Flame back into its pocket dimension.

PLACEMENT

Between **The Shadow of the Scourge #13** and the **Companion Chronicle** release **The Prisoner's Dilemma #3.8**

TRIVIA

- This was novelist Trevor Baxendale's first script for Big Finish. The play makes use of elements such as Black Light converters from the first segment (**The Mysterious Planet**) of the 1986 TV story **The Trial of a Time Lord**.
- Michael Praed, who here plays Slyde, is best known for his role as Robin Hood in the ITV series *Robin of Sherwood*.
- Sylvester McCoy was only available for the first of the two recording days, so it was a long one!
- The Cult of the Dark Flame returns to menace Benny in the **Bernice Summerfield** adventure **The Draconian Rage #4.2**.
- The play also provides an origin story for Joseph, one of the original regulars in the **Bernice Summerfield** range.

PRODUCTION SUMMARY

"After **The Rapture**, this was a much more traditional play. I remember thinking at the time that it would have suited Tom Baker very well because it had so many elements that I associate with his era. I was also very fortunate that I got my first choice of actor for every part in the play. I'd met Michael Praed just before I read the script and he'd said he'd be interested in acting for us if he could play a villainous role. So when I read the script I was hearing Michael's voice. It was a good fit."
Jason Haigh-Ellery

WORKING TITLES(S)

None.

RETURNING MONSTERS/CHARACTERS

None.

CREW

Writer	**Trevor Baxendale**
Director	**Jason Haigh-Ellery**
Producers	**Jason Haigh-Ellery**
	Gary Russell
Executive Producer (BBC)	**Jacqueline Rayner**
Music	**Andy Hardwick @ ERS**
Sound Design	**Gareth Jenkins @ ERS**
Cover Art	**Lee Binding**
Theme	**Keff McCulloch**

CAST

The Doctor	**Sylvester McCoy**
Ace	**Sophie Aldred**
Bernice Summerfield	**Lisa Bowerman**
Slyde	**Michael Praed**
Victor, Joseph	**Steven Wickham**
Remnex	**Andrew Westfield**
Lomar	**Hannah Smith**
Broke	**Toby Longworth**

TECHNICAL

Story Code	**SS4**
Recorded Date	**26 and 27 January 2003**
Release Date	**March 2003**
Place of Recording	**The Moat Studios, London**
Number of CDs	**2**
Total Duration	**115' 59"**
Number of Episodes	**4**
Duration of Episodes	**1 (27' 07")**
	2 (26' 51")
	3 (26' 14")
	4 (35' 47")
ISBN	**1-84435-025-8**

#43

DOCTOR WHO AND THE PIRATES

CREW

Writer	**Jacqueline Rayner**
Director	**Barnaby Edwards**
Producers	**Jason Haigh-Ellery**
	Gary Russell
Executive Producer (BBC)	**Jacqueline Rayner**
Music	**Timothy Sutton**
Sound Design	**David Darlington**
Cover Art	**Lee Binding**
Theme	**Dominic Glynn**

CAST

The Doctor	**Colin Baker**
Evelyn	**Maggie Stables**
Red Jasper	**Bill Oddie**
Jem	**Dan Barratt**
Sally	**Helen Goldwyn**
Swan	**Nicholas Pegg**
Mr. Merriweather	**Mark Siney**
Mate, Sailor, Pirate	**Timothy Sutton**

TECHNICAL

Story Code	**7C/H**
Recorded Date	**22, 23 and 24 January 2003**
Release Date	**April 2003**
Place of Recording	**The Moat Studios, London**
Number of CDs	**2**
Total Duration	**126' 04"**
Number of Episodes	**4**
Duration of Episodes	1 (31' 52")
	2 (30' 41")
	3 (28' 07")
	4 (35' 22")
ISBN	**1-84435-024-X**

SYNOPSIS

Evelyn tells a story to her student, Sally… She and the Doctor arrive aboard the merchant ship *Sea Eagle* as the ship comes under attack from the pirate Red Jasper and his crew aboard the *Adventurer's Fancy*. Evelyn admits to Sally that it she is not telling the story very well; she is embellishing and exaggerating. When The Doctor turns up at Sally's door he shares the telling of the story so they get it right. The pirates were actually hunting for the treasure of a man called Trent. Evelyn is saved by a cabin boy called Jem and together with Captain Swan they escape from the ship on a raft. It is revealed that Trent is dead, but that Jem is his son who knows where to find the treasure. Evelyn says she cannot tell any more of the story as it is too horrible. So the Doctor determines to treat the rest of the story as a musical. He sings about being the very model of a Gallifreyan buccaneer. Amazingly, Sally joins in the singing. Evelyn tells her that she knows about the tragic car accident that killed Sally's lover. The raft catches up with the pirate ship allowing Evelyn and Jem to climb aboard where they are captured and the Doctor is made to walk the plank. He is picked up by Swan in the raft and they head after the pirate ship as it makes for the treasure once more. Due to a mistake Evelyn makes, Jasper finds out that Jem is Trent's son and beats him to death. The Doctor and Swan reach the island on which the treasure is buried. While Jasper searches the island the Doctor gets back aboard the pirate ship with the loot and convinces the crew to maroon Jasper. The ship leaves with Swan once more in command and the Doctor leaves in the TARDIS with Evelyn. The Doctor sends Evelyn home and tells Sally that they came to see her through the first night after her lover's death to the renewed optimism of the morning…

PLACEMENT

Between **Jubilee #40** and **Project: Lazarus #45** and before **Arrangements for War #57**.

TRIVIA

- The 'Hecate - not sure that's canonical' line was added to the Major General's song by Barnaby Edwards.
- The ship Sea Eagle was named after a character from an old *Advanced Dungeons and Dragons* campaign that writer Jacqueline Rayner played as a teenager; only later did she find out it was an inn in **The Highlanders**, too!
- Red Jasper was named in honour of a ginger cat called Jasper of whom the author had been very fond.
- Jac's love of Gilbert & Sullivan started with seeing the TV broadcast of Jonathan Miller's production of *The Mikado* starring Eric Idle. She provided a tape of the various songs used in *Pirates* for Barnaby Edwards, including a number from this production.
- The Doctor/Merryweather battle was supposed to be to 'Anything You Can Do' from *Annie Get Your Gun*, but permission was refused to use this with altered words, so everything became Gilbert & Sullivan – which turned out to be a better idea anyway, so a blessing in disguise!
- The songs come from W. S. Gilbert and Arthur Sullivan's comic operas *HMS Pinafore*, *The Pirates of Penzance* and *The Mikado*.
- Jac's original proposal was a straight pirate story featuring the Fifth Doctor, Peri and Erimem.

PRODUCTION SUMMARY

"This one was really Barney and Jac's baby. Without Jac's brilliant script and songs we would have had nothing and without Barney's dedication and contacts book, we might have been, well, sunk! Jason and I knew this one would take a lot of extra time in terms of rehearsals and a bit of extra effort and money."
Gary Russell

WORKING TITLES(S)

The Pirates, Doctor Who in an exciting adventure with the Pirates, Doctor Who in an exciting adventure with some Pirates

RETURNING MONSTERS/CHARACTERS

None.

Check box - CD ■ MP3 ■

CREATURES OF BEAUTY

#44

SYNOPSIS

The Doctor and Nyssa arrive on the planet Veln, where the inhabitants have been the victim of a disfiguring genetic condition for 100 years. The disease came about when a Koteem ship transporting lethal toxins is destroyed when it avoids a collision with a mysterious ship that then disappears. Although the Koteem are extremely contrite for this disaster, the Veln want nothing to do with them: a feeling embodied by security officer Gilbrook who is fanatical about tracking down illegal Koteem immigrants. The planet is dying, no food will grow and the race is becoming ever more disfigured and mutated. Within Veln society there are those who have used cosmetic surgery to correct the disfigurement. These people are referred to as 'beauties' but are hated by the rest of the population.

This element of Veln society is represented by Lady Forleon, but it is revealed that she is in league with the Koteem, though only to find a cure for the diseases and safeguard the future of the Veln race. This is something that Gilbrook cannot understand nor conscience. It transpires that this cure means transferring the essence of a Koteem into the body of a Veln. Very little remains of the Koteem personality, but this is a price they seem willing to pay for their dreadful actions of the past. Instead of actively influencing events, the Doctor and Nyssa find themselves out of their depths — captured, interrogated and rescued — and instead help highlight the differing viewpoints and morals in the story. However, as they escape the planet, it is revealed that it was the TARDIS that caused the disaster in the first place…

PLACEMENT

Between **Spare Parts #34** and **The Game #66**.

TRIVIA

- Nick Briggs wrote the episodes and scenes in thematic order rather than in a linear order.
- The part of Gilbrook was originally offered to Clive Swift (who appeared in two **Doctor Who** stories on TV – **Revelation of the Daleks** and **Voyage of the Damned**) but he was not available and the role was instead played by David Daker (who also appeared in two **Doctor Who** stories on TV – **The Time Warrior** and **Nightmare of Eden**)!
- Nick wanted to play to the fact that we know the Doctor will survive by showing that he does in the very first scene.
- Big Finish received some of the discs back from customers who thought there was an error on them and that the scenes had been put together in the wrong order!

PRODUCTION SUMMARY

"When David Daker arrived I noticed that he wore two hearing aids. One of the actors who had worked with him before went up to him and was almost nose to nose speaking extremely loudly. And I thought 'ooh'. We went to put the headphones on him and he said 'I might have a problem with that', and there were a few moments where David's hearing aids did whistle. He's a great actor but because he was hard of hearing, he wasn't in control of when he was voiced and when he wasn't. So I had to do multiple takes of everything. I got all I needed but I had to put everything together in post-production and it was the hardest thing I've ever had to do on an audio."
Nicholas Briggs

WORKING TITLES(S)

None.

RETURNING MONSTERS/CHARACTERS

None.

CREW

Writer	**Nicholas Briggs**
Director	**Nicholas Briggs**
Producers	**Jason Haigh-Ellery**
	Gary Russell
Executive Producer (BBC)	**Jacqueline Rayner**
Music and Sound Design	**Nicholas Briggs**
Cover Art	**Paul Burley**
Theme	**Peter Howell**

CAST

The Doctor	**Peter Davison**
Nyssa	**Sarah Sutton**
Gilbrook	**David Daker**
Brodlik	**David Mallinson**
Lady Forleon	**Jemma Churchill**
Quain	**Nigel Hastings**
Seedleson	**Michael Smiley**
Murone	**Philip Wolff**
Veline	**Emma Manton**
Koteem, Morgue Attendant, Police Officer, Guard, Control, Captain Delarphim, Pilot	**Nicholas Briggs**

TECHNICAL

Story Code	**6C/F**
Recorded Date	**22 and 24 March 2003**
Release Date	**May 2003**
Place of Recording	**The Moat Studios, London**
Number of CDs	**2**
Total Duration	**109' 23"**
Number of Episodes	**4**
Duration of Episodes	**1 (26' 21")**
	2 (30' 01")
	3 (24' 40")
	4 (28' 21")
ISBN	**1-84435-026-6**

#45 PROJECT: LAZARUS

CREW

Writers	**Cavan Scott**
	Mark Wright
Director	**Gary Russell**
Producers	**Jason Haigh-Ellery**
	Gary Russell
Executive Producer (BBC)	**Jacqueline Rayner**
Music	**Andy Hardwick @ ERS**
Sound Design	**Gareth Jenkins @ ERS**
Cover Art	**Lee Binding**
Theme	**Dominic Glynn**

CAST

The Doctor	**Colin Baker**
Evelyn	**Maggie Stables**
The Doctor	**Sylvester McCoy**
Nimrod	**Stephen Chance**
Cassie	**Rosie Cavaliero**
Oracle	**Emma Collier**
Sergeant Frith	**Adam Woodroffe**
Dr. Crumpton	**Ingrid Evans**
Professor Harket	**Vidar Magnussen**
Soldier	**Mark Wright**

TECHNICAL

Story Code	**7C/J - 7X**
Recorded Date	**17 and 19 January 2003**
Release Date	**June 2003**
Place of Recording	**The Moat Studios, London**
Number of CDs	**2**
Total Duration	**125' 15"**
Number of Episodes	**4**
Duration of Episodes	**1 (26' 25")**
	2 (27' 52")
	3 (22' 48")
	4 (28' 10")
ISBN	**1-84435-027-4**

SYNOPSIS

The Doctor and Evelyn travel to Norway in 2004 to find Cassie because they have found a cure to the virus developed by the vampire Amelia in **Project: Twilight #23**. However, they find that she is now working for the Forge under the name Artemis. The Doctor is captured and Nimrod tries to force the Doctor to regenerate by electrocuting him so that he can record the results and use them. Evelyn manages to convince Cassie that Nimrod has brainwashed her; she has even forgotten about her son, whom she had put up for adoption. Evelyn also confides in Cassie that she has a heart condition which she has been hiding from the Doctor. Cassie then frees the Doctor, but is killed by Nimrod. Evelyn is furious and deeply upset with the Doctor as she thinks he abandoned her to her death. Some four years later, the Seventh Doctor follows an anomaly he has detected in the vortex to the Forge. He is surprised to find his Sixth self acting as the Forge's scientific advisor. Meanwhile, Nimrod is experimenting on an alien called a Huldran. When others of its species attack the Forge to free the Huldran, the Sixth Doctor has his arm cut off in the assault. The Seventh Doctor realises that this never happened and 'makes contact' telepathically to the 'Sixth Doctor'. He discovers that his earlier self is a clone, created from DNA extracted during Nimrod's experiments on the real Sixth Doctor. Working together, they discover that Nimrod has created countless other clones of the Doctor and in order to stop them, the Doctor clone impersonates Nimrod and activates the base's Hades protocol. The Seventh Doctor manages to escapes with the human Forge staff as well as the Huldran. However, despite being completely destroyed, the Forge's computer, Oracle, announces that the Forge Beta facility has been brought online...

PLACEMENT

For the Sixth Doctor: between **Doctor Who and the Pirates #43** and **Arrangements for War #57**.
For the Seventh Doctor: between the **Excelis** story **Excelis Decays #3** and **Master #49**.

TRIVIA

- Mark Wright and Cavan Scott pitched two separate four part stories to Gary Russell who decided to truncate them into one story. "This was anniversary year and seemed appropriate to release a multi-Doctor story in addition to **Zagreus**," says Mark.
- The decision to give Evelyn a heart condition was made at the same lunch meeting with Gary Russell at which the parentage of the Seventh Doctor's upcoming new companion, Hex, was decided.
- Norwegian Professor Harket was named after the lead singer of a-Ha, Morten Harket.
- When the Seventh Doctor telepathically melds with the clone of the Sixth Doctor, the sound FX used is that from **The Three Doctors** when the Time Lords link minds.
- The Forge vaults contain a sample of Axonite
- This story was released with two different CD covers; one for each Doctor that the story featured. Both covers could be placed side by side to create one complete image.
- The story of the Forge between **Project: Twilight #23** and **Project: Lazarus #45** is told in the Big Finish *New Worlds* novel *Project: Valhalla*.

PRODUCTION SUMMARY

"I don't recall this being two stories, but I do remember giving them permission to do a multi-Doctor story. Sort of. Then the first draft scripts came in and they were in serious need of work. Then we had a debate about where to set the first episode and in the end I got my way – as I usually do! I think Cav and Mark agree with me in hindsight. I think my friend Robert Dick suggested that the release have two covers on a train back from a *Doctor Who* convention in Stockton."
Gary Russell

WORKING TITLES(S)

The Forge, Project: Forge, BioForge, Project: Artemis, Project: Enigma

RETURNING MONSTERS/CHARACTERS

Nimrod, Cassie.

FLIP-FLOP

SYNOPSIS

BLACK

While Slithergee patrols are searching for them, the Doctor and Mel arrive on Puxatornee in the year 3090 to find leptonite crystals. They are arrested by Potter, who seems to know them. This is witnessed by Stewart and Reed. President Bailey meets with the Slithergee Community Leader to discuss reparation. The Doctor and Mel are interrogated by Capra, but are rescued by Stewart and Reed. The Doctor takes the leptonite crystals from Capra's machine and they leave. Reed explains that 30 years ago the Slithergee arrived and asked for sanctuary on the Puxatornee moon because their homeworld had been destroyed. President Bailey allowed them to do so. However the laws became bias towards the aliens and now humans are second class citizens who are only good to serve as sight guides to the blind Slithergee. Stewart and Reed know about the TARDIS and intend to use it to travel back in time and assassinate Bailey. While the Slithergee finally take over, the TARDIS travels back to 3060 where Stewart kills Bailey and her lover, Clarence. Assuming Clarence was a Slithergee assassin, Bailey's deputy, Mitchell, takes over and declares war on the Slithergee. The Doctor and Mel return Stewart and Reed to 3090. They learn that the humans won the war against the Slithergee but the planet is now a radioactive wasteland. Stewart and Reed demand the Doctor takes them back to the previous day to prevent themselves from going back. There, Stewart and Reed have alternative versions of themselves – security officers. The Doctor and Mel are arrested and taken to the palace. They reveal they know about Capra and his leptonite-powered machine, but Capra reveals he hasn't come up with the right power source yet. The Doctor and Mel escape with the leptonite in the TARDIS – just as another version of the TARDIS materialises…

WHITE

While human security patrols are searching for them the Doctor and Mel arrive on Puxatornee in the year 3090 to find leptonite crystals. This is witnessed by Stewart and Reed who arrest them as known fugitives. Reed tells them that 30 years ago the Slithergee arrived and asked for sanctuary on the Puxatornee moon. Before President Bailey could make a decision she was killed by a Slithergee agent. The humans then attacked and the planet became a radioactive wasteland. All that is going to change because Professor Capra has built a time machine which will allow them to go back and change the past. The other Stewart and Reed then turn up to rescue the Doctor and Mel but are killed by Potter. The Doctor and Mel make it to Capra's lab but the time machine has been activated and Mel and Stewart are sent back in time. The Doctor takes the leptonite crystals from Capra's machine and he leaves with Reed as the machine explodes. The TARDIS travels back to 3060 where Stewart kills Clarence, believing him to be a Slithergee assassin. The Doctor decides that letting Bailiey live is the lesser of two evils. Bailey tells Mitchell she killed Clarence and orders him to allow the Slithergee to settle on the moon. The Doctor and Mel return Stewart and Reed to 3090 where Bailey is still dead and Mitchell is President. Bailey completely surrendered the planet to the Slithergee. Stewart and Reed demand that the Doctor takes them back so they can prevent themselves from going back in time. When they do they find that President Bailey is alive and about to meet with the Slithergee Community Leader to discuss reparation for the race's treatment by the humans. When Mel meets this reality's Stewart and Reed she reveals that she has come here in a time machine. The Doctor and Mel escape with the leptonite crystals in the TARDIS – just as another version of time machine materialises…

PLACEMENT

Between **Bang-Bang-A-Boom! #39** and the TV story **Delta and the Bannermen**.

TRIVIA

- The story is told over two CDs, one black, one white and the CDs can be listened to in either order.
- The planet Puxatornee is named after the town that appears in the film *Groundhog Day*.
- The story borrows elements from *It's a Wonderful Life*. The professor is named after director Frank Capra, the two lieutenants are named after the films' stars (James Stewart and Donna Reed), the president's lover is named after Clarence Odbody, while the President himself is named after the film's protagonist (George Bailey).
- The line that Leptonite will cause a Quark to 'go berserk and explode' was inspired by the classic track 'Quark Goes Berserk and Explodes' on the *Doctor Who Sound Effects* album.

PRODUCTION SUMMARY

"What we wanted to achieve with **Flip-Flop** was something new. The idea came to me in the bath and Jonny delivered in spades. Of course, the whole thing was criticised at the time because two releases earlier we had **Creatures of Beauty**, which also played with the idea of narrative structure!

WORKING TITLES(S)

Vice Versa.

Check box - CD ■ MP3 ■

CREW

Writer	**Jonathan Morris**
Director	**Gary Russell**
Producers	**Jason Haigh-Ellery**
	Gary Russell
Executive Producer (BBC)	**Jacqueline Rayner**
Music and Sound Design	**David Darlington**
Cover Art	**Lee Binding**
Theme	**Keff McCulloch**

CAST

The Doctor	**Sylvester McCoy**
Melanie	**Bonnie Langford**
Mitchell	**Richard Gibson**
Bailey	**Pamela Miles**
Stewart	**Francis Magee**
Reed	**Audrey Schoelhammer**
Potter	**Trevor Littledale**
Professor Capra	**Trevor Martin**
Slithergee, Clarence	**Daniel Hogarth**
Security Guard	**David Darlington**

TECHNICAL

Story Code	**7E/B**
Recorded Date	**16 and 17 March 2003**
Release Date	**August 2003**
Place of Recording	**The Moat Studios, London**
Number of CDs	**2**
Total Duration	**125' 50"**
Number of Episodes	**2 x 2**
Duration of Episodes	**BLACK:**
	1 (34' 41")
	2 (28' 41")
	WHITE:
	1 (31' 35")
	2 (30' 53")
ISBN	**1-84435-028-2**

#47 OMEGA

CREW

Writer	**Nev Fountain**
Director	**Gary Russell**
Producers	**Jason Haigh-Ellery**
	Gary Russell
Executive Producer (BBC)	**Jacqueline Rayner**
Music	**Russell Stone**
Sound Design	**Gareth Jenkins @ ERS**
Cover Art	**Clayton Hickman**
Theme	**Peter Howell**

CAST

The Doctor	**Peter Davison**
Omega	**Ian Collier**
Sentia	**Caroline Munro**
Professor Ertikus, Luvis	**Patrick Duggan**
Daland	**Hugo Myatt**
Tarpov, Rassilon	**Conrad Westmaas**
Zagreus	**Jim Sangster**
Maven	**Faith Kent**
Glinda	**Anita Elias**
MediBot, VidiBot, Scintillans, Mugging Machine	**Gary Russell**

TECHNICAL

Story Code	**6E/A**
Recorded Date	**4 and 5 February 2003**
Release Date	**August 2003**
Place of Recording	**The Moat Studios, London**
Number of CDs	**2**
Total Duration	**140' 46"**
Number of Episodes	**4**
Duration of Episodes	**1 (31' 17")**
	2 (36' 18")
	3 (30' 27")
	4 (42' 44")
ISBN	**1-84435-029-0**

SYNOPSIS

The Doctor joins a Jolly Chronolidays ship as it sets out to recreate the history of the renegade Time Lord called Omega. He meets the tour guide, Sentia, and an historian called Ertikus and together they board a mock-up of Omega's ship, *Eurydice*. There, actors Daland and Tarpov perform the roles of Omega and his assistant Vandekirian. The story goes that Vandekirian was secretly working for Rassilon and cut off his hand as a penitence for his betrayal. However, Omega cuts his other hand off and places it in a stellar manipulator. Later, Tarpov is found with his hand chopped off. However, the Doctor realises that Tarpov could not have done it himself and must have been attacked by someone else. The Doctor then encounters Omega on an ethereal plane. Omega explains that he has been using Sentia's telepathic ability to pull his dissipated body back together. The Doctor cannot work out how Omega is managing to appear to him but then the real Eurydice appears. Ertikus is revealed to be a Time Lord and, as the Doctor says his TARDIS is 'unavailable', Ertikus uses his own time ship to take the Doctor to Omega's TARDIS. Omega tells the Doctor that he wishes to return to the anti-matter universe. However, it slowly becomes apparent to the Doctor that someone else must be acting on Omega's behalf but it cannot be any of the people on board… All is revealed when the TARDIS materialises and the real Doctor emerges. It transpires that Omega has developed a schizophrenic personality after the bungled attempt to take over the Doctor's body in Amsterdam; his personality is half Doctor and half Omega. Due to this madness, Omega kills Tarpov and Ertikus and beats Sentia – the woman he loves. To save the tourists, the Doctor and Daland usher them aboard the TARDIS and Omega is sent back into his anti-matter universe although Sentia is killed in the process.

PLACEMENT

Between the TV stories **Arc of Infinity** and **Snakedance**.

TRIVIA

- The first story in the 'villains' trilogy was originally going to feature the Celestial Toymaker. However, Gary Russell decided to use the character of Omega instead. The Celestial Toymaker does eventually turn up in **The Magic Mousetrap #120** and the **Companion Chronicles** release **Solitaire #4.12**.
- Writer Nev Fountain is perhaps best known for his comedy writing for the sketch series, *Dead Ringers* but he was also script editor on the BBC's webcast, **Death Comes to Time**.
- The play features Ian Collier, reprising the role of Omega, which he last played in the 1983 TV story **Arc of Infinity**.
- Nev Fountain had already sent in an idea to Gary but the producer had not picked it up. "It probably exploded any fanboy-o-meters in the vicinity," Nev explains. "Well, you've got to start somewhere haven't you?"
- Nev wanted his story for Omega to be about history. "It's the perception of history, and how easy it is for history to distort how you remember characters and people," the writer says. "The fact we see Richard III as a villain and Richard the Lionheart as a hero is simply down to accidents of history!"
- The script of this story appeared with a detailed behind-the-scenes essay on its writing in *Doctor Who: The Audio Scripts – Volume Four*.
- The casting of Jim Sangster in the one-line role of the tour guide 'Zagreus' was a deliberate tease for the audience after the events of **Neverland #33**. Sangster was asked to use his own Liverpool accent as a reference to Paul McGann's home town.

PRODUCTION SUMMARY

"I actually wanted to do a Celestial Toymaker story originally, but Michael Gough didn't want to play the part again and I didn't want to recast. I did have a back-up plan – I always did. I'd directed Ian Collier in Craig Hinton's **Excelis** play and I thought it would be a wheeze if we had an Omega story. And I knew that Nev wanted to write for us as he had already been in contact. As it turned out, the timings were mad because of Peter's schedule on *At Home with the Braithwaites* and I had to edit episodes one and two in a big hurry!"
Gary Russell

WORKING TITLES(S)

None.

RETURNING MONSTERS/CHARACTERS

Omega.

DAVROS

SYNOPSIS

A husband and wife team, Arnold and Lorraine Baynes attack a freighter carrying Davros's body in suspended animation. They take the body and leave in their interceptor space craft, returning to the domed headquarters of their galactic corporation, Trans Allied Inc (TAI). Meanwhile, the Doctor has arrived there, too, summoned by a journalist – Willis – who is investigating rumours that Baynes intends to shut down all the mining operations in the galaxy. As soon as the Doctor sees Davros he becomes involved with TAI and when Arnold offers Davros a job, the Doctor offers his services instead. However, the CEO offers them both a job and reluctantly the Doctor goes to work with Davros. Lorraine is a big Davros fan and believes he is a misunderstood genius. Meanwhile the Doctor, Willis and another TAI worker, Kim Todd, discover a secret production line of robots. Davros has analysed the stock market and hatches a plan to

make it redundant so that he can impose a "war-time" economy of slave labour, armament factories and a scientific elite. Davros detonates a nuclear bomb that he has built, apparently killing the Doctor and Arnold and allowing him to seize control of the company from Lorraine. The bomb has fractured a subterranean lake. Separated from the Doctor, Arnold takes the opportunity to kill Willis and then escapes with the Doctor. They confront Davros and the Doctor uses the robots on the production line to rescue the trapped workers in the dome. Davros kills Arnold and then escapes in the interceptor, taking Kim with him as a hostage. Realising that the Doctor won't act while she is alive, Kim takes her own life and the Doctor reluctantly operates the ship's hyperdrive remotely, forcing it to explode on the planet's surface. He then retrieves the record of the Baynes's attack on the freighter so that Lorraine will be arrested for her crimes.

PLACEMENT

Between the TV stories **The Two Doctors** and the subscriber bonus story **Cryptobiosis #IV** as well as the TV story **Timelash**.

TRIVIA

- This play was part of Big Finish's celebration of **Doctor Who**'s 40th anniversary, along with **Omega #47** and **Master #49**.
- This play does not feature any Daleks; this is the first time that Davros appears on his own in a Big Finish audio drama. In the Doctor's timeline this is the first Big Finish audio to feature the character.
- Peri is mentioned – attending a botany symposium – but she is not in the play.
- This play is the first to use the Season 22 arrangement of the theme and the first Sixth Doctor adventure to conform to the format of two long episodes rather than four shorter ones. The next story to do this is **The Reaping #86**, three years later.
- It was shortly after the release of this play that the BBC announced the return of **Doctor Who** to TV in 2005.
- "Gary was quite happy with all the stuff I thought I wouldn't get away with" says writer Lance Parkin. "There are some fun things with the structure and storytelling that I got to do that really help the story. Gary also told me to delve into Davros's origins. The thing I brought to the table was my belief that Davros was almost certainly a complete git well before his accident!"
- The original script for **Davros** was in four parts but was edited into two not only to mimic the era in which the story is set but also because the play was very long and there was no room for three reprises from previous episodes!

PRODUCTION SUMMARY

"I always wanted us to do a play that featured Davros but that didn't have any Daleks. I also knew that Lance would be perfect for it. I also loved this cast. I'd known Terry Molloy for ages and of course, because it was Colin it had to be his Davros. Then we had the lovely Wendy Padbury – who was Colin's agent – and Bernard Horsfall, whose participation was down to an introduction by David Bickerstaff."
Gary Russell

WORKING TITLES(S)

None.

RETURNING MONSTERS/CHARACTERS

Davros.

CREW

Writer	**Lance Parkin**
Director	**Gary Russell**
Producers	**Jason Haigh-Ellery**
	Gary Russell
Executive Producer (BBC)	**Jacqueline Rayner**
Music	**Jane Elphinstone**
Sound Design	**Jim Mortimore**
Cover Art	**Clayton Hickman**
Theme	**Peter Howell**

CAST

The Doctor	**Colin Baker**
Davros	**Terry Molloy**
Arnold Baynes	**Bernard Horsfall**
Lorraine Baynes	**Wendy Padbury**
Willis	**Eddie de Oliveira**
Kimberly Todd	**Ruth Sillers**
Shan, Computer, Earpiece Voice	**Katarina Olsson**
Ral	**David Bickerstaff**
Kaled Medics	**Louise Faulkner**
	Karl Hansen
Pilot	**Andrew Westfield**

TECHNICAL

Story Code	**6W/A**
Recorded Date	**27 and 28 January 2003**
Release Date	**September 2003**
Place of Recording	**The Moat Studios, London**
Number of CDs	**2**
Total Duration	**151' 56"**
Number of Episodes	**2**
Duration of Episodes	**1 (73' 52")**
	2 (78' 04")
ISBN	**1-84435-030-4**

Me and India got on like a house on fire which made life much easier.

Paul is an accomplished voice actor and I learnt a lot from him. There was a ludicrous rumour that he recorded all his dialogue separately – we howled with laughter at that one.

How was your relationship with Gary Russell?

Gary is like a big brother to a lot of us. He does things his own way and can be an easy target for some of his more 'out there' ideas, but if it wasn't for his imagination, passion and big heart, fandom and Doctor Who as we know it would have savaged itself to bits long ago.

What changed when Nick Briggs took over?

Me and Nick became good friends and I was blown away by the generosity and commitment he and Barnaby Edwards put into my send-off – they were under no obligation to ask me back and I'll always be grateful to them for the care they took over it. I haven't heard any of the range since but I'm sure it's flourishing.

How were Big Finish to work with as a whole?

Big Finish were great to work with. Like anything that people are passionate about it can be hard to keep perspective but if there were any backstage politics we were kept out of it. If India or I ever started to lose the plot, we'd just go for a drink or a run and remind ourselves we were lucky to be working!

The toughest bit of the job was the internet in-fighting that Russell T. Davies rightly describes as a 'carrion feast'. Some fans simply have no idea how damaging and futile all that jealous sniping can be. **Doctor Who** is a creative, optimistic show but is sometimes stifled by what amounts to boys squabbling over train sets. Thankfully, it was more than made up for by all the people who were constructive or supportive.

If you could start over with C'rizz what would you do differently?

With the benefit of hindsight, I'd worry less about what people thought and just jump in with something bolder. C'rizz seemed contradictory and changeable and I was pretty inexperienced at the time so I just did my best to fit in with Paul and India, learn fast and throw ideas in where I could. One thing I might have pushed for was a character name that was pronounceable – we were forever explaining to the guest cast how to say it! I think he was originally called 'Kriz' but that had been done before.

How satisfied were you with your character's demise?

I was very pleased with his departure. With the new

TV series and a change of hands at Big Finish I hadn't expected any leaving story at all. He was only supposed to be a short-term companion so to notch up five years was way more than I expected. Right from the start we'd discussed how he should leave and there was talk of a *Hellraiser*-style TARDIS-bound story with the Fendahl which would have been interesting given C'rizz's relationship with death. I think it was always the plan for C'rizz to die somehow and I said I didn't want any half-measures, so when I found out that he'd get Jedi-trained by Robert Glenister, turn into the devil and absorb a planet's-worth of souls before saying goodbye, I had no complaints!

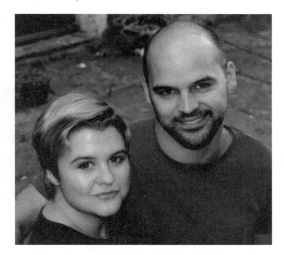

Left:
'Me and India got on like a house on fire…'
Conrad with his partner in crime, India Fisher.

Below:
Conrad and Paul McGann share a laugh during recording of the Eighth Doctor audios.

THE NATURAL HISTORY OF FEAR

#54

CREW

Writer	**Jim Mortimore**
Director	**Gary Russell**
Producers	**Jason Haigh-Ellery**
	Gary Russell
Executive Producer (BBC)	**Jacqueline Rayner**
Music and Sound Design	**Jim Mortimore**
Cover Art	**Steve Johnson**
Theme	**David Arnold**

CAST

The Doctor, The Editor	**Paul McGann**
Charley, The Wife, The Nurse, The New Conscience	**India Fisher**
Crizz, The Conscience	**Conrad Westmaas**
Other Characters	**Geoff Searle**
	Alison Sterling
	Sean Carlsen
	Wink Taylor
	Jane Hills
	Ben Summers

TECHNICAL

Story Code	**8Q**
Recorded Date	**11 and 12 May 2003**
Release Date	**February 2004**
Place of Recording	**Christchurch Studios, Bristol**
Number of CDs	**2**
Total Duration	**129' 19"**
Number of Episodes	**4**
Duration of Episodes	**1 (29' 02")**
	2 (32' 07")
	3 (26' 05")
	4 (42' 32")
ISBN	**1-84435-038-X**

SYNOPSIS

After an incident in the totalitarian Light City, a female Prole (who sounds like Charley) is arrested by the Conscience, a type of thought police (who sounds like C'rizz). He sends her for personality revision and reports this to the Editor (apparently the Doctor). The Conscience then visits the Disc Jockey, the man in charge of Light City's 'infotainments', which are based on the Doctor's adventures. The Editor and the Conscience then discover that the female Prole is harbouring strange images in her memory, including a spinning top. The Conscience reveals to the Nurse that he is part of a revolution. He tells her that they had pieced together all the Doctor's memories from the infotainments. She was going to use them to become the Doctor, but it failed. The Conscience is arrested but as he is taken away for revision, the Editor confesses that he believes in the revolution, too.

Later, several terrorist attacks take place and believing he is going mad, the Editor confronts the DJ. He makes the Editor listen to a tape of the Doctor, who has the same voice. It is revealed that the Editor is carrying out the attacks. The new Conscience – the former Nurse – arrests him but the Editor escapes. The Conscience catches up with him, but she begins to remember Charlotte Pollard and confesses that the Doctor's original memories are hidden in the spinning top. The Editor then destroys the tape, saving the state he loves so much. It turns out that the Doctor, Charley and C'rizz were in Light City, but the Doctor gave the state his memories in return for his friends' lives. The state has used these memories to ferment a revolution, thus helping it to evolve. The Doctor and his companions actually left the city a long, long time ago.

PLACEMENT

Between **The Creed of the Kromon #53** and **The Twilight Kingdom #56**.

TRIVIA

- There is no cast list given either on the CD or the Big Finish website. Inside the CD it states this is because: "the performances were more important than the actual names of characters".
- In the course of the story, Light City's DJ mentions an unmade adventure of the Hero called 'Dark Rising'. This was a reference to the unused story by Mark Michalowski (see **Master #49**).
- "Jim was the only writer in 2004 that I had worked with previously, back in the days of the amateur *Audio Visuals* plays of the 1980s," says Gary Russell.
- "I have an aversion to doubling up actors normally," says Gary Russell, "but Jim opted to provide me with a script where not only could the actors double up but in fact needed to – resulting in probably our largest character list in a play so far. But that's what's so clever about this play, it subverts your expectations – particularly mine. When Paul McGann turned up on his first day (we recorded this one first), he announced that this was one of the best scripts he'd ever read – not just **Who**-wise – but of all. He liked the political touches and said when we'd finished 'more like this, please'."
- Jim Mortimore wanted to direct this play himself.

PRODUCTION SUMMARY

"They're all spiders at the end! Only on audio can you pull off something like that! Jim's best thing he's ever written! And we had a great cast for that. It was a really fun day. It was hard because there was all this dialogue going on in the background of the people walking through the city talking in rote. And we actually had people walking in a circle with two of the microphones in the middle of the room. So we created a whole soundscape actually in the studio with people going every which way. That was Alistair's idea and it worked brilliantly."
Gary Russell

WORKING TITLES(S)

None.

RETURNING MONSTERS/CHARACTERS

None.

THE TWILIGHT KINGDOM

#55

SYNOPSIS

The Doctor, Charley and C'rizz become involved in the hunt for war hero turned rebel, Major Koth, who is hiding out with his rebels in a cave system on a jungle planet. While Charley is captured and taken to the rebel base in the caves, the Doctor and C'rizz are taken prisoner by the soldiers seeking Koth and his base. However, since coming to the planet, Koth has gained powers while living in the cave and is spoken to by two voices. When the Doctor enters the cave, he manages to stave off a massive psychic attack. They find Koth and it soon becomes clear that whatever is at work in the caves is affecting everyone, including Charley and C'rizz. It also becomes clear that the other camps where Koth sends people he 'promotes', do not exist. The Doctor confronts Koth but finds a charnel house of living organs, harvested from the rebels. He surmises that the cave system is actually a living entity akin to a Venus flytrap. When it consumed Koth it also consumed his anger and loss and it has been drawing new recruits to itself to feast. The Time Lord then realises that Koth's life is coming to an end and the creature needs another to take his place. The creature summons the TARDIS and the Doctor suspects that although the circumstances of its creation are an accident, it has been set up by a third party. To prevent the powerful creature from killing everyone, the Doctor merges with it. However, one of Koth's followers, Janto, takes his place and his love for his dead wife effectively kills the creature. This allows the Doctor and his friends to escape but the TARDIS dematerialises before they can board. As the Kro'ka opens up the interzone, the Doctor now knows he must search for Rassilon...

PLACEMENT

Between **The Natural History of Fear #54** and **Faith Stealer #61**.

TRIVIA

- Will Schindler was one of the 'new to Big Finish' writers Gary Russell wanted to use in 2004. He had been a script editor on *Doctors* and *Born and Bred* and was story editor on *The Bill* at the time he wrote this play.
- Gary Russell gave Will the brief that the story needed to contrast with both Philip Martin's and Jim Mortimore's scripts. He also asked that it be set in a cave system.
- Alan Rothwell (who here plays Byzar Janto) is famous in the UK for presenting the children's TV programme *Picture Box* between 1969 and 1990, and for playing David Barlow in the first few years of *Coronation Street*. He is also the man who – at the time – Gary Russell would have cast as the Doctor if he'd been given the chance!
- "I met Michael Keating before Big Finish started," says Gary. "He's one of the most underrated actors around. As soon as I read the script, I could hear Mike as the villain of the piece and asked him to do it."
- Michael Keating is best known as revolutionary Vila Restil in *Blake's 7*, and also appeared as Goudry in the **Doctor Who** TV story **The Sunmakers**.

PRODUCTION SUMMARY

"Will was a friend of Rob Shearman's and he was Rob's script editor on *Born and Bred*. Rob introduced me in a Starbucks on Regents Street and said 'this is Will, he wants to write *Doctor Who* for you'. So I said, 'yeah' and he turned in the script and I really liked it because everything in that first season was weird and this was a straightforward **Doctor Who** story. It was a romp, good guys versus bad guys. But it was really clever and had some interesting characters. Although all the main characters were male and only had surnames! So I made one a woman and gave everyone first names."
Gary Russell

WORKING TITLES(S)

None.

RETURNING MONSTERS/CHARACTERS

The Kro'ka.

CREW

Writer	**Will Shindler**
Director	**Gary Russell**
Producers	**Jason Haigh-Ellery**
	Gary Russell
Executive Producer (BBC)	**Jacqueline Rayner**
Music and Sound Design	**ERS**
Cover Art	**Steve Johnson**
Theme	**David Arnold**

CAST

The Doctor	**Paul McGann**
Charley	**India Fisher**
C'Rizz	**Conrad Westmaas**
Koth	**Michael Keating**
Janto	**Alan Rothwell**
Vayla	**Ann Carus-Wilson**
Quillian	**Dale Ibbetson**
Bryn	**Jeremy James**
Tysus	**Vivien Parry**
Koth's Wife	**Alison Sterling**
The Kro'ka	**Stephen Perring**

TECHNICAL

Story Code	**8R**
Recorded Date	**14 and 15 May 2003**
Release Date	**March 2004**
Place of Recording	**Christchurch Studios, Bristol**
Number of CDs	**2**
Total Duration	**121' 03"**
Number of Episodes	**4**
Duration of Episodes	**1 (27' 29")**
	2 (27' 05")
	3 (33' 51")
	4 (32' 38")
ISBN	**1-84435-037-1**

#56 | THE AXIS OF INSANITY

CREW

Writer	**Simon Furman**
Director	**Gary Russell**
Producers	**Jason Haigh-Ellery**
	Gary Russell
Executive Producer (BBC)	**Jacqueline Rayner**
Music and Sound Design	**ERS**
Cover Art	**Lee Binding**
Theme	**Peter Howell**

CAST

The Doctor	**Peter Davison**
Peri	**Nicola Bryant**
Erimem	**Caroline Morris**
The Overseer	**Roy North**
The Jester	**Garrick Hagon**
Jarra To	**Liza Ross**
Tog	**Marc Danbury**
Bird Trader	**Stephen Mansfield**
Carnival Barker	**Daniel Hogarth**

TECHNICAL

Story Code	**6Q/E**
Recorded Date	**22 and 23 January 2004**
Release Date	**April 2004**
Place of Recording	**The Moat Studios, London**
Number of CDs	**2**
Total Duration	**96' 09"**
Number of Episodes	**4**
Duration of Episodes	1 (26' 17")
2 (23' 50")
3 (21' 11")
4 (24' 51")
ISBN	**1-84435-094-0**

SYNOPSIS

The TARDIS is drawn to an area of inter-dimensional space that the Doctor identifies as the Axis – a place where all confused timelines are kept. The Doctor leaves Peri and Erimem in the TARDIS and outside he meets a jester who leads him through a bizarre environment to the Overseer. Meanwhile, Peri and Erimem rescue a man called Tog from some dragons and he agrees to help them find the Doctor. Peri and Tog set off, leaving Erimem in the TARDIS. The Doctor finally reaches the Overseer, but he is a very old man and dies. The Jester takes over and the Doctor realises he has escaped from one of the twisted realities. He then leaves to find his companions. When he does, Tog tells the Doctor of the rip in space-time that brought him there and the Doctor realises that the Jester is after his TARDIS. The Jester takes the Doctor's appearance and fools Erimem into letting him in. He then pilots the time ship to a research facility on Tog's home world, Pangorum. Erimem realises that he is an impostor and the Jester shows that she is really a woman called Jarra To who was working on a time scoop. When a Time Lord called Protok came to investigate she killed him by sucking his brain out. Now she wants a TARDIS but cannot find his so forced the Overseer to summon the Doctor. With the Axis now collapsing, the Doctor and his party pass through the rip and in the final confrontation, Tog and Jarra fall to their deaths. The Doctor arranges for a new Overseer and then pilots Protok's TARDIS to a pocket dimension where all TARDISes come when their owners die. The Doctor, Peri and Erimem then travel back to Pangorum to erase the broken timeline.

PLACEMENT

Between **Nekromanteia #41** and **Three's a Crowd #69**.

TRIVIA

- The play was originally meant to feature Nyssa and an adult Adric as companions.
- The TARDIS 'elephant's graveyard' in this play was mentioned in **Omega #47**.
- Simon Furman is a comic book writer who is perhaps best known for his work on *Transformers* comics for the likes of Marvel, Dreamwave and IDW.
- Garrick Hagon, who plays The Jester, is most famous for playing Biggs Darklighter in *Star Wars Episode IV: A New Hope*. He also appeared as Ky in the **Doctor Who** TV story **The Mutants**.
- Garrick appears here with his wife, Liza Ross, who had played opposite Peter Davison in *At Home with the Braithwaites*.
- The Axis would feature again in **Gallifrey** Series 4.

PRODUCTION SUMMARY

"Simon was one of the people I'd known at Marvel because he'd worked on the **Doctor Who** comic strip. He was one of the first people I wanted to get involved when I started at Big Finish. I liked the idea of the nexus points of reality. I think he put the Toymaker in the original synopsis. And I said 'no' and then he came up with the Jester. Simple, straightforward and exactly what we needed after the Eighth Doctor Divergent Universe season. And what a cover by Lee Binding! Bloody lovely!"
Gary Russell

WORKING TITLES(S)

None.

RETURNING MONSTERS/CHARACTERS

None.

ARRANGEMENTS FOR WAR

#57

SYNOPSIS

A few hours after the event of **Project: Lazarus #45**, Evelyn is very upset by the Doctor's reaction to Cassie's death. She says she wants to go somewhere with normal people – and no danger. So the Doctor takes her to Világ where a peace between two warring countries, Galen and Malendia, has been brokered. The Doctor assures her that they will arrive after this event and before an invasion by the Killorans – which will be prevented by the combined strength of the two countries. However, the two become separated and the Doctor upsets the future history by convincing a young Lieutenant, Marcus Reid, to declare his love for a princess of Galen, Krisztina. The trouble is the princess is supposed to marry Malendia's Prince Viktor and thus cement the alliance. Evelyn meets Governor Rossiter of Kozepén who is in charge of the consolidation talks. While the Doctor helps the two lovers to write to each other secretly, Evelyn is appointed a special envoy. Then, the secret romance is exposed by Suskind and Pokol who wish the alliance to break up. Within weeks,

the two countries are once again at war. The Doctor is imprisoned and Evelyn extradited. In prison, the Doctor tries to convince Suskind that there is an alien threat coming. He doesn't believe the Doctor but the idea that the war could leave the planet open to attack phases him. Princess Krisztina helps the Doctor escape only to discover that the Killoran fleet has arrived. Having escaped by jumping off the train that was taking her away, Evelyn is in hospital. She confesses to Rossiter that she has a heart condition and he comforts her. Meanwhile, the Killorans are winning the war until Rossiter sends the army of Kozepén to help. In the battle for the palace, both Krisztina and Marcus are killed and the Doctor storms off. Evelyn realises what he is going to do and despite her desire to stay with Rossiter she goes with him and prevents the Time Lord from stopping Marcus declaring his love for the princess. Grateful to Evelyn for this, the Doctor apologises for his apparent lack of reaction to Cassie's death and they leave Világ in the TARDIS.

PLACEMENT

Between the television adventures **The Trial of a Time Lord** and **Time and the Rani**, and after the Big Finish audio adventure **Project: Lazarus #45**.

TRIVIA

- Gabriel Woolf (Rossiter) played Sutekh in the TV adventure **Pyramids of Mars** and was the voice of The Beast in **The Impossible Planet/The Satan Pit.**
- The character Princess Krisztina is named after Paul Sutton's wife.
- The moment he read the part of Krisztina, Gary Russell knew he wanted Katarina Olsson to play the part.
- This play is in Gary's all-time top 10 Big Finish plays that he ever produced.
- The Killorans appear in the sequel to this play, **Thicker Than Water #73** as well as the **Bernice Summerfield** adventures in which Adrian is a Killoran who works at the Braxiatel Collection and is the father of Benny's son, Peter.
- The aliens also appear in the **Gallifrey** audio dramas **Lies #2.01** and **Pandora #2.03**.
- Gary thinks that – along with Joe Lidster – Paul Sutton is one of his best discoveries.
- The same month that this play was released, Gary Russell posted the following message on the Big Finish website: "Oh and in case anyone's wondering, of course we hope to ask Christopher Eccleston to join us one day, but let's allow him to get settled into the role first, eh?"

PRODUCTION SUMMARY

"Paul Sutton had submitted an idea for **Excelis** which was great; it was fourth favourite of three! And then I lost his contact details. I tried to track him down but I couldn't and I'd given up. The first proposal that arrived in the new open submissions window was from Paul in Hungary. And I wrote straight back and said, 'this submission is nonsense. Forget it! But I've been searching for you for the last year – let's talk!' He was on the phone straight away. So he submitted something else and it was this. And I think I hesitated about two seconds and then I said to everyone in the office: 'this is going to be one of the best *Doctor Who* stories we've ever made'.
Gary Russell

WORKING TITLES(S)

None.

RETURNING MONSTERS/CHARACTERS

The Killorans.

CREW

Writer	**Paul Sutton**
Director	**Gary Russell**
Producers	**Jason Haigh-Ellery**
	Gary Russell
Executive Producer (BBC)	**Jacqueline Rayner**
Music and Sound Design	**Steve Foxon**
Cover Art	**Lee Binding**
Theme	**Dominic Glynn**

CAST

The Doctor	**Colin Baker**
Evelyn	**Maggie Stables**
Governor Rossiter	**Gabriel Woolf**
Plenipotentiary Suskind	**Philip Bretherton**
Paramount Minister Mortund	**Geoffrey Leesley**
Princess Krisztina	**Katarina Olsson**
Corporal Reid	**Lewis Rae**
Commander Pokol	**Kraig Thornber**

TECHNICAL

Story Code	**7C/K**
Recorded Date	**19 and 20 February 2004**
Release Date	**May 2004**
Place of Recording	**The Moat Studios, London**
Number of CDs	**2**
Total Duration	**120' 14"**
Number of Episodes	**4**
Duration of Episodes	**1 (30' 20")**
	2 (27' 11")
	3 (27' 02")
	4 (35' 41")
ISBN	**1-84435-095-9**

#58 | THE HARVEST

CREW

Writer	**Dan Abnett**
Director	**Gary Russell**
Producers	**Jason Haigh-Ellery**
	Gary Russell
Executive Producer (BBC)	**Jacqueline Rayner**
Music and Sound Design	**David Darlington**
Cover Art	**Lee Binding**
Theme	**Keff McCulloch**

CAST

The Doctor	**Sylvester McCoy**
Ace	**Sophie Aldred**
Hex	**Philip Olivier**
Subject One	**William Boyde**
Doctor Farrer	**Richard Derrington**
Garnier	**David Warwick**
Doctor Mathias	**Paul Lacoux**
System	**Janie Booth**
Polk	**Mark Donovan**

TECHNICAL

Story Code	**7W**
Recorded Date	**30 and 31 March 2004**
Release Date	**June 2004**
Place of Recording	**The Moat Studios, London**
Number of CDs	**2**
Total Duration	**116' 52"**
Number of Episodes	**4**
Duration of Episodes	**1 (26' 27")**
	2 (29' 47")
	3 (33' 12")
	4 (27' 28")
ISBN	**1-84435-096-7**

SYNOPSIS

The Doctor and Ace are looking into strange activity at St Gart's hospital in 2021. Dr Stephen Farrer is examining one of his patients, Subject One, from the C-Programme. Head of Security Garnier reports that Subject Four has rejected a graft and there are no more tissue matches. A staff nurse at the hospital, Thomas Hector Schofield – Hex – becomes embroiled in this when a friend of his called Damien Boyd is brought in following a road accident. Farrer operates on Damien, but he dies. Ace (calling herself McShane) questions Hex about Dr Farrer and the C-Programme and is almost killed by a man called Polk. Hex saves Ace and takes her 'home' – to the TARDIS – where he meets the Doctor. The three of them infiltrate the hospital but are captured by Cybermen. Farrer confides in Garnier that all the subjects are rejecting the grafts which are in fact human tissue and organs harvested from brain-dead patients such as Damien. The Doctor finds out that those being cybernised are astronauts and pilots and that C-Programme is being run by the Central European Government using captured cyber-technology from a crashed ship. Subject One is a Cyberman being turned back into a human. He recognises the Doctor and asks for his help in stabilising the process but the new Cyber-humans start to attack humans as the enemy. The Doctor realises that Subject One is the Cyber-Leader, lying for its own aims. It has been in control all along; fooling the Euro Government into helping them subjugate the human race. However, Farrer has installed a master cut-out circuit which will destroy the Cyber-humans. He, Ace and Hex trigger the device but Farrer dies in the process. The new Cyber-humans are deactivated and Subject One dies from massive organ failure. Hex joins the TARDIS crew.

PLACEMENT

Between **The Rapture #36** and **Dreamtime #67**.

TRIVIA

- This is Hex's first story (see character profile, right).
- David Warwick (Garnier) had previously appeared as Kimus in the TV adventure **The Pirate Planet** and as a Police Commissioner in **Army of Ghosts**.
- The story makes mention of the events of **Spare Parts #54** and ties in with the conflict between Europe and the US in **The Time of the Daleks #32**.
- It is also closely linked to **Project: Lazarus #45** because Hex is Cassie's son, later revealed in **Thicker Than Water #73**.
- **Project: Destiny #139** would see the Doctor, Ace and Hex return to St Gart's hospital a few years after the events of this story.
- The Doctor has a sonic screwdriver. Chronologically, this is the first time the device is used since the Fifth Doctor TV story **The Visitation** and ties in with the **Doctor Who** TV movie in which the Seventh Doctor is seen using it.
- To keep the fact that the story featured the Cybermen a secret, this release had two covers: a teaser cover, which appeared quite ordinary and the real cover which was the same as the original but with a circuit board design behind the image.

PRODUCTION SUMMARY

"**The Harvest** is another play that's in my top 10. Dan is a man I have loved for years. I employed him at every opportunity at Marvel and he has never done anything bad in his life. I created Hex and gave him to Dan and told him that Philip Olivier was going to be playing him. It's funny: Evelyn and Hex were definitely mine whereas Charley was very much Alan's, really. But Phil brought so much to Hex; he really brought it alive."
Gary Russell

WORKING TITLES(S)

None.

RETURNING MONSTERS/CHARACTERS

Cybermen.

HEX

Of all the companions created by Big Finish, the character of Thomas Hector Schofield – Hex to his friends – is perhaps the most interwoven into the mythology the company has created for its **Doctor Who** range.

Played to perfection by Philip Olivier (famous for his role as "Tinhead" O'Leary in **Brookside**), Hex actually started life as a throwaway line in Cavan Scott and Mark Wright's **Project: Twilight #23**, in which the character of Cassie talks about her son, little "Tommy". Cassie abandoned Tommy to seek her fortune in London, where she encounters the Doctor and is turned into a vampire during the Doctor's very first battle with the top secret organisation known as the Forge.

He is also mentioned again in the sequel, **Project: Lazarus #45**, 'By this time I knew that Tommy was going to come into it,' says Gary Russell. 'At that time I thought he could be a companion with Evelyn but then I realised he should be paired with Ace. By that time we'd been through the whole "McShane" thing and Ace was now mid-to-late twenties and so she could have this kind of younger brother character. The Doctor had taught her everything and now she was teaching Hex.'

Hex made his first appearance in **The Harvest #58** as a staff nurse working at St. Gart's Hospital in the London of 2021. He helps the Seventh Doctor and Ace foil a plot by the Cybermen to convert the whole of humanity and joins the TARDIS crew. It is later revealed – in **Thicker than Water #73** – that the Seventh Doctor knows that Hex is Cassie's son.

'With Hex, everything about him was mine,' says Gary emphatically. 'The part was written specifically for Philip and I thought it would be just another job for him. But he brought something special to that role and absolutely nailed it. He made it his own.'

However, to say that Philip wasn't that familiar with the format of **Doctor Who** is something of understatement. Gary remembers his first day in studio with Sophie Aldred. 'Phil said to Sophie: "it's set in a hospital and it's called **Doctor Who** but it doesn't seem to be a medical thing!" and she just looked at him!'

He can be forgiven for this because, having been born in 1980, Philip is one of the lost generations of **Doctor Who**. Not only had it vanished from our screen by the time he was nine, he was brought up in South Africa. Fortunately, whatever Philip may have lacked in knowledge of the series he more than made up for in charm. 'He got on really well with Sophie,' says Gary. 'And I thought, "thank God!" because she and Sylv could easily have felt their noses were being put out of joint, but they didn't. From the first day you could see that Sophie and Phil were going to be mates.'

Hex enjoyed 13 adventures with the Seventh Doctor and Ace. Then things started to go awry for "Mr Hex". In Paul Sutton's **The Angel of Scutari #122**, Hex is shot and the Doctor must take him back to St Gart's Hospital in a cliffhanger that leads directly into the next story to feature Hex, **Project: Destiny #139**, some 17 releases later.

In **Project Destiny**, Hex meets the man responsible for his mother's death: Nimrod (although, of course, Nimrod tries to convince him that it is the Doctor who is at fault). In the following story, **A Death in the Family #140**, the Doctor is killed and Hex finds himself on the planet Pelechan where he is taken under the wing of Evelyn Smythe who tells him about his mother.

Having exorcised the shadow of his mother's demise, Hex elected to stay in the TARDIS and continue travelling with the Doctor. But nothing would ever be the same again.

Left:
Thomas Hector Schofield, aka Hex
(Philip Olivier)

#59

THE ROOF OF THE WORLD

CREW

Writer	**Adrian Rigelsford**
Director	**Gary Russell**
Producers	**Jason Haigh-Ellery**
	Gary Russell
Executive Producer (BBC)	**Jacqueline Rayner**
Music	**Russell Stone**
Sound Design	**Gareth Jenkins @ ERS**
Cover Art	**Lee Binding**
Theme	**Peter Howell**

CAST

The Doctor	**Peter Davison**
Erimem	**Caroline Morris**
Peri	**Nicola Bryant**
Lord Mortimer Davey	**Edward de Souza**
Pharaoh Amenhotep II	**William Franklyn**
General Alexander Bruce	**Sylvester Morand**
John Matthews	**Alan Cox**

TECHNICAL

Story Code	**6Q/F**
Recorded Date	**19 and 20 January 2004**
Release Date	**July 2004**
Place of Recording	**The Moat Studios, London**
Number of CDs	**2**
Total Duration	**119' 48"**
Number of Episodes	**4**
Duration of Episodes	**1 (27' 08")**
	2 (36' 25")
	3 (26' 46")
	4 (29' 29")
ISBN	**1-84435-097-5**

SYNOPSIS

Lord Davey and his expedition are attacked and killed in the Himalayas. Meanwhile, the TARDIS materialises aboard a train to Darjeeling because the Doctor has been invited to play a cricket match at the Imperial Hotel there by the expedition's organiser, General Alexander Bruce. Once in the city, the Time Lord and his companions are observed by an alien disguised as Lord Davey. He manages to kiss Erimem's hand and infects her with his masters' voices. Later, while the Doctor, Alexander et al are playing the cricket match a black cloud appears and, possessed by the voices, Erimem steps into it and is apparently killed. At her funeral, Erimem cannot work out why the Doctor and Peri cannot see her. However, Davey takes her away, showing visions of her past in Egypt as well as the TARDIS in which everyone seems to hate her. Finally, Davey takes her to the mountain – the white pyramid – where the dead Doctor convinces her that she is the key in returning an ancient race of beasts to the Earth. However, none of this is real and the Doctor and Peri set up a new expedition to go to the mountains and see what has happened there. When the expedition's equipment and supplies are destroyed by a psionic attack, the Doctor is forced to use the TARDIS to travel to the mountain. Here he is attacked by the cloud and learns that the creatures he faces are the Great Old Ones, immensely powerful and destructive beings from the dawn of time. Peri, meanwhile, works out that the cloud is affected by temperature and takes a canister of liquid nitrogen from the TARDIS. The Doctor confronts the beings and tells them he does not fear them because he has seen far greater evil and they are now old and weak. Peri and Alexander freeze the creatures and then blow up the white pyramid with explosives from the TARDIS. The Doctor takes the survivors back to London and tends to the traumatised Erimem.

PLACEMENT

Between **The Axis of Insanity #56** and **Three's a Crowd #69**.

TRIVIA

- Lord Davey is related by marriage to George Cranleigh, the disfigured explorer from the 1982 TV story **Black Orchid**.
- Lord Davey is played by Edward de Souza, who previously played Marc Corey in the TV episode **Mission to the Unknown**. He also played Sheik Hosein in the 1977 James Bond film *The Spy Who Loved Me* as well as 'The Man' in the final assignment of the *Sapphire and Steel* TV series.
- This play shares its title with that of the first episode of the 1966 TV story **Marco Polo**.
- Gary Russell wanted to do a story that involved Erimem's father, Amenhotep, and asked Adrian Rigelsford to include that. William Franklyn was Gary's first choice to play the role.
- Alan Cox, who plays John Matthews, is perhaps best known for playing John Watson in the 1985 film, *Young Sherlock Holmes*, and appears in Big Finish's own *Sherlock Holmes* range as Moriarty.

PRODUCTION SUMMARY

"**Roof of the World** was a risk. I stand by my mates and Adrian is a good writer. And, bless him, he was one of the few people during that period who delivered on time. I do remember the script being long, but it was on time! And there were lots of rumours because I had said let's do a story set in the Himalayas and that was just me making everyone think I was bringing the Yeti and the Great Intelligence back! Ha ha!"
Gary Russell

WORKING TITLES(S)

None.

RETURNING MONSTERS/CHARACTERS

None.

MEDICINAL PURPOSES

#60

SYNOPSIS

The TARDIS materialises in 1828. In Greyfriars Graveyard, the Doctor confirms to Evelyn that they are in Edinburgh at the time of the notorious body-snatchers Burke and Hare. Hare is drinking with a prostitute called Mary and her companion 'Daft' Jamie. When he hears about the strangers' interest in his handiwork, he goes to his employer, Dr Robert Knox, who is performing autopsies while explaining his actions aloud. The Doctor decides he would like to meet the infamous pair but it appears that Burke does not exist in this timeline. The Doctor then persuades Jamie to take him to Hare's lodgings but he has little luck with the man. Meanwhile Evelyn meets Knox who makes reference to Jekyll and Hyde. When the Doctor hears this, he points out that the book's author, Robert Louis Stevenson, has not yet been born. This means that Knox is a time traveller. Furthermore, it is revealed that his house is a Type 70

TARDIS, but Knox is no Time Lord. He is a human from the future who claims to be trying to cure a virus that is affecting his alien clients, replaying the same events repeatedly so he does not have to infect too many people. Indeed, he only infects the people who are meant to die – such as Mary and Daft Jamie. He is also making a nice profit on the side by broadcasting the events to the rich and bored of the future. To break the time loop, the Doctor takes Daft Jamie to 1829 to watch Burke's execution. When Knox turns up, the Doctor reveals that Knox will make Jamie famous and in misplaced gratitude, Jamie shakes Knox's hand, unaware that Knox has now infected him with the virus. Knox returns to his TARDIS to try and find a cure while the Doctor sadly takes Jamie back in time so he, too, can meet his destiny at the hands of Burke and Hare.

PLACEMENT

Between **Arrangements for War #57** and **Pier Pressure #78**.

TRIVIA

- This was the first play to feature Robert Ross's time-meddling character, Doctor Robert Knox, who would turn up again in **Assassin in the Limelight #108**.
- Leslie Phillips, who plays Doctor Robert Knox, is famous for his roles in the *Doctor* series of films, amongst countless film and TV roles.
- David Tennant, who would go on to play the Tenth Doctor on TV, is cast here as Daft Jamie!
- The planet on which Knox buys his Type 70 TARDIS from a Nekkistani dealer is Gryben, which is also mentioned in **Gallifrey Weapon of Choice #1.1**.
- The original proposal for the story involved Jack the Ripper, not Burke and Hare.
- Ross's original idea was to include the Meddling Monk and to have him played by Tyler Butterworth, the son of Peter Butterworth who played the character in the original 1965 TV story, **The Time Meddler**.
- Gary recalls that it was during the recording of this play (19th March 2004) that Christopher Eccleston had been cast as the Doctor. "I remember a discussion about the casting with myself, Colin, Robert Ross and David Tennant!"

PRODUCTION SUMMARY

"This was one of the longest scripts I have ever seen and we did record a lot of it. I remember sitting with Davy Darlington and him telling me that each episode was about 90 minutes long. We had to cut out whole storylines and great swathes of dialogue had to go. It is possible that I may have – may have – compromised Robert Ross's story by having to cut so much of it out."
Gary Russell

WORKING TITLES(S)

None.

RETURNING MONSTERS/CHARACTERS

None.

CREW

Writer	**Robert Ross**
Director	**Gary Russell**
Producers	**Jason Haigh-Ellery**
	Gary Russell
Executive Producer (BBC)	**Jacqueline Rayner**
Music and Sound Design	**David Darlington**
Cover Art	**Lee Binding**
Theme	**Dominic Glynn**

CAST

The Doctor	**Colin Baker**
Evelyn	**Maggie Stables**
Doctor Robert Knox	**Leslie Phillips**
Daft Jamie	**David Tennant**
Mary Patterson	**Glenna Morrison**
William Burke	**Kevin O'Leary**
Billy Hare	**Tom Farrelly**
Old Woman	**Janie Booth**

TECHNICAL

Story Code	**7C/L**
Recorded Date	**18 and 19 March 2004**
Release Date	**August 2004**
Place of Recording	**The Moat Studios, London**
Number of CDs	**2**
Total Duration	**138' 39"**
Number of Episodes	**2**
Duration of Episodes	**1 (71' 22")**
	2 (67' 17")
ISBN	**1-84435-098-3**

#61   FAITH STEALER

CREW

Writer	**Graham Duff**
Director	**Gary Russell**
Producers	**Jason Haigh-Ellery**
	Gary Russell
Executive Producer (BBC)	**Jacqueline Rayner**
Music and Sound Design	**Gareth Jenkins @ ERS**
Cover Art	**Steve Johnson**
Theme	**David Arnold**

CAST

The Doctor	**Paul McGann**
Charley	**India Fisher**
C'Rizz	**Conrad Westmaas**
The Kro'Ka	**Stephen Perring**
Laan Carder	**Christian Rodska**
The Bordinan	**Tessa Shaw**
Miraculite	**Jenny Coverack**
Bishop Parrash	**Ifan Huw Dafydd**
Jebdal	**Helen Kirkpatrick**
Director Garfolt	**Neil Bett**
The Bordinan's Assistant	**Chris Walter-Evans**
Bakoan	**John Dorney**
L'Da	**Jane Hills**

TECHNICAL

Story Code	**8S**
Recorded Date	**11 and 12 June 2004**
Release Date	**October 2004**
Place of Recording	**Christchurch Studios, Bristol.**
Number of CDs	**2**
Total Duration	**102' 20"**
Number of Episodes	**4**
Duration of Episodes	**1 (27' 26")**
	2 (23' 09")
	3 (26' 07")
	4 (25' 38")
ISBN	**1-84435-103-3**

SYNOPSIS

In search of rest, the Doctor and Charley bring C'rizz to the Multihaven, a place in which many religions peacefully co-exist. C'rizz is reliving the death of L'da (his former lover – see **The Creed of the Kromon #53**). The fastest-growing faith in the Multihaven is the Church of Lucidity. Its leader, Lann Carder, shows the priest of another faith, Bishop Parrash, a strange wardrobe that is bigger within than without. Carder claims he can harvest lucid crystals from people's dreams and Parrash enters the wardrobe. While C'rizz is taken to a Bakoran temple to be soothed by its eternal hymn, the Doctor and Charley explore, several times hearing the TARDIS, although they cannot find it. Parrash becomes lost in the wardrobe's endless corridors but stumbles upon the heart of the Lucidity Accumulator – a bright light that burns his mind and identifies itself as Miraculite. Carder and his followers enter the Bakoran temple and take C'rizz to the Church of Lucidity where, riven with guilt, he agrees to enter the Lucidity Accumulator. Here he finds Parrash a broken man. The Bishop tries to warn C'rizz about the light but Miraculite obliterates him. Meanwhile the Doctor discovers that the Lucidian followers are all suffering from a lack of REM sleep. Charley then finds C'rizz, and the Doctor puts him into a mild hypnotic state to stabilise him. Carder communes with Miraculite and is told everyone in the Multihaven must be harvested. The Doctor works out that Lucidianism is robbing its followers of their dream energy. By now nearly everyone in the city is a believer. To prevent the final harvest the Doctor enters the Lucidity Accumulator and confronts Miraculite, identifying it as a crystalline entity created by the friction between two realities. The Doctor reveals that Carder is merely an entity brought into being by Miraculite. Learning this, Carder disappears and Miraculite becomes unstable. The Doctor and Charley escape from the wardrobe as Miraculite collapses.

PLACEMENT

Between **The Twilight Kingdom #55** and **The Last #62**.

TRIVIA

- This season of Eighth Doctor stories was brought forward when it was announced that **Doctor Who** was returning to TV in 2005. Gary Russell wanted to ensure that new listeners were not alienated by the Divergent Universe arc so it was curtailed and brought forward to late 2004.
- Graham Duff was another writer who Gary Russell invited to submit a proposal for Big Finish during 2004. His previous credits included writing and producing the TV series *Dr. Terrible's House of Horrible* and subsequently went on to script seven series of the sitcom *Ideal*. He also wrote the BBC Radio 4 science fiction comedy *Nebulous*, which involved many Big Finish luminaries such as Nicholas Briggs, Mark Gatiss and David Warner.
- Although released first, **Faith Stealer** was the third play of the season to be recorded.
- In his first minor role, you will find John Dorney who has gone on to appear in many Big Finish plays – and write quite a few, too!
- Graham has been quoted as saying that he admires Donald Cotton's **Who** stories for the mix of comedy and pacing without undermining its overall gravitas. He says he wanted to achieve that balance.

PRODUCTION SUMMARY

"I'd been listening to Nick editing the *Nebulous* pilot and I thought it would be nice to have a more humorous Eighth Doctor story. So I just approached Graham and he's quite a fan so he said 'yes'! There've been criticisms that the ending was rushed, but I think Graham was in the midst of *Ideal* by then so he had very little time he could expend on the re-writes. The original ending was a bit more open with the Doctor not knowing what Miraculite was, or what had happened. I wanted more explanation!"
Gary Russell

WORKING TITLES(S)

None.

RETURNING MONSTERS/CHARACTERS

The Kro'ka.

Check box - CD ☐   MP3 ☐

THE LAST

#62

SYNOPSIS

The Doctor is tormented by the Kro'ka about the deaths of his companions Adric and Katarina before leaving the interzone and arriving in a ruined city, ravaged by atomic warfare. In a bunker are the survivors of Bortresoye's war: Excelsior, the planet's leader, and her ministers: Voss and Tralfinial. She also has a mysterious advisor, Landscar, whom no one seems to know. The building in which the Doctor, Charley and C'rizz are sheltering collapses and C'rizz leaves to find help. Landscar brings the Doctor and Charley to the bunker but Charley has been paralysed in the accident. Meanwhile, C'rizz meets a strange man called Requiem who tells him that all life has been wiped out. Despite this, there appear to be survivors in the ruins and C'rizz leads them all to the bunker. When they arrive, only C'rizz can be seen; the others have vanished. It becomes apparent that Excelsior is insane. She can hear the voices of

the dead, but ignores them, telling Charley that her race does not reproduce; they have reached the pinnacle of evolution. She then smothers Charley to death and goes to a rocket that used to be a nuclear missile. Once C'rizz is aboard, the Doctor pilots it into orbit. Excelsior then kills C'rizz, too. The rocket returns to the surface, where Landscar explains that the planet itself brought the ship back. The people failed to protect the Bortresoye, so it must start again. However, it cannot do so until the Last is dead. When Excelsior is killed in a volcanic eruption, the Doctor realises that he is the Last and must die in order for the planet to be re-born. With his friends dead and the TARDIS gone he has nothing to live for and so detonates the warhead on the rocket. The Doctor then awakens to find everyone alive. The planet has re-set. Together with Charley and C'rizz, he leaves as soon as the interzone opens.

PLACEMENT

Between **Faith Stealer #61** and **Caerdroia #63**.

TRIVIA

- Writer Gary Hopkins used to be involved with the in-depth *Doctor Who* reference series, *CMS*. He has written for many TV series including the Jeremy Brett version of *Sherlock Holmes*.
- Hopkins originally submitted a story called Virtuosi, but the plot was too similar to that of the preceding play, **Faith Stealer #61**.
- Gary Hopkins went on to contribute to the **Doctor Who Main Monthly Range** with **Other Lives #77**, the first instalment of the **I, Davros** range, **Innocence #1.1** and the initial release in the fourth series of **Gallifrey** audios, **Reborn #4.1**.
- This was the last Eighth Doctor story recorded in Bristol to date.

PRODUCTION SUMMARY

"This story was one that, I thought, kind of showed what the Divergent Universe was really like. Because there was no idea of one timeline, and things were being repeated, this is the sort of thing I think I was aiming for when I came up with the idea of having no concept of time in this arc. It's also a notable story because I remember Paul coming in during the recording of it and saying 'tell you what guys, I've made a mistake and we should do these in London!' so we moved to the Moat for the Eighth Doctor recordings."
Gary Russell

WORKING TITLES(S)

None.

RETURNING MONSTERS/CHARACTERS

The Kro'ka.

CREW

Writer	**Gary Hopkins**
Director	**Gary Russell**
Producers	**Jason Haigh-Ellery**
	Gary Russell
Executive Producer (BBC)	**Jacqueline Rayner**
Music and Sound Design	**David Darlington**
Cover Art	**Steve Johnson**
Theme	**David Arnold**

CAST

The Doctor	**Paul McGann**
Charley	**India Fisher**
C'Rizz	**Conrad Westmaas**
The Kro'Ka	**Stephen Perring**
Excelsior	**Carolyn Jones**
Minister Voss	**Ian Brooker**
Minister Tralfinial	**Robert Hines**
Landscar	**Richard Derrington**
Requiem	**Tom Eastwood**
Nurse	**Jane Hills**
Make-Up Assistant	**John Dorney**

TECHNICAL

Story Code	**8T**
Recorded Date	**9 and 10 June 2004**
Release Date	**October 2004**
Place of Recording	**Christchurch Studios, Bristol**
Number of CDs	**2**
Total Duration	**141' 37"**
Number of Episodes	**4**
Duration of Episodes	**1 (37' 28")**
	2 (36' 24")
	3 (35' 04")
	4 (32' 41")
ISBN	**1-84435-102-5**

#63 CAERDROIA

CREW

Writer	**Lloyd Rose**
Director	**Gary Russell**
Producers	**Jason Haigh-Ellery**
	Gary Russell
Executive Producer (BBC)	**Jacqueline Rayner**
Music and Sound Design	**Steve Foxon**
Cover Art	**Steve Johnson**
Theme	**David Arnold**

CAST

The Doctor	**Paul McGann**
Charley	**India Fisher**
C'Rizz	**Conrad Westmaas**
The Kro'Ka	**Stephen Perring**
Rassilon	**Don Warrington**

TECHNICAL

Story Code	**8U**
Recorded Date	**8 June 2004**
Release Date	**November 2004**
Place of Recording	**Christchurch Studios, Bristol.**
Number of CDs	**2**
Total Duration	**105' 53"**
Number of Episodes	**4**
Duration of Episodes	**1 (25' 13")**
	2 (26' 39")
	3 (22' 36")
	4 (31' 25")
ISBN	**1-84435-104-1**

SYNOPSIS

The Kro'ka finds that he cannot move the Doctor on to the next experiment through the interzone while he sleeps. When he wakes, the Doctor has worked out a great deal about the interzone and how to block the Kro'ka from his thoughts. However, the Kro'ka then uses a device to access the innermost part of the Time Lord's mind – exactly where the Doctor wants him. He works out that the Kro'ka is disobeying his masters, the Divergents. The Kro'ka admits that the TARDIS still exists and that the Divergents control their experiments from a planet called Caerdroia. However, when the Doctor and his companions get there, the Doctor has been split into three versions. Travelling to a nearby town, Charley dubs the grumpy one 'Eeyore' and the scatterbrained one as 'Tigger'. The calm, rational version retains his own name. They split up and explore but, via circuitous routes, are all brought back together in an underground maze containing a Minotaur. A man called Wayland then appears, claiming to have built the labyrinth. He asks them to help him break into the central core so he can make it safe once more. However the Doctor and Eeyore deduce that he is the Kro'ka and the central core represents access to the TARDIS. The Kro'ka disappears and leaves the two Doctors to escape the Minotaur. When they do, the Kro'ka captures Tigger and locks the calm Doctor in a chamber full of peeling bells. Before the alien can torture Tigger to gain his knowledge of the TARDIS, Eeyore appears and easily invades the Kro'ka's mind. He finds out where the others are and leaves. The Kro'ka then finds himself confronted by his true master – Rassilon. The Doctors combine and work out that the TARDIS has been communicating its whereabouts to them – in the centre of the labyrinth. Recombined, the Doctor sets the controls of the TARDIS knowing a showdown with the Divergents is now inevitable.

PLACEMENT

Between **The Last #62** and **The Next Life #64**.

TRIVIA

- Lloyd Rose has written for the US drama series *Homicide: Life on the Street* and *Kingpin*. She is also the author of several **Doctor Who** novels for the BBC.
- The play was produced with an alternative cover, which was available exclusively through the UK specialist shop, 10th Planet for the 2004 Dimensions convention.
- 'Caerdroia' is a Welsh word meaning 'the Castle of Turning' or 'the Labyrinth'.

PRODUCTION SUMMARY

"Lloyd was another person I wanted to write for Big Finish after seeing her excellent BBC books. And of course, she had some amazing US TV credits, too! Originally there were going to be four seasons to this arc and I had it all mapped out. This story would have closed the second season but instead it had to act as the lead in to what would tie up all the loose ends. That said, it's still a magnificent script!"
Gary Russell

WORKING TITLES(S)

None.

RETURNING MONSTERS/CHARACTERS

The Kro'ka, Rassilon.

Check box - CD ■ MP3 ■

Top-left:
Eight not out – Nicholas Courtney added another Doctor to his collection when he appeared with Paul McGann in **Minuet in Hell**.

Top-right:
The cast of **The Marian Conspiracy** (l-r): Barnaby Edwards, Sean Jackson, Colin Baker, Maggie Stables (seated), Jeremy James and Nicholas Pegg.

Left:
Caroline Morris (Erimem) and Peter Davison (Fifth Doctor) at the recording of the DWM special **No Place Like Home** in 2002.

#64 THE NEXT LIFE

CREW

Writers	**Alan Barnes**
	Gary Russell
Director	**Gary Russell**
Producers	**Jason Haigh-Ellery**
	Gary Russell
Executive Producer (BBC)	**Jacqueline Rayner**
Music and Sound Design	**ERS**
Cover Art	**Steve Johnson**
Theme	**David Arnold**

CAST

The Doctor	**Paul McGann**
Charley	**India Fisher**
C'Rizz	**Conrad Westmaas**
Perfection	**Daphne Ashbrook**
Keep	**Stephane Cornicard**
Guidance	**Paul Darrow**
L'Da	**Jane Hills**
The Kro'Ka	**Stephen Perring**
Rassilon	**Don Warrington**
Lady Louisa Pollard	**Anneke Wills**
Simon Murchford	**Stephen Mansfield**
Mother of Jembere-Bud	**Jane Goddard**

TECHNICAL

Story Code	**8V**
Recorded Date	**24, 25 and 31 August, and 3 September 2004**
Release Date	**December 2004**
Place of Recording	**Christchurch Studios, Bristol.**
Number of CDs	**3**
Total Duration	**187' 45"**
Number of Episodes	**6**
Duration of Episodes	**1 (33' 13")**
	2 (31' 35")
	3 (28' 26")
	4 (28' 02")
	5 (26' 53")
	6 (39' 36")
ISBN	**1-84435-105-X**

SYNOPSIS

As the TARDIS appears to burn up in the atmosphere of a blue moon, its occupants are split up. C'rizz is with his lover, L'da. It is the day before his wedding. Charley is with her mother at RAF Cardington, before the R101 takes off. They are being manipulated by the Kro'ka, but Charley is resisting. Rassilon enters her dream and tells her the Doctor is dead. In C'rizz's dream, the Eutermesan reveals that he was a very proficient killer for the Foundation. He joined the Doctor to expunge his guilt. Meanwhile, the Doctor has washed up on a beach and is about to be eaten by giant crabs when he is rescued by a familiar-looking woman called Perfection. Rassilon shows this to Charley and C'rizz on a screen and tells them that Perfection and her followers are looking for a way out of the Divergent Universe. He tries to convince the two companions that the Doctor has been lying to them about his anti-time infection and that he has abandoned them. The Doctor then meets Perfection's husband, Daqar Keep, and their servant, Guidance, who is the same species as C'rizz. They are both members of the Church of the Foundation as C'rizz once was. Rassilon tells Charley that he too was infected with anti-time but is now free of it and once he can rescue the Doctor, they can go home. Charley and C'rizz insist on being set free to find the Doctor themselves, however C'rizz believes Charley has betrayed the Doctor and leaves her. He then finds Guidance who takes him to a well, claiming it to be the Foundation itself and that he is C'rizz's father. As the Doctor and Perfection discuss the planet and the story of the Divergent Universe, the Time Lord realises that this universe has no fixed space-time co-ordinates because it is caught in an endless loop and that Rassilon has given the Divergents the ability to create a being that understands time. Perfection tells him that the creature escaped and fled to her home galaxy. They then find Charley and the three of them locate the entrance to the Foundation – a sort of trap door – where Guidance, C'rizz and Keep all appear at the same time. It transpires that this is the door back to the normal universe and that Keep is an amalgam of Charley and the Doctor created during the events of **Scherzo #52**. Keep wants to escape into our universe so he can absorb all life there. He then kills Guidance and is shot by C'rizz, who then turns the gun on the Doctor and Charley as Rassilon arrives in the TARDIS and takes C'rizz away. Keep escapes to track down Rassilon and the Doctor, accompanied by Perfection and Charley, follows him. In the end Keep reveals that he has manipulated Rassilon and that this is his 84th attempt to free himself in the looped universe. Keep tosses Rassilon back to the beginning of the Divergent Universe and is about to leave when Perfection is finally revealed to be Zagreus. She incapacitates Keep and boards the TARDIS, only to find it is actually a manifestation of Keep. He has trapped Zagreus and as they struggle the two universes come into synch and the Doctor escapes with Charley and C'rizz in the real TARDIS. However, when they emerge – once more into our universe – they are immediately captured by Davros and the Daleks…

PLACEMENT

Between **Caerdroia #63** and **Terror Firma #72**.

TRIVIA

- This story brings to an end the Divergent Universe arc begun in **Zagreus #50** and continued through the previous two seasons and Eighth Doctor stories (**Scherzo #52**, **The Creed of the Kromon #53**, **The Natural History of Fear #54**, **The Twilight Kingdom #55**, **Faith Stealer #61**, **The Last #62** and **Caerdroia #63**).
- In one draft, Perfection was indeed called 'Grace' (see right).
- This was the first time that Paul McGann and Daphne Ashbrook worked together since the 1996 **Doctor Who** TV movie (in which she played Dr. Grace Holloway, a character owned by Universal).
- In one version of the story, Alan Barnes had everyone dead by the end of episode three, except the Doctor. "I was obviously trying to top Rob Shearman," Alan says. "But I was very keen on this one-hander idea and Gary just said 'no'!"
- Several people pointed out in reviews that the Doctor isn't present when Rassilon gets his comeuppance and said that was a mistake. "And they're right!" says Alan Barnes. "I would change that. But there was so much going on in that last episode…"
- This was the last release in which Paul McGann was the 'current' Doctor. The next story, **Terror Firma #72**, was released in August 2005, two months after both Christopher Eccleston and David Tennant had been seen in the role on TV!

Check box - CD ■ MP3 ■

#64

PRODUCTION SUMMARY

"I never mind having a shopping list or a specific mission to accomplish. I like having lots of different elements to play with. Often when people see a list they might think 'oh my god, how do I do that?' but I just think 'I'll put that bit with this bit and that then becomes one thing' and so on until you have a few different plot strands and then it flows quite nicely from there. You've just got to boil them down into manageable entities! It's an interesting intellectual exercise that gets me through the awfulness of actually having to plot something out. I do remember that the fact it was six episodes is down to me because I knew we'd need a lot of room for explanations."
Alan Barnes

WORKING TITLES(S)

None.

RETURNING MONSTERS/CHARACTERS

Rassilon, the Kro'ka, Zagreus, Davros, the Daleks.

THE ORIGINAL SYNOPSIS

The Kr'oka offers the Doctor knowledge of Rassilon's whereabouts, in exchange for protecting him from his former interzone masters – and leads him to an island paradise dominated by a vast volcano and inhabited by 'devolved' ape-men and terrifying dinosaur-like creatures, all thought long-extinct. Separated from Charley and C'rizz when a tidal wave strikes the shore, the Doctor and the Kr'oka join forces with a group of shipwreck survivors, including 'Grace', and follow Charley's trail. Charley falls foul of a group of death-worshipping fundamentalists led by Rassilon, who believe themselves to have returned to the place of the Universe's Foundation… and who are on a mission to destroy it. C'rizz, meanwhile, is picked up by the Kr'oka and his ancestors – the troglodytic scientists who rule this world from beneath the surface – only to become a subject for their experiments in 'devolution'.

In the planet's hollow core, the Doctor learns that this 'timeless' Universe is 'decreated' over and over again by the passing of this planet – a vast seeding machine that spews 'devolving' matter across the cosmos once every x thousand years.

The Doctor agrees to help Rassilon destroy this 'Decreator', to give the people of this 'divergent' Universe the opportunity to properly develop and evolve – but soon realises that Rassilon only means to use the Decreator for his own ends, spreading the essence of an amended, augmented race of 'Mark II' Time Lords, the creatures he once called 'the Divergence'.

Rassilon is defeated (devolved in his own genetic swamp?) – and the Doctor and friends flee to the TARDIS while the island falls apart as the Decreator collapses in on itself, giving temporal co-ordinates back to the 'timeless' universe. The TARDIS will take Charley and C'rizz back into the 'real' universe – but the Doctor says he can't go with them: he's still infected with anti-time. The TARDIS dematerialises, leaving the Doctor behind. The Decreator finally implodes …

Inside, 'Grace' reveals herself to be the Doctor's 'Zagreus' infection, separated out from him when they first entered the 'Divergent' universe. Zagreus has triumphed at the last …

Only he/she/it hasn't, and somehow the Doctor is waiting. Zagreus is left abandoned and alone in the middle of nowhere – and the Doctor, Charley and C'rizz cross over into the real world and an appointment with the Daleks…

#65 THE JUGGERNAUTS

CREW

Writer	**Scott Alan Woodard**
Director	**Gary Russell**
Producers	**Jason Haigh-Ellery**
	Gary Russell
Executive Producer (BBC)	**Jacqueline Rayner**
Music and Sound Design	**Steve Foxon**
Cover Art	**Lee Binding**
Theme	**Dominic Glynn**

CAST

The Doctor	**Colin Baker**
Mel	**Bonnie Langford**
Davros	**Terry Molloy**
Sonali	**Bindya Solanki**
Geoff	**Klaus White**
Kryson	**Peter Forbe**
Brauer	**Paul Grunert**
Loewen	**Julia Houghton**
Dalek, Mechonoid Voices	**Nicholas Briggs**

TECHNICAL

Story Code	**7C/S**
Recorded Date	**20 and 21 April 2004**
Release Date	**February 2005**
Place of Recording	**The Moat Studios, London**
Number of CDs	**2**
Total Duration	**122' 56"**
Number of Episodes	**4**
Duration of Episodes	**1 (23' 02")**
	2 (29' 50")
	3 (35' 39")
	4 (34' 25")
ISBN	**1-84435-101-7**

SYNOPSIS

The Doctor and Mel have to leave a medical ship when it is destroyed by a foe the Doctor thinks he recognises. Mel leaves in an escape pod that transports her to the planet Lethe where she gets a job as a programmer, updating some old service robots under the good-humoured Dr Vaso, who calls the machines 'Juggernauts'. The Doctor has been time-scooped away from the exploding ship by the Daleks. The Black Dalek explains that they need his help, which he agrees to provide when the Daleks reveal they know where Mel is. As they show him on the screen, the Doctor sees that Dr Vaso is not the nice old man in a wheelchair, but Davros! Meanwhile, executives Kryson and Brauer arrive from the Outreach Corporation who sponsor the programme. They are pleased with what they see and decide to take the project into their own hands. Davros is furious and coerces Kryson to change his mind. The Doctor then confronts Davros, but some badly damaged white Daleks emerge from hiding and kill Brauer while Davros reveals that the Juggernauts – actually Mechonoids – have been modified to become the ultimate Dalek killers. The Doctor and Mel manage to deactivate one of the Mechonoids and find to their horror that Davros has augmented them with human tissue, making them cyborgs rather than just robots. The Doctor calls in his temporary allies – the grey Daleks – and there is a battle between the Daleks and the Mechonoids. Initially, the Daleks win and reveal that they attacked the medical ship and engineered the situation so that the Doctor would help them. They intend to take the Doctor back to Skaro and learn the secrets of the TARDIS. However, more Mechonoids arrive and the Doctor and Mel flee as the Daleks call for reinforcements. The colonists escape on the Outreach shuttle and Davros apparently blows up taking all the Daleks with him.

PLACEMENT

Between **The One Doctor #27** and **Catch-1782 #68**.

TRIVIA

- The Mechonoids previously appeared in the TV story **The Chase**.
- The **Specials** release **Her Final Flight** was originally slated to appear as release **#65**. It was announced on the Big Finish website that it would be removed from the regular schedule on 30th September 2004.
- Davros originally used the name 'Vorsad', but this proved to be too obvious, thus he became 'Dr Vaso', a more oblique anagram of his real name.
- Scott Alan Woodard's original storyline went by the title 'Domes'. This changed to 'Spider in the Web' and then 'The Second Coming' before Gary Russell and he settled on **The Juggernauts**. This title was first mentioned in an email Scott sent to Gary dated 25 November, 2003.
- Sonali is named after the host of a Los Angeles-based political radio show that Scott admires. In Classical Greek, the word Lethe literally means 'oblivion', 'forgetfulness,' or 'concealment'. "The perfect name for a planet where Davros can work in secret," Scott says.
- Reference to 'Sooty, Sweep and Sue' was changed from 'Moe, Larry and Curly' as it was made apparent that a reference to The Three Stooges might be lost on a predominantly British audience.
- Mention of the drug "oxypoxydrin" is a reference to a joke from episode 1 of the comedy series, Spaced.
- "Davros' claim that he has 're-imagined' the Daleks comes from the overused term that many Hollywood execs toss about when presenting remakes of older films,' Scott says. "Personally, I despise this term, but it seemed timely and appropriate!"
- Paul Grunert (Brauer) is married to Bonnie Langford.

PRODUCTION SUMMARY

"I rang up Scott in November, 2003 and asked if he was interested in writing a Doctor Who for us. At the time, he was employed as a Writer/Producer with the children's television arm of The Warner Brothers' Television Network, WB Kids. He was another Who fan and writing professional who was new to Big Finish and whose idea I loved. I used Scott again for the I, Davros range and he was one of my last commissions – for release 101: **Absolution**."
Gary Russell

WORKING TITLES(S)

Domes, Spider in the Web, The Second Coming.

RETURNING MONSTERS/CHARACTERS

Daleks, Mechonoids, Davros.

Check box - CD ☐ MP3 ☐

THE GAME

#66

SYNOPSIS

The Doctor takes Nyssa to the planet Cray where a peace negotiator hero of his, Lord Darzil Carlisle, is set to broker his last pact. However, there appears to be no war in progress; there is merely an obsession with a game called 'naxy'. As the Doctor agrees to a game and is taught how to play by Sharz, Nyssa has found Carlisle and Ambassador Faye Davis. When she tells Carlisle she is travelling with the Doctor, Carlisle becomes very interested. Then, on the TV they see that the Doctor is about to play a game of naxy – the game is the war between the opposing teams of Lineen and Gora! The Doctor not only survives the game but is hailed as a strategic genius who has led the Gora to victory. Nyssa discovers that Carlisle is a fraud and that a future Doctor will end up negotiating all the peace accords for which the human is given credit. The Doctor is challenged to one-on-one combat and Nyssa discovers that

a crime lord called Morian has been sabotaging the peace effort. During the combat, the Doctor is disarmed but convinces his opponent, Hollis, that naxy is senseless brutality and wrong. However, dog-like Velosian bornoxes appear and start firing into the crowd, before being ordered to kill the naxy players and their families. Morian has heard rumours that the Doctor is behind Carlisle's reputation, so he set up the whole situation to get his hands on the TARDIS. The Doctor refuses to give Morian the secrets of the TARDIS but before the criminal can kill the Time Lord, Hollis arrives to free the prisoners. In the escape, Morian kills Carlisle. Then both the Gora and Lineen team up and overpower the bornoxes while Morian and Faye, who is revealed to have been working for the crime lord, flee the planet. Nyssa departs with the Doctor who ensures that the credit for the peace negotiations goes to Carlisle.

PLACEMENT

Between **Creatures of Beauty #44** and **Renaissance of the Daleks #93**.

TRIVIA

- Christopher Ellison is best known to British audiences as DCI Frank Burnside in police drama *The Bill.*
- The story initially featured the Sixth Doctor.
- Originally Gary Russell had comic book and scriptwriter Simon Jowett pencilled in for this slot and that story would have also featured Nyssa.
- The play swapped places with **The Juggernauts #65** in the release schedule.
- This was the first Big Finish release to have 6 episodes on a standard 2-CD release.
- Jonathan Pearce who plays 'naxy' commentator Garny Diblick is well-known as a TV football commentator in the UK.
- The play was announced on the Big Finish website as 'a three CD release by *Seinfeld* writer Darin Henry, who also counts *The Muppets Tonight, Grosse Point* and *Futurama* amongst his writing credits. This will be a fifth Doctor story entitled Game Time.' The story later had a change of title…

PRODUCTION SUMMARY

"Wonderful, wonderful William Russell. Or Russell Enoch as he really is. What an absolute joy he was to work with. All along it had been my intent to cast **Doctor Who** actors in new parts because I didn't want to bring back every single companion for another story but I wanted to give something to their fans. I did the same for many of them: Wendy Padbury, Anneke Wills. They were all absolutely brilliant."
Gary Russell

WORKING TITLES(S)

Game Time.

RETURNING MONSTERS/CHARACTERS

None.

CREW

Writer	**Darin Henry**
Director	**Gary Russell**
Producers	**Jason Haigh-Ellery**
	Gary Russell
Executive Producer (BBC)	**Jacqueline Rayner**
Music and Sound Design	**ERS**
Cover Art	**Lee Binding**
Theme	**Peter Howell**

CAST

The Doctor	**Peter Davison**
Nyssa	**Sarah Sutton**
Ambassador Faye Davis	**Ursula Burton**
Ockle Dirr	**Robert Curbishley**
Coach Bela Destry	**Gregory Donaldson**
Morian	**Christopher Ellison**
Hollis Az	**Andrew Lothian**
Garny Diblick	**Jonathan Pearce**
Lord Darzil Carlisle	**William Russell**
Coach Sharz Sevix	**Dickon Tolson**

TECHNICAL

Story Code	**6C/G**
Recorded Date	**27, 28 and 29 October 2004**
Release Date	**February 2005**
Place of Recording	**The Moat Studios, London**
Number of CDs	**2**
Total Duration	**118' 10"**
Number of Episodes	**6**
Duration of Episodes	1 (18' 37")
	2 (18' 22")
	3 (19' 18")
	4 (21' 45")
	5 (20' 17")
	6 (19' 51")
ISBN	**1-84435-100-9**

#67 DREAMTIME

CREW

Writer	**Simon A. Forward**
Director	**Gary Russell**
Producers	**Jason Haigh-Ellery**
	Gary Russell
Executive Producer (BBC)	**Jacqueline Rayner**
Music and Sound Design	**Steve Foxon**
Cover Art	**Lee Binding**
Theme	**Keff McCulloch**

CAST

The Doctor	**Sylvester McCoy**
Ace	**Sophie Aldred**
Hex	**Philip Olivier**
Trade Negotiator Vresha	**Tamzin Griffin**
Co-Ordinator Whitten	**Jef Higgins**
Dream Commando Wahn	**Brigid Lohrey**
Toomey	**Josephine Mackerras**
Dream Commando Mulyan	**Andrew Peisley**
Commander Korshal	**Steffan Rhodri**
Baiame	**John Scholes**

TECHNICAL

Story Code	**7W/A**
Recorded Date	**9 and 11 November 2004**
Release Date	**March 2005**
Place of Recording	**The Moat Studios, London**
Number of CDs	**2**
Total Duration	**106' 07"**
Number of Episodes	**4**
Duration of Episodes	**1 (25' 02")**
	2 (24' 18")
	3 (28' 29")
	4 (28' 18")
ISBN	**1-84435-136-X**

SYNOPSIS

The Doctor, Ace and Hex arrive on an asteroid where there is a deserted city containing strange statues. Not long afterwards a Galyari ship touches down. Commander Korshal and Trade Negotiator Vresha wish to trade with the city's inhabitants. The time travellers are surprised to find Uluru – Ayres Rock – is part of the asteroid and decide to investigate. However, some 'dream commandoes' arrive and arrest them. The Galyari are then attacked by shapes in the shadows and decide to find the dream commandoes Leanne speaks of. The Doctor's party is attacked by Bunyips, legendary monsters from the Aboriginal Dreamtime, who turn the Time Lord and Leanne into stone statues – they have been lost to the Dreaming. Hex, Ace and the dream commandoes then meet up with the Galyari and together they fend off the Bunyips. The Doctor finds himself in the past of the Dreaming and meets a man called Whitten whose job it is to evacuate the Aborigines who live near Uluru before the Earth is destroyed. However he is being frustrated by Baiame who is promising the native Australians a spiritual alternative to evacuation. The Doctor meets with Baime and discovers that he will use his link to the people and the Dreamtime to launch the rock into space. The Doctor realises that Uluru has acted as a kind of mythological terraforming device but it has gone wrong, beginning its work too early and not waiting to find a new planet. Baiame agrees to help the Doctor put things right, but Korshal believes Baiame is a madman, responsible for the monsters. He sets out to kill Baiame while the Doctor makes for the Galyari ship. There he magnifies the effects of the dream commandoes' Bullroarer instrument/weapon and the creatures from the Dreaming fade away. The city's occupants all wake from their sleep and the travellers depart, leaving the people of Uluru to put things right once more.

PLACEMENT

Between **The Harvest #54** and **Live 34 #74**.

TRIVIA

- The Galyari appear in **The Sandman #37** and the **Bernice Summerfield** story **The Bone of Contention #5.02**.
- Because Gary Russell had cast Steffan Rhodri as the Galyari Commander (as he had in **The Bone of Contention**, see above), he asked Simon A. Forward if the character could be the same one – Korshal.
- The play makes broad use of names and terminology from Australian Aboriginal mythology: The Dreamtime itself is the core of the mythology and includes terms such as 'Galeru', 'Bunyip' and 'Yowie' which can mean 'rainbow snake', 'swamp-dwelling evil spirit' and 'humanoid spirit' (similar to the Bunyip) respectively.
- Tamzin Griffin, who here plays Trade Negotiator Vresha went on to play the part of Sheree Folkson in Russell T Davies's *Casanova* in 2005, opposite David Tennant.

PRODUCTION SUMMARY

"I wanted a sequel to **The Sandman** and I wanted the Galyari because they were well realised. I had no idea the storm we would unleash by using the Australian Aborigine mythology. It was something that a lot of people were upset by and accused us of plundering a belief system to create a science fiction story; although the majority of complainants were neither Aborigine or Australian. To this day I am not entirely sure what people are on about."
Gary Russell

WORKING TITLES(S)

None.

RETURNING MONSTERS/CHARACTERS

The Galyari

CATCH 1782

SYNOPSIS

The Doctor takes Mel to The National Foundation for Scientific Research. It is based in Hallam Hall where Mel's uncle, Dr John Hallam, lives. The house has been in his family for some 300 years and is now leased to the Foundation. The building has a reputation for being haunted by Eleanor Hallam, who wanders the top floors claiming to be trapped. Mel investigates her family history in John's upstairs apartment while the Doctor attends a ceremony to bury a time capsule. John tells him that it is constructed from a new alloy they have developed at the Foundation and the prototype is in his apartment. However, an old chest is discovered where the time capsule is to be buried and when the Doctor examines it, it turns out to contain the prototype. A bad reaction between the TARDIS and the alloy from which the canister is made has sent Mel back to 1781. She meets her ancestor, Henry Hallam, and his housekeeper, Mrs McGregor. Thanks to her ordeal, Mel is suffering from memory loss and dizziness. Dr Wallace is summoned and mishears her name as 'Nell'. Due to her ramblings about time travel he concludes she is mad and should be committed. Henry, himself suffering mentally because his wife died recently, takes pity on her and insists that she stay. The Doctor and John travel back to find Mel but arrive six months later, in 1782. They discover that Mel (now referred to as 'Eleanor') is confined to the upper floor of the house for her own safety. Mel is half convinced she is Eleanor and that her memories of time travel are madness but the Doctor manages to cure her. Discovering that Mrs McGregor is in love with Henry, John convinces her to tell him. They bury the prototype time capsule in the garden and leave, with Wallace and McGregor tending to Henry who finally suffers a breakdown over the loss of his wife.

PLACEMENT

Between **The Juggernauts #65** and **Thicker than Water #73**.

TRIVIA

- Keith Drinkel previously appeared in the TV story **Time-Flight**, while Ian Fairburn was a regular performer in TV stories directed by Douglas Camfield, including **The Invasion** and **Inferno**.
- This play swapped places with the next release in the schedule, **Three's a Crowd #69**, due to cast availability.
- It was originally called 'The Time Sprite' and concerned a mischievous Sprite that took Mel back in time.
- John Hallam is a mix of Alison's two friends John Bunney and Laurence Hallam, both huge **Doctor Who** fans!
- Dr Wallace is named after Alison's mum's family – a long line of Wallaces. Her brother's name is David Wallace Lawson.
- While Alison was writing the play she was working at the National Foundation for Educational Research, which did bury a time capsule to mark the completion of a new building in December 2002. The old building was a mock-Tudor house, which is shown on the cover of the CD.
- The then Director of the Foundation, Dr Seamus Hegarty, read and approved all the scripts prior to submission. Mrs McGregor is named for Alison's husband, Stuart, whose middle name is McGregor.

PRODUCTION SUMMARY

"I remember reading the original outline that Alison sent through and thinking 'I really like this, but we could lose the sprite', so I asked her to remove it and come up with another way of moving Mel through time, which she did. Alison's clever like that!"
Gary Russell

WORKING TITLES(S)

The Time Sprite.

RETURNING MONSTERS/CHARACTERS

None.

CREW

Writer	**Alison Lawson**
Director	**Gary Russell**
Producers	**Jason Haigh-Ellery**
	Gary Russell
Executive Producer (BBC)	**Jacqueline Rayner**
Music	**Russell Stone**
Sound Design	**ERS**
Cover Art	**Lee Binding**
Theme	**Dominic Glynn**

CAST

The Doctor	**Colin Baker**
Mel	**Bonnie Langford**
John Hallam	**Derek Benfield**
Dr Wallace	**Michael Chance**
Henry Hallam	**Keith Drinkel**
Professor David Munro	**Ian Fairburn**
Rachel	**Rhiannon Meades**
Mrs McGregor	**Jillie Meers**

TECHNICAL

Story Code	**7C/T**
Recorded Date	**25 and 26 October 2004**
Release Date	**April 2005**
Place of Recording	**The Moat Studios, London**
Number of CDs	**2**
Total Duration	**102' 51"**
Number of Episodes	**4**
Duration of Episodes	**1 (27' 07")**
	2 (23' 12")
	3 (28' 11")
	4 (24' 21")
ISBN	**1-84435-135-1**

#69 THREE'S A CROWD

CREW

Writer	**Colin Brake**
Director	**Gary Russell**
Producers	**Jason Haigh-Ellery**
	Gary Russell
Executive Producer (BBC)	**Jacqueline Rayner**
Music and Sound Design	**David Darlington**
Cover Art	**Stuart Manning**
Theme	**Peter Howell**

CAST

The Doctor	**Peter Davison**
Peri	**Nicola Bryant**
Erimem	**Caroline Morris**
Auntie	**Deborah Watling**
Bellip	**Lucy Beresford**
Khellian Queen	**Sara Carver**
General Makra'Thon	**Richard Gauntlett**
Laroq	**Daniel Hogarth**
Butler	**Charles Pemberton**
Vidler	**Richard Unwin**

TECHNICAL

Story Code	**6Q/G**
Recorded Date	**26 January and 3 March 2005**
Release Date	**May 2005**
Place of Recording	**The Moat Studios, London**
Number of CDs	**2**
Total Duration	**109' 53"**
Number of Episodes	**4**
Duration of Episodes	**1 (29' 54")**
	2 (27' 04")
	3 (24' 37")
	4 (28' 18")
ISBN	**1-84435-144-0**

SYNOPSIS

The TARDIS arrives aboard the apparently empty space station, Medusa. The Doctor, Peri and Erimem split up. The two women discover hundreds of alien eggs – and then Erimem is transported away by accident. The Doctor is captured and brought to the colony's leader, Auntie. She explains to him that because the terraforming of the planet below is taking too long the colonists must remain in almost solitary confinement where they have become agoraphobic and anti-social. Erimen arrives in a cell where Laroq is meeting his friend Vidler. Laroq panics when the Egyptian arrives because he has never seen three people together before. Erimem finds a way out of the cell and the two men reluctantly follow her. Peri, meanwhile, discovers that there are only 16 colonists on the entire planet. One of these is Belip, who has a massive panic attack brought on by Peri's presence.

The Doctor and Erimem meet up on the space station and find that the reptilian alien Khellians have been using the colonists as a food supply. Vidler and Laroq find out that they are not on the planet but still on the original colony ship. The Doctor confronts Auntie and she confesses that she made a deal with the Khellians: sending them colonists as food in return for the aliens keeping her family alive. She has also been hoping to buy time for the terraforming to complete so she can wake the frozen colonists aboard the Medusa and attack the Khellians. The Doctor tells her that her family has been eaten. She then helps the Doctor to destroy the colony ship and wipe out the Khellians. Auntie is reunited with her granddaughter, Bellip, and the planet is now ready for colonisation and the humans in cryogenic store on the Medusa awakened.

PLACEMENT

Between BFP **The Roof of the World #59** and **The Council of Nicaea #71**.

TRIVIA

- This play swapped places with the previous release in the schedule, **Catch-1782 #68**, due to cast availability.
- Deborah Watling (Auntie) played TV companion to the Second Doctor Victoria Waterfield.
- Richard Gauntlett (General Makra'Thon) played Urak, bat-like Tetrap henchmen to the Rani in the TV story **Time and the Rani**.
  Colin Brake had written the one-part **Bernice Summerfield** adventure, **Silver Lining**, which was given away as a cover-mounted CD on *Doctor Who Magazine*. "It must have gone down okay," Colin Brake says, "because Gary sent another email asking how quickly I could do a script for a non-Earthbound adventure for Fifth Doctor, Peri and Erimem?"
- Colin Brake was a Script Editor at the BBC, working on **EastEnders**, around the time of season 24, 25 and 26 of **Doctor Who**. "I spent lots of time hanging around with Andrew Cartmel and nicking his writers for EastEnders!" Colin says. He was mooted as Andrew's possible replacement.
- During the recording of **Ghost Light** Colin made a studio visit and got introduced to Sylvester McCoy. "This was the first time I'd met a Doctor and thought I'd get the chance to make that two but when I visited the Big Finish studio I managed to miss getting introduced to Peter!" Colin explains. "Not meeting **Doctor Who** actors is a bit of a habit; an episode of *Doctors* that I wrote featured Colin Baker as a guest star and I didn't find out until it was about to be broadcast!"
- Colin did meet Nicola Bryant and promised he'd write her a "meaty role" if he got the chance – which he did in **The Mind's Eye #102**.
- The story was inspired by E. M. Forster's 1909 short story *The Machine Stops*.

PRODUCTION SUMMARY

"I loved working on Big Finish and I did not write anything, other than some with Alan as I don't believe in commissioning myself – but what I can do is I can direct. There's a practicality to that in that I had commissioned the writers and I had a vision of where everything needed to be going. So it made sense for me to direct them all myself so I directed every play for 18 months [actually every play between **Project: Lazarus #45** and this play]. And I was working too hard. Yes. I was working seven days a week, ten hours a day."
Gary Russell

WORKING TITLES(S)

None.

RETURNING MONSTERS/CHARACTERS

None.

Check box - CD ☐ MP3 ☐

UNREGENERATE! #70

SYNOPSIS

In 1957, a German man called Rausch is trying to get work. He meets a mysterious man called Louis who agrees to improve his life if Rausch will go with him to a place of scientific study on the day of his death. 50 years in the future, Mel is waiting for the Doctor. When the TARDIS turns up he is not onboard, but he has left her a message. With a cabbie, she follows Rausch and Louis to an Institute, where the Doctor is an inmate and cannot remember who he is. Klyst, the woman in charge, discusses the escape of an inmate called Shokhra with her head of security, Rigan. Mel discovers that the building is in fact a hollow shell and the TARDIS identifies a section of wall that is a hologram. Mel then enters the building with the cabbie and finds both Shokhra and the Doctor. They flee, pursued by Rigan. In the lab, Klyst superimposes another mind onto Rausch who then goes mad and has to be sedated. Upset by this, Klyst seeks out the Doctor. It is revealed that Klyst, Rigan and Louis are all Time Lords and the institute is trying to implant 'TARDIS minds' into species that are capable of developing time travel so that the High Council can control them. However, these TARDIS minds are far too complex to be meshed with a humanoid and have been driven mad. The Doctor was sabotaging the experiments when one of the AIs discharged into his mind, but he is restored to full health when he merges with the Shokhra entity. The Rausch creature escapes and returns with the TARDIS, which then helps calm all the nascent AIs. All the subjects – including Klyst – decide to become renegades and use the techniques taught them by the Doctor's TARDIS to avoid detection and capture. Rigan and Louis are returned to Gallifrey.

PLACEMENT

Between the TV story **Time and the Rani** and BFP **The Fires of Vulcan #12**.

TRIVIA

- This slot was originally going to be filled by a play called Dead Man's Hand (which was announced on the Big Finish website) by John Ostrander.
- McIntee's original play featured the Daleks.
- Chronologically, this is meant to be the Seventh Doctor's first Big Finish audio adventure.
- Jennie Linden, who plays Klyst, is well-remembered for the role of Barbara in the 1965 film, **Dr Who and the Daleks**.
- This is one of only two plays in the monthly release range to contain an exclamation mark; the other is **Bang-Bang-A-Boom! #39**. (The only other unusual punctuation mark used is an ellipsis in **...ish #35**.)

PRODUCTION SUMMARY

"I gave **Unregenerate!** to John Ainsworth. Occasionally you come across a story that you think you either won't be as good at directing it as someone else or you think you won't enjoy it as much. As time went on from here, I gave away more and more. I was going completely loopy and I must have resigned about six times a week. And that is when Alan Barnes came in – mid 2005. Because I said to Jason that he needed bring someone in and Alan was the best man for the job'."

Gary Russell

WORKING TITLES(S)

None.

RETURNING MONSTERS/CHARACTERS

Time Lords.

CREW

Writer	**David A. McIntee**
Director	**John Ainsworth**
Producers	**Jason Haigh-Ellery** **Gary Russell**
Executive Producer (BBC)	**Jacqueline Rayner**
Music and Sound Design	**Ian Potter**
Cover Art	**Lee Binding**
Theme	**Keff McCulloch**

CAST

The Doctor	**Sylvester McCoy**
Mel	**Bonnie Langford**
Louis #2	**John Aston**
Rigan	**Gail Clayton**
Johannes Rausch	**Hugh Hemmings**
Shokhra	**Sam Peter Jackson**
Professor Klyst	**Jennie Linden**
The Cabbie	**Toby Longworth**
Louis	**Jamie Sandford**

TECHNICAL

Story Code	**7D/A**
Recorded Date	**16 and 17 November 2004**
Release Date	**June 2005**
Place of Recording	**The Moat Studios, London**
Number of CDs	**2**
Total Duration	**107' 50"**
Number of Episodes	**4**
Duration of Episodes	**1 (26' 12")** **2 (24' 31")** **3 (27' 44")** **4 (29' 23")**
ISBN	**1-84435-158-0**

Check box - CD ■ MP3 ■

no further announcement was made by Big Finish concerning the play until August, when it was announced that the story would get its CD release in December. Following on from the earlier release, the packaging for Shada bore the cover spine number II, a convention that would continue despite a slight hiccup further down the line.

The idea of a special release as a subscriber bonus was not pursued in 2003, but it was back in 2004, with **Her Final Flight #III**. On 22 September 2005 Big Finish announced the story, which would be sent out as a free CD accompanying **The Next Life #64**, and would — perhaps logically — be assigned the release number of #65.

This caused a lot of complaints from those who did not subscribe, saying that there would be a sequential gap on the cover spines of their collection. Eight days later Big Finish relented. 'Always willing to listen, we've opted thus to take **Her Final Flight** out of the sequential system and list it instead alongside **The Maltese Penguin** (our previous subscriber-only free disc), **Real Time** and **Shada** as a 'special'. Thus January's regular release, **The Game** becomes 65, **The Juggernauts**, 66 and so on.'

As well as its numbering, the play set many precedents in that it was released as a subscriber bonus with December's release and then received a general release a year later. Every subscriber bonus

story since has followed that pattern — with the exception of 2010's **The Four Doctors**, which Big Finish say will never see a wider release.

Her Final Flight #III, had initially been a play sent in by writer Julian Shortman during the open submissions window the previous year. This experiment was repeated the following year when one of the storylines submitted during 2003's round of open submissions was chosen for the subscriber-only role: **Cryptobiosis #IV** by Elliot Thorpe.

With subsequent releases, this idea would be dropped, but then ahead lay Zarbi, Daleks, Krotons and a quarter of Doctors, subjects that new executivep producer Nicholas Briggs felt would be better handled by experienced writers…

Top:
Robert Jezek and Colin Baker enjoy a further adventure for the Sixth Doctor and Frobisher in **The Maltese Penguin**.

Above-left:
Colin Baker and Maggie Stables at the recording of **Real Time** *- a sidestep adventure for the Doctor and Evelyn.*

#33½ THE MALTESE PENGUIN

CREW

Writer	**Robert Shearman**
Director	**Gary Russell**
Producers	**Jason Haigh-Ellery**
	Gary Russell
Executive Producer (BBC)	**Stephen Cole**
Music and Sound Design	**David Darlington**
Cover Art	**Lee Binding**
Theme	**David Darlington**

CAST

The Doctor	**Colin Baker**
Frobisher	**Robert Jezek**
Josiah W. Dogbolter	**Toby Longworth**
Alicia Mulholland	**Jane Goddard**
Chandler	**Alistair Lock**

TECHNICAL

Story Code	**BFPDWCDSS3**
Recorded Date	**2 November 2001**
Release Date	**July 2002 (subs) November 2002 (general)**
Place of Recording	**The Moat Studios, London**
Number of CDs	**1**
Total Duration	**68' 14"**
Number of Episodes	**1**
Duration of Episodes	**68' 14"**
ISBN	**1-903654-90-4**

SYNOPSIS

After Frobisher has finished travelling in the TARDIS, the Doctor returns to see him and ask if he would like some help. Frobisher refuses because he hasn't had a partner since his last one, Francine, left him. The Doctor leaves and Frobisher is confronted by Alicia Mulholland. She explains that her fiancé, Arthur Gringax, is being unfaithful and she wants him to investigate. To blend in more with the humans, the Whifferdill takes the form of the Sixth Doctor. He then follows Arthur to a hotel where he is killed. A corrupt police officer arrives and takes Frobisher to Josiah W. Dogbolter. The toad-like alien businessman tells Frobisher that he was Arthur's employer and is looking for something that Arthur made. Frobisher refuses to tell Dogbolter anything and is thrown from a cliff. He survives by morphing back into a penguin and meets with Alicia again. The two of them are recaptured and taken back to Dogbolter's office where he admits that on this planet it is most profitable for his businesses to do nothing. However, it all went wrong when Arthur managed to create something. Trouble is, no one knows what it is and he threatens to kill Alicia. It is revealed that the thing is a computer chip and when Dogbolter puts it in his machine it beams a message to every other computer in his business saying: "You don't have to be crazy to work here, but it helps". The three then hear laughter coming from all over the complex. This will cause people to start making things! Dogbolter is ruined and pulls a gun on Frobisher and Alicia. However, at that moment the TARDIS arrives, shielding them from the gunshots. As Dogbolter flees, Alicia admits to being Francine (and Arthur, too, using her shape-changing abilities). She has been trying to bring Dogbolter to justice and needed Frobisher's help. She leaves to pursue the businessman while Frobisher steps aboard the TARDIS once more.

PLACEMENT

Between the *Doctor Who Magazine* comic-strip **The World Shapers** and the Big Finish adventure **The Holy Terror #14**.

TRIVIA

- This story was originally released free to subscribers with **Neverland #33**, but subsequently made available on general release three months later – a great deal sooner than most subscriber bonus stories.
- It was given the release number "33 ½" because it was given away with release **#33** and before **#34**! No other Special release has been numbered in this way.
- **The Maltese Penguin** was the first subscriber bonus story; previously *Big Finish Magazine* had been given away as a subscriber bonus.
- This story was recorded on the same day and with the same cast as the *DWM* release **The Ratings War #3**.
- John Ridgeway, the *DWM* artist who drew Frobisher, is name-checked in the list of famous artists that Dogbolter reels off.
- The play features a special arrangement of the *Doctor Who* theme tune by David Darlington – a film noir version!

PRODUCTION SUMMARY

"It was actually Jason that asked Rob to do this one. I had no objection of course because I love both Rob and Robert Jezek is perfect as Frobisher; and when you add Colin to the mix… well! I did suggest Dogbolter as the villain because it tied in so well with Frobisher's adventures in the comic strip."
Gary Russell

WORKING TITLE(S)

None.

RETURNING MONSTERS/CHARACTERS

Frobisher, Dogbolter.

REAL TIME

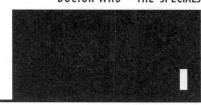

SYNOPSIS

The Doctor and Evelyn accompany an expedition to the planet Chronos where Cybermen are active and two survey teams have gone missing near a mysterious temple. While Evelyn gets to know Dr Reece Goddard, an expert on the Cybermen, the Doctor investigates the temple and discovers a time portal through which emerge three Cybermen. The Doctor escapes to the camp but is caught again by a Cyberman, who demands the TARDIS key. The Doctor learns that the Cybermen are coming from the distant future but the time portal is making their implants malfunction. This is why they need the TARDIS. Evelyn and Goddard go to the temple but are captured and taken through the portal. They meet the Cyber Controller, who tells them that they can use Evelyn's mind and wire it to the TARDIS, converting her into a time-travelling Cyber Controller. Back on Chronos, it is revealed that

Goddard is a super-advanced cyborg from 1927. In his time stream, the Cybermen attacked Earth with a techno-virus that killed or transformed all humans. The cybernetic rebels have sent him to this nexus point to change history back to the way it should be using a virus that attacks cyber implants. The Doctor realises that the virus Goddard is carrying will be retro-engineered by the Cybermen and used to attack the Earth in 1927 using the time portal. Together, the Doctor and Goddard travel through the portal to save Evelyn. The Doctor manages to get her away as Goddard holds off the Cyber Controller. It is then not only revealed that the Controller has infected Evelyn with the techno-virus but that the Cyber Controller *is* Evelyn. As the Doctor gets his Evelyn back to the TARDIS, she asks to see Goddard's time to check that all is well. The Doctor sets the co-ordinates for Earth, 1927…

PLACEMENT

Although this story was originally meant to be placed between the TV stories **The Trial of a Time Lord** and **Time and the Rani**, as well as after **Project: Twilight #23**, it is now seen as a sidestep and should not be considered part of Evelyn's story.

TRIVIA

- This story was produced by Big Finish productions for BBCi and was webcast as an animated adventure between 2 August and 6 September 2002.
- The CD release of this play includes extra scenes not included in the original broadcast, one featuring Robert Curbishley and Mark Wright recorded on the first day of recording for **The Church and the Crown #38** on 5th September 2002. A full-length, behind-the-scenes Making Of documentary is also featured on the CD release.
- The first story Big Finish came up with in 2001 for BBCi was **Dalek Invasion** by Rob Shearman. This would later be re-worked as **Jubilee #40** in 2003 and then again as the 2005 TV story **Dalek**.
- The names of all the supporting characters came from those suggested by entrants to a BBCi competition.
- This story produced the first ever Big Finish action figure; a Sixth Doctor in the blue costume he is shown wearing in the audio's animations and illustrations by Lee Sullivan was released as a San Diego Comic Con exclusive by Forbidden Planet in 2009.

PRODUCTION SUMMARY

"To me – because we never did the sequel – **Real Time** might as well have Doctor Who Unbound written across it. If one day **Real Time II** ever gets written then it could rejoin the Big Finish canon. And I would do that story now. I wouldn't have done it a few years ago, because now I know what I'd do with it! Its time has passed. I don't think this story represents Evelyn's future. She would never have been left as a Cyberman!"
Gary Russell

WORKING TITLE(S)

None.

RETURNING MONSTERS/CHARACTERS

Cybermen.

CREW

Writer	**Gary Russell**
Director	**Gary Russell**
Producers	**Jason Haigh-Ellery**
	Gary Russell
Executive Producer (BBCi)	**Martin Trickey**
Music and Sound Design	**Alistair Lock**
Cover Art	**Lee Sullivan**
Theme	**Delia Derbyshire**

CAST

The Doctor	**Colin Baker**
Evelyn Smythe	**Maggie Stables**
Administrator Isherwood	**Christopher Scott**
Doctor Goddard	**Yee Jee Tso**
Doctor Savage	**Jane Goddard**
Renchard	**Richard Herring**
Carey	**Stewart Lee**
Cyber Controller	**Nicholas Briggs**

TECHNICAL

Story Code	**BFPDWBBCiCD01**
Recorded Date	**19 March 2002**
Release Date	**December 2002**
Place of Recording	**The Moat Studios, London**
Number of CDs	**2**
Total Duration	**127' 32"**
Number of Episodes	**6**
Duration of Episodes	**1 (22' 54")**
	2 (10' 31")
	3 (14' 36")
	4 (15' 15")
	5 (15' 00")
	6 (14' 24")
	Documentary (34' 52")
ISBN	**1-903654-78-5**

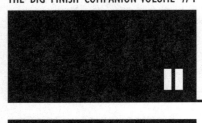

SHADA

CREW

Writer	**Douglas Adams**
Adapted by	**Gary Russell**
Director	**Nicholas Pegg**
Producers	**Jason Haigh-Ellery**
	Gary Russell
Executive Producer (BBCi)	**Martin Trickey**
Music	**Russell Stone**
Sound Design	**Gareth Jenkins**
Cover Art	**Clayton Hickman**
Theme	**Delia Derbyshire**

CAST

The Doctor	**Paul McGann**
Romana	**Lalla Ward**
K9	**John Leeson**
Chris Parsons	**Sean Biggerstaff**
Constable	**Stuart Crossman**
Professor Caldera	**Barnaby Edwards**
Professor Chronotis	**James Fox**
The Ship	**Hannah Gordon**
Clare Keightley	**Susannah Harker**
Wilkin	**Melvyn Hayes**
Think Tank Voice	**Nicholas Pegg**
Skagra	**Andrew Sachs**

TECHNICAL

Story Code	**BFPDWBBCiCD02**
Recorded Date	**12, 13 & 14 November 2002**
Release Date	**December 2003**
Place of Recording	**Christchurch Studios, Bristol**
Number of CDs	**2**
Total Duration	**142' 26"**
Number of Episodes	**6**
Duration of Episodes	**1 (22' 40")**
	2 (22' 41")
	3 (20' 56")
	4 (27' 17")
	5 (24' 04")
	6 (24' 47")
ISBN	**1-84435-039-8**

SYNOPSIS

The Eighth Doctor reunites with President Romana and K9 on Gallifrey, and persuades them to travel with him to Cambridge and visit their old friend Professor Chronotis, a retired Time Lord now living as an academic in a college. One of Professor Chronotis's students, Chris Parsons, borrows some books and notices that one of them is written in a strange language and shows it to his friend, Clare. The book is *The Worshipful and Ancient Law of Gallifrey*, which Chronotis wants the Doctor and Romana to return to Gallifrey. Also in Cambridge is an alien criminal called Skagra who is looking for the book. He attacks Chronotis with his mind sphere and leaves the Time Lord for dead. The Doctor and Romana then trace Skagra's ship but are captured by Skagra who wants the books translated. He uses the sphere to take a copy of the Doctor's mind and then takes Romana with him to the TARDIS. He is after a man called Salyavin, an infamous Time Lord criminal (and boyhood hero of the Doctor's) and pilots the TARDIS to his command ship in space. Here Romana discovers he has an army of rock-like Krargs that are grown in vats. It is also revealed that the book is actually the key to the Time Lord's prison planet, Shada. He connects the book to the TARDIS and it pilots the ship there. Meanwhile, Clare discovers that Chronotis's rooms are a TARDIS and when she operates the controls, the time field brings the Professor back to life. Escaping some Krargs, the Doctor and Chris stumble across the old TARDIS and together they travel to Shada. Here, Skagra and Romana have already arrived. In reality, Chronotis is really Salyavin and the sphere takes his mind as well as that of Chris's. The Doctor manages to turn the tables in a mental battle and Skagra is imprisoned. When Chronotis recovers Romana agrees not to imprison him again and they all return to Cambridge for tea.

PLACEMENT

After the 1996 **Doctor Who** TV Movie and prior to the Big Finish adventure **Storm Warning #16**.

TRIVIA

- This story was created by Big Finish productions for BBCi and was webcast as an animated adventure on the 2, 9, 16, 23 30 May, and 6 June.
- In the original version of **Shada**, the character of Chris Parsons went to a school in Bristol. Because Scottish actor Sean Biggerstaff (who had appeared in the *Harry Potter* franchise as Gryffindor Quidditch captain Oliver Wood) was cast, the reference was changed to St Aloysius College, which was a school near to where Sean had grown up in Glasgow.
- Big Finish did approach Tom Baker to reprise his role in **Shada**, but he declined.
- It was the casting of Susannah Harker in this play that led Jason Haigh-Ellery to suggesting her to Nigel Fairs for the part of Sapphire in Big Finish's **Sapphire & Steel** range in 2004.

PRODUCTION SUMMARY

"It was Jason's idea to do **Shada** and James Goss at BBCi was very taken with the notion. When I adapted Douglas Adams's script I took real care that we didn't cause the bits from **The Five Doctors** to become null and void! So we have the scene in the beginning where the McGann Doctor travels to Gallifrey and says to Romana: 'we've got to go back: there's unfinished business'. And I also took out the punting scene as we'd already seen that with the Fourth Doctor on TV. I also knew that as it wasn't really my cup of tea that we'd need someone who loved that era to direct it. That's why we got Nick Pegg in."
Gary Russell

WORKING TITLE(S)

None.

RETURNING MONSTERS/CHARACTERS

Romana, K9, Time Lords.

HER FINAL FLIGHT

SYNOPSIS

The TARDIS materialises on the desolate planet Refiloe. Before the Doctor can leave, though, he is shot and upon waking finds himself being looked after by Peri. However, he knows that he left Peri on Thoras Beta, so how can she be there? She tells him that she left King Yrcanos and crashed on this planet, setting up a distress call, which the TARDIS answered. The planet's inhabitants have taken the TARDIS to their temple, believing it to be a gift from their god, Sohile. There, the high priest Damus is pleased with the miraculous power that emanates from the TARDIS. The Doctor keeps collapsing during this time and hearing the voice of a feline creature called Rashaa. However, the Doctor keeps being pushed into this artificial reality where things go from bad to worse. As buildings and people are either aged to death or cured of a disease, the Doctor discovers that the time distortion is caused by the TARDIS

leaking chronon radiation. It has also been causing a native virus to develop but the Doctor develops an antidote. But he falls unconscious once more and when he wakes it is two days later and the virus has mutated beyond the vaccine's ability to control it. With little option, the Doctor shuts down the TARDIS. Peri then dies of the disease and, distraught, the Doctor sets the medical scanner to a higher setting. It reveals that there is no virus; instead his body has been implanted with an alien device, which he removes. As he does so, the temple and all the characters disappear and he finally confronts Rashaa. Using the same implant, he causes her to believe she has killed him. However, it is revealed that Rashaa was working for an Agent who has learned that the Doctor will kill him in the future. As the Doctor leaves in the TARDIS, the Agent kills Rashaa for her failure.

PLACEMENT

Between the 1986 TV story **The Trial of a Time Lord** and the Big Finish adventure **I.D. & Urgent Calls #94**.

TRIVIA

- This story was originally given away to subscribers to the main **Doctor Who** range whose subscriptions included **The Next Life #64**.
- The story was originally written with the Seventh Doctor and Mel. Cover artist Stuart Manning even produced a cover featuring this TARDIS team.
- Julian Harris offered the services of his acclaimed choir, The Saint James' Singers, to the production. The music they sing is composed by the story's author, Julian Shortman.
- Conrad Westmaas, who here plays High Priest Damus, is better known as C'rizz, companion to the Eighth Doctor in his Big Finish adventures.
- The story features Nekkistani time technology that was first mentioned in **The Apocalypse Element #11** and later in the **Gallifrey** range. It was a Nekkistani who sold Robert Knox his TARDIS in **Medicinal Purposes #60** and Davros acquired a Nekkistani time cruiser to lure the Doctor into a trap in **Terror Firma #72**.

PRODUCTION SUMMARY

"This was a nice little story that came through the slush pile. I liked that it set out its stall from the beginning with the whole false reality thing. And it was a nice way of having Nicola play an older Peri who wasn't bitter about the Doctor leaving her behind. It was a mystery. It had unanswered questions and I think sometimes it is quite neat not to tie up all the loose ends in a story."
Gary Russell

WORKING TITLE(S)

None.

RETURNING MONSTERS/CHARACTERS

None.

CREW

Writer	**Julian Shortman**
Director	**Gary Russell**
Producers	**Jason Haigh-Ellery**
	Gary Russell
Executive Producer (BBC)	**Jacqueline Rayner**
Music and Sound Design	**David Darlington**
Cover Art	**Stuart Manning**
Theme	**Dominic Glynn**

CAST

The Doctor	**Colin Baker**
Peri	**Nicola Bryant**
The Agent	**Steven Bugdale**
Hamiyun	**Jonathan Owen**
Rashaa	**Heather Tracy**
Damus	**Conrad Westmaas**

TECHNICAL

Story Code	**BFPDWCD7CPREA**
Recorded Date	**16 September 2004 (choral music: 6 October 2004)**
Release Date	**December 2004 (Subs); December 2005 (general)**
Place of Recording	**The Moat Studios, London**
Number of CDs	**1**
Total Duration	**73' 47"**
Number of Episodes	**2**
Duration of Episodes	**1 (37' 43") 2 (36' 04")**
ISBN	**1-84435-113-0**

THE BEAUTIFUL PEOPLE

#1.4

SYNOPSIS

In search of doughnuts, the Doctor takes Romana to the Vita Novus Health Spa where all is fitness and healthy eating. The travellers meet Sebella Bing who digs up a chocolate cake from where she buried it and shares it with them. However, a trainer robot arrives and removes Sebella to the treadmill. The Doctor and Romana then meet the health spa's owner, Dame Monserrat Karna. She tells them people leave the spa after only a few days as an entirely new person: thinner, fitter and happier. Believing them to be representatives of a publication, she gives them a tour of the facility, with its pervasive aroma of pine. Romana is attacked by a strange seaweed creature but saved by Sebella. Together they go to the basement where they are confronted by Karna who reveals that she uses a cellular reduction process to remove any extraneous body materials, leaving the person wholly regenerated. The removed tissue is then processed into the spa's exclusive range of products. Karna also re-programmes their minds to remain healthy and to recommend the Vita Novus to everyone and that this plan will one day result in a spa on every planet, those who do not wish to participate being killed. She places Romana in a slimming booth and sets it to remove 100 per cent of her body tissue, but the Doctor and K9 arrive to save her. The computer controlling the process is destroyed in the fight and, as Romana had rigged the process to work in reverse, the Doctor climbs into another slimming booth. Anyone left outside the booths will be processed and although Karna tries to enter a booth she is processed, losing 100 per cent of her body mass. Later, as they are about to leave, Sebella gives the Doctor a doughnut she has programmed the robots to make. She has taken over the health spa!

PLACEMENT

Between the TV stories **Nightmare of Eden** and **The Horns of Nimon**.

TRIVIA

- Lalla Ward has appeared as Romana in many Big Finish plays across several ranges prior to this: in the **Main Monthly Range** stories **The Apocalypse Element #11**, **Neverland #33**, **Zagreus #50**, **The Chaos Pool #119** as well as appearing in the **Special Release Shada #II** and taking the lead in the **Gallifrey** series.
- This story was written in two weeks as a replacement for Mark J. Thompson's 'Psychomorph', which wasn't deemed right for the series by script editor Alan Barnes.
- The story is broken down into chapters ("Too Good to be True", "The Complete Makeover", "Slim Chances and Narrow Escapes" and "Live and Let Diet").
- Being set during the period when Douglas Adams was script editor of the TV show, this story has many references to Adams's *Hitchhikers Guide t o the Galaxy* series of books, including the Doctor claiming that he and Romana are researchers for "a well-known guide for the space traveller on a budget".

PRODUCTION SUMMARY

"Jonathan Morris created this cute little tale in double-quick time, and he wrote well for Lalla's Romana. Comedy is always a difficult area in **Doctor Who**: it seems to divide fans (think of **Love & Monsters**) and is not something I'm keen on personally. However, the flavour he created fitted very well as a Season 17 story. I was keen that each story fitted in each season seamlessly so as not to jar with established continuity."
Mark J. Thompson

WORKING TITLE(S)

Psychomorph.

RETURNING MONSTERS/CHARACTERS

None.

CREW

Writer	**Jonathan Morris**
Director	**Mark J Thompson**
Producer	**Mark J Thompson**
Executive Producer	**Jason Haigh-Ellery**
Music	**Lawrence Oakley**
Sound Design	**Lawrence Oakely and Robert Dunlop**
Cover Art	**Simon Holub**
Theme	**Delia Derbyshire**

CAST

Romana	**Lalla Ward**
Karna	**Marcia Ashton**

ERA

Fourth Doctor – read by Romana II

TECHNICAL

Story Code	**BFPDWCC04**
Recorded Date	**28 November 2006**
Release Date	**January 2007**
Place of Recording	**Soundmagic Studios, Essex**
Number of CDs	**1**
Total Duration	**66' 28"**
Number of Episodes	**4**
Duration of Episodes	**1 (24' 52")**
	2 (17' 44")
	3 (12' 05")
	4 (11' 47")
ISBN	**978-1-84435-266-1**

#2.1 MOTHER RUSSIA

CREW

Writer	**Marc Platt**
Director	**Nigel Fairs**
Producer	**Sharon Gosling**
Executive Producer	**Jason Haigh-Ellery**
Executive Producer (BBC)	**Jacqueline Rayner**
Music and Sound Design	**David Darlington**
Cover Art	**Simon Holub**
Theme	**Delia Derbyshire**

CAST

Steven	**Peter Purves**
The Interrogator	**Tony Millan**

ERA

First Doctor – Read by Steven

TECHNICAL

Story Code	**BFPDWCC05**
Recorded Date	**6 June 2007**
Release Date	**October 2007**
Place of Recording	**Wolf Studios, London**
Number of CDs	**1**
Total Duration	**67' 41"**
Number of Episodes	**2**
Duration of Episodes	**1 (33' 36"), 2 (34' 05")**
ISBN	**978-1-84435-290-6**

SYNOPSIS

Steven is being questioned by an unknown interrogator, accusing him of being an impostor. So Steven tells him of his most recent adventure… The TARDIS has brought him, the Doctor and Dodo to Russia in 1812 as Napoleon Bonaparte is advancing on Moscow. For weeks, the travellers enjoyed their 'holiday' with Steven befriending local man, Semian. Semian is to be married to Glasha and he asks Steven to be his best man. However, on the first night of the wedding celebrations, everyone is terrified to see lights in the sky which the Doctor identifies as a space battle. They see something crash to Earth so Steven and Semian go to investigate. They become separated and Steven is attacked by a bear before being rescued by the Doctor and Dodo. When Semian returns he is behaving strangely and the villagers lock him up. The Doctor releases him but Steven and Dodo discover Semian's dead body elsewhere. When they try to warn the Doctor of this they find evidence of a struggle and the Doctor acting out of character. Steven runs off to the village but Dodo appears and knocks him out. When he wakes, Napoleon's army has taken the Doctor, Dodo and the TARDIS to Moscow. Arriving at the Kremlin, Steven finds the Doctor advising Napoleon on how he should negotiate Russia's surrender. The Doctor gives orders for Steven to be taken outside and shot but then apparently stops the firing squad. The Time Lord explains that the alien is a shape thief. He then confronts the alien pretending to be him, who tries to escape in the TARDIS – but the time ship is not fooled. Desperate, the alien changes into Napoleon, hoping to escape as Moscow burns. It is revealed that the interrogator is the alien who also pretended to be Semian, the bear and Dodo as well, but not Steven. Believing him to be the French Emperor, the alien shape-shifter is then carried away by an angry mob of Muscovites.

PLACEMENT

Between the TV stories **The Gunfighters** and **The Savages**.

TRIVIA

- This was Peter Purves's first appearance as Steven Taylor for 41 years (since **The Savages** in 1966).
- Napoleon's retreat from Moscow in 1812 is also mentioned in Marc Platt's **Doctor Who Main Range** story **Loups-Garoux #20** as the time and place where Ileana de Santos first encountered Pieter Stubbe.
- The sequences in the Russian countryside echo Pushkin's *Eugene Onegin* and Turgenyev's *A Month in the Country*. The Moscow sequences echo Tolstoy's *War and Peace*. The Russian peasant wedding was inspired by Stravinsky's ballet *Les Noces*.

PRODUCTION SUMMARY

"I'd so been looking forward to meeting Peter Purves, and vowed that I wouldn't mention *Blue Peter*. Of course, the first thing I said when he walked through the door was, 'You and Valerie Singleton were my heroes when I was growing up!' He was absolutely charming about it and shared some very happy memories of his time on it. And listening to him reading Marc's splendid script was just like hearing him narrate one of those Blue Peter film items, you know, the ones with the line drawings. I was taken right back! What I didn't know was that Val went to RADA. I told Sharon she should commission one with the pair of them – imagine that! I'd be in *Blue Peter* heaven!"
Nigel Fairs

WORKING TITLE(S)

None.

RETURNING MONSTERS/CHARACTERS

Dodo.

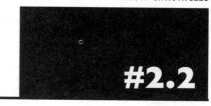

HELICON PRIME

#2.2

SYNOPSIS

As he recovers from an injury to his head, Jamie's mind clears and he tells his nurse about the time he and the Doctor went to an exclusive luxury resort called Helicon Prime. They soon meet Mindy Voir, a singer who the Doctor admires. She tells them that her father augmented her vocal range and she can even tie knots in pieces of string using just her voice. Later, Jamie meets a glass creature called Romea who tells him that Ambassador Dromeo is watching him and the Doctor. Later, Romea is poisoned and, when the Doctor asks Jamie to search Dromeo's suite, Mindy follows him. As they investigate together, the ambassador returns and they hide. Dromeo calmly poisons two further aliens but not before revealing that he is looking for a hidden treasure – the collected minds of a former colony. Jamie and Mindy escape and over dinner they tell the Doctor what they heard.

They also learn that Helicon Prime is drifting away from the Golden Section. When Dromeo arrives in the restaurant, the Doctor persuades Mindy to give a spontaneous concert while he puts his plan into action. Jamie then follows Dromeo to a series of rooms that he searches but does not find what he is looking for. The Doctor claims that he has found the treasure and intends to return it to the colonists' descendants. Dromeo flees as the Doctor stabilises the resort using the TARDIS. Jamie finishes his story but the nurse reveals that she is Mindy who has also been looking for the treasure. The Doctor did not give it to the colonists and she believes Jamie has it. As she attacks him with her voice, it is revealed that the collective memories are trapped in a special pendant that Jamie is wearing. The device then traps Mindy but wipes Jamie's memories of his time with the Doctor once more.

PLACEMENT

Between the TV stories **The Two Doctors** and **Spearhead from Space**.

TRIVIA

- This was Frazer Hines's first appearance as Jamie McCrimmon for 22 years (since **The Two Doctors** in 1985).

PRODUCTION SUMMARY

"I adore Frazer Hines! He's so sweet and generous and funny and does a superb Troughton, of course. He's so committed to the role and his own nostalgia for his time on *Doctor Who* is huge and quite moving."
Nigel Fairs

WORKING TITLE(S)

None.

RETURNING MONSTERS/CHARACTERS

None.

CREW

Writer	**Jake Elliott**
Director	**Nigel Fairs**
Producer	**Sharon Gosling**
Executive Producer	**Jason Haigh-Ellery**
Music and Sound Design	**David Darlington**
Cover Art	**Simon Holub**
Theme	**Delia Derbyshire**

CAST

Jamie	**Frazer Hines**
Mindy Voir	**Suzanne Proctor**

ERA

Second Doctor - read by Jamie

TECHNICAL

Story Code	**BFPDWCC06**
Recorded Date	**Unknown**
Release Date	**November 2007**
Place of Recording	**Wolf Studios, London**
Number of CDs	**1**
Total Duration	**63' 15"**
Number of Episodes	**2**
Duration of Episodes	**1 (32' 35")** **2 (30' 40")**
ISBN	**978-1-84435-291-3**

#2.3 OLD SOLDIERS

CREW

Writer	**James Swallow**
Director	**Nigel Fairs**
Producer	**Sharon Gosling**
Executive Producer	**Jason Haigh-Ellery**
Executive Producer (BBC)	**Jacqueline Rayner**
Music and Sound Design	**David Darlington**
Cover Art	**Simon Holub**
Theme	**Delia Derbyshire**

CAST

Brigadier Alistair Lethbridge-Stewart	**Nicholas Courtney**
Konrad/Schrader	**Toby Longworth**

ERA

Third Doctor - Read by his friend, Brigadier Lethbridge-Stewart

TECHNICAL

Story Code	**BFPDWCC07**
Recorded Date	**Unknown**
Release Date	**December 2007**
Place of Recording	**Wolf Studios, London**
Number of CDs	**1**
Total Duration	**61' 35"**
Number of Episodes	**2**
Duration of Episodes	**1 (32' 11")**
	2 (29' 24")
ISBN	**978-1-84435-292-0**

SYNOPSIS

The Brigadier visits a UNIT base at Kreigskind Castle in Germany at the request of his friend Kolonel Heinrich Konrad. However, he finds the man in the medical wing on the brink of death and muttering about ancient soldiers rising up. Later in bed, the Brigadier is attacked by a Roman soldier. He shoots it and it fades away. Elsewhere, the base's troops, led by second-in-command, Major Schrader, endure a similar attack by phantom soldiers. It transpires that the castle was built on the site of a Roman garrison and that the manifestations have been happening with increasing regularity. The Brigadier calls in the Doctor, who in typical style, parachutes in! The Time Lord puts forward the idea of the events being down to a time fissure. The Brigadier discovers that Konrad was in charge of something called Project 995 involving six men of whom only the Kolonel had survived, the rest of the team apparently having been poisoned. He shows this to the Doctor but then Nazi soldiers from World War II start to attack and they are forced to withdraw. Schrader reveals that the toxin is in fact a drug extracted from an alien plant. Both Konrad and Schrader were working to create super soldiers to defend the planet from alien threats. They believe the Doctor to be just such an alien threat and have called in an airstrike to destroy the castle thus preventing the information falling into "enemy" hands. The Doctor discovers that the drug enhances psychic ability and the Romans and Nazis are projections of the castle's history, created by Konrad's uncontrolled psychic powers. He builds a device that nullifies the psychic energy, freezing the phantoms. As the airstrike closes in, the Brigadier rushes the UNIT troops to safety and Konrad volunteers to operate the device until the air strike takes place. Konrad is killed as the castle is destroyed, eradicating the alien plant.

PLACEMENT

Between the TV stories **Doctor Who and the Silurians** and **The Ambassadors of Death**.

TRIVIA

- An early version of this story featured the Doctor and Liz Shaw trapped inside UNIT's equivalent of Area 51, with only the Brigadier able to rescue them.
- During the story, the Brigadier refers to UNIT's encounters with several alien invaders, including the Cybermen, Nestene and Autons.
- Director Nigel Fairs had worked with Nicholas Courtney when they had both been in *The Mousetrap* for a year back in the mid-1990s. During this stint, Nick got married to his second wife. "The ceremony was in the morning, and then he came in and did two shows the same day," Nigel recalls. "That man was such an old pro! I was sitting with him in the wings and he turned to me and said, with a tear in his eye: 'This is one of the happiest days of my life'."

PRODUCTION SUMMARY

"**Old Soldiers** was such a strange experience. It was always good to see Nick and he was always brilliant. But on the first studio day he did seem a little tired and of course it turned out that he was rushed into hospital that night and we had to cancel the second day. I had an idea of replacing the stuff we hadn't done with Richard Franklin, who's another old friend, but thank God Nick recovered and was actually far more energetic for the second day, really back to his old self. I loved the man and miss him so much."
Nigel Fairs

WORKING TITLE(S)

None.

RETURNING MONSTERS/CHARACTERS

None.

Check box - CD ■ MP3 ■

THE CATALYST

SYNOPSIS

Leela is being interrogated. Gallifrey is gone and she is aging. She recalls a visit she and the Doctor made to Lord Joshua Douglas in Edwardian times. Joshua's daughter, Jessica, tells Leela that her father used to travel with the Doctor. Leela then hears a voice in her head and she breaks down a locked door to find a secret room where an alien is being kept prisoner in stasis. When they activate it, the alien comes to life and explains that his name is H'mbrackle, last of the noble race of Z'nai. He tells the women that the Doctor destroyed the Z'nai and confined H'mbrackle to this perpetual prison. When Leela goes to confront the Doctor he tells her that Joshua did travel with him but that they parted company because they fell out over something. They discover that the Z'nai has killed Jessica and escaped. Then they track him to the main house where H'mbrackle has killed everyone before attacking Joshua. The Doctor pleads with the Z'nai not to kill him, but H'mbrackle reminds him that he is merely purifying the system of lesser races. He then collapses, sick with a virus, and the Doctor takes him back to his prison. He explains to Leela that it was Lord Joshua who had released the original virus to kill the Z'nai for the greater good. The Doctor had found a cure but the Z'nai were too untrusting to let him use it. Then a vast Z'nai spacecraft lands outside and troops enter the house. However, Leela has become the carrier of the diseases and every Z'nai soldier she touches dies. Later, the Doctor douses the whole house in petrol and sets fire to it. The interrogator is revealed to be a Z'nai and Leela knows she can kill him with a touch.

PLACEMENT

Between the TV story **The Talons of Weng-Chiang** and the **Companion Chronicle Empathy Games #3.4.**

TRIVIA

- This story is apparently set after the events of the **Gallifrey** series and, indeed, the TV series plot strand of the Time War.
- Originally, the story had the Daleks in it but they were dropped. "The brief for **The Catalyst** was originally to write 'Leela meets the Daleks'," Nigel Fairs says. "I love it when the Daleks are so dangerous that they signal the end of a Doctor, or a planet, or a Universe, so that's why I set it at the end of her life, with Leela becoming the ultimate Dalek destroyer!"
- As the story was initially set in Nazi Germany, Nigel Fairs used that as an anagram for the alien race he created to take the place of the Daleks.
- "I was particularly fascinated by the greyness of Nazi morality – how could these monsters be art lovers?" Nigel says. "And all that business with Hm'Brackle creating his people in his own image was Hitler. Timothy Watson, who played him, had been touring *Bedroom Farce* with Lou and Colin Baker and I thought he was great. What a voice!"
- Nigel was going to bring the Z'nai back in **The Tomorrow People** but then the licence for that range was not renewed.
- It is revealed that the name 'Leela' is that of the Sevateem's greatest female warrior and the most revered figure in the tribe's history.

PRODUCTION SUMMARY

"I love writing for Lou. I've never met anyone who comes to a studio or rehearsal room as prepared as she does. She's also a truly inspirational director and I think the most frightening and yet enthralling moment I've ever had on stage was playing Gloucester opposite her Lady Anne in a Shakespeare anthology recently – awesomely good, she makes it look so easy! The post production and music was a labour of love for this one. I based Leela's theme on the one I'd written for the first theatre production of *Acid Bath Murderer* back in 1999, so the fact that Lou has now directed me in it has a weird symmetry!"
Nigel Fairs

WORKING TITLE(S)

None.

RETURNING MONSTERS/CHARACTERS

None.

CREW

Writer	**Nigel Fairs**
Director	**Nigel Fairs**
Producer	**Sharon Gosling**
Executive Producer	**Jason Haigh-Ellery**
Executive Producer (BBC)	**Jacqueline Rayner**
Music and Sound Design	**Nigel Fairs**
Cover Art	**Simon Holub**
Theme	**Delia Derbyshire**

CAST

Leela	**Louise Jameson**
The Z'nai	**Timothy Watson**

ERA

Fourth Doctor - read by Leela

TECHNICAL

Story Code	**BFPDWCC08**
Recorded Date	**3 June 2007**
Release Date	**January 2008**
Place of Recording	**The Moat Studios, London**
Number of CDs	**1**
Total Duration	**73' 29"**
Number of Episodes	**2**
Duration of Episodes	**1 (42' 47"), 2 (30' 42")**
ISBN	**978-1-84435-293-7**

Above:
Nyssa (Sarah Sutton) had an encounter with the Dar
Traders in **The Darkening Eye**.

Top-right:
Another coup for **The Companion Chronicles** –
Jean Marsh returns as Sara Kingdom, joined by Niall
MacGregor as Robert for **Home Truths**.

Right:
Anneke Wills (Polly) and John Sackville (Pilot) at the
recording of **Resistance**, May 2008.

Above:
Nicholas Briggs provides monster voices for many
of **The Companion Chronicles**.

Top-left:
Louise Jameson (Leela) was thrilled to be
working with David Warner (Co-ordinator Angell)
on **Empathy Games**.

Left:
The Mahogany Murderers, starring Trevor
Baxter and Christopher Benjamin, started a whole
new series of adventures for those
infernal investigators Jago and Litefoot!

THE MAGICIAN'S OATH

#3.10

SYNOPSIS

Mike Yates drops into UNIT HQ, recalling old times and old friends. He recently met up with Jo Grant who gave him an old playing card. Yates hands it to the duty officer, and says he wants to make a statement. Mike recalls freak weather conditions in central London, such as frosty lawns in July and a tube train being covered in snow, as the Doctor detected energy spikes in the area. UNIT is summoned when half of Hyde Park is frozen over, killing many people on what had been a warm Saturday afternoon. The Doctor locates the source of the energy waves, Highgate Cemetery, and heads off with the Brigadier to investigate. Meanwhile, Yates and Jo find a magician, Diamond Jack, performing amazing tricks. As Yates takes a call on his radio, Jo vanishes, and he confronts Jack about it. The magician then levitates and explodes into tiny pieces, leaving behind a jack of diamonds playing card, with his name and address on it. Mike, realising it's a trap, goes to the address and finds

Jo. Jack appears behind them, and they discover he has no memories of his childhood. The Doctor and Brigadier arrive soon after, carrying a red cylinder from a spaceship in the cemetery. The Doctor hands it to Jack, whose memories return, and he tells them he was exiled to Earth by his alien people for misuse of his powers. By removing his memories they want to give him a second chance. Jack vanishes, so the Doctor, Brigadier and Yates return to the spaceship, where they find a giant insect – Jack's original body. It follows the new Jack, who has taken Jo to Tower Bridge. Here, Yates confronts him again, as the magician draws power from the capital. Jack is wounded by his old body and then hands Jo a playing card as he tries to transfer his mind to her body, damaging her memory. Yates shoots him through the head. Years later, Jo found the card and remembered the events – including Mike expressing his love for her. He gives UNIT the playing card, and leaves.

PLACEMENT

Between the TV stories **The Dæmons** and **Day of the Daleks**.

TRIVIA

- This is the first appearance by Richard Franklin as Mike Yates for the first time since 1974's **Planet of the Spiders**. He would subsequently return to the role alongside Tom Baker as the Doctor in AudioGO's *Hornets' Nest* series, and its sequels, written by Paul Magrs.
- Mike Yates says that the acronym UNIT no longer stands for the same thing it used to. This is a reference to the fact that Russell T Davies changed it from United Nations Intelligence Taskforce to Unified Intelligence Taskforce for the 2008 TV story **The Sontaran Stratagem/The Poison Sky**.

PRODUCTION SUMMARY

"I nearly wrote this one myself. I'd come up with the story, and started to plan it. But I'm a wimp. I actually can't cope with the idea of writing something, and the possibility it might get a bad review. It would actually destroy me! So I chickened out, passed my notes to Scott Handcock, and he did the rest. Most of my ideas were in episode one, with the magician and his dual life – I think episode two was pretty much all Scott."
David Richardson

WORKING TITLE(S)

None.

RETURNING MONSTERS/CHARACTERS

None.

CREW
Writer **Scott Handcock**
Director **Nigel Fairs**
Producer **David Richardson**
Executive Producer **Jason Haigh-Ellery**
Music **Jamie Robertson**
Sound Design **Rob Thrush**
Cover Art **Simon Holub**
Theme **Delia Derbyshire**

CAST
Mike Yates **Richard Franklin**
Diamond Jack **Michael Chance**

ERA
Third Doctor - read by Captain Mike Yates

TECHNICAL
Story Code **BFPDWCC18**
Recorded Date **13 June 2008**
Release Date **April 2009**
Place of Recording **The Moat Studios, London**
Number of CDs **1**
Total Duration **76' 59"**
Number of Episodes **2**
Duration of Episodes **1 (34' 03")**
2 (36' 10")
ISBN **978-1-84435-379-8**

#3.11

THE MAHOGANY MURDERERS

CREW

Writer **Andy Lane**
Director **Lisa Bowerman**
Producer **David Richardson**
Executive Producer **Jason Haigh-Ellery**
Music and
Sound Design **David Darlington**
Cover Art **Simon Holub**
Theme **Delia Derbyshire**

CAST

Jago **Christopher Benjamin**
Litefoot **Trevor Baxter**
Ellie **Lisa Bowerman**

ERA

Fourth Doctor - Read by Jago and Litefoot

TECHNICAL

Story Code **BFPDWCC19**
Recorded Date **22 September 2008**
Release Date **May 2009**
Place of Recording **The Moat Studios, London**
Number of CDs **1**
Total Duration **70' 59"**
Number of Episodes **2**
Duration of Episodes **1 (26' 57")**
2 (34' 40")
ISBN **978-1-84435-380-4**

SYNOPSIS

Henry Gordon Jago meets Professor George Litefoot in a local hostelry, where they're served by Ellie, the barmaid. Litefoot tells Jago that the previous evening, two officers brought a body to him in a wheelbarrow, the cadaver having been found in mudflats. Litefoot examined the corpse, only to find it was, in fact, made of wood with real teeth and glass eyes. Litefoot sends a telegram to Jago asking him to investigate the area where the body was found. Jago does so and the smell of ozone leads him to a warehouse full of electrical equipment. Meanwhile, three men enter Litefoot's lab to reclaim the mahogany body, but are scared off when the police officers return. Litefoot then watches as the mannequin climbs off his table and walks off into the night! The Professor gives chase. Meanwhile, Jago is knocked out by a hard hand and carried away on equally hard shoulders. When he fully comes to, he's face to face with a group of wooden men. One of these men, Jack Yeovil, was killed three weeks previously and was the "body" that Litefoot examined in his lab. It is revealed that the wooden men have been created by a man called Dr Heinrich Tulp. He has taken criminals from their prisons and transferred their beings into these new bodies. Elsewhere, Litefoot follows his mannequin – Speedle – to a meeting with the other wooden men. Speedle tells his story: he overheard Tulp saying he would return the men to their original bodies unless he received regular payments. When Tulp saw that Speedle had been eavesdropping, he attacked him and the next thing Speedle knew he was on Litefoot's table. The wooden men plan to take Tulp's equipment and free their former prison colleagues and transfer them into new bodies, but this time made of metal. Litefoot throws his lamp into the room, setting some of the men on fire. The wooden men retreat to the warehouse as Litefoot gives chase. By taking a cab, he manages to arrive before them. There he pulls all the cables out of the equipment and the wooden marionettes collapse to the floor. It is only then that Jago and Litefoot realise Doctor Tulp is still at large…

PLACEMENT

After the TV story **The Talons of Weng-Chiang**.

TRIVIA

- This is the first **Companion Chronicle** not to feature the Doctor in the story.
- This play was originally scheduled for release in June, but was moved up when a planned story by Peter Anghelides was pulled because it was set during the original **Key to Time** season and it was felt it clashed with Big Finish's **Key2Time** sequel. The story was finally released two years later as **Ferril's Folly #5.11**.
- Shortly after this, a full-cast series of **Jago & Litefoot** was commissioned by Big Finish.
- The play reunited Christopher Benjamin and Trevor Baxter for the first time in many years (although they had made one convention appearance together). Producer David Richardson was amazed how quickly they found both the characters and their friendship again.

PRODUCTION SUMMARY

"The **Companion Chronicle** that started a whole new spin-off! It was an obvious decision the moment Christopher and Trevor came back together again. This was such a joy to listen to during recording, and Lisa and I hoped and prayed that everyone would love it as much as we did. Thankfully it was a huge hit – the first pressing sold out within two months, and we actually didn't have any stock at all when Christopher and Trevor made a convention appearance in Wales in September 2009. But the sense of love for them from the fans was palpable, and long may Jago and Litefoot endure."
David Richardson

WORKING TITLE(S)

None.

RETURNING MONSTERS/CHARACTERS

Henry Gordon Jago, Professor George Litefoot.

Check box - CD ■ MP3 ■

THE STEALERS FROM SAIPH

#3.12

SYNOPSIS

France, 1929. The Doctor and Romana are enjoying a stay in a hotel. Here they encounter an elderly astrologer called Madame Arcana. She tells the Time Lords that according to her star charts, the stars haven't been shining properly for 100 years. They then accompany an archaeologist, Sir Henry Chavallier, to a pre-historic cave he's found near the Mediterranean Sea. Romana notices that the ground is covered in a reddish-brown substance, while the Doctor spots the incongruous figures of creatures from the planet Saiph among the cave paintings. Romana then attends a party aboard the yacht Hermes, owned by millionaire Broderick Crane. There she notices odd behaviour and finds a reddish-brown slime trail on the boat. Returning to shore, Romana finds the Doctor and Arcana. The astrologer gives Romana a diamond for safekeeping before retiring to bed. Romana goes to the cave, and watches in horror as the slime gathers together to form a giant octopus-like creature. Covered in what look like maggots, it catches Romana and pulls her towards its beak. But she's saved when one of the hotel residents, Tommy, arrives and switches on the lights. Arcana again tries to get the Doctor to look at her charts but is ushered off to bed by the professor. The Time Lords look at the chart and notice an extra star has appeared over the years. Next morning, Arcana is found dead. The Doctor and Romana then confront the professor. It is revealed that he is under the control of the Saiph and has been travelling the area for generations, preparing to turn it into a breeding ground for his masters. He has set up a series of five relay stations in the form of a pentagram, ready to take a bolt of bio-plasmic energy from an orbiting satellite which will change the sea's composition. The satellite is the additional star they saw on the chart. Using a mirror and Arcana's diamond, the Doctor and Romana deflect the beam onto the yacht and destroy the professor and the other Saiph in the sea.

PLACEMENT

Between the TV stories **The Armageddon Factor** and **Destiny of the Daleks**.

TRIVIA

- This is the first **Companion Chronicle** not to feature cover art by Simon Holub.
- This is the only **Companion Chronicle** not to feature a second voice – although one had been planned in early drafts of the script. However David Richardson felt that this threw the balance in a murder mystery story, so it was rewritten for Mary Tamm to perform solo.

PRODUCTION SUMMARY

"In my past life I'd been a journalist and I'd interviewed Mary Tamm. I just remember she was hysterical – I laughed so much. Hence I was very keen to work with her in my first year on the **Chronicles**. Sadly the original script, Ferril's Folly, fell through, to be recorded at a later date, so I got my old mate Nigel Robinson in. He did a great job, and Mary loved this story. And, yes, she was brilliant fun to work with, just as I'd expected."
David Richardson

WORKING TITLE(S)

None.

RETURNING MONSTERS/CHARACTERS

None.

CREW

Writer	**Nigel Robinson**
Director	**Lisa Bowerman**
Producer	**David Richardson**
Executive Producer	**Jason Haigh-Ellery**
Music and Sound Design	**Howard Carter**
Cover Art	**Lee Johnson**
Theme	**Delia Derbyshire**

CAST

Romana I	**Mary Tamm**

ERA

Fourth Doctor - read by Romana I

TECHNICAL

Story Code	**BFPDWCC20**
Recorded Date	**16 February 2009**
Release Date	**June 2009**
Place of Recording	**The Moat Studios, London**
Number of CDs	**I**
Total Duration	**76' 05"**
Number of Episodes	**2**
Duration of Episodes	**I (27' 45")**
	2 (36' 36")
ISBN	**978-1-84435-381-1**

SECTION 4

DOCTOR WHO – THE LOST STORIES

There were two projects that producer David Richardson was keen to get his hands on when he started at Big Finish. One was **The Companion Chronicles** (see Section 03) and the other was something that didn't even exist at that point.

'The whole idea of doing the **Lost Stories** wasn't original,' says David. 'It had been mentioned to Big Finish many times before I came on the scene.' Indeed, Target Books had pursued the idea back in late 80s/early 90s. So what was special about 2008? 'I nagged

Jason and Nick into submission,' jokes David. In actual fact, his timing was just right...

'We'd just done the stage plays, taking **Doctor Who** theatre scripts from the 60s, 70s and 80s and doing them on audio,' says David. 'They were successful and so it seemed the right time to do something that was an extension of that.'

The **Stage Plays** (see Section 06) had been in studio during June and July of 2008 and were released later that year to an enthusiastic reception. David's badgering and the success of the stage plays led him to a central London restaurant and dinner with Jason Haigh-Ellery. Jason gave him the go ahead on a new range of stories that would focus on the 'lost' season 23: the stories that would have been made and broadcast had the BBC not put **Doctor Who** on hiatus in 1985.

'As soon as we knew we were going to do the series it involved about three months of research,' says David. 'We needed to find out exactly what the scripts were and how to find the writers.'

Because of those Target novels, almost every **Doctor Who** fan can name three stories from that lost season without batting an eyelid. A fourth is also embedded in the fan consciousness due to its mythic status as a lost Robert Holmes script that would have been set in Singapore.

Top:
Nabil Shaban (Sil) returned for a rematch with the Sixth Doctor in **Mission to Magnus**.

Right:
Some of the team behind **The Lost Stories** (l-r): sound engineer Toby Hrycek-Robinson, director Ken Bentley, producers David Richardson and Nicholas Briggs.

SERIES 1

'The series started off as being purely the missing Season 23 and that fell apart when we failed to agree terms with Wally K Daly on *The Ultimate Evil*,' explains David. 'There were also discussions about whether we should do *Yellow Fever and How to Cure It*, which is the lost Robert Holmes story featuring the Autons, the Master and Rani. But not enough of that existed. I think there's just a brief story outline and ideas for episode one – not enough for us to work with.'

With two stories of the best-known four out of the window, David set about ensuring the other two would form part of the line-up. He contacted Graham Williams's widow, Jackie, and sent her a copy of the **Main Monthly Range** release **Kingdom of Silver #112**. She was very positive about the idea and generously gave her permission for Big Finish to make an adaptation of **The Nightmare Fair #1.1**.

Because Philip Martin had already contributed to Big Finish's **Doctor Who** range (**The Creed of the Cromon #53**) it was easy for David to ring him and ask if he would adapt his earlier script for audio. Philip said 'yes' right away.

As David had now spread his net a little further than Season 23, he was free to poke into corners he might not otherwise have considered. 'In the process of looking around, I had found all these other interesting things we could do instead,' he says. 'So the *Lost Season* became the **Lost Stories**. We took things on board which expanded it into something I think is more interesting.'

David also went after a story from another writer who had previously contributed to Big Finish – Christopher H Bidmead. Bidmead had acted as

script editor for **Doctor Who** in the 1980s as well as contributing three stories during that time – **Logopolis**, **Castrovalva** and **Frontios**. For Big Finish he had provided the basis for **Renaissance of the Daleks #93**. The script David was interested in was a sequel to **Frontios** featuring the Tractators and the Gravis, called **The Hollows of Time**.

Big Finish went public with news of the **Lost Stories** range on 10 February 2009 when a brief news story was added to the website. The statement read: "Big Finish is to launch a new series of audio adventures in January 2010… Colin Baker stars as the Sixth Doctor and Nicola Bryant as Peri in these adaptations of scripts that were commissioned but never made for television in the mid-80s." The announcement went on to confirm that the line-up of releases included **The Nightmare Fair** and **Mission to Magnus**. It also stated that there would be a further five stories.

While David had done a lot of legwork exploring script possibilities, one story that turned up unexpectedly was **Leviathan**. The writer of the story was Brian Finch, who had helped create **The Tomorrow People**, co-writing the entire first season for ITV. Unfortunately he had died in 2007, but his son, Paul, had read the announcement about the **Lost Stories** and got in contact. David was bowled over by the story and quickly agreed to Paul adapting his father's script for audio.

It was also clear that **The Nightmare Fair** would need to be adapted and David chose long-term Big Finish contributor John Ainsworth for the job,

Left:
The guest-cast of **Mission to Magnus** (l-r) : Tina Jones (Ulema), Maggie Steed (Madamme Zandusia) and Susan Franklyn (Jarmaya).

SECTION 4
DOCTOR WHO – THE LOST STORIES

who would also direct five of the first season's plays. John was delighted – as was David. 'I think he did a fantastic job,' he says.

With the first four stories in place, Moat Studios was booked for initial recording blocks in February, March and April 2009. The recording schedule was slightly out of order with the running order: **Mission to Magnus #1.2** was recorded first (its completion was announced online the day after recording finished), followed by **The Nightmare Fair #1.1** (attended by Graham Williams's widow, Jackie, along with her two sons), **The Hollows of Time #1.4** and finally **Leviathan #1.3**.

The **Lost Stories** also represented an opportunity for Colin Baker and Nicola Bryant to deal with what must have felt like unfinished business. David grins. 'Colin said to me that it was lancing a boil! I think it had been a difficult time in his life and it has now been given back to him.'

By this stage four other scripts were being prepared or investigated: **Point of Entry** by Barbara Clegg, **Paradise 5** by P J Hammond and **The Space Whale** by Pat Mills. 'Gary Russell suggested **Paradise 5** while approving the script for **The Nightmare Fair**,' says David. 'Peter was just one of the nicest people we could ever hope to contact!'

Barbara Clegg's story had been brought to David's attention by Keith Barnfather at Reeltime Pictures. 'Keith had been working on a documentary with Barbara and she'd apparently discussed the story,' says David. 'So Keith contacted me about it, and when I read the synopsis it just intrigued me!'

However, with both Clegg and Hammond busy, David brought in Marc Platt and Andy Lane to work on the respective scripts. When it comes to choosing writers to work as adapter or co-writer, David has a foolproof method of selection. 'Gut instinct!' he says with a smile. 'It's a case of whoever you think would be a good fit. I thought Andy Lane was a good fit with P J Hammond and I thought that Marc Platt would work well with Barbara Clegg. There are two writers who come up with fantastic ideas!'

There was a fourth script under consideration at this point, but it never made the final cut. Wait... There's even a **Lost Stories**' lost story? 'Yes,' confesses David. 'We didn't get to make **The Children of January** by Michael Feeney Callan, which was on the cards for a long time. We just ran out of time because Michael became too busy. Maybe one day we'll come back to it. Who knows?'

As such a replacement was needed but negotiations were on-going when the Big Finish website was updated on 3 April 2009 with details of all eight plays now in the series – save this one: TBA! The

running order was also a little off with this new story supposedly being numbered **#1.5**, **Paradise 5** at **#1.7** and **The Space Whale** coming in as **#1.8**.

The replacement became apparent on 21 July 2009 when it was announced that among the other entries to the season would be **The Macros**, co-written by actress Ingrid Pitt. By this stage, **Paradise 5** had been recorded, going into studio on the 13th and 14th of that month.

The final story in the line up was **The Space Whale** by Pat Mills. Mills had recently written for Big Finish, contributing **The Scapegoat #3.5** to the **Eighth Doctor Adventures**. While the play was in studio during October 2008, David had asked Mills about his unmade **Doctor Who** story. 'Of all the **Lost Stories**, this one probably had the most complicated history,' David says. 'It has this reputation of being the cursed **Doctor Who** story. It started off in the late 70s and was rewritten two or three times but just never happened. I find it hard to see why. It came in as a fully-formed audio script which didn't need many changes.'

The story was the last to be recorded and would undergo one final hurdle before the curse was lifted. The play had been announced as **The Space Whale** and even recorded as such in late September 2009. However, it would have to alter its title one last time, to **The Song of Megaptera** at the request of the **Doctor Who** production office in Cardiff because it was too similar to the Star Whale featuring in the 2010 television story **The Beast Below**.

The first **Lost Story** was released only two months later and proved to be a big hit with fans. David has a theory as to why that is. 'The **Lost Stories** are something different – a little experiment!' he says. 'It's a chance to do something archival, something that would really please **Doctor Who**

Top:
The Celestial Toymaker (david bailie) finally had a rematch with the Doctor in **The Nightmare Fair**.

144

SECTION 4

purists in that they were uncovering these adventures that have been locked away in the vault for years.'

For David himself it has been a fascinating insight into the history of **Doctor Who** production. 'Why didn't some of these scripts get made?' he asks. 'Well, with **Song of Megaptera** it must have been budgetary, but with a script like **Leviathan** I'm kind of scratching my head. Perhaps it was due to the amount of film scenes. With PJ Hammond's script it was a case of his script being championed by Eric Saward but John Nathan-Turner not liking it.'

Fate can be a fickle editor it seems, but this means that there are still such gems to be found in dusty corners of life's cutting room floor. 'It's been an interesting journey uncovering these stories as I hope it has been for the fans to listen to them,' says David.

After the first season, the journey continues with a trip back to the very earliest days of **Doctor Who** and then a jump forward to a set of stories set after **Doctor Who** was 'suspended' in 1989. But those **Lost Stories** must wait for us to find them in their proper time…

Top:
Putting ghosts of the past to rest – Colin Baker and Nicola Bryant recording **The Lost Stories**.

Left:
Beth Chalmers would return as Raine in series two of **The Lost Stories**, but series one saw the actress playing Althya in **Leviathan**.

#1.1 THE NIGHTMARE FAIR

CREW

Writer	**Graham Williams**
Adapted by	**John Ainsworth**
Director	**John Ainsworth**
Producer	**David Richardson**
Executive Producer	**Jason Haigh-Ellery**
Music and Sound Design	**Jamie Robertson**
Cover Art	**Alex Mallinson**
Theme	**Peter Howell**

CAST

The Doctor	**Colin Baker**
Peri	**Nicola Bryant**
The Celestial Toymaker	**david bailie**
Kevin	**Matthew Noble**
Stefan	**Andrew Fettes**
Woman	**Louise Faulkner**
Shardow, Attendant	**William Whymper**
Yatsumoto, Truscott, Manager, Man	**Toby Longworth**
Humandroid, Security Man, Geoff, Guard	**Duncan Wisbey**

TECHNICAL

Story Code	**6Y/AA**
Recorded Date	**9 and 10 March 2009**
Release Date	**November 2009**
Place of Recording	**The Moat Studios, London**
Number of CDs	**2**
Total Duration	**137' 33"**
Number of Episodes	**2**
Duration of Episodes	**1 (38' 36")** **2 (57' 04")**
ISBN	**978-1-84435-444-3**

SYNOPSIS

A young man, Kevin Stoney, reports to the police that his brother has gone missing at Blackpool Pleasure Beach, where he's seen a seven-foot tall creature glowing green and red. The Doctor and Peri are enjoying an off-season break in Blackpool, where they are observed by a mysterious stranger – and the Doctor notices they're being followed by Kevin. Separated on their next ride, the Doctor is taken captive inside the ghost train. Kevin approaches Peri when the Doctor fails to return, just as both are taken away by a funfair worker. They jump their captor and escape into a gold mine ride. The Doctor comes face to face with his enemy, the Celestial Toymaker. He tells the Time Lord he has been on Earth for many years, playing and learning the planet's games, and the Doctor agrees to play one final game. The Toymaker has a new prototype game activated, an electronic arcade machine, and when programmer Yatsumoto loses, a creature emerges to consume him. The Toymaker plans to roll these machines out across the planet. The Doctor escapes from his cell and meets his fellow captives – a humandroid and a Venusian mechanic. Taken to the Toymaker, the Doctor plays the arcade machine, and realises the Toymaker was hurled out of his own universe and into ours, having a lifespan which lasts for millions of years. The Doctor continues to play the game, and soon beats his rival's high score. The mechanic builds a special helmet that operates on the Toymaker's telepathic wavelength, which is activated and allows the Doctor to escape. The Doctor searches for and finds the Toymaker's tele-mechanical relay, which is powered by his own mental power, so as long as the Toymaker's brain works, he'll be imprisoned forever. Reunited, the Doctor and Peri depart in the TARDIS.

PLACEMENT

After **Revelation of the Daleks** and before **The Trial of a Time Lord.**

TRIVIA

- The story was published by Target Books as the first in its *Missing Episodes* range in May 1989.
- The role of the Toymaker is here played by david bailie, who had previously played Dask in the 1977 TV story **The Robots of Death**. He would go on to reprise the Toymaker in the **Companion Chronicle Solitaire #4.12**.
- Seven months before this audio was released, the Celestial Toymaker featured in the **Main Monthly Range** release **The Magic Mousetrap #120** although the character is played by a different actor (Paul Antony-Barber).
- The release includes over 40 minutes of extras.
- In the first draft of the script, episode one had a duration of 30 minutes and episode two had a duration of 1 hour and 15 minutes. David Richardson regretfully decided to change the episode ending for part one so that they were more evenly matched – instead of a climax in which Peri and Kevin are menaced by the robotic miners, it now ends with the Toymaker threatening the Doctor.
- Adapter John Ainsworth chose to use some scenes that Graham Williams wrote for the novelisation, but were not featured in the original script.
- William Whymper was cast as Shardlow after David Richardson had seen him appearing in a play with Lisa Bowerman.
- Director John Ainsworth arranged an official visit to the Blackpool Pleasure Beach and, with agreement, recorded some background ambiance for the fairground rides.
- Matthew Noble was cast as Kevin after his impressive performance in the *Doctor Who Magazine* covermounted give-away story **Cuddlesome**.

PRODUCTION SUMMARY

"My fondest memory of **The Nightmare Fair** is the fact that Graham Williams's widow, Jackie, and their two sons came along to the recording, and were so generous and enthusiastic about the project. They made the whole thing feel really special for me. And it did seem like a really momentous endeavour – here we were, over two decades later, making stories that the late John Nathan-Turner had hoped to produce in the 1980s. The young David Richardson would have been screaming with excitement had he known back then."
David Richardson

WORKING TITLE(S)

None.

RETURNING MONSTERS/CHARACTERS

The Celestial Toymaker.

MISSION TO MAGNUS

SYNOPSIS

The TARDIS is pulled off course to the 23rd century where the Doctor meets Anzor, a Time Lord bully from his class at the academy. His TARDIS, in the form of a blasted oak tree, is trapped in orbit around Magnus Epsilon, with an alien warship also above the planet, and the time ships swap places. Anzor materialises and is met by Sil and Madame Rana Zandusia, the ruler of the planet. The Doctor's TARDIS breaks free and lands on the female-dominated world. Rana tells Anzor that all men on the planet go blind and die before the age of 20. She wants the Time Lords to authorise her invasion of the male-ruled Salvak, by going back a year in time – but Anzor refuses. The Doctor is captured and the Magnus women try to glean the secrets of time travel from his brain, as Sil enters Anzor's TARDIS with Rana. He

forces everyone out of his ship, but it has been locked on a slow ride to the beginning of time by the Doctor. The Doctor and Peri escape to the ice tunnels where they are separated and she is taken captive by the Ice Warriors. Sil and Rana get into the Doctor's TARDIS, but view a possible future for the world when it is destroyed. Peri meets a group of Salvakian men who are being used by the Ice Warriors to work on setting up neutrino-based nuclear bombs, which they detonate to move Magnus Epsilon into a new, colder orbit, in a perpetual winter – ideal for the Martians. However, the Doctor finds their secondary bombs, and moves the planet into a warmer orbit, with the heat killing off the Ice Warriors. The Salvakians have a cure for the plague which kills Magnusian men, and they propose marriage to the rulers of Magnus.

PLACEMENT

After **Revelation of the Daleks** and before **The Trial of a Time Lord**.

TRIVIA

- The story was published by Target Books as the third in its *Missing Episodes* range in July 1990.
- An early draft of the script featured the Ice Warriors in the first scene. David Richardson chose to cut the sequence, in order to retain the impact of their arrival at the episode's climax.
- Maggie Steed was cast as Rana Zandusia on the recommendation of Colin Baker, who had just worked with her on stage in *Noises Off*. The actress has been a well-known face on British television for many years, with appearances in *Shine on Harvey Moon*, *Red Dwarf*, *Pie in the Sky* and *Jam and Jerusalem*.
- The recording was split over two days, with the first day given over to the Sil scenes, while the second focused on Ice Warriors and the young children.
- A short sequence was cut from episode one for timing reasons, in which Rana's henchmen attempt to read the mind of the Doctor for a second time.
- The release includes over 47 minutes of extras.

PRODUCTION SUMMARY

"Sil! Ice Warriors! The Rana Zandusia! Anzor! No one could ever accuse **Mission to Magnus** of being short of villains. It is, in the best possible sense, a monster romp and a jolly bit of fun. Nabil was absolutely thrilled to be back in the role of Sil, and Colin and Nicola were delighted to see him. Again, **Mission to Magnus** was a piece of the 1980s finally being realised after being in suspended animation for so long."
David Richardson

WORKING TITLE(S)

Planet of Storms.

RETURNING MONSTERS/CHARACTERS

Sil, The Ice Warriors.

CREW

Writer	**Philip Martin**
Director	**Lisa Bowerman**
Producer	**David Richardson**
Executive Producer	**Jason Haigh-Ellery**
Music and Sound Design	**Simon Robinson**
Cover Art	**Alex Mallinson**
Theme	**Peter Howell**

CAST

The Doctor	**Colin Baker**
Peri	**Nicola Bryant**
Sil	**Nabil Shaban**
Anzor	**Malcolm Rennie**
Madame Rana Zandusia	**Maggie Steed**
Jarmaya, Tace	**Susan Franklyn**
Ulema, Soma	**Tina Jones**
Vion	**William Townsend**
Asam	**Callum Witney Mills**
Brorg, Vedikael, Grand Marshall, Ishka	**Nicholas Briggs**
Skaarg, Jarga, Hussa	**James George**

TECHNICAL

Story Code	**6Y/AB**
Recorded Date	**18 & 19 February 2009**
Release Date	**December 2009**
Place of Recording	**The Moat Studios, London**
Number of CDs	**2**
Total Duration	**155' 21"**
Number of Episodes	**2**
Duration of Episodes	**1 (57' 24")** **2 (49' 06")**
ISBN	**978-1-84435-445-0**

#1.3   LEVIATHAN

CREW

Writer	**Brian Finch**
Adapted by	**Paul Finch**
Director	**Ken Bentley**
Producer	**David Richardson**
Executive Producer	**Jason Haigh-Ellery**
Music and Sound Design	**Simon Robinson**
Cover Art	**Alex Mallinson**
Theme	**Peter Howell**

CAST

The Doctor	**Colin Baker**
Peri	**Nicola Bryant**
Gurth	**Howard Gossington**
Herne the Hunter	**John Banks**
Althya	**Beth Chalmers**
Wulfric	**James Parker**
Siward	**Derek Carlyle**

TECHNICAL

Story Code	**6Y/AC**
Recorded Date	**28 and 29 April 2009**
Release Date	**January 2010**
Place of Recording	**The Moat Studios, London**
Number of CDs	**2**
Total Duration	**147' 26"**
Number of Episodes	**2**
Duration of Episodes	**1 (55' 13")** **2 (59' 58")**
ISBN	**978-1-84435-446-7**

SYNOPSIS

A young man, Burth, is chased through a forest, as the TARDIS is pulled off course to land nearby in what appears to be England in the Middle Ages. Gurth is being chased by Herne the Hunter, and as the Doctor and Peri join him, they're watched by a band of outlaws, the Pariah. They drive Herne away but find the dogs are actually androids. Peri is taken by the Pariah as the Doctor goes to see the ruling Baron in his castle. Peri noticed the majority of her captors are in their late teens, and is shown a crossbow dropped by Herne – which fires a laser bolt. The Baron confers with the unseen Zeron that the Doctor's existence is a surprise to him. The pair duel, with the Doctor winning and escaping, but the Pariah attack a door which sets off an electronic alarm - and Herne. Meeting up with an escaped Peri and Gurth, the Doctor notices the world is wrong – the moat is two feet deep and the walls are thin. They find a concealed door and step through – to find they're on a spaceship. They notice another ship, the Icarus, flying alongside them. Onboard, the Icarus crew have been watching the people living around the Baron's castle. They have been placed on board a deep space Leviathan transporter, taking them to colonise a new world, and are being ruled over by the Zeron, acting on orders from the Icarus' captain Chandris. They regularly recycle the lifeforms living in the Leviathan when they reach their late teens and start to question their environment more. The Zeron is given orders to run the population down, so the Leviathan can be scrapped and sold, with the crew profiting. The Doctor takes command of the Zeron and teleports to the Icarus, confronting the crew. He wants the Leviathan's population transferred to the Icarus, and he threatens them with the Herne unless they obey. The people are taken to live a new life.

PLACEMENT

After **Revelation of the Daleks** and before **The Trial of a Time Lord**.

TRIVIA

- This story was originally written by Brian Finch for inclusion in Season 22 of the TV series. The script was adapted for audio by his son, Paul.
- Paul has since written a prequel to Leviathan for the **Companion Chronicles** range featuring Liz Shaw, called **The Sentinels of the New Dawn #5.10**.
- According to *Doctor Who Magazine*, this story was originally commissioned under the title 'Livanthian', although this is a typographical error and not a working title.
- The story was not originally included in the six-story line-up for Season One. However Paul Finch emailed the script to *Doctor Who Magazine*, who forwarded the message to David Richardson, who soon realised Leviathan had to be added to the list.
- Herne the Hunter does not speak in the original TV script. However, David Richardson suggested the character needed dialogue in order to have the right impact on audio.
- Beth Chalmers (Althya) was subsequently cast as new companion Raine Creevy in Season Two of the **Lost Stories**.
- Finch's script features far too many characters for a standard audio budget. Director Ken Bentley ingeniously had his cast triple up, so that every actor plays multiple roles – sometimes in the same scene.
- Jamie Parker (Wulfric) is best known for the stage and film versions of *The History Boys*. He also starred alongside Tom Cruise in the movie *Valkyrie*.
- The release includes over 30 minutes of extras.

PRODUCTION SUMMARY

"A personal favourite of mine from Series One, and also a hit with **Doctor Who** fans. Which is interesting because no one knew anything about **Leviathan** before the script landed on my desk – I must confess, at first I thought it was a hoax… until I read the authentic pages from the 1980s. Paul Finch told me how his father had dreamed of getting a **Doctor Who** story made. I was so pleased that his wish had finally been fulfilled, albeit sadly after his death."
David Richardson

WORKING TITLE(S)

None.

RETURNING MONSTERS/CHARACTERS

None.

THE HOLLOWS OF TIME

#1.4

SYNOPSIS

The Doctor and Peri recall their trip to Hollowdean to visit the Doctor's old friend Reverend Foxwell, a former World War II codebreaker. Peri meets a young boy, Simon, who is taking part in a fancy dress party, dressed as a creature he's seen in the sand. They attend a local fundraiser for Professor Stream, a wheelchair-bound genius who made his money from electronics in the 1970s, but is now regarded as a local swami. Simon shows the Doctor a glowing reptile scale he found on the beach, which they analyse in Foxwell's lab. The vicar is working on a project which scans organic brains which can be put into an artificial intelligence. The Doctor tells Foxwell they've arrived after detecting gravitational blips in Hollowdean, then realises the scale is from a Tractator. The Doctor returns to the TARDIS, as Simon and Peri go to the beach and fall down a deep hole into a tunnel system. Professor Stream's colleague Steel Specs links Foxwell's car – a primitive time machine – to the TARDIS and they swap places, in his quest for the supreme Tractator, the Gravis. The Doctor manages to materialise the car, crashing it into the caves below the beach, where he finds Peri. In the church hall, they find Foxwell has placed a series of large encasements in a circle to form a quantum gravity engine. Steel Specs materialises the TARDIS and with Professor Stream, delivers the Gravis to complete the circle. Stream reveals he used the real intelligence machine as a cover for his engine, to master the Tractators' gravity powers. The TARDIS rematerialises above the gravity circle, but the Doctor convinces the Gravis to use the Tractators to stop Stream, who plans to become one with the gravity engine and the TARDIS to control all time and space. The Tractators apparently tear him apart. The Doctor and Peri depart, with the Time Lord concerned that the professor knew how to operate his ship… Could he be more than he seems?

PLACEMENT

After **Revelation of the Daleks** and before **The Trial of a Time Lord**.

TRIVIA

- This is the first appearance by the Tractators since the 1984 TV story **Frontios**.
- In the original story, Professor Stream was to have been revealed as the Master – another anagram of the renegade Time Lord's name. In this adaptation it is left up to the listener to decide.
- The **Doctor Who** production office requested that the Master not be included in the story because of the proximity of the play's release with the broadcast of **The End of Time**, which also featured the character as played by John Simm.
- Colin Baker had requested that the role of Simon be given to Susan Sheridan, who is well-known for her uncanny radio performances as young children. She also played Trillian in the original radio series of *The Hitchhiker's Guide to the Galaxy*.
- The release includes over 32 minutes of extras.

PRODUCTION SUMMARY

"In some ways I took a bit of a back seat on this one, as Christopher Bidmead had requested up front that he didn't want his scripts to be tampered with before they were recorded. So although I did provide notes (a couple of scenes were removed from part one at my request, and the very lengthy church hall scene in part two was broken up a little) it very much remained Chris's vision for the story."
David Richardson

WORKING TITLE(S)

In the Hollows of Time.

RETURNING MONSTERS/CHARACTERS

The Tractators, The Master… or was it?.

CREW

Writer	**Christopher H. Bidmead**
Director	**John Ainsworth**
Producer	**David Richardson**
Executive Producer	**Jason Haigh-Ellery**
Music and Sound Design	**Nigel Fairs**
Cover Art	**Alex Mallinson**
Theme	**Peter Howell**

CAST

The Doctor	**Colin Baker**
Peri	**Nicola Bryant**
Professor Stream	**David Garfield**
Reverend Foxwell	**Trevor Littledale**
Mrs Streeter	**Susan Sheridan**
Steel Specs	**Hywel John**
Jane	**Victoria Finney**

TECHNICAL

Story Code	**6Y/AD**
Recorded Date	**30 and 31 March 2009**
Release Date	**February 2010**
Place of Recording	**The Moat Studios, London**
Number of CDs	**2**
Total Duration	**153' 56"**
Number of Episodes	**2**
Duration of Episodes	**1 (62' 04")**
	2 (58' 19")
ISBN	**978-1-84435-447-4**

#1.5 | PARADISE 5

CREW

Writers	**PJ Hammond**
	Andy Lane
Director	**Barnaby Edwards**
Producer	**David Richardson**
Executive Producer	**Jason Haigh-Ellery**
Music and Sound Design	**Simon Robinson**
Cover Art	**Alex Mallinson**
Theme	**Peter Howell**

CAST

The Doctor	**Colin Baker**
Peri	**Nicola Bryant**
Gabriel	**Alex McQueen**
Michael	**James D'Arcy**
Stella, Bella	**Helen Goldwyn**
Lorelei	**Andrée Bernard**
Mr Gelter, Mr Bliss, Elohim Voice	**Teddy Kempner**
Ms Aht	**Claire Wyatt**
Mr Tapp, Mr Winterbourne	**Richard Earl**

TECHNICAL

Story Code	**6Y/AE**
Recorded Date	**13 and 14 July 2009**
Release Date	**March 2010**
Place of Recording	**The Moat Studios, London**
Number of CDs	**2**
Total Duration	**153' 11"**
Number of Episodes	**2**
Duration of Episodes	**1 (58' 04") 2 (60' 29")**
ISBN	**978-1-84435-448-1**

SYNOPSIS

The Doctor and Peri arrive on Targos Delta to visit his old friend Professor Albrecht Thompson. They learn he went to the orbiting holiday resort of Paradise 5 three months earlier, but never returned. Peri gets a job as a hostess on Paradise 5 where she meets its public face, Gabriel, and the station's diminutive servitors, the Cherubs. The Doctor smuggles himself on board as one of the visitors, Mr Gelter, whom Peri befriended, disappears. Gabriel and his partner Michael discuss the next arrivals, describing them as: "a depressingly average catch." The new visitors want to see the Paradise Machine, which will put them in a hypnotic state to take away their fears and worries, leaving them more relaxed than they've ever been. The Doctor meets a Cherub, supposedly with limited intelligence, which warns him to beware. Peri, trying to find the Doctor, is surrounded by the skull-like Elohim in the station's infrastructure, and the Doctor soon finds her, unconscious. Michael discovers the Doctor and Peri have no records on Targos Delta, as the pair find an alien shuttlecraft hidden onboard. Alerted, Gabriel decides to crash Paradise 5 onto the planet below, as he and Michael plot their escape. One by one, Gabriel summons the guests to the communications suite, and when the Doctor goes he is grabbed and taken to the alien shuttle, where some of the missing guests are chained up. He is freed by a Cherub, which scratches out the words 'I am Professor Albrecht Thompson.' The Doctor and the Cherub find Peri and learn the Elohim are creatures from a higher dimension, fighting a civil war, and have struck a deal with Gabriel and Michael to provide them with foot-soldiers through the Paradise Machine, their remains being recycled as Cherubs. The Doctor and Peri escape to the arrival shuttle as the station comes under attack, while Gabriel and Michael have a last gin and tonic before Paradise 5 crashes.

PLACEMENT

After **Revelation of the Daleks** and before **The Trial of a Time Lord**.

TRIVIA

- **Paradise 5** was written to be the third section of the 1986 TV season-long story **The Trial of a Time Lord**. The original script actually includes scenes in the Time Lord trial room, but David Richardson chose to excise these along with other changes.
- The story originally featured Mel. Due to Bonnie Langford's busy schedule and to make the story in keeping with the rest of the season, the character was replaced by Peri.
- PJ Hammond's paperwork for this story included a complete script for episode one, plus the storyline for the remaining episodes. However, upon commencing work, adapter Andy Lane soon realised that the removal of the trial sequences left just enough plot for three episodes. So he wrote a brand new episode one, which sits before Hammond's episode one (now episode two), in which the Doctor and Peri become embroiled in the mystery of Paradise 5. PJ Hammond was thrilled with Andy's work on the story, and wrote a long letter of thanks.
- P J Hammond is well known as the creator of TV series and Big Finish range **Sapphire & Steel.** He has also contributed two stories to **Doctor Who** TV spin-off Torchwood – Small Worlds and From Out of the Rain.
- The release includes several tracks of extras.

PRODUCTION SUMMARY

"Working at Big Finish is full of special moments. And, when you're a fan of **Sapphire and Steel** like me, and when you love PJ Hammond's episodes of Torchwood… well, does it get any more exciting than working with the man himself? Peter was just the single nicest man on the planet. Enthusiastic, endlessly helpful and generous, he made the whole production feel like something special and it's no surprise that **Paradise 5** has gone on to become one of the most popular of the **Lost Stories**. I think it's superb."
David Richardson

WORKING TITLE(S)

End of Term.

RETURNING MONSTERS/CHARACTERS

None.

Check box - CD ■ MP3 ■

POINT OF ENTRY

#1.6

SYNOPSIS

In 1590, playwright Christopher "Kit" Marlow is writing *Doctor Faustus*, when he is visited by an emaciated Spaniard, Don Lorenzo Velez, who wants him to help him find the blade of a knife which was stolen in South America. In the TARDIS, the Doctor and Peri hear a strange cry in deep space, then a reply, as they avoid colliding with an asteroid. The TARDIS lands in Elizabethan England, where the Doctor and Peri find a man known as Mad Jack, who has had his tongue cut out in an Aztec ritual. Trying to find help in a tavern, they meet Marlowe and his friend Tom, but the writer storms off when the Doctor asks him about his spying work. Marlowe goes to Velez, followed by Peri and Tom who find Jack chained up – and is later sacrificed, allowing Velez's decaying body to be restored. At the Tower of London, the Doctor warns spymaster Sir Francis Walsingham of Velez's influence on Kit. Velez, who has the knife's

hilt, can hear the knife approaching as it calls to its other half. Peri's mind is sent to the astral plane by Velez, and the Doctor follows soon after, learning of the world of the Omnim, which was destroyed. Its population projected their mental energies into an asteroid to try and survive, and have followed the TARDIS like a homing beacon to Earth. The Aztecs had previously found a remnant of the Omnim and carved it into a blade, transmitting the blood sacrifices back to the asteroid. The Omnim were driven mad when the blade was broken. Velez found the hilt in a vault in Madrid, and aims to reunite them, and with an eclipse due it will give them a point of entry. The Omnim link is affected by resonance, so the Doctor has the blade placed in a casket at the centre of a ring of glasses, as every bell in London is rung on Sir Francis's orders. The increasing resonance breaks the link with the Omnim.

PLACEMENT

After **Revelation of the Daleks** and before **The Trial of a Time Lord**.

TRIVIA

- Writer Barbara Clegg wrote the 1983 TV story **Enlightenment** for season 20.
- The story was suggested to Big Finish by Keith Barnfather of Reeltime Pictures, who had made a *Myth Makers* documentary with Barbara.
- Barbara Clegg was delighted for the production to proceed but felt unable to write the script at the time. Marc Platt was chosen for the adaptation as David Richardson felt he was the perfect fit.
- A few elements were dropped from Clegg's original storyline, including a scene in which Peri dresses as a boy, and uses a personal stereo in Victorian London.
- David Richardson felt that the early effects edit was too gruesome and asked for the sound of Velez's creeping flesh to be replaced by a more sci-fi sound.
- Ian Brooker (Sir Francis Walsingham) is a long-time Big Finish performer, and played the regular character of DJ Wayne Foley in radio soap *The Archers*, making a brief return to Ambridge in 2011.
- The release includes several tracks of extras.

PRODUCTION SUMMARY

"Colin and Nicola loved this script – the days of the studio recording just felt right. Marc's script was beautifully written and the cast was just brilliant. I've got to give special plaudits to Matt Addis, who ran with the guest star role of Kit Marlowe and did something really special with it."
David Richardson

WORKING TITLE(S)

None.

RETURNING MONSTERS/CHARACTERS

None.

CREW

Writers	**Barbara Clegg**
	Marc Platt
Director	**John Ainsworth**
Producer	**David Richardson**
Executive Producer	**Jason Haigh-Ellery**
Music and Sound Design	**Steve Foxon**
Cover Art	**Alex Mallinson**
Theme	**Peter Howell**

CAST

The Doctor	**Colin Baker**
Peri	**Nicola Bryant**
Kit Marlowe	**Matt Addis**
Velez	**Luis Soto**
Iguano, Captain Garland	**Sean Connolly**
Tom	**Tam Williams**
Alys	**Gemma Wardle**
Sir Francis Walsingham	**Ian Brooker**

TECHNICAL

Story Code	**6Y/AF**
Recorded Date	**4 and 5 November 2009**
Release Date	**April 2010**
Place of Recording	**The Moat Studios, London**
Number of CDs	**2**
Total Duration	**154' 59"**
Number of Episodes	**2**
Duration of Episodes	**1 (62' 04")**
	2 (67' 16")
ISBN	**978-1-84435-449-8**

BLOOD OF THE DALEKS (PART 2)

#1.2

SYNOPSIS

The Doctor manages to trick Martez's Daleks and escapes. Despite their claim to have received the colony distress call, the Daleks have actually been asked to come to the planet by Martez who wants help with his Dalek experiments. However, the real Daleks are repulsed by the ersatz Daleks and see them as an impurity that could contaminate the Dalek race. As such, they intend to destroy them. Because they temporarily share a common goal, the Doctor appears to team up with the real Daleks in order to destroy Martez's Daleks. Behind the scenes he is also working with Tom Cardwell to destroy all the Daleks on Red Rocket Rising. It is then revealed that the true Daleks caused the meteorite strike in the first place in order to destroy Martez's Daleks. Because of the speed of their production, the impure Daleks initially have the advantage, but the Doctor manages to persuade Martez that his 'creations' will only bring hatred and death. Martez stops the production line and is then killed by his Daleks for treachery. Ultimately, the two groups of Daleks annihilate one another and the human colonists can begin to look to the future. Indeed, there seems to be an offer of rescue from another planet already... When she attempts to stay on Red Rocket Rising, Lucie and the Doctor discover that the Time Lords want them to leave the planet together. Meanwhile, the mysterious Mister Hulbert is giving a woman called the Headhunter a mission: to find Lucie Miller wherever she is in space and time...

TRIVIA

- This story was originally broadcast on BBC Radio 7 on 7 January, 2007.
- A documentary about the series called *Beyond the Vortex* followed this episode in the BBC 7 schedules.
- The name of the planet that offers the colonists rescue is never heard in full, but Steve Lyons says that it was his intention for there to be a joke that it *could* be Telos, the second home of the Cybermen. However, he'd like to think the survivors of Red Rocket Rising *weren't* actually 'rescued' by the Cybermen, as that would just be horrible.
- The CD/download includes extras totalling over 20 minutes.
- Gareth Jenkins actually created Foley sound effects for the Daleks moving.
- One of the battle scenes includes a Dalek swearing somewhere amongst all the other audio tracks!

PRODUCTION SUMMARY

"Jason and I stripped off the names and titles and went through to see what we liked. Nick came on a bit later, but what grabbed me about this one was that the Daleks were basically coming to rescue people. And we'd agreed that we wanted Daleks to kick off the series. Possibly I would have wanted to start with a one-parter, which we did in subsequent seasons, but I was happy with it."
Alan Barnes

WORKING TITLE(S)

Exodus, The Enemy Gene, Exodus of the Daleks (Part 2).

RETURNING MONSTERS/CHARACTERS

Daleks, Time Lords.

CREW

Writer	**Steve Lyons**
Director	**Nicholas Briggs**
Producers	**Nicholas Briggs**
	Sharon Gosling
Executive Producer	**Jason Haigh-Ellery**
Music and Sound Design	**ERS**
Cover Art	**Alex Mallinson**
Theme	**David Arnold**

CAST

The Doctor	**Paul McGann**
Lucie	**Sheridan Smith**
Headhunter	**Katarina Olsson**
Eileen Klint	**Anita Dobson**
Tom Cardwell	**Kenneth Cranham**
Asha	**Hayley Atwell**
Lowell	**Gerry O'Toole**
The Daleks	**Nicholas Briggs**

TECHNICAL

Story Code	**BFPDWCDMG002**
Recorded Date	**21 and 29 August 2006**
Release Date	**February 2007**
Place of Recording	**The Moat Studios, London**
Number of CDs	**1**
Total Duration	**72' 22"**
Number of Episodes	**1 (50' 50")**
ISBN	**978-1-84435-256-2**

#1.3 HORROR OF GLAM ROCK

CREW

Writer	**Paul Magrs**
Director	**Barnaby Edwards**
Producers	**Nicholas Briggs**
	Sharon Gosling
Executive Producer	**Jason Haigh-Ellery**
Music and Sound Design	**ERS**
Cover Art	**Alex Mallinson**
Theme	**Tim Sutton**

CAST

The Doctor	**Paul McGann**
Lucie	**Sheridan Smith**
Arnold Korns	**Bernard Cribbins**
Flo	**Una Stubbs**
Tommy Tomorrow	**Stephen Gately**
Trisha Tomorrow	**Clare Buckfield**
Pat	**Lynsey Hardwick**
The Headhunter/ The Only Ones	**Katarina Olsson**

TECHNICAL

Story Code	**BFPDWCDMG003**
Recorded Date	**25 and 29 August 2006**
Release Date	**March 2007**
Place of Recording	**The Moat Studios, London**
Number of CDs	**1**
Total Duration	**69' 15"**
Number of Episodes	**1(48' 49")**
ISBN	**978-1-84435-257-9**

SYNOPSIS

The Doctor tries once more to return Lucie to her own time, but instead ends up at a service station off the M62 in 1974. Slade, the Sweet and Suzi Quatro top the charts and outside there is a blizzard blowing. In the car park, the time travellers find the mutilated body of a glam rock band member. The Doctor and Lucie then meet the pop group, The Tomorrow Twins and their manager, Arnold Korns who is determined to make them a success. The service station is under attack by vicious bear-like creatures that are being controlled by a hidden enemy. Whoever it is, they are secretly communicating with Tommy Tomorrow, using his 1970s electronic instrument, the stylophone. It transpires that the hidden enemy are a race called the Only Ones and they are using Tommy as the first stepping stone on their way to world domination. They intend to use the fans of The Tomorrow Twins so that Earth can be a re-fuelling spot for their race. Realising that the aliens use sonic technology, the Doctor manages to trap them using Lucie's MP3 player, which transforms them into harmless sound waves. As the Doctor and Lucie depart in the TARDIS, the Headhunter arrives on her trail…

TRIVIA

- This story was originally broadcast on BBC Radio 7 on 14 January 2007.
- A documentary about the series called *Beyond the Vortex* followed this episode in the BBC 7 schedules.
- Arnold Korns is played by Bernard Cribbins who is one of the UK's best-loved comic and character actors. He is well known for the role of Donna Noble's 'gramps', Wilfred Mott, in the new series of *Doctor Who* between 2007 and 2009, as well as PC Tom Campbell in the 1966 Amicus film, *Daleks - Invasion Earth: 2150 AD*.
- Auntie Pat reappears in **The Zygon Who Fell to Earth #2.6**.
- The song *Children of Tomorrow* sung by Stephen Gately and Clare Buckfield is included as a bonus track on the CD and download.
- The story also uses a special 'Glam Rock' version of the theme tune, composed by Tim Sutton
- The CD/download includes extras and music tracks totalling over 18 minutes.
- The first line of this script is Alan Barnes's favourite of the whole series because it captures Lucie so well.
- The working title was taken from a line in David Bowie's 1972 single *Starman*.

PRODUCTION SUMMARY

"When we mapped out the season, this was the comedy script. I say we picked up the story ideas blind, but it was obvious which one was Paul Magrs's! What was really attractive about this was the scope to do interesting things with the audio environment."
Alan Barnes

WORKING TITLE(S)

Hazy Cosmic Jive.

RETURNING MONSTERS/CHARACTERS

The Headhunter.

Check box - CD ■ MP3 ■

IMMORTAL BELOVED

#1.4

SYNOPSIS

The TARDIS brings the Doctor and Lucie to what they think is Ancient Greece and manage to prevent two lovers, Kalkin and Sararti, from taking their lives. However, when they are menaced by helicopters, it transpires that they are on a lost colony planet. They then witness the ailing General Ares having his mind transferred into a younger man's body. The Doctor meets Zeus and berates him for the way the planet is run. Zeus admits he is not a god, but a human that has survived for generations since the original colonists arrives by a spaceship that he himself piloted. Zeus, his wife Hera and the other 'gods' are using illegal technology to create clones of themselves. They can remain alive forever by transferring their minds into younger bodies. However, not only is the machinery running down, but Kalkin – whom the Doctor thought to be Zeus's son – is actually Zeus's next clone who has rebelled against his purpose. Living so long has driven Zeus quite mad and he forces the Doctor to fetch parts to repair the immortality machine using his TARDIS. The Doctor agrees to do so but only after Zeus has threatened to torture and kill Lucie and an eternity of clones he will create. Then Hera has a heart attack and her mind is transferred into her next clone – Sararti. However, the process fails and while pretending to be Hera, Sararti kills Zeus. When he is taken for emergency transfer into Kalkin, the Doctor ensures that the process fails again. The two lovers then take on the roles of Hera and Zeus but remain themselves with no one any the wiser. The Doctor and Lucie leave, with the Doctor wondering about Kalkin and Sararti's future, given that they are just younger versions of the 'gods' they have helped destroy.

TRIVIA

- This story was originally broadcast on BBC Radio 7 on 21 January, 2007.
- A documentary about the series called *Beyond the Vortex* followed this episode in the BBC 7 schedules.
- Jake McGann (Ganymede) is the son of Paul McGann. For Big Finish, he would go on to play the Doctor's great grandson, Alex, in the subscriber special release, **An Earthly Child**, and later in **Relative Dimensions 4.7**.
- Jonathan Clements had Baron Harkonnen, a character from Frank Herbert's 1965 novel *Dune*, in mind when he wrote the character of Zeus. He did not know that Ian McNeice who here plays Zeus, had played Baron Harkonnen in the Sci Fi Channel's *Dune* mini-series in 2000. Ian, of course, would go on to play Churchill in the 2010 TV story **Victory of the Daleks**, which also featured Nicholas Briggs (producer of this series) as the voice of the Daleks… who would later go onto play the role of Churchill in *Doctor Who Live*!
- The story started life as a **Strontium Dog** proposal for the **2000AD** range. When that range was cancelled, it became a proposal for a Richard E. Grant *Doctor Who* animation called Kingmaker.
- As well as Sins of the Father, Jonathan gave Alan Barnes several ideas for possible titles including Karma Police, Together Forever, and Immortal Beloved.
- The CD/download includes extras and music tracks totalling over 18 minutes.

PRODUCTION SUMMARY

"So this was the high-concept, science fiction story. I really rated this one. I'm not sure everyone else did. But I loved the fact that it was based around one really good SF idea. I don't think we do enough of this kind of high concept thing. I think we can get distracted by the adventure aspect of **Doctor Who**. I also loved the Romeo & Juliet element, too."
Alan Barnes

WORKING TITLE(S)

Sins of the Father.

RETURNING MONSTERS/CHARACTERS

None.

CREW

Writer	**Jonathan Clements**
Director	**Jason Haigh-Ellery**
Producers	**Nicholas Briggs**
	Sharon Gosling
Executive Producer	**Jason Haigh-Ellery**
Music and Sound Design	**ERS**
Cover Art	**Alex Mallinson**
Theme	**David Arnold**

CAST

The Doctor	**Paul McGann**
Lucie	**Sheridan Smith**
Zeus	**Ian McNeice**
Hera	**Elspet Gray**
Sararti	**Jennifer Higham**
Kalkin	**Anthony Spargo**
Tayden/Ares	**David Dobson**
Ganymede	**Jake McGann**

TECHNICAL

Story Code	**BFPDWCDMG004**
Recorded Date	**23 August 2006**
Release Date	**April 2007**
Place of Recording	**The Moat Studios, London**
Number of CDs	**1**
Total Duration	**67' 36"**
Number of Episodes	**1 (49' 14")**
ISBN	**978-1-84435-258-6**

#1.5 PHOBOS

CREW

Writer	**Eddie Robson**
Director	**Barnaby Edwards**
Producers	**Nicholas Briggs**
	Sharon Gosling
Executive Producer	**Jason Haigh-Ellery**
Music and Sound Design	**ERS**
Cover Art	**Alex Mallinson**
Theme	**David Arnold**

CAST

The Doctor	**Paul McGann**
Lucie	**Sheridan Smith**
Headhunter, Amy	**Katarina Olsson**
Kai Tobias	**Timothy West**
Eris	**Nerys Hughes**
Drew	**Ben Silverstone**
Hayd	**John Schwab**
Farl	**Tim Sutton**

TECHNICAL

Story Code	**BFPDWCDMG005**
Recorded Date	**22 August 2006**
Release Date	**May 2007**
Place of Recording	**The Moat Studios, London**
Number of CDs	**I**
Total Duration	**74' 14"**
Number of Episodes	**I(51' 49")**
ISBN	**978-1-84435-259-3**

SYNOPSIS

Landing on the Martian moon Phobos in 2589, the Doctor and Lucie meet extreme winter sports fans Drew and Hayd, adrenaline junkies known as Drennies. They are there to experience 'the wormhole', an apparently natural gravitational anomaly in a vertical shaft, which no one knows the depth of. Centre boss Kai Tobias tells human Amy and Githian husband Farl he's seen monsters on the mountain, warning them to leave. The Doctor and Lucie then find the body of a man which has been ripped in half. Lucie finds a Phobian monster – and discovers it's actually a robot. The Doctor confronts Kai, who admits he has been behind the killings, before stunning them and taking them to the wormhole, which he plans to throw them into. However, they are saved when Drew arrives with Kai's partner Eris. Kai tells them that there is a god of fear from another reality, which is trapped between dimensions in the hole. It created Phobos's atmosphere to draw creatures to it. It then feeds on the pleasurable fear that extreme sports fans experience in an attempt to force its way through to our reality. However, it is hurt by real fear and Tobias made the robots to create real fear. The Doctor then dives into the wormhole, letting the creature feed on the fears of the monsters he has experienced. The creature can't handle it and withdraws, killing Eris as it does so. The Doctor is unsure whether the entity is dead or not, as Lucie ponders whether he's scarier than the monsters. The Doctor feels closing down Phobos would prevent the creature's return. As the Doctor and Lucie leave, the Headhunter awakens in the moon's sickbay, angry that she has missed Lucie again.

TRIVIA

- This story was originally broadcast on BBC Radio 7 on 28 January, 2007.
- A documentary about the series called *Beyond the Vortex* followed this episode in the BBC 7 schedules.
- Nerys Hughes, who here plays Eris, is perhaps best known for her role as Sandra Hutchinson in the BBC sitcom *The Liver Birds* between 1972 and 1979. She appeared in **Doctor Who** on television in the 1982 story **Kinda**, and later returned to the **Doctor Who** universe in the season two *Torchwood* episode *Something Borrowed* (2008).
- The CD/download includes extras and music tracks totalling over 23 minutes.
- Eddie Robson says he hadn't planned to rewrite so much of the original script but that once he had made small tweaks to each scene it was then easier for him to go back and write the whole scene from scratch.
- Eddie remembers doing the notes for the story on a train a few hours before the broadcast of the TV *Doctor Who* story **The Impossible Planet**, but failed to notice the similarity until Phobos aired and people pointed it out. "I'm not sure anyone ever believes me when I say these things aren't intentional," he says. "But when you get close to an idea you really don't always notice."
- An earlier pitch submitted for this slot by writers Iain McLaughlin and Claire Bartlett featured a funfair on the moon and would have featured the Yeti as well as the Great Intelligence.

PRODUCTION SUMMARY

"I wanted this to represent the horror element for the season. The original pitch was set in a futuristic theme park and Justin Richards pointed out that we seemed to do a lot of stories like this one. So I came up with the idea of extreme sports and suggested making it **Phobos**. The original writers then produced a first draft based on these new ideas but it just seemed a bit flat, a bit detached from the modern, extreme sports aspect. Nick and I talked and decided that, having had **Human Resources** in, we'd give it to Eddie. Not a lot remained of the original."
Alan Barnes

WORKING TITLE(S)

Helter Skelter, Jumping At Shadows, The Feast of Fear.

RETURNING MONSTERS/CHARACTERS

The Headhunter.

Check box - CD ☐ MP3 ☐

NO MORE LIES

SYNOPSIS

On a disintegrating spaceship, the Doctor and Lucie corner the criminal time traveller Dr Nick Zimmerman. At the same time, ferocious alien raiders called the Tar-Modowk appear riding Vortisaurs and board his vessel. Zimmerman catches the Doctor in his time whip, planning to sell time technology he has obtained to the highest bidder, which could result in the deaths of millions. Zimmerman gets away in an escape pod, travelling through the vortex. The Doctor and Lucie give chase in the TARDIS, with the Tar-Modowk in pursuit. Landing on Earth, they meet Zimmerman again. Some 30 years have passed for him, however, and he has married a woman called Rachel, for whom he is throwing a birthday party. The Doctor can sense a disturbance which turns out to be a time loop running over and over again. Then the

Tar-Modowk raiders arrive and break through into the time loop in order to feast on it. The Doctor knows the only way to get rid of the Tar-Modowk is to break the loop. However, Zimmerman runs off to protect it, and the Doctor gives chase on a Vortisaur to finds its source. This turns out to be the heart of the disintegrating time ship, which is hidden in a mausoleum in the grounds of Zimmerman's home. The Doctor disables the time loop, sending the Tar-Modowk away. Rachel then correctly guesses that her husband created the time loop to keep her alive, repeating the same evening over and over again. With the loop broken, Rachel dies. As Lucie returns to the TARDIS, the Headhunter appears and takes her away, leaving the Doctor trapped in his ship, unable to leave without her.

TRIVIA

- This story was originally broadcast on BBC Radio 7 on 4 February 2007.
- A documentary about the series called *Beyond the Vortex* followed this episode in the BBC 7 schedules.
- The play features the song *Bucimeana* sung by Julia McKenzie with music by Tim Sutton and lyrics by Paul Sutton from a traditional Hungarian poem.
- The Vortisaurs first appeared in **Storm Warning #16**, which is where the Doctor acquired his "pet" referred to here. That Vortisuar was called Ramsay (after Ramsay McDonald, the UK Prime Minister between 1931 and 1935). There is a Vortisuar in this story called Margaret (after another UK Prime Minister...)
- Writer Paul Sutton is based in Hungary and so uses Hungarian words for alien names. For example: "tar-modowk" comes from the word for "attackers".
- The CD/download includes extras totalling over 22 minutes.

PRODUCTION SUMMARY

"The tragic/romantic element to the season. I remember Paul had the Vortisaurs even in the original pitch and thought "oh, he's trying to please me"! Huh! I didn't get paid any more for their use! Seriously, it landed on my desk pretty fully-formed. There was one real risk that it could have been slow and died, but it really didn't. The one thing I wasn't keen on was the title. I am not keen on pompous titles; they seem so self-important and any writer who sits down to write a *Doctor Who* story and thinks he's going to change the world is utterly mad!"
Alan Barnes

WORKING TITLE(S)

None.

RETURNING MONSTERS/CHARACTERS

The Headhunter, Vortisaurs.

CREW

Writer	**Paul Sutton**
Director	**Barnaby Edwards**
Producers	**Nicholas Briggs**
	Sharon Gosling
Executive Producer	**Jason Haigh-Ellery**
Music and Sound Design	**ERS**
Cover Art	**Alex Mallinson**
Theme	**David Arnold**

CAST

The Doctor	**Paul McGann**
Lucie	**Sheridan Smith**
Headhunter	**Katarina Olsson**
Nick	**Nigel Havers**
Rachel	**Julia McKenzie**
Gordon	**Tom Chadbon**
Tar-Modowk Leader	**Tim Hudson**

TECHNICAL

Story Code	**BFPDWCDMG006**
Recorded Date	**24 and 29 August 2006**
Release Date	**June 2007**
Place of Recording	**The Moat Studios, London**
Number of CDs	**1**
Total Duration	**71' 01"**
Number of Episodes	**1 (48' 58")**
ISBN	**978-1-84435-260-9**

#1.7

HUMAN RESOURCES (PART 1)

CREW

Writer **Eddie Robson**
Director **Nicholas Briggs**
Producers **Nicholas Briggs**
Sharon Gosling
Executive Producer **Jason Haigh-Ellery**
Music and
Sound Design **ERS**
Cover Art **Alex Mallinson**
Theme **David Arnold**

CAST

The Doctor **Paul McGann**
Lucie **Sheridan Smith**
Headhunter **Katarina Olsson**
Hulbert **Roy Marsden**
Straxus **Nickolas Grace**
Jerry **Owen Brenman**
Karen **Louise Fullerton**
Malcolm **Andy Wisher**
The Cybermen **Nicholas Briggs**

TECHNICAL

Story Code **BFPDWCDMG007**
Recorded Date **26 and 30 August
2006**
Release Date **July 2007**
Place of Recording **The Moat Studios,
London**
Number of CDs **1**
Total Duration **60' 33"**
Number of Episodes **1 (48' 19")**
ISBN **978-1-84435-261-6**

SYNOPSIS

Lucie – believing her travels with the Doctor were just a dream – starts work in a new office job at Hulbert Logistics. In the TARDIS, the Time Lord Straxis arrives, gives the Doctor a time ring and sends him off to find her. Meanwhile, Lucie meets Karen, another girl who recently started at the company. They were even interviewed for the job at the same time. Lucie is then summoned to an office where the Doctor breaks her conditioning. Back to her old self, Lucie realises that this is the job she was meant to start when she was first kidnapped by the Time Lords. While she returns to her data input duties, the Doctor stumbles across a meeting at which the suggestion of using laser cutters and knock out gas appears to be the norm. Lucie is fired after admitting to distracting Karen and both are ejected from the office. Outside, they discover the building is actually a giant, armoured robot, stomping through a dry jungle. Karen and Lucie meet Malcolm, who used to be a manager in the office before being fired. Meanwhile, the Doctor finds a dimensional corridor in the human resources department, which leads to an office in London run by a man called Todd Hulbert, who is a problem solver in galactic matters. His current job involves using non-military people and getting them to work in a familiar setting, translating their work into waging war to wipe out the creatures on planet Lonsis. Meanwhile, the Headhunter is outraged when she hears Lucie has been fired and sets off to find her. Hulbert travels with the Doctor to Lonsis to meet with his clients. His base of operations comes under fire, but Hulbert says there will be no problems from their attackers as it's fully shielded. However, the Doctor tells him he's already lowered the defences as the enemies arrive - the Cybermen.

TRIVIA

- This story was originally broadcast on BBC Radio 7 on 11 February 2007.
- A documentary about the series called *Beyond the Vortex* followed this episode in the BBC 7 schedules.
- Roy Marsden (Hulbert) is perhaps best-known for his portrayal of police inspector Adam Dalgliesh in the ITV series based on the novels by P. D. James. He also appeared as Mr Stoker in the 2007 **Doctor Who** TV story **Smith and Jones**.
- The CD also includes an extras track and bonus interviews with the cast, totalling over 12 minutes.
- In Eddie Robson's original pitch, this was a one-parter in which the Doctor and Lucie simply turned up at the office in the TARDIS and investigated. Instead of the Cybermen turning up at the end of Part One, the Doctor and Lucie sorted it all out and left. But Nick and Alan liked the idea, decided to make it part of Lucie's backstory and asked him to add the Cybermen in when it was selected as the season finale. They also came up with the Headhunter as part of that world.

PRODUCTION SUMMARY

"This was always designed to be the big Cybermen season finale and it was brilliant from minute one. A real stand out for the season. I love the way it goes in a totally different direction after episode one. I was disappointed we couldn't keep the Cybermen a secret but I understand why these things have to be done!"
Alan Barnes

WORKING TITLE(S)

Human Resources (no parts!)

RETURNING MONSTERS/CHARACTERS

The Headhunter, Cybermen, Time Lords.

Check box - CD ■ MP3 ■

HUMAN RESOURCES (PART 2)

#1.8

SYNOPSIS

The Headhunter arrives looking for Lucie, but the rebel forces tie her up. In Hulbert's base, it's revealed the alien Shinx wanted to have the Cybermen wiped out on Lonsis, which the cyborgs have colonised. The Shinx fear the Cybermen will try to invade their planet, so they engaged Hulbert's services to eradicate them. Lucie returns to her old office and senses a time disruption and a humming from underneath the carpet. The Doctor is amazed to find that the office has a perfect success rate in the war, something which is statistically improbable. He then finds the reason: a Quantum Crystaliser under the floor. Its job is to sift through time lines until it finds the desired outcome, before making that outcome a reality. Using the time ring the Doctor and Lucie return to the TARDIS, where they learn the CIA installed the Crystaliser in an attempt to wipe out the Cybermen. While working on that project, they foresaw a time line in which the woman interviewed for the job would become the powerful leader of an oppressive right-wing regime, putting the planet on an aggressive interplanetary footing. So, the Time Lords pulled her out of time and placed her with the Doctor. Returning to Lonsis, an upset Lucie takes the Crystaliser just as the Cybermen invade the building, intent on seizing the device. The Doctor realises that the woman the CIA identified as a future dictator was Karen not Lucie! The Doctor explains that the Crystaliser has been programmed to ensure that the Cybermen are defeated, so he simply increases its range, causing all of the Cybermen to be killed, and burning out the device at the same time. The Headhunter finds Karen injured and decides to take her on as her new assistant. The Doctor tells the surviving human group to go through the portal and return home while a happier Lucie decides to continue her travels in the TARDIS.

TRIVIA

- This story was originally broadcast on BBC Radio 7 on 18 February 2007.
- A documentary about the series called *Beyond the Vortex* followed this episode in the BBC 7 schedules.
- The CD/download also includes three extra tracks, a trailer for season three and one for the **The Girl Who Never Was #103** – the last full-length Eighth Doctor story to appear in the **Main Monthly Range** release schedule for four years (**The Company of Friends #123** being an anthology release.)
- Andrew Wisher (Malcolm) is the son of Michael Wisher, who played the part of Davros in the 1975 TV story **Genesis of the Daleks**.
- When given the Cybermen as an extra for the season finale, Eddie says his first attempt at expanding the storyline was "rubbish". He split the story between two offices, one of which had been captured by the Cybermen. Eddie says he thought that was over-complicated, and the original idea had got lost. In the end he took inspiration from the TV story **Bad Wolf**, where they let the whole gameshow idea play out for an episode and then brought the Daleks in. "That was what I wanted to do in the first place," Eddie says. "But it felt like cheating!"

PRODUCTION SUMMARY

"I remember that we originally wanted to do different episode titles for the two parts of this and **Blood of the Daleks**, but because that's what was being done in the TV series, we didn't. Nothing to do with being asked NOT to; we just didn't want people to think we were aping the new TV series."
Alan Barnes

WORKING TITLE(S)

Hostile Takeover.

RETURNING MONSTERS/CHARACTERS

The Headhunter, Cybermen, Time Lords.

CREW

Writer	**Eddie Robson**
Director	**Nicholas Briggs**
Producers	**Nicholas Briggs**
	Sharon Gosling
Executive Producer	**Jason Haigh-Ellery**
Music and Sound Design	**ERS**
Cover Art	**Alex Mallinson**
Theme	**David Arnold**

CAST

The Doctor	**Paul McGann**
Lucie	**Sheridan Smith**
Headhunter	**Katarina Olsson**
Hulbert	**Roy Marsden**
Straxus	**Nickolas Grace**
Jerry	**Owen Brenman**
Karen	**Louise Fullerton**
Malcolm	**Andy Wisher**
The Cybermen	**Nicholas Briggs**

TECHNICAL

Story Code	**BFPDWCDMG008**
Recorded Date	**26 and 30 August 2006**
Release Date	**August 2007**
Place of Recording	**The Moat Studios, London**
Number of CDs	**I**
Total Duration	**65' 57"**
Number of Episodes	**I (47' 52")**
ISBN	**978-1-84435-262-3**

THE VENGEANCE OF MORBIUS

#2.8

SYNOPSIS

Orthena tells the Doctor that Zarodnix drove the Sisterhood from Karn, as he has a Morbius fixation. Zarodnix is told that extraction has been a total success, as the Sisterhood say he plans to revive Morbius. Rosto's ship lands on Karn and Straxus is terrified, as Zarodnix has been scouring the universe for a Time Lord. When the Sisterhood warned Gallifrey of the menace, the Time Lords quarantined themselves and used the time scoop to collect all errant TARDISes. The Doctor and Lucie are put in the chamber which is activated, but the Sisterhood stop when they deduce that Zarodnix already has a Time Lord in his possession – Straxus. The Doctor realises Zarodnix has found a fragment of Morbius's brain and he plans to blend his DNA with that of Straxus, to create a new incarnation. They return to the TARDIS and are time-scooped back to Gallifrey. The new Morbius contacts his homeworld and demands they surrender to him, as he has his own stellar manipulator and starts to drain the Eye of Harmony. The Doctor and Lucie use the TARDIS's reserve power to travel to Karn where they find Straxus. He tells them ten years have passed, during which time Morbius has conquered much of time and space, using Straxus to top up his constantly draining life-force. The Doctor contacts Orthena using the TARDIS's telepathic circuits and asks her to remove the stellar manipulator control from Morbius's neck when he gives her the signal. The Doctor confronts Morbius on the edge of the canyon where the Sisterhood confronted him all those years before, and switches off the manipulator. The pair plunge into the abyss to their deaths. With Morbius dead, the Time Lords have the energy needed to restore the original timeline, erasing the last decade. With the Doctor dead, too, Lucie is returned home to Blackpool. But then the Headhunter shows up at her door...

TRIVIA

- This episode was broadcast on BBC Radio 7 on 18 December 2009.
- The BBC broadcasts of Episodes 7 and 8 of Series 2 were delayed from the original broadcast of the series in October and November 2008.
- Samuel West (Morbius) was a member of the **Doctor Who** Appreciation Society (DWAS). His previous brush with Doctor Who was as the Rani's companion in the Children in Need story **Dimensions in Time**.
- The Headhunter makes a surprise appearance at the end of the story.
- The CD/download also includes extras and bonus tracks totalling over 16 minutes.
- Alan Barnes has said that what he wanted to make people really believe that Big Finish had killed the Doctor.

PRODUCTION SUMMARY

"We didn't have the faintest idea of how we were going to get out of that ending and we didn't have a plan until well through the commissioning of the third season! It was quite a long haul getting out of that one. When you're writing one of these things, the key is to have someone who can deliver a script that can go into studio tomorrow, with dialogue that can be spoken in a studio tomorrow and sound effects that can be used for a template for a production by a sound designer tomorrow. There are some writers who get it quite naturally and those that don't. You can't teach it; you have to have it in your bones. So it's a huge weight off your shoulders to know Nick's working on the season finale. But I did send him notes just like everyone else!"
Alan Barnes

WORKING TITLE(S)

None.

RETURNING MONSTERS/CHARACTERS

Morbius, Time Lords, Straxus, Sisterhood of Karn, the Headhunter.

CREW

Writer	**Nicholas Briggs**
Director	**Nicholas Briggs**
Producer	**Nicholas Briggs**
Executive Producer	**Jason Haigh-Ellery**
Music and Sound Design	**ERS**
Cover Art	**Grant Kempster**
Theme	**Nicholas Briggs**

CAST

The Doctor	**Paul McGann**
Lucie	**Sheridan Smith**
Revenant	**Samuel West**
Zarodnix	**Kenneth Colley**
Rosto	**Alexander Siddig**
Straxus	**Nickolas Grace**
Bulek	**Barry McCarthy**
Haspira	**Nicola Weeks**
Orthena	**Katarina Olsson**

TECHNICAL

Story Code	**BFPDWCDMG016**
Recorded Date	**23 August 2007**
Release Date	**August 2008**
Place of Recording	**The Moat Studios, London**
Number of CDs	**1**
Total Duration	**66' 09"**
Number of Episodes	**1 (49' 12")**
ISBN	**978-1-84435-311-8**

SECTION 6

DOCTOR WHO – THE STAGE PLAYS

'**T**he Stage Plays were Jason's pet project,' says range producer, Nicholas Briggs. 'He'd been mentioning it for years and we'd always said, "oh, shut up"! But then I thought it was quite an exciting idea – so we did it.'

Producing the **Stage Plays** meant that the writers of the originals had to be contacted (or their estates) and permission sought to adapt them. This was reasonably straightforward as Nick knew Terrance Dicks of old and Jason had been in contact with the David Whittaker estate. Terrance agreed to adapt his own scripts for **The Ultimate Adventure #1** and **The Seven Keys to Doomsday #2**, while Nick took on those duties for **Curse of the Daleks #3**.

'That was quite a mammoth task because of the re-writing,' recalls Nick. 'I wanted to keep it as faithful to the original sexist, slightly old-fashioned script!' he jokes. 'I had to make the decision to put the narration in because it was so visual in places – particularly the pivotal scene in which the Dalek first comes to life. It starts moving but the people on stage don't notice it. Now, this is meant to be a terrifying moment but how can you do that on audio? I thought about cutting to the Dalek control room perspective and the Dalek reporting back that it was moving, but it wouldn't have had the same effect. But if you do it with a bit of narration: "unbeknownst to them..." and all that, you can create the same atmosphere that the play was originally trying to create.'

While casting for **The Stage Plays** was up to Jason and Nick, they knew they wanted to ask David Banks back to reprise his stage role in **The Ultimate Adventure** as mercenary Karl. There was also an initial hiccup in the casting of the Doctor in **The Seven Keys to Doomsday**.

'We weren't originally going to do it with Trevor Martin,' reveals Nick. 'We had all sorts of mad ideas of who we were going to use in that and John Ainsworth just said, "go and get Trevor Martin"! We thought he might have given up acting or was too old but John had seen him in a play and he was jumping about all over the place. So it was fine.'

Another casting suggestion came from Gary Russell. 'Wendy Padbury – although ever youthful – we all know is not a teenager and it was important that her part was played by a young girl. Gary had worked with Wendy's daughter Charlie Hayes on **Master #49** so suggested her as a natural replacement.'

With scripts and casting in place, recording sessions were booked for June and July 2008, with **The Ultimate Adventure** going into studio first on 5 June.

The news was announced in issue 396 of *Doctor Who Magazine* and a few days later on 30 June as a press release on bigfinish.com saying: 'Big Finish will open the curtains on **Doctor Who**'s theatrical past with audio adaptations of the three **Doctor Who** stage plays... Each play will be released as a double CD with **The Ultimate Adventure** being available from September, **The Seven Keys to Doomsday** in October and **The Curse of the Daleks** in November.'

It was also noted that **The Stage Plays** replaced **Cyberman 2** in the Big Finish schedules, with the Cyber mini-series pushed back to December 2009, although the statement said February. **The Stage Plays** themselves kept to their announced schedule and all came as a two-CD release with a great deal of behind-the-scenes bonus material.

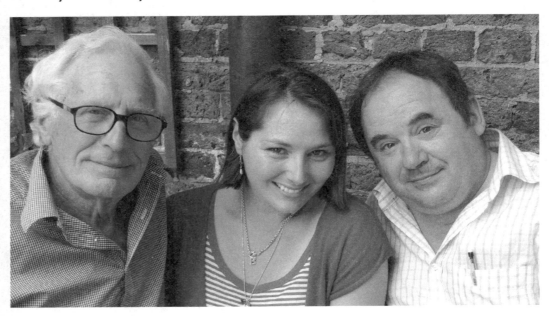

Right:
Facing **The Curse of the Daleks** on Skaro (l-r): John Line (Professor Vanderlyn), Beth Chalmers (Marion Clements), Nick Wilton (Rocket Smith).

'The moment we announced the news everyone went wild for it and we got very enthusiastic about it because everyone else got enthusiastic about it!' says Nick. '*Doctor Who Magazine* gave us a huge splash on the news page. Normally we're fighting for two paragraphs or two columns and they gave over a whole page to it.'

Nick was baffled by this unprecedented reaction. 'I asked Peter Ware, who's the assistant editor, and he said, "It's like finding an old piece of forgotten **Doctor Who**". Everyone knows about the stage plays but most fans never saw them. I'd only seen one of them – **The Ultimate Adventure**. It was one of the worst evenings of my life! Being such a serious fan, the Daleks didn't look like Daleks – they looked like bad drawings of Daleks!'

Ultimately, however, **The Stage Plays** range did not prove to be as massively successful as the response

to their arrival might have indicated. 'There was an awful lot of noise made about them,' recalls Nick. 'People were saying things like "this will be the first Big Finish I've ever bought" and we thought it was going to be so huge that it was going to transform our fortunes. But it didn't!'

That didn't prevent the production team from discussing a possible future for the range. 'We loved them so much we had meetings about how we were going to do sequels to them all,' says Nick. 'I desperately wanted to do a sequel to **Curse of the Daleks** that had the Doctor from **The Seven Keys to Doomsday**! We were really up for all this. Jason had even spoken to Gary Russell at the BBC to see if that would be all right. Gary just laughed and said, "well, if you want to..."!'

Although a full second season did not materialise, there would eventually be a second chance for the cast of **The Ultimate Adventure**. December 2011 would see the release of **Beyond the Ultimate Adventure #6.6**, starring Colin Baker, Claire Huckle and Noel Sullivan as part of the sixth season of **The Companion Chronicles**.

However, the experience of working on these missing adventures did play a part in the decision to start investigating the possibility of producing the stories from the original lost season 23. This, in turn, led to the successful range of **Lost Stories** (see Section 04).

And who knows where those ideas that the team had for sequels might lead? They may yet receive a curtain call in some form or other...

Top:
The Ultimate Adventure lives on, 20 years later (l-r): Claire Huckle (Crystal), Colin Baker (the Doctor) and Noel Sullivan (Jason).

Left:
The Stage Plays producer Nicholas Briggs.

#1 | THE ULTIMATE ADVENTURE

CREW

Writer	**Terrance Dicks**
Director	**Jason Haigh-Ellery**
Producer	**Nicholas Briggs**
Line Producer	**David Richardson**
Executive Producer	**Jason Haigh-Ellery**
Music	**Andy Hardwick**
Sound Design	**Matthew Cochrane**
Orchestration	**David Darlington**
Cover Art	**Grant Kempster**

CAST

The Doctor	**Colin Baker**
Jason	**Noel Sullivan**
Crystal	**Claire Huckle**
Karl	**David Banks**
Delilah, Mrs T	**Nadine Cox**
Nightclub MC	**Bryan Pilkington**
Envoy, Zog	**Derek Carlyle**
Daleks, Cybermen	**Nicholas Briggs**

TECHNICAL

Story Code	**BFPDWSPCD01**
Recorded Date	**5 and 6 June 2008**
Release Date	**September 2008**
Place of Recording	**The Moat Studios**
Number of CDs	**2**
Total Duration	**100' 47"**
Number of Episodes	**2**
Duration of Episodes	**1 (47 26")**
	2 (51' 28")
ISBN	**978-1-84435-373-6**

SYNOPSIS

The Doctor is summoned to London where an alien plot has been discovered to kidnap an American envoy and blow up the peace conference he will be attending the next day. A squad of Cybermen lead by Karl, a mercenary, seize the envoy at a nightclub and take him to the Emperor Dalek on Skaro. The Doctor locks the TARDIS onto an energy trail that leads to Altair III, where the Cybermen are waiting. With the help of Crystal and Jason – who he met in the nightclub – they escape the trap and follow a lead to Sentos. Again, they are expected but manage to get away from Karl, this time with Zog, a hairy creature who has befriended them. However, the TARDIS is ensnared by a tractor beam and brought aboard a Dalek ship. Under duress, the Doctor allows a Dalek into the TARDIS but manages to electrocute it. He and his companions then travel back to Sentos. There, the Daleks betray Karl and kill his men. The mercenary joins the Doctor and they all travel to Skaro. Zog occupies the electrocuted Dalek's casing and with Karl playing along, they fool the Daleks and gain access to a high security area whey they find the US envoy, but are unable to free him. While Jason and Zog stand guard, the Doctor and Crystal return to the TARDIS, where the Time Lord creates a time tunnel, which penetrates the cell and frees the envoy. However, they are all captured and taken before the Emperor. Karl sacrifices himself so that the Doctor, his companions and the envoy can escape. They return to Earth where the Doctor discovers that the envoy is carrying a Dalekenium bomb and has forged evidence incriminating each world power in the explosion. With the conference due to start, the Doctor manages to defuse the bomb and break the hold the Daleks have on the envoy.

TRIVIA

- The original stage production ran from 23 March 1989 with Jon Pertwee playing the Doctor. Colin Baker then took over the role on 5 June and continued until the play finished its run on 1 August.
- Although David Banks played the Cyber Leader in four **Doctor Who** TV stories, the voice of the Cybermen was provided by Oliver Gary in the stage production. Dalek voices were performed by Chris Beaumont and Troy Webb. Here both are provided by the current TV voice artist, Nick Briggs.
- Noel Sullivan was a member of the pop group Hear'Say. He appeared in the final episode of the BBC comedy series *Gavin & Stacey* opposite Sheridan Smith, who plays companion Lucie Miller in the **Eighth Doctor Adventures** range.
- The Doctor makes reference to Evelyn when listing the companions he has travelled with.

PRODUCTION SUMMARY

"This was the only one of the three that I had actually seen. I remember thinking it was one of the worst nights of my life because I took the whole Dalek thing so seriously back then and to me the ones they used on stage looked like bad drawings of Daleks!"
Nicholas Briggs

WORKING TITLE(S)

None.

RETURNING MONSTERS/CHARACTERS

Daleks, Cybermen.

Check box - CD ■ MP3 ■

SEVEN KEYS TO DOOMSDAY

SYNOPSIS

When the TARDIS materialises on a stage and the Doctor falls out, two audience members, Jimmy and Jenny, help him back inside, where he regenerates. They travel to Karn where the Doctor took a large crystal before being ambushed. They arrive in a ruined Citadel where the Doctor finds another crystal and meets some rebels, led by Jedak and Tara. Avoiding a half-man, half-crab creature called a Clawrantular, they find a maintenance tunnel. This leads to a super-computer that tells them it was built by the Masters of Karn, the last of whom lives in the Great Hall. When they go to the Great Hall, the last Master tells them of the brilliant scientists who invented the Ultimate Weapon, which they turned on themselves in a terrible civil war. A Dalek appears, demanding the Crystal, which the Doctor throws into the shadows allowing them to escape to the TARDIS. Jedak thinks the Daleks have a spy because they are so well informed and accuses Jimmy. The boy refutes the allegation and the Doctor says the Daleks might have a surveillance device. The two groups return to the Dalek base but Jenny is captured. Tara admits that she has been working for the Daleks who are holding her brother, Marco, hostage. The Doctor says they must rescue Marco and go to the prison centre. When they arrive they also free Jenny. Realising that the Daleks plan to build the Ultimate Weapon, they go to the chamber where it's located and the rebels cause a diversion that allows the Doctor to slip into the control room. However, after a bluff by Jimmy, they are all captured and the Emperor forces the Doctor to put the final segment in place and operate the machine. But he has swapped the crystal for a fake and the machine backfires. The Doctor, his companions and the rebels escape as the Dalek base blows up.

TRIVIA

- In the original production, Wendy Padbury (who played Zoe in the TV series) was cast as Jenny. Here it is her daughter, Charlie Hayes, who plays the part. She has also appeared in the **Main Monthly Range** release **Master #49** and the **Companion Chronicles Bernice Summerfield and the Criminal Code #4.6** and **The Memory Cheats #6.3**, alongside her mother.
- Trevor Martin, who here plays the Doctor, appeared in the TV series as one of the very first Time Lords ever seen in the 1969 story **The War Games**. He also appeared in the **Main Monthly Range** release **Flip-Flop #46**.
- Nick Briggs plays the previous Doctor in an uncredited role.
- The story is set on the planet Karn, location of the 1975 TV story **The Brain of Morbius**, also written by Terrance Dicks.

PRODUCTION SUMMARY

"Originally the assistants were chosen from the audience and we wanted to stick with that. It is fair to say that in recreating these stage plays and deciding what remained and what had to change we were very much setting up the production template for **The Lost Stories.**"
Nicholas Briggs

WORKING TITLE(S)

None.

RETURNING MONSTERS/CHARACTERS

Daleks,

CREW

Writer	**Terrance Dicks**
Director	**John Ainsworth**
Producer	**Nicholas Briggs**
Line Producer	**David Richardson**
Executive Producer	**Jason Haigh-Ellery**
Music and Sound Design	**Richard Fox and Lauren Yason**
Cover Art	**Grant Kempster**
Theme	**Delia Derbyshire**

CAST

The Doctor	**Trevor Martin**
Jenny	**Charlie Hayes**
Jimmy	**Joe Thompson**
Jedak	**Nicholas Deal**
Tara	**Christine Brennan**
Garm, The Master of Karn	**Steven Wickham**
Computer, Marko	**Paul Thornley**
Daleks	**Nicholas Briggs**

TECHNICAL

Story Code	**BFPDWSPCD02**
Recorded Date	**15 and 16 July 2008**
Release Date	**October 2008**
Place of Recording	**The Moat Studios**
Number of CDs	**2**
Total Duration	**142' 59"**
Number of Episodes	**2**
Duration of Episodes	**1 (51' 24")**
	2 (35' 12")
ISBN	**978-1-84435-374-3**

Left:
Lisa Bowerman (Bernice Summerfield) and Katy Manning (Iris Wildthyme) at the Moat Studios during the recording of **Bernice Summerfield and The Plague Herds of Excelis**.

Below:
The cast of **Excelis Decays** (l-r): Yee Jee Tso, Ian Collier, Sylvester McCoy, writer Craig Hinton, Stuart Piper and Penny MacDonald.

SECTION 8
BERNICE SUMMERFIELD

It all started with an archaeologist called Professor Bernice Summerfield…

As Big Finish lore has previously established, Gary Russell had approached the BBC about producing a series of **Doctor Who** audios in the 1990s, but because of the Paul McGann TV movie, that idea had been rejected. This had arisen after a discussion with Nicholas Briggs about producing some professional versions of their Audio Visuals plays. After the knock back from the BBC, Gary then mooted doing something that tied in with Virgin Books' series of *New Adventures* novels.

'We knew we weren't going to get anything out of the BBC,' says Gary. 'So I said, "you know what would be really good? We should do Bernice Summerfield", because she was popular, she was staying on in the books and I thought that Paul Cornell would be easy enough to talk to.'

Gary approached Paul Cornell, who had created the character for his *New Adventures* novel *Love and War*. He was very keen, so Gary went to see editor Rebecca Levene at Virgin. 'We agreed that we would adapt the existing books and we'd get Jac Rayner to do them,' says Gary. 'I think Jac was probably Paul's suggestion.'

After that first meeting, Gary met with Jason Haigh-Ellery. 'I took Jason out for dinner at Pizza Express – Jason always knows that when someone takes him out for dinner, there's a catch!' laughs Gary. 'Jason had always been interested in audio drama and I said, "here's a great idea: I've got the rights from Virgin and Paul to do Bernice Summerfield".'

Paul Cornell was already known to Gary and Jason, and they thought the idea could work well. 'I basically said to Jason, "I want you to give me all your money and I'll go and spend it"!'

With Jason and his company, Big Finish, on board, Gary went back to Nick Briggs and they started to plan. As well as asking Jacqueline Rayner to write the scripts, they also needed to find an actress to play of Benny herself. So they went about drawing up a shortlist to interview for the part.

It was Gary's friend Peter Griffiths who suggested Lisa Bowerman for the role. He had seen the Reeltime Pictures documentary *I Was a Doctor Who Monster* in which Gary had interviewed Lisa about her role as Kara in the 1989 TV story **Survival**. 'I thought she'd be absolutely perfect because she's mad and fun and bouncy, so we got her along for the interviews and she just was Bernice the moment she walked in through the door.'

The first season is particularly notable for its inclusion of many **Doctor Who** alumni in guest-starring roles, such as Colin Baker (the Sixth Doctor), Nicholas Courtney (Brigadier Lethbridge-Stewart), Sophie Aldred (Ace), Elisabeth Sladen (Sarah Jane Smith), Anneke Wills (Polly) and Richard Franklin (Captain Mike Yates) – all of whom would go on to reprise their original *Doctor Who* roles for Big Finish in later years. Stephen Fewell was also cast in the pivotal role of Bernice's husband, Jason Kane, having been recommended to Gary by Lisa.

Because of the initial agreement with Paul Cornell and Virgin, the first season of **Bernice Summerfield** consists of six adaptations of *New Adventures* novels. Each of the plays was released as a double CD except for the last play in the initial run, **Dragon's Wrath #1.6**, which was a single CD. The plays differ to varying degrees from the original novels, especially **Birthright #1.4** and **Just War #1.5**, which originally included the character of the Doctor.

'It became clear very quickly that doing adaptations was not a good idea,' says Gary. 'They were big books and trying to condense them onto a double or single CD just didn't make any sense. We got into all sorts of problems with Kate Orman over **Walking to Babylon #1.3**, which is entirely my fault… And then there was **Dragon's Wrath #1.6** which was written at the same time but took a whole year-and-a-half to be released. They probably weren't our brightest moments.'

Gary decided that the only way forward was to produce original plays. 'I thought it was time to let Benny stand on her own two feet,' he says. Even before **Dragon's Wrath** was recorded, Gary had David Bailey and Lance Parkin working on scripts for a second season of adventures.

'It was Justin who came up with Brax and KS-159 and the Collection and all of that,' Gary says of the decision to introduce an ongoing story arc for the second and subsequent seasons. Big Finish also started publishing **Bernice Summerfield** books that tied in closely with the audios. For example, Benny actually became pregnant in the novel *The Squire's Crystal*, which was first mentioned in the audio range in David Bailey's **The Skymines of Karthos #2.4**.

The third season was used to flesh out the cast of characters that had been introduced in season two with Jason, Adrian Wall and Irving Braxiatel all given major parts to play in the storyline. As the third series progressed, Brax in particular was developed to hint at a mysterious character who was harbouring some terrible secrets.

Season three also boasted **The Plague Herds of Excelis** – a coda of sorts to the **Doctor Who Excelis** trilogy. Though it takes place between **The Green-Eyed Monsters #3.2** and is followed directly by **The Dance of the Dead #3.3**, it was produced between the first and second stories of the season. As a side-step from the ongoing Bernice story arc, this is why there is no number on the spine of the **Excelis** release.

SERIES 1 - 4

The fourth run of releases would be Bernice's 'monster season', acknowledging Benny's origins with a number of links back into the history of **Doctor Who**: **The Bellotron Incident #4.1** features the Rutans and has the Sontarans as a presence – although they are never heard; **The Draconian Rage #4.2** has a cast dominated by the noble reptiles from **Frontier in Space**; **The Poison Seas #4.3** has a plot that portrays the Sea Devils as intelligent aliens rather than monsters; and Paul Cornell's **Death and the Daleks #4.4** brings the season to a shattering, double-CD climax that follows on from the acclaimed short story collection *Life During Wartime*.

Gary stands by all the **Bernice Summerfield** plays, but concedes that with Lisa, who he describes as: 'the greatest ambassador the range could have', played a crucial role in the success of the range. 'Once you've got Lisa in something she could make rubbish sound like a sonnet. Luckily she never had to deal with rubbish,' says Gary. 'I'm very happy with all the Bennys; I'm very proud of them.'

The origins and production of the **Bernice Summerfield** range is dealt with in magnificent detail in Simon Guerrier's fascinating book, **Bernice Summerfield: The Inside Story**, published by Big Finish in June 2009.

Top:
Lisa Bowerman with Philip Bretherton, who guest-starred in The Draconian Rage as Emperor Shenn.

Left:
Lisa Bowerman as Professor Bernice Summerfield, Big Finish's original audio heroine.

#1.1   OH NO IT ISN'T!

CREW

Writer	**Paul Cornell**
Adapted by	**Jacqueline Rayner**
Director	**Nicholas Briggs**
Producer	**Gary Russell**
Executive Producer	**Jason Haigh-Ellery**
Music and Sound Design	**Alistair Lock**
Cover Art	**John Sullivan**
Bernice Art	**Lee Sullivan**

CAST

Bernice Summerfield	**Lisa Bowerman**
Wolsey the Cat	**Nicholas Courtney**
Jayne Waspo/Bitchy	**Jo Castleton**
Michael Doran, Cute	**Jonathan Brüün**
Captain Balsam, King Rupert	**Colin McIntyre**
Lt Prince, Prince Charming	**Nicholas Briggs**
Professor Candy, Dame Candy	**James Campbell**
The Grand Vizier	**Mark Gatiss**
The Grel Master	**Alistair Lock**

TECHNICAL

Story Code	**BFPCD1**
Recorded Date	**25 and 26 June 1998**
Release Date	**September 1998**
Place of Recording	**Intergalactic Arts, London**
Number of CDs	**2**
Total Duration	**111' 06"**
Number of Episodes	**2**
Duration of Episodes	**1 (56' 14"); 2 (54' 52")**
ISBN	**1-903654-30-0**

SYNOPSIS

Bernice Summerfield leads an expedition to the quarantined planet of Perfecton. She returns to the ship, the *Winton*, as the alien Grel prepare to attack it. But a missile approaches the *Winton* from Perfecton and hits the ship. When Benny awakes, she finds herself in a strange world where her cat Wolsey is now walking upright and talking, and thinks she's a lad named Dick. They soon encounter other members of the expedition – her students have been transformed into seven dwarves, Professor Candy has taken on the persona of a dame, the ship's captain is now the king, and a lieutenant is now a prince. Benny finds her environment familiar, but can't quite put her finger on it, after being mistaken for a princess, meeting her fairy godfather and attending the king's ball in order to find a husband. Perfectons have been the audience, hissing whenever the king's vizier appeared. The Perfectons condensed their entire civilisation and placed it in a missile, which would be fired at any passing spaceship and transform it, restoring the race. But when the missile hit the *Winton*, it happened at the same time Benny was about to read her colleague Professor Archduke's thesis on the nature of pantomime, with the result being a reshaping of reality, transforming everyone into characters from an ancient British theatrical tradition. Benny realises that to escape the story and return to normality she must place a magic lamp, containing the Perfecton's leader, on a special pedestal. She tricks the leader into returning to the lamp and as she places it into position the scenario ends.

TRIVIA

- This was the first ever release from Big Finish Productions and as such was Nicholas Briggs's directorial debut for the company.
- Nicholas Courtney (Wolsey) is better known to **Doctor Who** fans for playing the recurring character of Brigadier Lethbridge-Stewart.
- **Oh No It Isn't** was the first of the *New Adventures* books not to feature the Doctor.
- The original story by Paul Cornell started life as simply 'Behind You' in 1996.
- Paul suggested that Jacqueline Rayner adapt his story because he was busy on his TV series, *Wavelength*.
- Jac shares a birthday with Benny – June 21st.
- Jo Castleton, who here plays Jayne Waspo/Bitchy, auditioned for the part of Bernice Summerfield.
- The original theme for **Bernice Summerfield** had actually been composed by Alistair Lock for another Paul Cornell project called *Phoenix Ryan*.

PRODUCTION SUMMARY

"As this had been Virgin's pilot for Doctor-less *New Adventures*, we decided that this one should be ours, too. I must say I wasn't very keen on it being the first. I originally wanted to kick off the series with what ended up being the final release in the first season: **Dragon's Wrath #1.6**. But we went with this one because Paul persuaded me, basically. It is a good book, but I just felt **Dragon's Wrath** was what Benny was all about." *Gary Russell*

WORKING TITLE(S)

None.

RETURNING MONSTERS/CHARACTERS

None.

BEYOND THE SUN

SYNOPSIS

Bernice and two students, Tameka and Emile, explore the remains of a Chelonian site, when her former husband Jason Kane shows up. He has been working with a business partner, and shows Benny a crystal statue, which he believes was part of an ancient and powerful weapon. The couple spend the night together, but while she's in the shower, Jason is kidnapped, leaving the figurine behind. Benny leaves with Emile and Tameka, but their ship comes under attack from the race known as the Sunless, and they crash onto the planet Ursa below. Benny and her friends meet Scott, one of the Ursulans. They are born from blooms as one of a family group of eight. The blooms were originally taken from the Sunless homeworld to Ursa, which were re-engineered to give birth to the planet's children without the need for biological breeding, and each of the children was based on the eight races who populated the planet in a state of peace. Scott,

however, was born into a bloom of nine, with eight of the family sharing genetic traits with each other, with only his sister Miranda untouched. Looking at a picture of Miranda, they recognise her as Jason's business partner. Scott's brother Leon betrays them to the Sunless, who take them to their dying world. Thinking about the situation, Benny realises that the bloom was always programmed to give birth to one offspring at this time, on the Sunless homeworld, before being taken to Ursa. Miranda is the extra child. Benny realises that a translation on the statue that it will give power beyond the sun was wrongly read, as it meant it would extend the power of the sun beyond its natural life. Miranda falls into a pit with the same inscription around it, and revitalises the planet's star. Benny and her friends return to Ursa, as Tameka discovers she's pregnant with Scott's child, and Emile takes Scott as his lover.

TRIVIA

- This play guest-stars two well-known *Doctor Who* actors: Sophie Aldred who played Ace and Anneke Wills who played Polly. They would both go on to reprise their **Doctor Who** roles for Big Finish.
- This is the first appearance in the Big Finish series for Jason Kane, Benny's husband. It was actually Lisa Bowerman that suggested Stephen Fewell for the part.
- The alien Ursulans were so named by Matt Jones after SF novelist Ursula K. Le Guin.
- Matt submitted the revised version of another *New Adventures* idea to Gary Russell in 1999 but it did not feature Benny and so was not taken up. (You can read the full synopsis of this idea in Simon Guerrier's excellent work, **Bernice Summerfield: The Inside Story**.)
- Gary Russell would go on to script-edit Matt's episode of the **Doctor Who** spin-off, *Torchwood* (*Dead Man Walking* in 2008).
- This release marks Gary Russell's directorial debut for Big Finish.
- The original cover for this release (as well as the first play) featured the image of Benny that had been drawn by Lee Sullivan to accompany Paul Cornell's interview about the character in *Doctor Who Magazine*. This was replaced when the cover was re-issued featuring the Professor Bernice Summerfield logo.

PRODUCTION SUMMARY

"This is the only play of the first season not to be adapted by Jac. Matt Jones adapted his own Virgin *New Adventures* story and I think he did a superb job. It actually wasn't down as one of the books I wanted to adapt but Matt asked me if it could be and told me how he would adapt it. And what he said was good, so I said 'yes'!"
Gary Russell

WORKING TITLE(S)

None.

RETURNING MONSTERS/CHARACTERS

Jason Kane.

CREW
Writer	**Matt Jones**
Director	**Gary Russell**
Producer	**Gary Russell**
Executive Producer	**Jason Haigh-Ellery**
Music and Sound Design	**Harvey Summers**
Cover Art	**Mark Salwowski**
Bernice Art	**Lee Sullivan**

CAST
Bernice Summerfield	**Lisa Bowerman**
Miranda	**Sophie Aldred**
Doctor Kitzinger	**Anneke Wills**
Jason Kane	**Stephen Fewell**
Tameka Vito	**Jane Burke**
Emile Mars-Smith	**Lewis Davis**
Scott	**Nicholas Pegg**
Leon	**Barnaby Edwards**

TECHNICAL
Story Code	**BFPCD2**
Recorded Date	**6 and 7 August 1998**
Release Date	**September 1998**
Place of Recording	**Crosstown Studios, London**
Number of CDs	**2**
Total Duration	**100' 27"**
Number of Episodes	**2**
Duration of Episodes	**1 (47' 44")** **2 (52' 43")**
ISBN	**1-903654-34-3**

#1.3 WALKING TO BABYLON

CREW

Writer	**Kate Orman**
Adapted by	**Jacqueline Rayner**
Director	**Gary Russell**
Producer	**Gary Russell**
Executive Producer	**Jason Haigh-Ellery**
Music	**Harvey Summers**
	Chinook Lodge
Sound Design	**Harvey Summers**
Cover Art	**Colin Howard**

CAST

Bernice Summerfield	**Lisa Bowerman**
Ninan-ashtammu	**Elisabeth Sladen**
Jason Kane	**Stephen Fewell**
John Lafayette	**Barnaby Edwards**
WiRgo!xu	**Nigel Fairs**
!Ci!ci-tel	**Anthony Keetch**
The Drone	**Steven Wickham**
Miriam	**Louise Morell**
Babylonian Child	**Alex Canini**

TECHNICAL

Story Code	**BFPCD3**
Recorded Date	**5 and 6 November 1998**
Release Date	**January 1999**
Place of Recording	**Crosstown Studios, London**
Number of CDs	**2**
Total Duration	**92' 10"**
Number of Episodes	**2**
Duration of Episodes	**1 (55' 53")**
	2 (36' 17")
ISBN	**1-903654-19X**

SYNOPSIS

Jason visits Bernice with a man who claims to be a fan, but she soon discovers that he has stolen her wedding ring – a time ring. Jason, with two members of the People, !Ci!Ci-tel and WiRgo!xu, use him to forge an illegal link to the past, known as the Path, and travel back to ancient Babylon, taking an unwilling Jason with them. Benny meets another of the People, who learns what has happened, and wants !Ci!Ci-tel and WiRgo!xu stopped, as they have broken the terms of the People's Treaty with their enemies, forbidding the People from travelling in time. Benny is given just 48 hours to find them and rescue her errant husband, before the People back in the 26th century send a singularity bomb to destroy the Path – and Babylon. Benny tries to track them down using her chrono-connetiscope device, but along the way meets Edwardian time-sensitive John Lafayette, who stumbled upon the Path. Benny meets and befriends the priestess Ninan, before locating the rogue People. They tell Benny they wanted to experience a simpler way of life when there was no guarantee of any specific outcomes in life, and want to bring back more people to experience the same way of life in ancient Babylon. But they admit the People became complacent after their victory in the last war and want to provoke another conflict, which they couldn't be sure they would win. John touches !Ci!Ci-tel, aging him to death through the release of temporal energy from the Path, and WiRgo!xu agrees to travel the world with Ninan, who dreams of exploring new realms. Lafayette is returned along the path to 1901, taking the chrono-connetiscope with him. Benny and Jason shut down the Path, the pair of them being knocked through time in the back blast.

TRIVIA

- Elisabeth Sladen (Ninan-ashtammu) is well known for playing Sarah Jane Smith not only in **Doctor Who** but also in her own spin-off series, *The Sarah Jane Adventures*, as well as Big Finish's own **Sarah Jane Smith** series (see Section 10).
- This is the first story in the 'Time Ring Trilogy'. The cover design features a ring as a motif.
- Gary Russell released news of the play's adaption before Kate Orman, the original author, had been informed because he wanted to announce the range at the Icon 2 convention in Cheshire. This caused false news stories to circulate on the internet regarding the nature of the contract Big Finish held with the authors. In fact, none existed. The only contract was with Virgin who owned the rights to the authors' stories.
- The cover had to differ from the one used on the book essentially because it was the wrong shape. As such, Gary commissioned Colin Howard to supply artwork of Lafayette and the drone.
- The artwork was used one way round (with Lafayette looking to the right) in the original release. In the re-issue (which features the Professor Bernice Summerfield logo designed by Paul Vyse) this image was flipped.
- Several **Doctor Who** fans were invited to the play's recording including Paul Ebbs who would go on to write **The Greatest Shop in the Galaxy #3.1**.

PRODUCTION SUMMARY

"The problems we had with Kate Orman are probably my fault. I wanted to announce everything and we had not had time to contact everyone. I think it was the fact that we hadn't told her that Kate objected to, not the fact that we were adapting her story. I thought I had told [Kate's husband] Jon via email and assumed he would tell his wife. Of course, this is not hugely professional and naturally Kate was annoyed. But, we managed to sort it out, even if the delay caused problems to the marketing of the range."
Gary Russell

WORKING TITLE(S)

None.

RETURNING MONSTERS/CHARACTERS

Jason Kane.

BIRTHRIGHT

#1.4

SYNOPSIS

The time rings deposit Benny and Jason at either end of the Great Divide, an unstable wormhole in time and space. Benny arrives in Edwardian London, while Jason finds himself in the future on Antykhon, where he has the insectoid Charrl for company. Learning she's in 1909 Benny realises her friend from Babylon, John Lafayette, should still be alive. She goes to a library, where a librarian hands her a note – Lafayette supposed she would arrive in his time one day, so left identical messages for her in places she was likely to visit. Lafayette, who's recently married, tells her he's left the chrono-connetiscope in a safety deposit box with a bank on Guernsey. On Antykhon, Jason learns the Charrl have made contact with a human, Jared Khan, who is assisting them in their attempted migration to a new home. Several Charrl have been sent across the Great Divide, but have died soon after arriving due to the condition of the wormhole.

Queen Ch'tizz wants to use Benny's time ring to stabilise their journey, in conjunction with Jason's. Jason initially refuses, and soon learns that the Charrl have made their home in a tunnel beneath the sea – the Channel Tunnel. Antykhon is a ravaged Earth in the future, with the Charrl keeping humans to devour. Another Charrl is sent through the divide as Benny, investigating a series of grisly murders in the East End, is bitten by it before it dies. Benny becomes unwell as Jason convinces Ch'tizz to send him to find Benny and her time ring. Benny and several others have been infected with Charrl eggs, as first Jason, then the aliens, arrive. Benny recovers to convince the Queen to go to another planet, and by using their time rings, she and Jason are able to send them to Analyas VI. Without the Charrl influence the eggs in the infected humans die, as Benny and Jason are once more thrown through time.

TRIVIA

- Colin Baker (Mikhail Vladamir Popov) is the first actor to have played the Doctor to appear in a Big Finish release; **Birthright #1.4** was recorded four months before the **Main Monthly Range** release **The Sirens of Time #1**.
- This is the second story in the 'Time Ring Trilogy.'
- 'The Time Ring Trilogy' was the first-ever Big Finish special offer. The three plays were sold together with a CD of extras at a reduced price – see **Buried Treasures** further on in this section.

PRODUCTION SUMMARY

"Everyone goes on about 'retconning' and 'canon' and I don't give a stuff. To me, these first plays were like having six pilots for the series. That's how I view them now. To me the series really gets going in the second season and in the books that Big Finish published at around this time."
Gary Russell

WORKING TITLE(S)

None.

RETURNING MONSTERS/CHARACTERS

Jason Kane, John Lafayette.

CREW

Writer	**Nigel Robinson**
Adapted by	**Jacqueline Rayner**
Director	**Nicholas Briggs**
Producer	**Gary Russell**
Executive Producer	**Jason Haigh-Ellery**
Music	**Harvey Summers Chinook Lodge**
Sound Design	**Harvey Summers**
Cover Art	**Peter Elson**

CAST

Bernice Summerfield	**Lisa Bowerman**
Mikhail Vladamir Popov	**Colin Baker**
Jason Kane	**Stephen Fewell**
John Lafayette	**Barnaby Edwards**
Jared Khan	**John Wadmore**
Queen Ch'tizz	**Jane Shakespeare**
Chf. Insp. Prior	**Jonathan Reason**
Charlie	**Benjamin Roddy**

TECHNICAL

Story Code	**BFPCD4**
Recorded Date	**5 and 6 November 1998**
Release Date	**February 1999**
Place of Recording	**Crosstown Studios, London**
Number of CDs	**2**
Total Duration	**127' 50"**
Number of Episodes	**2**
Duration of Episodes	**1 (63' 54") 2 (63' 56")**
ISBN	**1-903654-36-X**

#1.5 JUST WAR

CREW

Writer	**Lance Parkin**
Adapted by	**Jacqueline Rayner**
Director	**Nicholas Briggs**
Producer	**Gary Russell**
Executive Producer	**Jason Haigh-Ellery**
Music and Sound Design	**Harvey Summers**
Cover Art	**Nik Spender**

CAST

Bernice Summerfield	**Lisa Bowerman**
Jason Kane	**Stephen Fewell**
Oberst Oskar Steinmann	**Michael Wade**
Standardtenführer Joachim Wolff	**Mark Gatiss**
Ma Doras	**Maggie Stables**
Nurse Rosa Kitzel	**Nicky Golding**
Private Franz Hutter	**Anthony Keetch**
Private Gerhard Flur	**Simon Moore**

TECHNICAL

Story Code	**BFPCD5**
Recorded Date	**13 & 14 March 1999**
Release Date	**August 1999**
Place of Recording	**Crosstown Studios, London**
Number of CDs	**2**
Total Duration	**115' 42"**
Number of Episodes	**2**
Duration of Episodes	**1 (55' 32")**
	2 (60' 10")
ISBN	**1-903654-35-1**

SYNOPSIS

Arriving on Earth in 1936, Jason travels to Guernsey, knowing Benny will be heading there to find the chrono-connetiscope. There he meets German Emil Hartung, and hints at the concept of radar, which fascinates the scientist. On learning he's a Nazi, Jason storms off. Benny arrives on the island five years later, when it's occupied by German forces. She poses as the daughter of boarding house owner Ma Doras, and flirts with a young German trooper, Gerhard. They walk one night, Benny using it as a cover to investigate the airstrip, and Benny goes out after seeing what she thinks is a crashing UFO. Gerhard finds her out of her disguise, and she kills him to protect Ma Doras. Benny is soon captured by German officer Standardtenführer Joachim Wolff, while Jason, now a captain with the British military, observes all communications from the island, looking to find any traces of Benny. When he learns a woman has been captured for killing a German soldier, he heads for the island, where he too is captured and taken before Wolff's superior, Oberst Oskar Steinmann. Steinmann wants him to look over plans for a new German plane. Jason realises to his horror the plane was developed by Hartung, who made it out of the same futuristic material as the chrono-connetiscope – which he'd found – and Jason's flippant comments about radar, to create two radar resistant planes, *Hugin* and *Munin*. After being tortured by Wolff, Benny is reunited with Jason, and they learn he died when Hugin exploded, as she recovered the chrono-connetiscope from his charred remains. Benny and Jason steal Munin and fly back to Britain before destroying the aircraft, enabling history to run its normal course, before using their time rings to finally return them back to the 26th century.

TRIVIA

- Gary Russell originally planned to cast Wendy Padbury as Ma Doras.
- Instead, the role went to Maggie Stables – her Big Finish debut. She would go on to be cast as Evelyn Smythe and appear opposite Colin Baker in **The Marian Conspiracy #6** seven months later.
- This is the third story in the 'Time Ring Trilogy'.
- This was the first play recorded after Big Finish had been awarded the *Doctor Who* licence by the BBC. Coincidentally, the original novel on which the play is based was the only one adapted by Big Finish to actually include the character of the Doctor, albeit excised in the adaptation.
- Lance Parkin had bought back his rights to the original novel, which made negotiations more difficult than the other adaptations that make up the first season.
- The first studio session for the play on March 13th simply failed to record and had to be retaken the following day.

PRODUCTION SUMMARY

"I don't think I had ever read the book and I think I lied through my teeth to Lance and said it was magnificent because everyone else had said it was! Of course, this is now my favourite of the first season. It was a great story to begin with and Jac did a really good job of adapting it for audio. It's one of the plays I am most proud of."
Gary Russell

WORKING TITLE(S)

None.

RETURNING MONSTERS/CHARACTERS

Jason Kane.

#1.5

BURIED TREASURES

Included with the release of **Just War #1.5** was a free disc that contains two original **Bernice Summerfield** stories; the very first original stories from Big Finish, in fact. The disc also includes an interview with Paul Cornell (who also contributes one of the CD's stories) plus a musical suite (as heard in **Just War**) and trailer for the rest of the range.

TRIVIA

- These stories were the first original *Bernice Summerfield* plays to be recorded.
- **Making Myths** was the first Big Finish play to be directed by Jason Haigh-Ellery.
- Keri the Pakhar featured in Gary Russell's *New Adventures* novel *Legacy* and went on to appear in **The Goddess Quandary #6.4**, albeit voiced this time by Rob Shearman's wife, Jane Goddard (who also played the part of Geri the Pakhar in **Bang-Bang-A-Boom! #39**).

MAKING MYTHS

SYNOPSIS

The first of the two is a funny and enjoyable comedy written by Jacqueline Rayner, entitled **Making Myths**. The story starts off with Benny appearing on a live satellite radio broadcast talking about the oft-referenced Lost Mudfields of Agravan. Lisa Bowerman gives another wonderful performance here; the skill with which she plays our favourite archaeologist is quite unnerving, almost as if Cornell had her in mind for the part all those years ago when he first created Bernice (although he had apparently visualised her as resembling a short-haired version of actress Emma Thompson). Sarah Mowat (who also appeared in Big Finish's first **Doctor Who** release **The Sirens of Time #1**) appears as the *New Adventures* stalwart Keri Pakhar, hosting the radio broadcast. Both Bowerman and Mowat seem to enjoy the comic interplay, keeping the whole tale moving along.

CLOSURE

SYNOPSIS

The second of the two tales, written by Paul Cornell, is a story of Benny travelling back in time to confront the mother of a future dictator. She's given the choice of deciding whether to kill for the greater good, or stick to her morals regardless of the cost to future generations. Very different from **Making Myths**, this one is very much a dark and chilling tale because everything is based on fact. Once more, both Bowerman and Mowat are the only two actors involved, and their interaction here is fantastic.

CREW

Making Myths Writer	**Jacqueline Rayner**
Closure Writer	**Paul Cornell**
Director	**Jason Haigh-Ellery**
Producer	**Gary Russell**
Executive Producer	**Jason Haigh-Ellery**
Music and Sound Design	**N/A**
Cover Art	**Lee Sullivan**

CAST

Bernice Summerfield	**Lisa Bowerman**
Keri Pakhar, Isabella	**Sarah Mowat**

TECHNICAL

Story Code	**N/A**
Recorded Date	**9 January 1999**
Release Date	**August 1999**
Place of Recording	**Gary Gillatt and Ed Salt's flat!**
Number of CDs	**1**
Total Duration	**127' 50"**
Number of Episodes	**2**
Duration of Episodes	**1 (63' 54")**
	2 (63' 56")
ISBN	**1-903654-36-X**

#1.6 DRAGONS' WRATH

CREW

Writer	**Justin Richards**
Adapted by	**Jacqueline Rayner**
Director	**Ed Salt**
Producer	**Gary Russell**
Executive Producer	**Jason Haigh-Ellery**
Music and Sound Design	**Toby Richards**
Cover Art	**Fred Gambino**

CAST

Bernice Summerfield	**Lisa Bowerman**
Romolo Nusek	**Richard Franklin**
Nicholas Clyde	**Nigel Fairs**
Truby Kamadrich	**Jane Burke**
Mappin Gilder	**Gary Russell**
Reddick	**Jez Fielder**

TECHNICAL

Story Code	**BFPCD6**
Recorded Date	**7 September 1999**
Release Date	**September 2000**
Place of Recording	**Harvey Summer's studio, Hastings**
Number of CDs	**1**
Total Duration	**72' 31"**
Number of Episodes	**1**
ISBN	**1-903654-033**

SYNOPSIS

Benny finds dying forger Newark Rappare at St Oscar's, then locates a beautiful dragon statuette in his study. Archaeologist Dr Truby Kamadrich tells Benny and historian Dr Nicholas Clyde that billionaire Romolo Nusek wants to pay for a dig on Stanturus III, which he claims his ancestor Gamaliel once controlled, giving him the right to assume his ancestor's mantle as ruler of the Sector. Benny is told it was the site of a famous triumph for Gamaliel, who captured the Gamalian Dragon, a jewel-encrusted statuette, from the legendary Knights of Jeneve after the Battle of Bocaro. Benny's dragon is an exact replica of the original, which has been in Nusek's vaults for decades. Benny and Clyde meet Nusek in his palace within a volcano, where they secretly inspect the original, and find librarian Reddick. On Stanturus III the party splits in two, Benny's party finding a third dragon, while Clyde is the only survivor when his party is destroyed, along with the site they were investigating. He blames it on a Nusek ship. Benny reckons the third dragon is a fake, and that the Knights of Jeneve weren't destroyed. Running Gamaliel's victory through battle computers, she can't see how he won, and suspects the Knights wanted him to take the dragon. A hearing is held into the expedition and Nusek's claim on the planet, where it's revealed the Gamaliel Dragon was lead lined to prevent it being scanned, as it contains a microphone and video camera, allowing the Knights to spy on their opponent. Clyde is revealed as a Knight, who destroyed his party when they found genuine evidence of Gamalien troopers, so killed them to stop Nusek expanding his empire. Benny and Clyde are taken before Nusek, as archivist Reddick – another Knight – reveals there's a bomb in the dragon. Clyde is killed as Benny activates the detonator, also destroying Nusek.

TRIVIA

- This play was recorded six months after **Just War #1.5** and released over a year later due to problems and delays in post-production.
- Richard Franklin (Romolo Nusek) is better known to **Doctor Who** fans as UNIT Captain Mike Yates.
- This is the last adaptation of a Virgin *New Adventure*; all subsequent **Bernice Summerfield** audios would be original plays.
- Director Ed Salt's first job had been at the **Doctor Who** Exhibition in Blackpool.
- After several false starts, the music and sound design was given to Justin Richards's brother Toby. "Considering what had happened, Toby did a magnificent job," Gary Russell says. "So much so, we continued to use him until we got back on our feet post-production wise."
- This was the first release in the range to bear the new 'Professor Bernice Summerfield' logo designed by Paul Vyse.

PRODUCTION SUMMARY

"God! This took an age to come out, didn't it? I seem to recall that this was adapted at the same time as all the others but was delayed for various nightmare reasons. We had to record it in a studio in Sussex somewhere. Something went wrong; the recording wasn't up to much. Harvey did his best to try and repair it but it all went hideously wrong! This was not one of our brightest moments."
Gary Russell

WORKING TITLE(S)

None.

RETURNING MONSTERS/CHARACTERS

None.

Check box - CD ▢

Above:
Benny's creator, Paul Cornell, joins the cast of
Death and the Daleks (clockwise from left):
Paul Cornell, Miles Richardson, Lisa Bowerman,
Louise Faulkner, Stephen Fewell, Harry Myers,
Nicholas Briggs, Steven Wickham and Ian Collier.

Left:
Companion piece – Anneke Wills and
Sophie Aldred guest-starred in series one's
Beyond the Sun.

Far left:
The Doctor himself, Colin Baker, joined Lisa as Mikhail Vladamir Popov in **Birthright**.

Left:
Nicholas Courtney and Lisa Bowerman in studio for the the very first Bernice Summerfield audio - **Oh No It Isn't!**

Below:
The cast of **The Bellotron Incident**
(l-r): Lisa Bowerman, Louise Faulkner, writer Mike Tucker, Karl Hansen and Peter John.

#4.1

THE BELLOTRON INCIDENT

CREW

Writer	**Mike Tucker**
Director	**Gary Russell**
Producer	**Gary Russell**
Executive Producer	**Jason Haigh-Ellery**
Music	**David Darlington**
Sound Design	**Andrew Swann**
Cover Art	**Adrian Salmon**

CAST

Bernice Summerfield	**Lisa Bowerman**
Bev Tarrant	**Louise Faulkner**
Irving Braxiatel	**Miles Richardson**
Joseph	**Steven Wickham**
Commander Ryan	**Karl Hansen**
Captain Quilby	**Peter John**

TECHNICAL

Story Code	**BFPCD16**
Recorded Date	**31 January 2003**
Release Date	**April 2003**
Place of Recording	**The Moat Studios, London**
Number of CDs	**1**
Total Duration	**70' 26"**
Number of Episodes	**1**
ISBN	**1-84435-040-1**

SYNOPSIS

Captain Quilby and Commander Ryan are monitoring the planet Bellotron as its orbit takes it from Rutan controlled space into a Sontaran sector. They detect electrical activity and discover it is coming from a cave in which rests a stone covered in hieroglyphs. At Quilby's request, Braxiatel sends Benny to Bellotron to investigate. Together with Ryan and some robot soldiers, she manages to open the stone and discovers an ancient structure on the other side. There, Bernice and Ryan see a local nomad and follow him to a sarcophagus where he is revealed to be a Rutan who seems very interested in what appears to be a burial urn. The Rutan then attacks Benny and Ryan but is killed by the robots. They then find a woman called Bev Tarrant, who is tomb-raiding. She shows them a subterranean river that they use to escape the temple. Ryan then takes them back to his ship, locks up Bev and refuses to go back to examine the urn because there are Sontaran ships approaching. However, when Benny goes to her cabin she finds Bev there. She claims to have escaped and convinces Benny to help her steal a shuttle and return to Bellotron. Meanwhile, Ryan finds Bev still in her cell. In the burial chamber on the planet Bev tells Benny that she is in fact a Rutan using Bev's appearance as a disguise. The urn is actually a Rutan bomb that will release a virus deadly to Sontarans and which will destroy the planet. The Rutan has come to repair the weapon following its sabotage by the other Rutan, which was part of a breakaway, pacifist faction. Before it can operate the bomb, the Sontaran ships arrive and bombard the caves, killing the Rutan and Benny. However, it is then revealed that the pacifist Rutans captured Benny earlier and that the Benny in the cave was one of their number. As the Earth ship departs, Benny and Bev start to discuss a mutual friend...

TRIVIA

- Bev Tarrant previously appeared in the **Main Monthly Range** releases **The Genocide Machine #7** and **Dust Breeding #21**.
- This is the first time the Rutans would appear in a Big Finish play. Although mentioned, the Sontarans would not show up properly until the **Main Monthly Range** release **Heroes of Sontar #146** in April 2011. A Rutan would be the main villain in the Main Monthly Range release **Castle of Fear #127**.
- Mike Tucker was asked by Gary Russell to write a second **Bernice Summerfield** play with a stipulation being that he included a **Doctor Who** monster. It was Mike's decision to write about a Rutan.
- "Jason originally wanted Sontarans," Gary Russell recalls, "but I like Rutans more because they're shape changers."

PRODUCTION SUMMARY

"I made a firm decision that the fourth season of Benny plays should include monsters from **Doctor Who**. I was concerned about sales and I thought this would give the range a shot in the arm. In the end I had a trade-off. Jason wanted all **Who** monsters and I wanted the Galyari and the Grel. I loved **The Sandman**, we had the rights to them and Jac wanted to do a Grel story."
Gary Russell

WORKING TITLE(S)

The Double Time Incident, The Gallotron Incident.

RETURNING MONSTERS/CHARACTERS

Rutans, Sontarans, Bev Tarrant, Irving Braxiatel, Joseph.

THE DRACONIAN RAGE

#4.2

SYNOPSIS

Bernice is invited to Draconia to identify a relic. Arriving at the Imperial Palace, Benny meets Lord Vasar. He tells her the relic was found on a planet called Tranagus on which 20 million Draconians recently committed suicide. Meanwhile, Lord Paranesh and Emperor Shen are discussing the incident on Tranagus and the seeming spread of unrest in the same sector of space. Shen is angry that the humans are referring to it as "the Draconian Rage". Bernice is shocked to discover that the relic is an object she is familiar with – the skull of Vilus Kull (which she encountered in **The Dark Flame #42**). Paranesh and Vasar are revealed to be members of the cult of the Dark Flame. They believe that when she was touched by the Dark Flame on Marran Alpha, the evil was trapped in her mind. They then drill a hole in her head to release it. Later, Vasar visits her and explains that Tranagus was the birth place of Vilus Kull and the

cult has spread throughout the Draconian empire. Paranesh intends to use the cult to incite a war between Draconia and Earth as well as overthrow Shen. Vasar says he is only working with Paranesh so that he can undermine him. As such he intends to help Benny escape so she can warn the Earth authorities. He gives her a gun and shows her to a hatch behind which he says is a shuttle bay. However, when Benny goes through she finds Emperor Shen. Under the control of the Dark Flame, Benny shoots the Draconian dead. Paranesh orders her arrested and knows that a human assassination of the Draconian Emperor will bring about the war he craves. Just then, Vasar appears and shoots Paranesh. Shen then recovers. It is revealed that they have used her to uncover Paranesh's treachery. However, Shen then kills Vasar saying he will have no cultists in his government. Disgusted, Benny leaves Draconia vowing never to return.

TRIVIA

- This play serves as a sequel to the **Main Monthly Range** title **The Dark Flame #42** released five months earlier and also written by Trevor Baxendale.
- Philip Bretherton (Emperor Shen) is best known for his role as Alistair Deacon in the BBC TV sitcom *As Time Goes By* that ran between 1992 and 2005.
- This slot was originally supposed to be for Jac Rayner's **The Grel Escape**, which would eventually appear as release **#5.1**.
- Miles Richardson recorded his scenes for the next play in the morning of the studio session for this.

PRODUCTION SUMMARY

"Jac was busy with the BBC books because she was editor of that range and it became apparent that she couldn't write the script in time. So I called up Trevor and asked if he'd like to do me a kind of sequel to his Seventh Doctor script. I told him it had to have Draconians in it. I remember that I wanted the cult explained a bit more but all in all I think his script was really good, really dark. Ed Salt liked it, too, and it's always important to impress your directors!"
Gary Russell

WORKING TITLE(S)

Draconians.

RETURNING MONSTERS/CHARACTERS

Draconians, Irving Braxiatel, Joseph.

CREW

Writer	**Trevor Baxendale**
Director	**Edward Salt**
Producer	**Gary Russell**
Executive Producer	**Jason Haigh-Ellery**
Music and Sound Design	**David Darlington**
Cover Art	**Adrian Salmon**

CAST

Bernice Summerfield	**Lisa Bowerman**
Irving Braxiatel	**Miles Richardson**
Emperor Shen	**Philip Bretherton**
Lord Paranesh	**Kraig Thornber**
Lord Vasar	**Johnson Willis**
Joseph	**Steven Wickham**
Commander Ryan	**Karl Hansen**
Captain Quilby	**Peter John**

TECHNICAL

Story Code	**BFPCD17**
Recorded Date	**27 Jun 2003**
Release Date	**August 2003**
Place of Recording	**The Moat Studios, London**
Number of CDs	**1**
Total Duration	**72' 32"**
Number of Episodes	**1**
ISBN	**1-84435-067-3**

#4.3 THE POISON SEAS

CREW

Writer	**David Bailey**
Director	**Edward Salt**
Producer	**Gary Russell**
Executive Producer	**Jason Haigh-Ellery**
Music and Sound Design	**David Darlington**
Cover Art	**Adrian Salmon**

CAST

Bernice Summerfield	**Lisa Bowerman**
Irving Braxiatel	**Miles Richardson**
Principal Lurnix	**Ifan Huw Dafydd**
Clinician Nedda	**Nicky Goldie**
Joanne Carver	**Jenny Livesay**
Ressix	**Matt Dineen**

TECHNICAL

Story Code	**BFPCD18**
Recorded Date	**28 June 2003**
Release Date	**September 2003**
Place of Recording	**The Moat Studios, London**
Number of CDs	**1**
Total Duration	**63' 16"**
Number of Episodes	**1**
ISBN	**1-84435-040-1**

SYNOPSIS

When Calabraxian terrorists threaten a colony of Sea Devils on the planet Chosan, Bernice is sent to uncover a terrorist agent. She hires Joanne Carver to take her to the colony, but Carver is the leader of the terrorists. When the defences are lowered for Benny to enter, Carver sneaks in too. However, the Sea Devils have other problems. Scientists Nedda and Ressix have discovered that a protein in the sea of Chosan is mutating the Sea Devil RNA. The Eocene's leader, Lurnix, seems unconcerned but it is revealed that he is a terrorist agent. Carver plants a bomb, but her escape route is cut off when her submarine is attacked by Chosan sharks. Benny tells Nedda that Lurnix is under suspicion by the Earth Reptile Council and they go to confront the leader. However, Carver captures Benny and, when Lurnix reveals he is under the control of the protein, he kills Ressix as Nedda escapes. Lurnix then finds Carver and attacks her, too, saying that the planet does not belong to the humans or the Sea Devils. Nedda finds Benny and the bomb. She frees her friend and calls in a security team to defuse the bomb. Nedda and Benny head back to the Sea Devil's lab where she concludes that the protein is a sentient gestalt entity. Together they track down Lurnix who has opened the colony's floodgates. His plan is to let all the Sea Devils become infected with the protein, giving it an army with which to wipe out the humans. Benny sends Nedda to evacuate the Sea Devils while she looks for Carver. When Bernice finds her, she convinces the terrorist to give her the bomb's remote detonator in return for her life. When the Sea Devils are all safe, Benny detonates the bomb, killing Lurnix but destroying the gestalt protein in the process. The Sea Devils will have to find another planet to settle on and Carver will have to stand trial. Benny contacts Braxiatel to tell him the news, but the transmission is cut short and Benny rushes back to the Collection to see what is wrong...

TRIVIA

- This is the only time the Sea Devils (Gary Russell's favourite monster) have appeared in a Big Finish audio drama, although the Silurians appeared in the **Main Monthly Range** release **Bloodtide #22**.
- The planet Chosan was visited by Benny in **The Secret of Cassandra #2.1**.
- The end of **The Poison Seas** leads into the short story collection *Life During Wartime*.
- Gary Russell had initially wanted Gareth Roberts and Clayton Hickman to close the season with a story that featured Gareth's alien race, the Chelonians. "I originally wanted them to include Banto Zame [from **The One Doctor #27**] as well," Gary says.

PRODUCTION SUMMARY

"Because Clay and Gareth were busy on a **Doctor Who** script, I rang up David and invited him to send me a proposal. I still wanted a Who monster in it and I was coming up with all sorts of crazy ideas, like the Malus, but eventually we settled on the Sea Devils. Why? We'll never know because I can't remember!"
Gary Russell

WORKING TITLE(S)

The Sea Devils.

RETURNING MONSTERS/CHARACTERS

Sea Devils, Irving Braxiatel.

Check box - CD ☐

DALEK WAR – CHAPTER TWO

SYNOPSIS

The Daleks threaten to exterminate the humans unless Suz surrenders to them, but she takes a gun and threatens to shoot herself, taking the Emperor with her. The crew are taken captive and placed in a cargo hold. There, Suz and Alby have a quick catch up, and he tells her he found Morli on board the abandoned research centre. Morli has a child-like manner, describing herself as a patient of the good Daleks, and it becomes clear she's the product of the alliance Daleks' experiments. Alby discovered the Emperor's casing was taken there, but when the enemy Daleks arrived they recovered it and left a convincing hologram behind. The enemy soon arrive at the hospital, and take Alby and Morli prisoner, and return in his ship to the rendezvous. Kalendorf is clashing with the Mentor over his strategies, especially the destruction of the cargo freighter and Mirana's presence on the *Defiant*, but the Mentor insists she still has confidence in her commander in chief. Back on the ship, the Daleks try to gas the humans, but Alby, Suz, Mirana and pilot Marber escape, the latter two making off in an escape pod. When Kalendorf and his crew arrive in the solar system, they find Jupiter has been terraformed and despite the Mentor's advice to the contrary, he elects to land some troops on the planet, which offers perfect conditions for human beings. The Mentor's sensors also detect the approach of the *Defiant*, which isn't returning signals from the alliance. The Daleks paralyse Alby and take Suz prisoner again. They scan her brain and she converses with the Emperor Dalek in her mind. When Suz regains consciousness, to Alby's horror, she declares, "I… We… I… am the Emperor of the Daleks!"

TRIVIA

- This is the first time since the very first **Dalek Empire** release (**Invasion of the Daleks #1.1**) that Alby Brooks and Susan Mendes actually meet.

PRODUCTION SUMMARY

"I think this story is where I focussed on the personal drama and didn't include quite so much of the epic war going on around the characters. And of course I had the reunion between Alby and Suz. I wanted it to be less a dramatic love scene and more an awkward meeting after so many years. It seemed more real. I was also quite pleased with Dannie Carr's Morli. Her voice was a nice contrast to most of the RP accents we had and Teresa's American accent, of course."
Nicholas Briggs

WORKING TITLE(S)

None.

CREW

Writer	**Nicholas Briggs**
Director	**Nicholas Briggs**
Producers	**Jason Haigh-Ellery**
	Nicholas Briggs
Executive Producer (BBC)	**Jacqueline Rayner**
Music and Sound Design	**Nicholas Briggs**
Cover Art	**Clayton Hickman**
Theme	**Nicholas Briggs**

CAST

Susan Mendes	**Sarah Mowat**
Mirana	**Teresa Gallagher**
Alby Brook	**Mark McDonnell**
Morli	**Dannie Carr**
Herrick	**Jeremy James**
Kalendorf	**Gareth Thomas**
Marber, Drudger	**Ian Brooker**
The Mentor	**Hannah Smith**
Siy Tarkov	**Steven Elder**
Saloran Haredew	**Karen Henson**
Daleks	**Nicholas Briggs**

TECHNICAL

Story Code	**BFPCDDE06**
Recorded Date	**27 October & 3, 4, 6 and 10 November 2002**
Release Date	**February 2003**
Place of Recording	**The Moat Studios, London**
Number of CDs	**1**
Total Duration	**58' 24"**
Number of Episodes	**1**
ISBN	**1-84435-019-3**

#2.3 DALEK WAR – CHAPTER THREE

CREW

Writer	**Nicholas Briggs**
Director	**Nicholas Briggs**
Producers	**Jason Haigh-Ellery**
	Nicholas Briggs
Executive Producer (BBC)	**Jacqueline Rayner**
Music and Sound Design	**Nicholas Briggs**
Cover Art	**Clayton Hickman**
Theme	**Nicholas Briggs**

CAST

Herrick, Trooper, Vaarga Man	**Jeremy James**
Kalendorf	**Gareth Thomas**
The Mentor	**Hannah Smith**
Scientist	**Simon Bridge**
Allenby	**Mark Donovan**
Sparks, Marber	**Ian Brooker**
Morli	**Dannie Carr**
Alby Brook	**Mark McDonnell**
Susan Mendes	**Sarah Mowat**
Mirana	**Teresa Gallagher**
Siy Tarkov	**Steven Elder**
Saloran Haredew	**Karen Henson**
Daleks	**Nicholas Briggs**

TECHNICAL

Story Code	**BFPCDDE07**
Recorded Date	**27 October & 3, 4, 6 and 10 November 2002**
Release Date	**March 2003**
Place of Recording	**The Moat Studios, London**
Number of CDs	**1**
Total Duration	**58' 44"**
Number of Episodes	**1**
ISBN	**1-84435-020-7**

SYNOPSIS

On board his ship the *Courageous*, Kalendorf is told of an unidentified transmission being made on an enemy Dalek frequency, but he is unperturbed. His ship is still receiving a signal from the *Defiant* as the first of the alliance troops touch down on Jupiter, where they find some strange plant life. Crew members are attacked by, and transformed into, Varga plants. Kalendorf orders his remaining troops to evacuate, but the Varga hybrids board the ships and attack the alliance fleet. Morli and Alby are with Suz when she wakes up, as herself. The enemy Daleks had temporarily awoken the Emperor as a test, and are happy to leave him dormant for now. In their escape pod, Mirana and Marber discuss Kalendorf's plan to rid the universe of the alliance Daleks, and she admits she didn't know what it was – she just trusted him – as they run out of fuel, then air. The Mentor confronts Kalendorf over the attack on the cargo freighter, Suz's survival, and his failed strategy on Jupiter. He is stripped of his command and is told he will be returned to Lopra Minor for brain correction. The enemy Daleks attack in force, allowing Kalendorf to escape and head for the *Defiant*. Morli has been thinking about Suz's survival. As her alliance Dalek mental conditioning kicks in, she realises that killing Suz would make their lives much easier. Morli tries to strangle Suz, but a Dalek arrives in time and exterminates her. Kalendorf boards the *Defiant*, and has a telepathic conference with Suz and reveals that his plan involves "pure destruction." Alby, untrusting of Kalendorf, who won't reveal his intentions, hears Suz announce that she intends to broadcast to the cosmos that the Angel of Mercy has returned and they have to work with the enemy Daleks to stop the Mentor's forces. Alby is horrified, and as Kalendorf prepares to transmit, a weapon discharges…

TRIVIA

- The murderous Varga plants first appeared in the 1965 TV story **Mission to the Unknown**. They also played a key role in the **I, Davros** Big Finish range (See Section 12) and appeared in the BBC online game, *City of the Daleks* in 2010.

PRODUCTION SUMMARY

"This is the one in this series where I upped the ante! We start to really see what the Mentor is capable of and why Kalendorf has been doing what he's been doing. I also wanted to make use of the good old Varga plants from the 60s. It's always nice to have bits and bobs from Dalek continuity for the fans – and I count myself among them!"
Nicholas Briggs

WORKING TITLE(S)

None.

DALEK WAR – CHAPTER FOUR

#2.4

SYNOPSIS

Some 2,500 years after the Dalek war, Saloran Haredew and Siy Tarkov discuss the Great Catastrophe. Haredew has been excavating the tomb of Kalendorf, and trying to find the cause of the Great Catastrophe which resulted in the collapse of civilisation across the galaxy. The tomb contains his memories, and they watch as Alby confronts Suz and Kalendorf, and a gun goes off. Suz shoots down her former lover, before the Daleks take her away to Earth. Three years pass, and Kalendorf is told an escape pod from the SS *Defiant* has been found and he goes to recover it. Once he boards the craft, he encounters an alliance Dalek, and is transported to face the Mentor. She wants to know why he betrayed her and the alliance to the enemy Daleks. He counters by telling her that he would rather live in a universe where he has freedom of thought. When Kalendorf tells her that he and the people of his universe will never give up, the Mentor withdraws her forces into their own reality. Kalendorf returns to the solar system and signals the enemy Daleks, saying he wants to see Suz. He is taken back to Earth where the Dalek Supreme brings him before her. She reveals that when she was taken by the Daleks they activated the dormant Emperor within her. It has retained her form, intending to broadcast to the universe again, urging the people to obey the Daleks. Kalendorf makes physical contact with her and they communicate telepathically. He finds Suz within the Emperor's mind and she takes over, sending a destructive wave throughout the Dalek command network, destroying everything, and forcing the destruction of many worlds and systems. Years later, Tarkov and Haredew realise this caused the Great Catastrophe. Tarkov has brought a recent recording with him, and it is unscrambled by Haredew's archaeological team. It is a Dalek, and they're coming back to conquer and destroy. Tarkov leaves to warn Earth…

TRIVIA

- This release also features a bonus CD of behind the scenes recordings: interviews, incidental music and even out-takes. It is called "Dalek Empire Strikes Back"!
- The play mentions the first Knight of Velyshaa, Sancroff, who appeared in the Main Monthly Range release **The Sirens of Time #1**.

PRODUCTION SUMMARY

"This was where I thought it would all end, really. The 'final end'! Ha! I should have known better. That's the thing about the Daleks: they never really go away; they never give up. They will always want to conquer and destroy – even hundreds of years after the events of the main storyline! It's only through the examples of the characters that fight the Daleks that there's a glimmer of hope – although it's never black and white…"
Nicholas Briggs

WORKING TITLE(S)

None.

CREW

Writer	**Nicholas Briggs**
Director	**Nicholas Briggs**
Producers	**Jason Haigh-Ellery**
	Nicholas Briggs
Executive Producer (BBC)	**Jacqueline Rayner**
Music and Sound Design	**Nicholas Briggs**
Cover Art	**Clayton Hickman**
Theme	**Nicholas Briggs**

CAST

Siy Tarkov	**Steven Elder**
Trooper	**David Sax**
Saloran Haredew	**Karen Henson**
Alby Brook	**Mark McDonnell**
Kalendorf	**Gareth Thomas**
Susan Mendes	**Sarah Mowat**
Godwin	**Helen Goldwyn**
Command, Computer, Technician	**Jack Galagher**
The Mentor	**Hannah Smith**
Herrick	**Jeremy James**
Daleks	**Nicholas Briggs**

TECHNICAL

Story Code	**BFPCDDE08**
Recorded Date	**27 October & 3, 4, 6 and 10 November 2002**
Release Date	**April 2003**
Place of Recording	**The Moat Studios, London**
Number of CDs	**2**
Total Duration	**139' 15"**
Number of Episodes	**2**
Duration of Episodes	**1 (67' 39")**
	2 (71' 36")
ISBN	**1-84435-021-5**

#3.1 THE EXTERMINATORS

CREW

Writer	**Nicholas Briggs**
Director	**Nicholas Briggs**
Producers	**Jason Haigh-Ellery**
	Nicholas Briggs
Executive Producer (BBC)	**Jacqueline Rayner**
Music and Sound Design	**Nicholas Briggs**
Cover Art	**Clayton Hickman**
Theme	**Nicholas Briggs**

CAST

Galanar	**David Tennant**
Selestru	**William Gaunt**
Frey Saxton	**Ishia Bennison**
Siy Tarkov	**Steven Elder**
Suz	**Sarah Mowat**
Kaymee	**Laura Rees**
Amur	**Claudia Elmhirst**
Japrice	**Octavia Walters**
Culver	**Peter Forbes**
Mivas	**Dot Smith**
Telligan	**Greg Donaldson**
Saloran	**Karen Henson**
Morli	**Dannie Carr**
Sergic, Snubby	**Jeremy James**
Seth	**Sean Jackson**
Mietok	**Ian Brooker**
Roozell	**Jane Goddard**
Chauley	**Philip Wolff**
Jake	**Colin McIntyre**
The Daleks	**Nicholas Briggs**

TECHNICAL

Story Code	**BFPCDDE09**
Recorded Date	**Between November 2003 and April 2004**
Release Date	**May 2004**
Place of Recording	**The Moat Studios, London**
Number of CDs	**1**
Total Duration	**72' 29"**
Number of Episodes	**1**
ISBN	**1-84435-082-7**

SYNOPSIS

Siy Tarkov sends out a distress signal to the galaxy, warning of an imminent Dalek invasion. The crew of his ship have died after the outbreak of a plague… Young Kaymee Arnod arrives on Graxis Major to join up with the Graxis Wardens, a group of ecologists led by commander Frey Saxton. Years after sending his warning, Tarkov's message – which was buried by the Galactic Union council – is investigated by agent Galanar, on the orders of his boss, security chief Georgi Selestru. The Galactic Union has distanced itself from the Border Worlds fearing that the NFS plague – Neurotransmitter Failure Syndrome – would be brought into the Union worlds. The Daleks have contacted the Confederation of Border Planets, offering them Variant 7, a treatment which can be used on NFS to cure its victims. Tarkov meets with Selestru, who tells him that his ship drifted in space for 20 years before being recovered, and it took another two years for his cryopod to be brought home to Planet 9. He had contracted NFS but was partially treated, leaving him with a constant buzzing in his head and causing his speech to stutter. On Graxis Major, the Wardens find one of their number dead and Saxton informs Provost Carneill of the Borderer Confederation of the situation. More Wardens then find what appears to be a drillhead, sticking out of the ground in the jungle, and are attacked by a Dalek, which jams their communications. It is destroyed as a ship approaches the planet with Carneill onboard, and he overrules Saxton on contacting the Galactic Council security forces. The Wardens suspect he knows more about the situation than he has let on. He lands and declares the planet to be under Borderer jurisdiction, as a party of Daleks disembark from his ship.

TRIVIA

- This release sees David Tennant (Galanar), facing up to the Daleks, a year before he took on the slightly more prominent role of the Tenth Doctor on TV. He is best-known for his role as the Tenth Doctor.
- William Gaunt (Selestru) is well-known for his lead roles in *The Champions* and the sitcom *No Place Like Home* as well as playing the part of Orcini in the 1985 TV story **Revelation Of The Daleks**.
- The original idea for **Dalek Empire III** was to have an anthology series. Nick asked Rob Shearman and Clayton Hickman to pitch for the series but in the end, all six parts were written by Nick.

PRODUCTION SUMMARY

"The original idea for **Dalek Empire III** was to have an anthology series. I asked Rob Shearman and Clayton Hickman to pitch for the series but they said they'd rather hear what happened next according to me, which was very nice of them! And it was obvious really where I should kick it off from and after conversations with John Ainsworth I started writing it. Then I showed it to Rob and John and as a result I started to flesh out the idea of the Graxis Wardens."
Nicholas Briggs

WORKING TITLE(S)

None.

THE HEALERS

SYNOPSIS

The Graxis Wardens are outraged as the Daleks access their database and absorb its contents. They protest, and one of their number is exterminated. The wardens in their headquarters, the Den, are rounded up, and confined to quarters by Carneill and the Daleks. The Daleks reveal they plan to geoform the planet and the others in the Graxis system, to turn them into healing zones to combat the NFS plague. Tarkov, still in pain from the side effects of his condition, appears before the Galactic Union council and he tries to warn them of the Daleks. They dismiss his fears, saying he is mentally unstable and Saloran Haredew has been discredited. Galanar, posing as eccentric medic Dr Dennis Grentrum, has crossed into the Border Worlds, hoping to find evidence of the Daleks' existence and their aggressive intentions, in the hope he can convince the Galactic Union of their menace. Tarkov, meanwhile, has discovered that he

has been declared dead, but is shocked when he goes to an address and finds that he has a daughter, Amur, whom he never knew existed. Back on Graxis Major, the wardens manage to escape from the clutches of the Daleks and leave the Den. In the jungle, they encounter more of their colleagues who were on patrol, as Kaymee starts to complain of having a sore head. Galanar wakes up to find himself on Scalanis VIII, which surprises him, and discovers that someone has activated a sleep inducer in his travel bay. He expected to arrive on Scalanis V, and is told that Scalanis VIII was geoformed and had a healing zone created on it. The Daleks are monitoring him as he is suspicious of what's going on, but they note a high level of electrical activity in his brain as he's shown NFS victims. In the Serifia Galaxy, the new female Dalek Supreme is connected to the command network. She tells her forces: "Now it begins…"

TRIVIA

- In this play the Daleks pretend to be "healers", a title that their creator, Davros, applied to himself ('The Great Healer') in the 1985 TV story **Revelation of the Daleks** (which, as stated before, starred William Gaunt).
- David Tennant asked Nick Briggs for a part in **Dalek Empire II** at a party hosted by Mark Gatiss.

PRODUCTION SUMMARY

"What I'd done with the last series was to contrast love with the hatred of the Daleks and it wasn't quite as diametrically opposed as I had originally thought because Daleks have a passion to them. So I focussed on the idea of friendship. And I was so lucky to have David Tennant playing Galanar, not only because he's brilliant but also because I really missed the actors from the original **Dalek Empire** series!"
Nicholas Briggs

WORKING TITLE(S)

None.

CREW

Writer	**Nicholas Briggs**
Director	**Nicholas Briggs**
Producers	**Jason Haigh-Ellery Nicholas Briggs**
Executive Producer (BBC)	**Jacqueline Rayner**
Music and Sound Design	**Nicholas Briggs**
Cover Art	**Clayton Hickman**
Theme	**Nicholas Briggs**

CAST

Galanar	**David Tennant**
Selestru	**William Gaunt**
Frey Saxton	**Ishia Bennison**
Siy Tarkov	**Steven Elder**
Suz	**Sarah Mowat**
Kaymee	**Laura Rees**
Amur	**Claudia Elmhirst**
Japrice	**Octavia Walters**
Culver	**Peter Forbes**
Carneill	**Oliver Hume**
Mivas	**Dot Smith**
Telligan	**Greg Donaldson**
Saloran	**Karen Henson**
Morli	**Dannie Carr**
Sergic/Snubby	**Jeremy James**
Seth	**Sean Jackson**
Mietok	**Ian Brooker**
Roozell	**Jane Goddard**
Chauley	**Philip Wolff**
Jake	**Colin McIntyre**
The Daleks	**Nicholas Briggs**

TECHNICAL

Story Code	**BFPCDDE10**
Recorded Date	**Between November 2003 and April 2004**
Release Date	**June 2004**
Place of Recording	**The Moat Studios, London**
Number of CDs	**1**
Total Duration	**70' 25"**
Number of Episodes	**1**
ISBN	**1-84435-083-5**

#3.3 | THE SURVIVORS

CREW

Writer	**Nicholas Briggs**
Director	**Nicholas Briggs**
Producers	**Jason Haigh-Ellery**
	Nicholas Briggs
Executive Producer (BBC)	**Jacqueline Rayner**
Music and Sound Design	**Nicholas Briggs**
Cover Art	**Clayton Hickman**
Theme	**Nicholas Briggs**

CAST

Galanar	**David Tennant**
Selestru	**William Gaunt**
Frey Saxton	**Ishia Bennison**
Siy Tarkov	**Steven Elder**
Suz	**Sarah Mowat**
Kaymee	**Laura Rees**
Amur	**Claudia Elmhirst**
Japrice	**Octavia Walters**
Culver	**Peter Forbes**
Carneill	**Oliver Hume**
Mivas	**Dot Smith**
Telligan	**Greg Donaldson**
Saloran	**Karen Henson**
Morli	**Dannie Carr**
Sergic, Snubby	**Jeremy James**
Seth	**Sean Jackson**
Mietok	**Ian Brooker**
Roozell	**Jane Goddard**
Chauley	**Philip Wolff**
Jake	**Colin McIntyre**
The Daleks	**Nicholas Briggs**

TECHNICAL

Story Code	**BFPCDDE11**
Recorded Date	**Between November 2003 and April 2004**
Release Date	**July 2004**
Place of Recording	**The Moat Studios, London**
Number of CDs	**1**
Total Duration	**73' 43"**
Number of Episodes	**1**
ISBN	**1-84435-084-3**

SYNOPSIS

Galanar enquires about who created the healing zones, asking if it was the Daleks, but is ignored when he mentions their name. Amur meets Selestru to discuss Tarkov, and she offers to find out more about the NFS plague and the Daleks. Kaymee, who's feeling worse, joins the other wardens as they try to escape Graxis Major on their ship Ranger 1. Onboard they encounter Carneill, who is keen to find a cure as he lost his whole family to NFS, and he decides to let them go. However, Saxton is informed that Kaymee has contracted NFS and she is left behind with Carneill to be cured by the Daleks. Tarkov, posing as a current victim of NFS, is accompanied by Amur as they make their way to the Border Worlds to find a cure for his condition – but in reality are trying to find out more about the Daleks. Galanar is shown a patient who has been treated with the cure for NFS, Variant 7, and appears to be recovering. He is left to monitor the patients but disappears off Dalek scanners. They soon find him following the Variant 7 supply line which is intravenously treating the patients, but as his brain's electrical activity increases, he disappears from their scanners again. Selestru is informed by Bulis Mietok of the Galactic Union that Tarkov's daughter was killed in an accident with his wife 15 years previously. The Dalek Supreme is told of Galanar's disappearance and states she knows what Galanar is, then orders him to be captured. She wants to speak with him. She knows he will be unable to maintain his electro-chemical levels without becoming visible. When Galanar becomes tired, he is captured and brought to speak with the Supreme. The Supreme says she thought he had been destroyed in the Great Catastrophe, before revealing: "You were created by the Daleks…"

TRIVIA

- This play shares its title with that of Terry Nation's 1970s series – and its short-lived 2009 re-make – *Survivors* about the near-extinction of the human race by a virus.
- This release also features bonus tracks of behind the scenes recordings: interviews, incidental music and even out-takes.

PRODUCTION SUMMARY

"With a lot of the **Dalek Empire** characters, I wanted to shade them in tones of grey. I wanted to make their motives questionable and allegiances unclear. I think it's vastly more interesting if you find out about a character by peeling away the layers rather than have someone who wears their motivation on their sleeve!"
Nicholas Briggs

WORKING TITLE(S)

None.

Check box - CD ☐ MP3 ☐

THE DEMONS

#3.4

SYNOPSIS

Susan Mendes recalls travelling through the Dalek Empire command network, destroying everything, as the Daleks realise what is happening. They prepare an isolated Dalek mutant to absorb the destructive wave Suz has generated, but their plan only has a 40 per cent chance of success. Suz and the creature merge, creating a new Dalek Supreme. On Planet 9, Bulis Mietok of the Galactic Union tells Selestru he knows of Galanar's mission. Galanar, meanwhile, is told of his origins by the Supreme – he is a Demon, who was found in a cryo tube on an abandoned space station, hidden in a particle cloud, by Selestru. He was a creation of the Daleks, and is then ordered to tend to a Variant 7 patient, Tarkov. The Wardens aboard Ranger 1 come under fire from a Dalek ship, but confuse then destroy it. They lay in a course for the Scalannis System. The Supreme summons Amur, a Dalek agent who was tasked with bringing Tarkov to them, as they know he has knowledge of the Daleks. Amur is shown an image of Tarkov and Galanar, whom she recognises – she too is a Demon. The Supreme wants her to find out where Velyshaa is, as it has a data store which could prove to be dangerous to the future of the Daleks. Amur tries to convince Galanar to join forces with her and the Daleks – and he recognises her as Elaria. They share memories – they, plus Morli, were once criminally insane but treated by the alliance Daleks to become super-strong beings that can change their form. Elaria realises she imprinted on the enemy Daleks, who found her on the space station. Galanar and Elaria go on the run with Tarkov, as she realises her true purpose, to defeat the enemy Daleks. They plan to steal a Dalek ship and escape, but are surrounded by a platoon of Daleks…

TRIVIA

- This story links back to the plot of **Dalek Empire II**.

PRODUCTION SUMMARY

"I really wanted to flesh out all the characters and situations in the third series and because I had six releases in which to do that I felt I could take my foot off the accelerator and take the time to look around, as it were. We had the whole backstory to Galanar being one of the Demons and how Suz had become the Dalek Supreme, and I didn't want to shirk those stories."
Nicholas Briggs

WORKING TITLE(S)

None.

CREW

Writer	**Nicholas Briggs**
Director	**Nicholas Briggs**
Producers	**Jason Haigh-Ellery Gary Russell**
Executive Producer (BBC)	**Jacqueline Rayner**
Music and Sound Design	**Nicholas Briggs**
Cover Art	**Clayton Hickman**
Theme	**Nicholas Briggs**

CAST

Galanar	**David Tennant**
Selestru	**William Gaunt**
Frey Saxton	**Ishia Bennison**
Siy Tarkov	**Steven Elder**
Suz	**Sarah Mowat**
Kaymee	**Laura Rees**
Amur	**Claudia Elmhirst**
Japrice	**Octavia Walters**
Culver	**Peter Forbes**
Carneill	**Oliver Hume**
Mivas	**Dot Smith**
Telligan	**Greg Donaldson**
Saloran	**Karen Henson**
Morli	**Dannie Carr**
Sergic/Snubby	**Jeremy James**
Seth	**Sean Jackson**
Mietok	**Ian Brooker**
Roozell	**Jane Goddard**
Chauley	**Philip Wolff**
Jake	**Colin McIntyre**
The Daleks	**Nicholas Briggs**

TECHNICAL

Story Code	**BFPCDDE12**
Recorded Date	**Between November 2003 and April 2004**
Release Date	**August 2004**
Place of Recording	**The Moat Studios, London**
Number of CDs	**1**
Total Duration	**72' 39"**
Number of Episodes	**1**
ISBN	**1-84435-085-1**

#3.5

THE WARRIORS

CREW

Writer	**Nicholas Briggs**
Director	**Nicholas Briggs**
Producers	**Jason Haigh-Ellery**
	Nicholas Briggs
Executive Producer (BBC)	**Jacqueline Rayner**
Music and Sound Design	**Nicholas Briggs**
Cover Art	**Clayton Hickman**
Theme	**Nicholas Briggs**

CAST

Galanar	**David Tennant**
Selestru	**William Gaunt**
Frey Saxton	**Ishia Bennison**
Siy Tarkov	**Steven Elder**
Suz	**Sarah Mowat**
Kaymee	**Laura Rees**
Amur	**Claudia Elmhirst**
Japrice	**Octavia Walters**
Culver	**Peter Forbes**
Carneill	**Oliver Hume**
Mivas	**Dot Smith**
Telligan	**Greg Donaldson**
Saloran	**Karen Henson**
Morli	**Dannie Carr**
Sergic, Snubby	**Jeremy James**
Seth	**Sean Jackson**
Mietok	**Ian Brooker**
Roozell	**Jane Goddard**
Chauley	**Philip Wolff**
Jake	**Colin McIntyre**
The Daleks	**Nicholas Briggs**

TECHNICAL

Story Code	**BFPCDDE13**
Recorded Date	**Between November 2003 and April 2004**
Release Date	**October 2004**
Place of Recording	**The Moat Studios, London**
Number of CDs	**1**
Total Duration	**73' 31"**
Number of Episodes	**1**
ISBN	**1-84435-086-X**

SYNOPSIS

Kaymee Arnod has been treated with Variant 7 and made a full recovery, impressing Carneill. Millions have arrived in the Graxis System and been cured, but Carneill tells Kaymee that none of them have returned home and some have gone missing. Kaymee, who regularly dreams of her dad, sleepwalks, and finds herself in a room full of Dalek spare parts on a conveyor belt. The Daleks feed her a special nutrition and monitor her condition as the first patient of the healing zone. Carneill is feeling unwell due to a rise in radiation in the healing zone, while Kaymee feels great. The Daleks want to find the missing Wardens, so Carneill offers to take Kaymee to find them, claiming she knows where they will be. Kaymee says her skin is feeling strange and her fingers are sticking together, and is mentally becoming quite distant. Carneill tries to convince her to leave, but she refuses, even though the Daleks have done something to her DNA. A Dalek arrives, and since Carneill knows what's happening, is exterminated. With few ships near Scalannis VIII, as the Daleks prepare a fleet to find Velyshaa, Ranger 1 easily swoops down to the planet and rescues Galanar and friends. They tell Saxton their story and agree to set course for Velyshaa to get the evidence needed to warn the Galactic Union, but their flight will take them seven months. As they depart, Saxton is still unsure what the Daleks are getting out of curing the plague. The Dalek Supreme is told mutations are now underway in all healing zones, as a battleship follows Ranger 1 on its course to Velyshaa, ready to attack on her orders…

TRIVIA

- Ian Brooker (Mietock) is a veteran of many Big Finish productions, including the very first **Dalek Empire** release, **Invasion of the Daleks #1.1**. He is an experienced voice actor, and some fans may recognise him as Wayne Foley, resident Radio Borsetshire DJ in *The Archers*, who made a brief return to the legendary Radio 4 drama in 2011, during the Bridge Farm E.coli scandal!

PRODUCTION SUMMARY

"I had to pull all the strands together here with Kaymee, the plague and what Variant 7 actually does. I also had to get Galanar away from the danger I'd left him in and of course I had the Wardens' ship to do that! It was interesting because I didn't want them all to be too friendly towards each other – why would you be when you were in the middle of such a bloody conflict – so there's a lot of suspicion that they have to get over in order to trust one another."
Nicholas Briggs

WORKING TITLE(S)

None.

Check box - CD ☐ MP3 ☐

THE FUTURE

#3.6

SYNOPSIS

The medical staff on Scalannis VIII discovers there are high levels of radiation on the planet, while on Ranger 1 Elaria hides in the engine room. She's struggling to come to terms with her conditioning to obey the enemy Daleks, while knowing what they're doing is wrong, and she goads Galanar about his morals. Galanar and Tarkov strike up a real friendship during the lengthy journey to Velyshaa. As Ranger 1 finally gets close to the planet, their sensors bounce off it and they realise a Dalek ship is in pursuit. The crew wonder whether Elaria has been signalling them their position all along. She denies she has, although every fibre of her being still wants to serve the Daleks. Elaria then details the Dalek plan to them, having first created the NFS plague and released it into the galaxy, then offering to help cure it when it had taken grip. However, their cure has a little added something, a command to change human DNA into

Dalek DNA. This will help bolster Dalek numbers which were massively depleted after the Great Catastrophe. Ranger 1 lands on Velyshaa and they find Saloran Hardrew, who gives them another copy of the evidence from the tomb of Kalendorf, to show the Daleks are a menace. A fight breaks out between the remaining Graxis Wardens and the newly arrived Daleks, as Galanar, Elaria and Tarkov board the Dalek ship and transmit Kalendorf's memories to the Galactic Union. But the Daleks arrive and take them captive, exposing Tarkov to radiation which triggers a mutation in him. Elaria mocks Galanar's optimism again, to the point he turns on her and kills her. Galanar speaks to the Supreme, telling her the Daleks will never understand the concept of friendship and why they will never be able to break the humans. The Supreme wants to know more, so Galanar says, "Let me tell you about my friend Siy Tarkov…"

TRIVIA

- Ishia Bennison (Frey Saxton) is best known for the role of Guizin Osmond in the very early days of *EastEnders*, playing the role from 1985 to 1989. She has appeared in many TV shows on UK screens, including *Bergerac*, *The Bill*, *Coronation Street*, *Holby City*, and also appeared with Fifth Doctor Peter Davison in the hit ITV drama *At Home with the Braithwaites*.

PRODUCTION SUMMARY

"I wanted everything to be ominous and started that off by having the Daleks simply killing people in the most casual of ways. I think that's what makes the Daleks so terrifying: they don't think about it; if you're of no use to them, they'll just kill you. I took exactly the same approach with **To The Death #4.10** many years later. And it still works. It's still shocking."
Nicholas Briggs

WORKING TITLE(S)

None.

CREW

Writer	**Nicholas Briggs**
Director	**Nicholas Briggs**
Producers	**Jason Haigh-Ellery**
	Gary Russell
Executive Producer (BBC)	**Jacqueline Rayner**
Music and Sound Design	**Nicholas Briggs**
Cover Art	**Clayton Hickman**
Theme	**Nicholas Briggs**

CAST

Galanar	**David Tennant**
Selestru	**William Gaunt**
Frey Saxton	**Ishia Bennison**
Siy Tarkov	**Steven Elder**
Suz	**Sarah Mowat**
Kaymee	**Laura Rees**
Amur	**Claudia Elmhirst**
Japrice	**Octavia Walters**
Culver	**Peter Forbes**
Carneill	**Oliver Hume**
Mivas	**Dot Smith**
Telligan	**Greg Donaldson**
Saloran	**Karen Henson**
Morli	**Dannie Carr**
Sergic/Snubby	**Jeremy James**
Seth	**Sean Jackson**
Mietok	**Ian Brooker**
Roozell	**Jane Goddard**
Chauley	**Philip Wolff**
Jake	**Colin McIntyre**
The Daleks	**Nicholas Briggs**

TECHNICAL

Story Code	**BFPCDDE14**
Recorded Date	**Between November 2003 and April 2004**
Release Date	**August 2004**
Place of Recording	**The Moat Studios, London**
Number of CDs	**1**
Total Duration	**72' 39"**
Number of Episodes	**1**
ISBN	**1-84435-087-8**

#4.1 THE FEARLESS – PART I

CREW

Writer	**Nicholas Briggs**
Director	**Nicholas Briggs**
Producers	**Jason Haigh-Ellery**
	Nicholas Briggs
Executive Producer (BBC)	**Jacqueline Rayner**
Music	**Nicholas Briggs**
Sound Design	**Chris Snyder**
	Nicholas Briggs
Cover Art	**Alex Mallinson**
Theme	**Nicholas Briggs**

CAST

Agnes Landen	**Maureen O'Brien**
The Daleks	**Nicholas Briggs**
Susan Mendes	**Sarah Mowat**
Lt Carlisle	**John Schwab**
Salus Kade	**Noel Clarke**
Egan Fisk	**Oliver Mellor**
Kennedy	**David Yip**
Lajitta	**Ginita Jimenez**
Colonel Baxter	**Colin Spaull**
General Croft/Shuttle Pilot	**Ian Brooker**
Computer/Pilot/Aide	**Sean Connolly**
Gaz	**Alex Mallinson**
Flight Control	**Esther Ruth Elliott**

TECHNICAL

Story Code	**BFPCDDE15**
Recorded Date	**16th, 17th, 18th, 23rd and 24th July 2007**
Release Date	**October 2007**
Place of Recording	**The Moat Studios, London**
Number of CDs	**1**
Total Duration	**61' 06"**
Number of Episodes	**1**
ISBN	**978-1-84435-300-2**

SYNOPSIS

As the Daleks conquer humanity with the assistance of Susan Mendez, Commander Agnes Landens has an idea to turn the tide of the war. She wants to create a division of Spacers, a human-controlled, super-strengthened spacesuit, to fight back against the Daleks. Made from an ultra-strong fabric, fused with an energy-source to create a new battle armour, it is strong enough to propel its user between solar systems, and has weapons powerful enough to crack open Dalek casings. On struggling colony world Talis Minor, Salus Kade is fighting hard to help the troubled planet survive. Earth Alliance Spacers arrive on a recruiting mission to join the Space Corps Cadets. When no one steps forward, Colonel Baxter conscripts all men and women of fighting age. Kade goes with them, leaving his wife Lajitta and daughter Kiri behind. Their ship comes under fire from Daleks and crashes towards Talis Minor, but Kade's quick thinking and skills avert a serious crash. The Daleks land, and take Lajitta and some of her friends hostage. However, Kade soon arrives and they destroy the invaders. Kade goes on the run with his friend Egan Fisk and Space Sergeant Kennedy. They hide from the Daleks in the mountains, then Landen arrives with her Spacer troops and wipe out the Dalek platoon. Landen spots a lot of potential in Kade and wants to recruit him. He signs up and quickly establishes himself as a leader of men, who inspires his troops, quickly becoming a lieutenant. Landen declares him the best Spacer she's ever seen. Kade soon leads his men into conflict with a Dalek ship, codenamed Dead Hand, which drains their power. The Daleks arm their missiles, target Kade's ship and open fire…

TRIVIA

- The role of Salus Kade is played by Noel Clarke, well-known to **Doctor Who** fans as Mickey Smith in the TV series between 2005 and 2009. He is also a BAFTA award-winning film actor, screenwriter and director.
- Nick Briggs is looking at adapting the story used in **Dalek Empire IV** as a movie script – although without any Daleks in it!
- Colin Spaull (Colonel Baxter) appeared one of a handful of actors to have appeared in both the classic and new series of **Doctor Who**. He played Lilt in Revelation of the Daleks, directed by Graeme Harper, who would cast him again in the 2006 story **Rise of the Cybermen/The Age of Steel** as Mr Crane – in which Nicholas Briggs provided the voices of the Cybermen. Colin played the role of Uncle Lindsay in the first episode of Big Finish's **Graceless**.
- Oliver Mellor (Egan Fisk) is best known as Doctor Carter in soap opera **Coronation Street**, and also had a minor role as Matt in the **Doctor Who** TV story **Army of Ghosts**.

PRODUCTION SUMMARY

"In order to make a splash we have to make announcements that will really get people's attention and having Noel in the new series was certainly a way of doing that. He and I are mates so I hoped he'd say 'yes' – and he did! That might sound mercenary, but we do have to think about sales in order to keep the productions going!"
Nicholas Briggs

WORKING TITLE(S)

None.

Check box - CD ☐ MP3 ☐

THE FEARLESS – PART 2

#4.2

SYNOPSIS

The Daleks arm their missiles, target Kade's ship and open fire, destroying the craft. Dead Hand moves into position to use its new weapon again, to drain Alliance ships of their power, but the Daleks find the ship's hull has been breached by Kade and the members of Maniac Squad. The Daleks try to seal the command deck, but Kade cuts his way through in seconds. Landen speaks with General Tanlee, telling him all is going to plan. She orders the reserve ships round Kedru 7 to join the main attack force, leaving the planet open to attack, and two trans-solar discs break through. Kade's family are on the planet below, and despite his best efforts to give chase in the Dead Hand, the discs up their speed. They overload their flight chambers as they plummet towards the planet on a suicide run, killing the population who had tried to take shelter. Kade

goes off the rails, but Landen has him brought in and tells him to divert his anger – she understands his pain having lost her own children to the Daleks. Landen plays him a message from Susan Mendes, explaining she has a mission for Kade and the Fearless, as the Spacers have become known. The Daleks take the Angel of Mercy to board a ship, the *Amaryst*, on a covert mission, where she is shown around by crew member Ollander. Ollander tells Suz the Daleks tortured her and damaged her memory – she can't even remember her first name. Ollander is later taken to the bridge to help them with a navigational beacon, and in return they promise to give her her memories and her name – Esther – back. Landen introduces Maniac Squad to their newly promoted commander, Kade. Their mission is simple – to find and kill Susan Mendes…

TRIVIA

• Maureen O'Brien (Agnes Landen) is best known for playing the First Doctor's companion, Vicki, in **Doctor Who**. She has had a recurring role in *Casualty,* and is now a best-selling novelist. She has reprised the role of Vicki in several releases from Big Finish's **Companion Chronicles** range, including the very first story, **Frostfire #1.1**.

PRODUCTION SUMMARY

"Kade is a real bad-ass and that was one of the things that Noel asked me to make the character when he agreed to be in **Dalek Empire**. He loves playing those roles and I don't think Mickey 'the idiot' did him any justice. Noel is very forthright so I think he asked them to beef up the role of Mickey. He's also very gentle and generous – but don't upset him! He says that everyone arrives with a full set of points and they lose them if they do something wrong!"
Nicholas Briggs

WORKING TITLE(S)

None.

CREW

Writer	**Nicholas Briggs**
Director	**Nicholas Briggs**
Producers	**Jason Haigh-Ellery Gary Russell**
Executive Producer (BBC)	**Jacqueline Rayner**
Music	**Nicholas Briggs**
Sound Design	**Jamie Robertson**
Cover Art	**Alex Mallinson**
Theme	**Nicholas Briggs**

CAST

The Daleks	**Nicholas Briggs**
Agnes Landen	**Maureen O'Brien**
General Croft, Spacer, PA, MP, Medic	**Ian Brooker**
Salus Kade	**Noel Clarke**
Egan Fisk	**Oliver Mellor**
Kennedy	**David Yip**
Lt Carlisle	**John Schwab**
Ernst Tanlee	**David Sax**
Lajitta	**Ginita Jimenez**
Susan Mendes	**Sarah Mowat**
Avers	**David Dobson**
Ollander	**Esther Ruth Elliott**
Computer, Kenzie, Soldier	**Sean Connolly**
PA	**Esther Ruth Elliot**

TECHNICAL

Story Code	**BFPCDDE16**
Recorded Date	**16th, 17th, 18th, 23rd and 24th July 2007**
Release Date	**November 2007**
Place of Recording	**The Moat Studios, London**
Number of CDs	**1**
Total Duration	**72' 39"**
Number of Episodes	**1**
ISBN	**978-1-84435-301-9**

#4.3 THE FEARLESS – PART 3

CREW

Writer	**Nicholas Briggs**
Director	**Nicholas Briggs**
Producers	**Jason Haigh-Ellery**
	Nicholas Briggs
Executive Producer (BBC)	**Jacqueline Rayner**
Music	**Nicholas Briggs**
Sound Design	**Jamie Robertson**
Cover Art	**Alex Mallinson**
Theme	**Nicholas Briggs**

CAST

Agnes Landen	**Maureen O'Brien**
Ernst Tanlee	**David Sax**
The Daleks	**Nicholas Briggs**
Salus Kade	**Noel Clarke**
Egan Fisk	**Oliver Mellor**
Kennedy	**David Yip**
Lajitta	**Ginita Jimenez**
Kenzie	**Sean Connolly**
Ollander	**Esther Ruth Elliott**
Avers	**David Dobson**
Susan Mendes	**Sarah Mowat**
Tren, Radio Voice	**Sean Connolly**

TECHNICAL

Story Code	**BFPCDDE17**
Recorded Date	**16th, 17th, 18th, 23rd and 24th July 2007**
Release Date	**December 2007**
Place of Recording	**The Moat Studios, London**
Number of CDs	**1**
Total Duration	**61' 01"**
Number of Episodes	**1**
ISBN	**978-1-84435-302-6**

SYNOPSIS

The Dalek Supreme informs the Emperor a small craft has been detected in the vicinity of the Amaryst, but he dismisses it. Kade and his men leave the drop ship in their Spacer suits, with 25 of them slowly closing in on their target over the course of a few months. Months pass, and onboard the Amaryst, the Daleks detect what they suspect is an Alliance probe so fire the engines to destroy it, but it is Kade. Dazed, he dreams of Legitta, but Fisk finds and revives him, and the Spacers deploy scramblers to confuse the Dalek sensors. The Daleks send one of their number outside to investigate the problem, as they shut down the main drive. The Spacers come under fire but destroy the Dalek then board the ship, destroying all but one of the Daleks. Kade is ready to kill Suz, but Ollander tells him the Angel of Mercy and Kalendorf are working on a secret plan to defeat the Daleks, a plan that will take time to come to fruition. The Daleks realise the Amaryst has drifted off course and send a ship to intercept it, but keep at a distance. The Spacers detect a homing beacon onboard the ship and try to locate it, and find a hyperlink decoder, monitoring Earth Alliance transmissions, which has given the Daleks an advantage in the war. They then realise the homing signal is coming from Suz – and Kade guns her down. But this isn't the real Angel of Mercy, it's a Dalek replicant. The signal cut off, the Daleks move in to attack the Amaryst, and as the Spacers prepare to depart, Kade overhears some talk on the decoder between General Tanlee and Landen. She reveals she has been using Kade, having found him single-handedly keeping Talis Minor alive – and she engineered the circumstances of his family's deaths...

TRIVIA

- David Yip (Kennedy) is best known for his lead role in the 1981 TV series *The Chinese Detective*. He also appeared in the 1979 TV story **Destiny of the Daleks**, as one of the Dalek slaves, Veldan. His film roles include *Indiana Jones and the Temple of Doom* and the James Bond movie *A View to a Kill*. He was also a regular in the Channel 4 soap opera *Brookside*.

PRODUCTION SUMMARY

"As well as the tough-guy action and attitude stuff, Noel does the touching, emotional scenes so well, too. Throughout this series and while I was writing as well as directing I was always looking for ways to play to Noel's great range and diversity."
Nicholas Briggs

WORKING TITLE(S)

None.

THE FEARLESS – PART 4

#4.4

SYNOPSIS

Kade's life support has been on minimal level for over a year, as he's been drifting in space, and it drops into the danger zone. Landen's command ship chances upon him, on a trans-solar disc, and they bring him on board. He recovers, and learns from Landen that the rest of the Fearless on his mission were lost in the failed assassination attempt on Susan Mendes. Landen shows Kade an approaching asteroid storm on the long-range scan, which is being led towards the solar system by the Daleks, using a gravity net to cause maximum damage to the heart of the Earth Alliance. Landen promotes Kade to captain of her ship the *Herald*, and they head off to stop the Daleks by destroying the gravity generators. She plans to blast a clear route through the Dalek defences for the Spacers to get through to the main gravity source and destroy it. Kade calmly confronts Landen about her past decisions, and as they prepare to leave on

their mission, he forces her at gunpoint to don a Spacer suit and go with the troops. The Daleks detect their presence and the Earth troops come under fire, landing 2km away from their Dalek base target. The Daleks surround the remaining troops and Landen surrenders, as the Daleks exterminate all bar Landen and Kade. Kade demands to speak to the Emperor as he knows of Suz and Kalendorf's plan for a secret rebellion. They are taken to Dalek command, but the Emperor says he knows of the planned betrayal - as he says so, Kade activates an explosive device, destroying the gravity net as he and Landen power up their suits and escape. Kade shoots Landen as she won't apologise for manipulating him, but they are rescued by the *Herald*. As Suz transmits her message, "Death to the Daleks," Kade resigns his command and heads to Talus Minor. But Landen expects him to be back to fight again: "For him, it's personal."

TRIVIA

- John Schwab (Lt Carlisle) had a previous encounter with the Daleks, in the 2005 TV story, **Dalek**.

PRODUCTION SUMMARY

"I knew that this would probably be the last **Dalek Empire** play so I did write it with that in mind. I was always building to this tying together of the various strands with Suz and Kalendorf. Yeah. I think it ends well; it's a nice way to round it all off."
Nicholas Briggs

WORKING TITLE(S)

None.

CREW

Writer	**Nicholas Briggs**
Director	**Nicholas Briggs**
Producers	**Jason Haigh-Ellery**
	Gary Russell
Executive Producer (BBC)	**Jacqueline Rayner**
Music	**Nicholas Briggs**
Sound Design	**Jamie Robertson**
Cover Art	**Alex Mallinson**
Theme	**Nicholas Briggs**

CAST

Agnes Landen	**Maureen O'Brien**
Ernst Tanlee	**David Sax**
Announcer, Computer, PA	**Sean Connolly**
Kade	**Noel Clarke**
Lt Carlisle	**John Schwab**
Officer	**Ian Brooker**
Lajitta	**Ginita Jimenez**
Dr Mezeran	**Jane Goddard**
Spacer 1	**Andrew Dickens**
The Daleks	**Nicholas Briggs**

TECHNICAL

Story Code	**BFPCDDE18**
Recorded Date	**16th, 17th, 18th, 23rd and 24th July 2007**
Release Date	**January 2008**
Place of Recording	**The Moat Studios, London**
Number of CDs	**1**
Total Duration	**60' 38"**
Number of Episodes	**1**
ISBN	**978-1-84435-303-3**

BURIED SECRETS

#2.1

SYNOPSIS

Both Miss Winters and Harris are killed in separate accidents leaving Sarah Jane Smith free once more. Nat has joined the Medici Project, a team of forensic archaeologists who are exhuming the famous family from tombs in the Italian town of San Lorenzo. The team's former leader – Professor Brunetti – has disappeared and Professor Edmons has replaced him. Sarah Jane is approached by a man who says he is Harry Sullivan's younger brother, Will, but then Josh arrives with a letter for Sarah Jane. She is furious and knows he is being over-protective so she leaves with Will. It transpires that he is working at an Antarctic Base and says that he should be able to arrange a visit for her. Meanwhile, in Italy the team open a coffin to discover the body of Professor Brunetti inside. Before Sarah Jane leaves for Italy, she reads the letter, which is from Miss Winters. It warns Sarah to beware the scarlet acolytes of the 'Orphans of the Future' and that the 'Book of

Tomorrows' is opening. In Italy, they meet with Nat, Edmons and his assistant Luca. Nat tells Sarah that her research has revealed that the Book of Tomorrows is a prophetic work written in the 16th century that was stolen by the Orphans of the Future. They believe mankind's development has been helped by aliens and would culminate in one final visitation. However, the sect is divided in two. The White Chapter believes the aliens are benign and the Crimson Chapter thinks the aliens will destroy humanity. The coming of the aliens would be preceded by a human herald. It is revealed that Sarah Jane is this herald due to her appearance in San Martino in the 15th century while travelling with the Doctor. Luca is from the Crimson Chapter. He murdered Brunetti and now kills Edmons (both of whom were White Chapter agents) before trying to shoot Sarah. However, when the lights fail, there is mayhem and in the confusion Josh shoots Luca.

PLACEMENT

Between the Big Finish audio dramas **Mirror, Signal, Manoeuvre #1.5** and **Snow Blind #2.2**; before the 2006 **Doctor Who** TV story **School Reunion**.

TRIVIA

- David Gooderson played Davros in the 1979 TV story **Destiny of the Daleks**.
- Tom Chadbon (Will Sullivan) appeared as Duggan in the next TV story from 1979's Season 17, **City of Death**, and as Merdeen in the first section (**The Mysterious Planet**) of the 1986 TV story **The Trial of a Time Lord** as well as the Big Finish **Eighth Doctor Adventures** story **No More Lies #1.6**.
- The character of Will Sullivan was originally Harry's nephew, not his brother.
- Like much of this second season of **Sarah Jane Smith** audios, the Medici tombs excavation was based on real-life events.
- Shaun Ley, who appears throughout the series, is a real BBC newsreader, often to be heard on Radio 4's *The World at One* and *The World This Weekend*.
- Like other stories of **Sarah Jane Smith II**, this story was a homage to a **Doctor Who** TV story: in this case 1976's **The Masque of Mandragora**.
- An abandoned early plotline for this story revolved around dodgy research using stem-cells to help the disabled walk again – something that would have involved Nat being used as a guinea pig.

PRODUCTION SUMMARY

"We were keen to give the second series of *Sarah Jane Smith* a globetrotting, adventure feel, a bit like *Department S* from the 60s. David Bishop had recently been on holiday in Florence, so that made an obvious location for our first story. There was quite a lot to set up in this first story, including the introduction of the new character, Will, but I was keen that it should be a self-contained adventure as well rather than just an introduction to the rest of the series. So, with that in mind, we were keen to wrap up the loose ends of the previous series as quickly as possible, hence the off-screen death of Miss Winters."
John Ainsworth

WORKING TITLE(S)

None.

RETURNING MONSTERS/CHARACTERS

None.

CREW

Writer	**David Bishop**
Director	**John Ainsworth**
Producer	**John Ainsworth**
Executive Producers	**Jason Haigh-Ellery Jacqueline Rayner (BBC)**
Music and Sound Design	**Steve Foxon**
Cover Art	**Lee Binding**
Theme	**Steve Foxon**

CAST

Sarah Jane Smith	**Elisabeth Sladen**
Josh	**Jeremy James**
Natalie Redfern	**Sadie Miller**
Will	**Tom Chadbon**
Professor Edmons	**Ivor Danvers**
Luca	**Daniel Barzotti**
Newsreader	**Shaun Ley**
With	**Jon Weinberg Jacqueline Pearce David Gooderson Partricia Leventon Stephen Greif**

TECHNICAL

Story Code	**SJ06**
Recorded Date	**3 November 2005**
Release Date	**January 2006**
Place of Recording	**The Moat Studios**
Number of CDs	**1**
Total Duration	**55' 25"**
Number of Episodes	**1**
Duration of Episodes	**1 (55' 25")**
ISBN	**1-84435-200-5**

#2.2 SNOW BLIND

CREW

Writer	**David Bishop**
Director	**John Ainsworth**
Producer	**John Ainsworth**
Executive Producers	**Jason Haigh-Ellery**
	Jacqueline Rayner
	(BBC)
Music and Sound Design	**Steve Foxon**
Cover Art	**Lee Binding**
Theme	**Steve Foxon**

CAST

Sarah Jane Smith	**Elisabeth Sladen**
Josh Townsend	**Jeremy James**
Will	**Tom Chadbon**
Munro	**Nicholas Briggs**
Morgane	**Julia Righton**
Jack	**Jack Galagher**
Newsreader	**Shaun Ley**
With	**Jacqueline Pearce**
	David Gooderson
	Stephen Greif

TECHNICAL

Story Code	**SJ07**
Recorded Date	**4 November 2005**
Release Date	**February 2006**
Place of Recording	**The Moat Studios**
Number of CDs	**I**
Total Duration	**54' 22"**
Number of Episodes	**I**
Duration of Episodes	**I (54' 22")**
ISBN	**1-84435-201-3**

SYNOPSIS

Sarah and Josh travel to Nikita Base in Antarctica to visit Will Sullivan. There they meet Will's fellow scientists, Morgane and team leader Munro. They are given a tour of the facility while Jack, the pilot, checks out a warning light that came on as they landed. Will has a black eye and Sarah asks him about it. He admits that Munro punched him. The team leader is becoming increasingly paranoid. Due to the problem with the plane, Sarah Jane and Josh are forced to stay the night so Sarah goes to speak with Munro. He says that Morgane is the real troublemaker. As Sarah Jane leaves him he advises her to wear goggles outside due to snow blindness. Josh goes with Will and Morgane to the drilling site where Morgane becomes excited about what they have discovered there before becoming dizzy. She returns to the base. Meanwhile, Sarah helps Jack with his aircraft who tells her he thinks that Munro and Will have been fighting over Morgane. Sarah returns to her room to find a note asking her to come to the storage hut. When she goes there she is knocked out and left in the snow as a big storm descends on the base. She manages to radio for help and eventually Josh and Will reach her only to discover she has become snow blind. It transpires that the thing they have found in the ice is a very rich form of uranium and that Morgane has been working with Jack to get the precious find out of Antarctica and make a fortune. Morgane is also a member of the Crimson Chapter but Jack shoots her so he can have the uranium for himself. Jack also shoots Munro and then tries to leave in the plane, but Sarah has sabotaged it. Elsewhere, a meeting is held of the Crimson Chapter. Its leader decrees that their agent, Will Sullivan, must kill Sarah Jane...

PLACEMENT

- Between the Big Finish audio dramas **Buried Secrets #2.1** and **Fatal Consequences #2.3**; before the 2006 **Doctor Who** TV story **School Reunion**.

TRIVIA

- Jacqueline Pearce (Keeper) is well known to SF fans as Supreme Commander Servalan in *Blake's 7*. She has also appeared in the **Doctor Who Main Monthly Range** release **The Fearmonger #5** and the **2000 AD** drama **Strontium Dog – Down to Earth #3**. Jacqueline also appeared in the TV **Doctor Who** story **The Two Doctors**, as Chessene, opposite Colin Baker and Patrick Troughton.
- The Antarctic setting was a deliberate nod to **The Seeds of Doom**, intended to keep listeners guessing whether the plot featured Krynoid pods.
- The graphic novels *Whiteout* and *Whiteout: Melt* by Greg Rucka and Steve Leiber were another inspiration.
- The part of pilot Jack was written for Australian actor Jack Galagher.

PRODUCTION SUMMARY

"I think this is my favourite of the four plays and is probably the most self-contained. I loved the Arctic setting which I thought was well realised in the script and the sound design. Nicholas Briggs gave an excellent performance and was really chilling. I particularly liked the idea that Sarah mistakenly thought that Krynoid seed pods had been discovered based on her previous Arctic experience. This was a nice little nod to her **Doctor Who** adventures without being too overt."
John Ainsworth

WORKING TITLE(S)

None.

RETURNING MONSTERS/CHARACTERS

None.

FATAL CONSEQUENCES

#2.3

SYNOPSIS

Sarah decides to take the fight to the Crimson Chapter. She has traced Miss Winters's movements and thinks that Rechauffeur Inc. has been used to make and sell biological weapons. Sarah Jane believes they are going to cleanse the Earth with a doomsday weapon of some sort. Then a man called Dr Dexter, working for the organisation Mandrake, contacts Sarah. When they meet, he tells Sarah, Josh and Will that Mandrake has been working on a cure for the deadly Marburg virus in their lab in Pangbourne. It is later revealed that, unbeknownst to Sarah, Dexter is working for the Crimson Chapter. Will and Josh go to Pangbourne to do some digging and Sarah is contacted by Sir Donald Wakefield, a billionaire who is about to become the first passenger on a commercial space shuttle. It is revealed that Sir Donald is the head of the White Chapter. He tells her that Will is an agent of the red faction and has orders to kill her. In Pangbourne, Dexter forces Will to administer injections to human guinea pigs – protestors who have been taken for this purpose. But this is not the cure, it is a super virus based on Marburg. Will refuses at first but Dexter tells him the orders come from the Keeper of the Crimson Chapter herself. When the 'patients' are released they will spread the virus at a stupendous rate. Sarah rushes to Pangbourne knowing there must be an antidote. There Sarah makes a deal with the Keeper: she will be given the antidote but cannot take it herself. It is revealed that the Book of Tomorrows is based on the journals of Giuliano – the Italian Duke she met with the Doctor when they battled the Mandragora Helix 500 years previously. Josh and Will then confront one another and struggle for the gun while a similar fight ensues between the Keeper and Sarah...

PLACEMENT

Between the Big Finish audio dramas **Snow Blind #2.2** and **Dreamland #2.4**; before the 2006 **Doctor Who** TV story **School Reunion**.

TRIVIA

- Stephen Greif (Sir Donald) is best known as Space Commander Travis in the first season of *Blake's 7*. Stephen also appeared in the Big Finish **Doctor Who Main Monthly** range release **Primeval #26**.
- The working title for this story was drawn from the policies of organisations such as the Animal Liberation Front.
- The script went through three drafts in the space of nine days during October 2005.
- Writer David Bishop could only attend the recording day for this story alone because he was studying for an MA in screenwriting at the time.
- This story was released one year before the character of Sarah Jane made her debut in the new TV series **The Sarah Jane Adventures** (*Invasion of the Bane*).

PRODUCTION SUMMARY

"I don't mean to be disrespectful to David, but this was both mine and Lis's least favourite of the four scripts. We weren't happy that Sarah was kept away from the action for most of the story. However, it was a difficult one to get the balance right as a lot of the explanations had to come out in this story which is hard to do without info-dumping. But it had a great, dramatic conclusion with a fantastic cliff-hanger ending. Tom Chadbon was disappointed to discover that he wouldn't be returning for the fourth and final story. Tom was great to work with, though I remember Lis only half-pretending to be offended that he gave her an acting note at one point!"
John Ainsworth

WORKING TITLE(S)

Direct Action.

RETURNING MONSTERS/CHARACTERS

None.

CREW

Writer	**David Bishop**
Director	**John Ainsworth**
Producers	**John Ainsworth**
Executive Producers	**Jason Haigh-Ellery Jacqueline Rayner (BBC)**
Music and Sound Design	**Steve Foxon**
Cover Art	**Lee Binding**
Theme	**Steve Foxon**

CAST

Sarah Jane Smith	**Elisabeth Sladen**
Josh	**Jeremy James**
Will	**Tom Chadbon**
Keeper	**Jacqueline Pearce**
Dexter	**David Gooderson**
Maude	**Patricia Leventon**
Emily	**Katarina Olsson**
Newsreader	**Shaun Ley**
Sir Donald	**Stephen Greif**

TECHNICAL

Story Code	**SJ08**
Recorded Date	**23 November 2005**
Release Date	**March 2006**
Place of Recording	**The Moat Studios**
Number of CDs	**1**
Total Duration	**56' 20"**
Number of Episodes	**1**
Duration of Episodes	**1 (56' 20")**
ISBN	**1-84435-202-1**

#2.4 DREAMLAND

CREW

Writer	**David Bishop**
Director	**John Ainsworth**
Producer	**John Ainsworth**
Executive Producers	**Jason Haigh-Ellery**
	Jacqueline Rayner
	(BBC)
Music and Sound Design	**Steve Foxon**
Cover Art	**Lee Binding**
Theme	**Steve Foxon**

CAST

Sarah Jane Smith	**Elisabeth Sladen**
Josh Townsend	**Jeremy James**
Natalie Redfern	**Sadie Miller**
Sir Donald	**Stephen Greif**
Kimmel	**Jon Weinberg**
Mission Control	**Toby Longworth**
Newsreader	**Shaun Ley**
With	**Patricia Leventon**

TECHNICAL

Story Code	**SJ09**
Recorded Date	**24 November 2005**
Release Date	**April 2006**
Place of Recording	**The Moat Studios**
Number of CDs	**1**
Total Duration	**60' 35"**
Number of Episodes	**1**
Duration of Episodes	**1 (60' 35")**
ISBN	**1-84435-203-X**

SYNOPSIS

Josh has killed Will and the Keeper of the Crimson Chapter. He injects Sarah Jane with the antidote and saves her life. With Sir Donald's help the plan to release the deadly Marburg virus has been stopped. Later Sarah meets with Nat and attends Will Sullivan's funeral. Afterwards they find Josh and Sir Donald waiting at Sarah's cottage. He wants her to come with him on the commercial space shuttle *Dauntless*. It is then revealed that the reason Sir Donald is going on the shuttle is to see a new comet that has been detected. He believes it represents humanity's salvation as was foretold by Giuliano 500 years before. Sarah asks him to leave and then sees the resemblance between Sir Donald and Josh – they are father and son. When they do leave, Sarah reminisces with Nat about the marvellous friend she used to travel with. She misses him and always hoped he'd come back for her but wonders if he abandoned her for a reason. So she and Nat go to Nevada so Sarah can undertake the astronaut training and meet the pilot for the mission, Ben Kimmel. At Sir Donald's deathbed, Sarah agrees to go into space and Josh says he will take his father's place. Sarah Jane and Josh then board the *Dauntless* and say goodbye to Nat – even though they will be back in time for lunch. When the space shuttle reaches its orbit in outer space everyone is shocked when the pilot is revealed as an agent of the Crimson Chapter. He is piloting the ship towards the comet. Josh then pulls a gun and there is a scuffle during which several shots are fired, damaging the shuttle and its controls. Josh is shot but manages to kill Ben. As he slips from consciousness, Sarah is left alone and as all hope fades, something hurtles towards the shuttle, something she has seen before – a lifetime ago – that arrives with a roar…

PLACEMENT

- After the Big Finish audio dramas **Fatal Consequences #2.3** and before the 2006 **Doctor Who** TV story **School Reunion**.

TRIVIA

- The idea to focus on space tourism came from Elisabeth Sladen herself.
- The space craft in **Dreamland** is based on the work of American aerospace pioneer Burt Rutan – a man with a wonderfully **Doctor Who** name – who was the winner of the X-Prize in 2004 for being the first person to produce the first privately funded spacecraft to reach space twice in two weeks.
- The final audio of series two was always intended to end on a cliffhanger and David Bishop had no particular resolution in mind either!

PRODUCTION SUMMARY

"With the bulk of the arc plot for the series wrapped up in the previous story, **Dreamland** became more of a character based epilogue. It was great to have Jon Weinberg in the cast, a totally genuine American who is a great actor who I call upon whenever I need a good American voice. There was a bit of an outcry at the ambiguous cliff-hanger ending. However, given that Lis is now sadly gone, I can't help feeling that this might be regarded as a fitting end to Sarah's story – alone in space, but encountering something fantastic and wonderful and she then vanishes having gone to who knows where."
John Ainsworth

WORKING TITLE(S)

None.

RETURNING MONSTERS/CHARACTERS

None.

Check box - CD ■ MP3 ■

Left:
The guest cast of **Comeback** (l-r): Robin Bowerman, David Jackson and Peter Sowerbutts at the Moat Studios, March 2002.

Below:
The cast of **The Tao Connection** (l-r): Robert Curbishley, Steven Wickham, Jane McFarlane, Jeremy James, Alistair Lock, Moray Treadwell, Wendy Albiston and Elisabeth Sladen.

SECTION 11 JAGO & LITEFOOT

The circumspect circumstances by which those Investigators of Infernal Incidents came to be cajoled and coaxed into co-starring in a spin-off serialisation of stories specific to the salubrious sleuths are thus...

David Richardson, producer of **The Companion Chronicles** had hit upon the idea of reuniting the characters of Henry Gordon Jago and Professor George Litefoot from the 1977 **Doctor Who** TV story **The Talons of Weng-Chiang**. **The Mahogany Murderers #3.11** was written by Andy Lane and recorded in September 2008. It was announced on the Big Finish website the following month, with the report stating that "both actors were thrilled by Lane's script, which stays true to the wit and imagination of Robert Holmes and finds the amateur sleuths on the trail of another mystery in Victorian London."

The play was released in May 2009 and proved to be the hit of the season with fans delighted by the return of not just such loveable characters but also the ebullient actors who brought them to life. In September both Trevor Baxter and Christopher Benjamin appeared together at the Regenerations convention in Swansea to a rapturous audience.

Unbeknownst to the ecstatic fans, plans were already underway for a spin-off series with David Richardson taking on producer's duties. 'When we first read Andy Lane's script, we thought it worked very well as a pilot,' says David. 'The groundwork had already been laid and we hoped we could follow it up with at least another **Companion Chronicle**. Then one day Jason Haigh-Ellery just said to me, "how do you fancy doing a set of four **Jago & Litefoot** plays?"'

The news was announced on the Big Finish website the day after the convention, with more details promised later in the year.

Behind the scenes, David was planning and scheming. He immediately approached Andy Lane to write one of the plays. Originally, he was offered the chance to outline all four stories and then actually write the last one. However, Andy was too busy with his new range of *Young Sherlock Holmes* books to take on such a job, so David turned to Justin Richards.

'I wanted to persuade Justin to write for me but I thought he'd be too busy with the **Doctor Who** books and everything,' says David. Fortunately, the timing couldn't have been better and not only was Justin available to write one of the plays he also agreed to taking on the role of script editor.

'David Richardson asked me if I would like to write for the first season and it actually fitted with my schedule,' recalls Justin. 'I immediately said, "yes"!'

Justin also has something of a confession... '**The Mahogany Murderers** had been out for a while and I hadn't got round to listening to it!' However, David supplied him with a download of the play and Justin could see the direction the new series should go in. 'There was the unresolved story of Dr Tulp and this first season follows on directly from **The Mahogany Murderers**.'

Justin knew he wanted a relatively straightforward story to kick off the series and wrote **The Bloodless Soldier #1.1** very early on. This provided the writers with a tonal template for the new series. With Justin down to write one play himself, Andy Lane promised another slot and Alan Barnes asking if he could write for the range, there was only one place remaining and Justin asked Jonathan Morris to pitch some ideas.

'Each of the writers gave me an idea of what they wanted to do,' says Justin. 'I then wrote a six-page overview of the series with a half page synopsis for each story. The writers then haggled over that and we discussed how the character of Tulp would be involved with each storyline. They then wrote a full

Right:
Recording series one's finale, **The Spirit Trap** (clockwise from left): producer David Richardson, Conrad Asquith (Sgt Quick), Christopher Benjamin (Jago), Trevor Baxter (Litefoot), Matt Steer (Smitty), DWM reporter Dan Tostevin, Toby Longworth (Dr Tulp) and director Lisa Bowerman, who also plays Ellie.

SERIES ONE

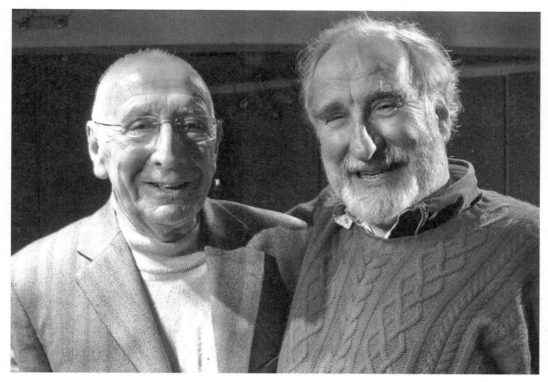

synopsis which had to go through the normal BBC approval process.'

The series was also in the very unusual position of being confirmed for a second season before recording began on the first. 'We knew that was going to happen,' says Justin. 'So we were able to incorporate where we were going with Season Two into the end of Season One. That's why the last play ends on a cliff-hanger that leads into the first story of the next season.'

It was also known that the series was going to be released as a box set and not as individual releases. As such, although the stories can be listened to out of sequence, the story arc is very much felt throughout and it is best to listen to them in order.

It was already apparent that Christopher Benjamin and Trevor Baxter could slip back into the roles with alacrity and ease so Justin went about building up a supporting cast for the main characters to play off. 'Ellie's role was beefed up so that she wasn't just a reason for Jago and Litefoot to tell each other a story,' says Justin. Ellie may not be in the plays as much as Jago and Litefoot but Justin wanted her to become a proper part of the team.

There was also a need for a police presence. 'I didn't want people saying, "why don't you just go to the police?" when something happens that would normally involve the police so we had a generic policeman pencilled in,' says Justin . 'Then David found he could get Conrad Asquith.' Conrad had played the part of PC Quick in **The Talons of Weng-Chiang** so he got a promotion to sergeant.

With the team complete, recording could get underway and the idea of a company of players was used across the block. This worked particularly well for the villain of the piece. 'The way we recorded the series meant that we could have Tulp crop up a little bit in most of the plays and take a major role in the last story,' says Justin. 'It also meant that we could have recurring characters such as Ellie and Sergeant Quick.'

Justin is very proud of what he and David have achieved with the new spin-off range. 'These are proper dramas,' he says. 'They're not just penny dreadful boys own adventures! The whole thing has been a joy and a delight.'

The first season of **Jago & Litefoot** was made available for pre-order in January 2010 with synopses for the stories added to the Big Finish website in March. A trailer was uploaded in April and the box set was finally released in June 2010. Only weeks earlier, season two had been announced. The press release quoted David as saying: 'Obviously we don't want to say too much about it yet as people have yet to enjoy the first four stories. But I can say that we have the brilliant David Collings joining the regular cast as Gabriel Sanders, while our guest stars in series two will include Vernon Dobtcheff and Simon Williams.'

So the cliff-hanger would be resolved, but not until January 2011…

Top:
Investigators of infernal incidents – Trevor Baxter and Christopher Benjamin, together again 32 years after **The Talons of Weng-Chiang**.

#1.1 THE BLOODLESS SOLDIER

CREW

Writer	**Justin Richards**
Director	**Lisa Bowerman**
Producer	**David Richardson**
Executive Producers	**Nicholas Briggs**
	Jason Haigh-Ellery
Script Editor	**Justin Richards**
Music &	**Kelly Ellis & Steve**
Sound Design	**McNichol @ Fool**
	Circle Productions
Cover Art	**Alex Mallinson**
Theme	**Jamie Robertson**

CAST

Henry Gordon Jago	**Christopher Benjamin**
George Litefoot	**Trevor Baxter**
Ellie Higson	**Lisa Bowerman**
Sergeant Quick	**Conrad Asquith**
Doctor Tulp	**Toby Longworth**
Private Higson, Hari Sunil, Captain Hertford	**John Banks**
Private Michaels	**Alex Lowe**
Private Smith	**Alex Mallinson**

TECHNICAL

Story Code	**BFPJLCD01**
Recorded Date	**16,17,18 & 21 December 2009**
Release Date	**June 2010**
Place of Recording	**The Moat Studios**
Number of CDs	**1**
Total Duration	**50' 28"**
Number of Episodes	**1**
Duration of Episodes	**1 (50' 28")**
ISBN	**978-1-84435-494-8**

SYNOPSIS

A creature in India attacks a platoon of soldiers and one of the men, Captain Hertford, is injured. Their overseas tour at an end, they return to London, but Hertford has apparently gone feral and escapes, killing a worker at the docks. Police Sergeant Quick summons Litefoot who examines the body, which has been dead for less than an hour, but has been drained of blood. The troops recapture Hertford, and one of the men summons Dr Tulp to look at him. Tulp says Hertford can be cured, given time. Jago comes off stage to meet Private Michaels, who offers him a new star attraction. Litefoot is visited by Hari Sunil, who has been following the bloodless beast. Jago and Litefoot meet up in the Red Tavern, and plan to meet Michaels at King's Cross Station. Barmaid Ellie Higson meets her brother Jim, newly returned from India, before he runs off. The soldiers find Hertford is missing as Jago and Litefoot head for their rendezvous, while Sunil follows them with Ellie. They meet Michaels and Sunil tells them Hertford was scratched by a beast in India, leading to his slow transformation. The creature kills again, as Michaels drags it into the train station, but it breaks free and kills him. Jago and Litefoot lure the creature out into the open for Jim Higson to shoot it in the head, and he eventually kills it – but not before being bitten. He starts to change into another bloodless killer, and as Ellie starts shouting for her brother, Jago kills Jim. Jago is stricken with grief, and Jim changes back to human form as Ellie arrives on the scene. Litefoot blames the incident on trauma, and tells Ellie how her brother stopped his former captain's rampage. The professor then gently reassures Jago that he did the right thing.

PLACEMENT

- After the **Doctor Who** TV story **The Talons of Weng-Chiang**, the **Companion Chronicle The Mahogany Murderers**, and before the Big Finish audio play **The Bellova Devil #1.2**.

TRIVIA

- Robin Bowerman (Corporal Lorton) is the older brother of Lisa Bowerman, the director of the play. He has also played the evil Mr Harris in the first season of Big Finish's **Sarah Jane Smith** series as well as Mordecan in the **Bernice Summerfield** story **The Bone of Contention #5.2** in which he played opposite his sister, rather than being directed by her. Robin's connection to **Jago & Litefoot** goes much further than his family connection to the director – he also appeared as an extra in **The Talons of Weng-Chiang**!
- Lisa Bowerman was given the regular role of Ellie as a thank you for playing the part in **The Mahogany Murderers** for nothing. Andy Lane's script for the **Companion Chronicle** featured three characters instead of two, and Lisa stepped in to stop it going over budget.
- Alex Lowe is a Big Finish regular and acclaimed comedy actor – his creation Barry from Watford is a regular on the Steve Wright Show, and appears in one-man performances. Alex is also known to **Doctor Who** fans as the novelizer Huxley in **The Companion Chronicles Ringpullworld #4.5** and **Find and Replace #5.3**.

PRODUCTION SUMMARY

"Whenever I think about **Jago & Litefoot**, it's always the banter inside the studio that comes to mind rather than the fiction… That's not to say I don't love these stories – I do passionately – but it's also the happiest production to work on, and Christopher and Trevor are just hilarious from the moment they arrive to the moment they leave the studio. My strongest memory of recording on Day 1? Christopher doing the first scene alone in the studio. Trevor then came in to join him and said, "Oh I thought you were in here." "Why's that?" asked Christopher. "Because I could get a word in edgeways in the green room!" said Trevor."
David Richardson

WORKING TITLE(S)

None.

RETURNING MONSTERS/CHARACTERS

Sergeant Quick, Dr Tulp.

Check box - CD ■ MP3 ■

THE BELLOVA DEVIL

#1.2

SYNOPSIS

Professor Litefoot is called in to give a colleague at St Thomas' Hospital, Dr Sacker, a second opinion on a body which has been found on the Circle Line, wearing the full dress uniform of a Turkish Army officer. A second body came in at the same time, which had been beheaded with a scimitar. Sacker identifies the first man as Clive Colville – a man whom he certified dead some six weeks previously. Jago and Litefoot travel to Highgate Cemetery, last resting place of Colville. There, they meet a couple of Bulgars, old enemies of Colville, whom they claim was once taken by the spirit of a frost and is a vampire who will return. Litefoot goes back to St Thomas' to ensure the body was secure, but finds Clive's son Reginald wants to re-bury it. Jago's enquiries lead the investigators to the Far-Off Traveller's Club, where Colville was introduced by his apparent victim, Francis Whitworth. Jago tries to gain entry to the club, while Litefoot is stunned to meet Sacker in the members' lounge. Jago learns he is applying to join a suicide club, which is full of people who are officially dead and buried, in return for signing over a portion of their estates in trust to the Friends of the Bolivian Tree Frogs. The chair of this club is Dr Tulp. Sergeant Quick arrives at the club and saves a rumbled Jago from being drowned by placing his feet in a bucket of concrete, in a technique Tulp learned from a Mr Capone in Chicago. Jago and Litefoot discover Clive Colville signed his estate over to the club rather than his son, so Reginald planned to use his father's reputation to get it back, by extorting the club members. But when they find Reginald, he has been decapitated, with a rose briar placed around his feet – a Bulgar tradition. However, Clive's body is still missing.

PLACEMENT

After the **Doctor Who** TV story **The Talons of Weng-Chiang** and between the Big Finish audio plays **The Bloodless Soldier #1.1** and **The Spirit Trap #1.3**.

TRIVIA

- Stephen Thorne (The Club Secretary) is well known to **Doctor Who** fans for playing Azal in the 1971 TV story **The Daemons**, as well as the renegade Time Lord Omega in 1973's **The Three Doctors**. His other **Doctor Who** roles hid Stephen behind the mask of an Ogron in **Frontier in Space**, and as the final form of Eldrad in **The Hand of Fear**. Stephen is also an experienced radio and voice artist, having appeared in the acclaimed BBC Radio adaptation of *The Lord of the Rings* as Treebeard, and has recorded over 300 talking books, including a highly entertaining reading of Donald Cotton's novelisation of his First Doctor story **The Myth Makers** for BBC Audio's Target Books range. He is a close friend of Christopher Benjamin, who suggested him to the producer.
- Dr Sacker – played by Duncan Wisbey – proved such a hit that the character returns in two episodes of the second season.
- During post production a couple of dialogue cuts were made to the early sequence in the graveyard, purely for pacing, as the producer and director felt that the story needed to get to the gentlemen's club more quickly.

PRODUCTION SUMMARY

"Writer Alan Barnes was there from the very first moment of **Jago & Litefoot**'s creation – we were having a Big Finish company meeting, and Jason had announced his decision to forge ahead with a series. Alan instantly put himself forward to script edit, before realising that the workload would just be too much given his other commitments. But I was keen that he would write a script for this first season and he did us proud with a head-scratching mystery. I say head-scratching because it all makes sense in the play and on the page, but in the studio (when we're recording out of order anyway) it took a lot of effort to follow. But we got there!"
David Richardson

WORKING TITLE(S)

None.

RETURNING MONSTERS/CHARACTERS

None.

CREW

Writer	**Alan Barnes**
Director	**Lisa Bowerman**
Producer	**David Richardson**
Executive Producers	**Nicholas Briggs**
	Jason Haigh-Ellery
Music and Sound Design	**Kelly Ellis & Steve McNichol @ Fool Circle Productions**
Cover Art	**Alex Mallinson**
Theme	**Jamie Robertson**

CAST

Henry Gordon Jago	**Christopher Benjamin**
George Litefoot	**Trevor Baxter**
Ellie Higson	**Lisa Bowerman**
Sergeant Quick	**Conrad Asquith**
Doctor Tulp	**Toby Longworth**
The Club Secretary	**Stephen Thorne**
Doctor Sacker, Bulgar	**Duncan Wisbey**
Reginald Colvile, Resurrection Joe	**Peter Silverleaf**
The Manchester Mangler	**Alex Mallinson**

TECHNICAL

Story Code	**BFPJLCD01**
Recorded Date	**16, 17, 18 & 21 December 2009**
Release Date	**June 2010**
Place of Recording	**The Moat Studios**
Number of CDs	**1**
Total Duration	**62 '08"**
Number of Episodes	**1**
Duration of Episodes	**1 (62 '08")**
ISBN	**978-1-84435-494-8**

#1.3 THE SPIRIT TRAP

CREW

Writer	**Jonathan Morris**
Director	**John Ainsworth**
Producer	**David Richardson**
Executive Producers	**Nicholas Briggs**
	Jason Haigh-Ellery
Script Editor	**Justin Richards**
Music & Sound Design	**Kelly Ellis & Steve McNichol @ Fool Circle Productions**
Cover Art	**Alex Mallinson**
Theme	**Jamie Robertson**

CAST

Henry Gordon Jago	**Christopher Benjamin**
George Litefoot	**Trevor Baxter**
Ellie Higson	**Lisa Bowerman**
Sergeant Quick	**Conrad Asquith**
Mrs Vanguard	**Janet Henfrey**
Toby	**Lex Shrapnel**
The Landlord	**John Ainsworth**

TECHNICAL

Story Code	**BFPJLCD01**
Recorded Date	**16, 17, 18 & 21 December 2009**
Release Date	**June 2010**
Place of Recording	**The Moat Studios**
Number of CDs	**1**
Total Duration	**68' 53"**
Number of Episodes	**1**
Duration of Episodes	**1 (68' 53")**
ISBN	**978-1-84435-494-8**

SYNOPSIS

Barmaid Ellie Higson believes that spiritualist Mrs Vanguard can really hear the voices of the dead, recounting her experience to Jago and Litefoot, but Jago thinks it's all superstition and theatrical trickery. But when she tells them Mrs Vanguard said he died after an altercation at King's Cross station, they decide to visit her. Before they go, the next morning Litefoot is woken early by Toby Barker, a hospital porter, saying his wife has gone missing after acting strangely. After their séance, which Jago knows is a fake, Ellie has a private séance. She fails to return home, as Mrs Barker is found burned alive, in an apparent case of spontaneous human combustion. Jago returns to Mrs Vanguard's home to be met by Ellie, who fails to recognise him, and sits in on another séance – this time being surrounded by spirits made of mist. Ellie prepares the spirit cabinet, and Jago's body is taken over by a being that plans to bring more people of influence to Mrs Vanguard with the ultimate aim of taking over Queen Victoria. Apparently trapped in the afterlife, Jago's consciousness finds Ellie, while Litefoot and Toby meet with his body. Litefoot can tell something is amiss with his fellow investigator, who fails to recognise him, and they discover burnt bodies in the spiritualist's home. The being in Jago's body claims to be from the 49th century and is evacuating a dying world by taking over the bodies of people in the past. Litefoot and Toby open the cabinet as the spiritualist returns, but Jago and Ellie's spirits exit the cabinet and return to their own bodies. Toby can hear his wife's voice calling to him from inside the cabinet, but a spirit tries to take him over. He burns up, and then explodes, seconds after Jago, Litefoot and Ellie have left. Mrs Vanguard wakes with no recollection of the events.

PLACEMENT

- After the **Doctor Who** TV story **The Talons of Weng-Chiang** and between the Big Finish audio plays **The Bellova Devil #1.2** and **The Similarity Engine #1.4**.

TRIVIA

- Janet Henfrey (Mrs Vanguard) previously appeared in Doctor Who in the 1989 TV story **The Curse of Fenric** as Miss Hardaker. After the recording of **The Spirit Trap**, she phoned the producer to say how much she'd enjoyed the experience of working on **Jago & Litefoot**.
- Lex Shrapnel (Toby) is best known for the lead role in Five's recent remake of *Minder*, alongside Shane Richie, and for being International Rescue hero John Tracey in the *Thunderbirds* movie. Film roles include *K-19: The Widowmaker* and *Captain America: The First Avenger*. Lex previously recorded a **Companion Chronicle**, **Shadow of the Past #4.9**, with Caroline John. He is the son of actor John Shrapnel.

PRODUCTION SUMMARY

"This is the only **Jago & Litefoot** episode directed by John Ainsworth. Lisa had directed the other three, but I was worried that – given the sheer amount of scenes that her character Ellie had in this episode – switching her two hats between acting and directing might have been too complicated. For subsequent seasons Lisa actually directed herself in all episodes. It proved easier in the end, as we can be recording scenes from different episodes on any single day – so the continuity of direction is important. But John did a great job, and loved his time with our daring infernal investigators."
David Richardson

WORKING TITLE(S)

None.

RETURNING MONSTERS/CHARACTERS

None.

Check box - CD ▪ MP3 ▪

THE SIMILARITY ENGINE

#1.4

SYNOPSIS

Sergeant Quick tells Professor Litefoot that some of his officers have had sores appearing on their bodies. Meanwhile, Jago has fallen down and is taken to hospital where he meets a man also with facial sores. The man's name is Smith. He is a police officer and, along with some colleagues, he has been moonlighting at a warehouse in the docks. He and his mates have been taken ill after unloading a strange black ore. Jago leaves the hospital and meets up with Litefoot to find the warehouse. Jago then tries to push Litefoot in front of a cart, but ends up being hit himself. 'Jago' turns out to be a wooden construct, controlled by Dr Tulp, who reveals he has glimpsed the future in his dreams. Through his astral projection he has brought ideas back into the past, to recreate them using Victorian technology, including the Similarity Engine. Before 'Jago' can attack him, Litefoot and Sergeant Quick set the wooden man ablaze and Tulp withdraws. Soon after, the real Jago is able to take over the charred remains of his wooden counterpart and tells his friends where to find him. Quick and Litefoot arrive, but soon after are captured, as Tulp reveals the black ore will one day become known as uranium and he wants to corner the market in it as a power source and weapon. Jago, having seen Tulp with his gloves off earlier, asks him to shake hands. When Tulp removes his glove, his fingers are like worms. It is revealed that during his astral projections, Tulp brought something back with him from the void, which starts to transform his body, shedding his skin. Jago and Litefoot push the creature into the Similarity Engine machinery, destroying it. At the Red Tavern, Ellie tells the professor a body drained of blood with puncture marks on the neck has been found at the docks, but Litefoot urges her not to inform Jago, muttering that, "This is a case for Litefoot and Sanders"…

PLACEMENT

After the **Doctor Who** TV story **The Talons of Weng-Chiang** and between the Big Finish audio plays **The Spirit Trap #1.3** and **Litefoot and Sanders #2.1**.

TRIVIA

- The story is a direct sequel to the **Companion Chronicles** story **The Mahogany Murderers #3.11**.
- Alex Mallinson, who appears in minor roles throughout the series, is perhaps better known as the designer responsible for many Big Finish CD cover designs as well as *Vortex* magazine. He has also appeared in a number of other Big Finish productions.
- The title of the story is a reference to the difference engine calculating machine created by Charles Babbage and the famous steampunk novel *The Difference Engine* by William Gibson and Bruce Sterling.
- All of Doctor Tulp's scenes from the four episodes were recorded on the final day of studio. David Richardson sent Toby Longworth a CD of **The Mahogany Murderers**, so he could hear how Tulp's voice had sounded in that story.
- John Banks and Alex Lowe recorded their scenes from this episode during the first studio day for **The Bloodless Soldier #1.1**.
- Andy Lane's script required a young child to appear in the first scene. This would have been not only expensive for a cameo, but would have required complicated licensing to hire a child. Ultimately, the lines were delivered by Alex Lowe, pitching his voice up.

PRODUCTION SUMMARY

"The season finale! I was really pleased that Andy wanted to continue the story from his **Companion Chronicle**, and it was great to have those Mahogany Murderers back. We found out just before recording began that we were getting a second series, so I asked Justin to write in a cliff-hanger. Part of our plan for season two was to split Jago and Litefoot up, and give the professor a new investigative partner. So that is alluded to here as he mentions working with Gabriel Sanders. At this stage, we had no idea who was going to play him — who'd have thought we'd get the brilliant David Collings!"
David Richardson

WORKING TITLE(S)

None.

RETURNING MONSTERS/CHARACTERS

None.

CREW

Writer	**Andy Lane**
Director	**Lisa Bowerman**
Producer	**David Richardson**
Executive Producers	**Nicholas Briggs** **Jason Haigh-Ellery**
Music and Sound Design	**Kelly Ellis & Steve McNichol @ Fool Circle Productions**
Cover Art	**Alex Mallinson**
Theme	**Jamie Robertson**

CAST

Henry Gordon Jago	**Christopher Benjamin**
George Litefoot	**Trevor Baxter**
Ellie Higson	**Lisa Bowerman**
Sergeant Quick	**Conrad Asquith**
Doctor Tulp	**Toby Longworth**
Smitty	**Matt Steer**
Sergeant Lange, Ragamuffin	**Alex Lowe**
Constable Lee	**John Banks**
Alf	**Alex Mallinson**

TECHNICAL

Story Code	**BFPJLCD01**
Recorded Date	**16, 17, 18 & 21 December 2009**
Release Date	**June 2010**
Place of Recording	**The Moat Studios**
Number of CDs	**1**
Total Duration	**56 '09"**
Number of Episodes	**1**
Duration of Episodes	**1 (56 '09")**
ISBN	**978-1-84435-494-8**

SECTION 12 | I, DAVROS

The genesis of **I, Davros** is a complicated one dating right back to the very early days of Big Finish's **Doctor Who** range. From the beginning, producer Gary Russell was against the idea of featuring Davros alongside his evil creations, the Daleks. As such, the character did not appear in the **Main Monthly Range** range for four years.

When it was decided that the "villains" trilogy of stories that led up to **Zagreus #50** should include Davros, Gary wanted something that examined the character without the baggage of the Daleks alongside. He wanted to find out what made Davros tick. 'Lance Parkin's script was everything I could have wished for,' says Gary. 'It was about Davros the man.'

It was this insight into the psychology of Davros that Lance captured that Gary wanted to develop in the mini-series. '**Davros #48** worked so well,' explains Gary. 'Then we did **The Juggernauts #65** and I thought there was a whole back story here to play with, rather as we had with the Master.'

Although both **The Juggernauts** and **Terror Firma #72** did feature the Daleks and their creator, the plays themselves examined Davros as a person, delving into his history and descent into madness.

In 2005, Gary met with Jason Haigh-Ellery to discuss what spin-offs Big Finish might produce for the following year. Gary was keen to work more with actor Terry Molloy who had played Davros in **Doctor Who** on TV since 1984 as well as in the three **Main Monthly Range** stories to feature the character.

It became apparent that the best way to do a Davros mini-series was to tell his life story rather than have a linked collection of stories about the character as the majority of the Big Finish audience already knew him. 'Somehow the story of Davros lent itself to an epic backstory,' says Gary. 'Terry Molloy was also keen to explore how the character had become the person he was when he first appeared. So I wanted the *I, Claudius*-like grand grotesques for the family and assembled some brilliant writers for it.'

I, Claudius (based on the books *I, Claudius* and *Claudius the God* by Robert Graves) was a major BBC TV drama, first broadcast in 1976. It charted the history of Rome through the eyes of the elderly Roman Emperor Claudius. It starred Sir Derek Jacobi in the title role and won many awards, including three BAFTAs.

Gary thinks he managed to rise to this self-imposed challenge. 'Along with the three **Gallifrey** mini-series, this I think is the pinnacle of my Big Finish career,' he says. 'I am immensely proud of **I, Davros.**'

With a broad idea of what he wanted to achieve, Gary sat down with Alan Barnes and began adding flesh to the bones of the plot. They knew that they wanted

to end the story just before the events of 1975's classic TV story **Genesis of the Daleks**.

Together they shaped the direction of the series and sent the writers a detailed brief, which included the dysfunctional family into which Davros was born. Alan subsequently dropped out of involvement on the series due to his other Big Finish commitments.

I, Davros was to draw on writers, cast and crew who all had experience of working for Big Finish. Part of this was due to the fact that Gary knew his time at Big Finish was coming to an end. 'I Davros was just Gary Russell's greatest hits cast-wise,' smiles Gary. 'I wanted to go out on a high with the best writers and actors.'

For the first story – **Innocence** – Gary Russell approached Gary Hopkins, who had written Eighth Doctor release **The Last #62**. Coincidentally, the actress Gary chose for the key role of Calcula, the mother of Davros, was Carolyn Jones, who had also appeared in **The Last** as the character Excelsior.

Gary Russell is keen to stress the difference between the two parts. 'Whereas Excelsior had been unstable, Calcula is far more logical.' She is also flawed in perhaps a more natural way, as she will do anything for her son. For Gary, she was also the most pivotal character and it was important her story arc was fluid. 'Calcula was the

This page:
Genesis of evil – Davros actor Terry Molloy was keen to explore the origins of the Daleks' creator in **I, Davros**.

Davros in the form of Shan. The story culminates in the attack that leaves the infamous Kaled scientist crippled and confined to his "chariot".

Scott Allan Woodard had been tasked by Gary to write the final part of the quartet – **Guilt**. Scott had previously written for Davros in the story **The Juggernauts**. 'The original storyline focused on the Mutos, but this was dropped to focus more on the Thals and the Kaleds,' says Scott. 'When researching, I focused most of my energies on **Genesis of the Daleks** – both the televised story and the novelisation – as well as Terry Nation's original script titled *Daleks: Genesis of Terror*. Even the physical formatting of the script drew inspiration from Terry's original script!'

The reason for this focus was the time period in which the play was set: a few months before the events of **Genesis of the Daleks**. As such, it would have to feature the character of Nyder, played by Peter Miles. 'I've known Peter for years,' says Gary. 'He was also in the first play I ever directed for Big Finish – **Whispers of Terror #3** – so it was something I simply knew we had to do.'

Finally, the play would also see the arrival of the universe's first Dalek, played by Nicholas Briggs. However, there was to be a sting in the tale. Nick plays a spy pretending to be a Muto. So the first-ever Dalek was not a Kaled but a Thal. Nick is convinced the irony of the idea was something cooked up by Gary and Alan Barnes.

character that I worked on most, making her consistent throughout the scripts,' explains Gary.

For Davros's father, Gary chose Richard Franklin, well known for playing Mike Yates in **Doctor Who** on TV during the Jon Pertwee era. 'When the script came in, I knew immediately that Richard would be absolutely right for the role,' says Gary.

The cast also included Rita Davies as Tashek who had been in **Primeval #26**; Lisa Bowerman, who plays Bernice Summerfield as well as numerous other parts for Big Finish; Katarina Olsson playing Shan, a character that had appeared in **Davros**; and Lizzie Hopley who plays Davros's older sister Yarvell and had already appeared in **Terror Firma**.

Because the series focused on a young Davros, it was important that the right actor be cast in this crucial role. Gary chose Rory Jennings, who played Tommy in the 2006 TV story **The Idiot's Lantern**. 'He was brilliant,' says Gary. 'He had watched and listened to Terry's performance and took it from there.'

Providing the second script – **Purity** – was the writing team of James Parsons and Andrew Stirling-Brown who had been commissioned following the success of their unique play, **Live 34 #74**, which had come to Gary's attention during a recent period of open submissions.

Lance Parkin wrote play three – **Corruption** – which reintroduced us to the idea of a love interest for

The series was announced on 3 February 2006 with a news story stating that the new mini-series would be released, "over four consecutive months on four single CDs from September 2006… Further story and casting details will be released soon." The website posted further details about the fist play on 4 August with a trailer and cover uploaded 24 days later. This was a very fast turnaround as the plays had only gone into studio over four consecutive days between 31 July and 3 August 2006.

3 August 2006 was not just the final day of recording on the series but also Gary's last official day at Big Finish. 'I was well ensconced in Cardiff by then,' says Gary. 'So I zoomed back and forth to London setting it up and then took a week out to come to the Moat to make it. I have rarely had so much fun. Toby made me a cake to say goodbye on the last day!'

The series was released between September and December 2006 and stands as a testament to Gary's creative verve. 'I wouldn't change a single beat of anything I did other than the odd quality control cock-up – the track spaces in **Davros**, typos on covers, that sort of thing,' he says. 'But I am proud of **I, Davros**. Always, always so proud.'

also introduced the character of Ruby (see interview with Lisa Bowerman on page 272) in the ever-expanding pantheon of elements that we actually got to meet.

Contrary to fan belief, the second season did not end on a cliffhanger because a third season was uncertain. 'It had always been our plan to do a fake "relaunch" of the series with very different leads,' says Nigel. Indeed, the opening of the third season was to have been a Joseph Lidster script entitled Reborn.

Again, the writer's other commitments became such that he had to pull out. This time, however, instead of having two weeks to pen a replacement, Nigel was left with six days before the studio session. He actually managed to write **Second Sight #3.1** in just two days.

Because the idea was to make people believe Big Finish had recast the leads, Blair McDonough and Anna Skellern played Steel and Sapphire. David Warner and Susannah Harker were listed on the CD booklet as guest stars, although at the end of the story, Ruby frees them and the two regular leads are restored in the remaining three stories of the third season.

The original announcement of season three was published on the Big Finish website on 27 October 2007. Naturally it still included Lidster's 'Reborn' and included one new writer among the four – John Dorney.

The stories were eventually recorded out of order with **Second Sight #3.1** and **Zero #3.3** being in the first recording block in December 2007. They were followed by a second block comprising **Remember Me #3.2** and **Wall of Darkness #3.4** in February 2008. They were then released in March, April, June and July 2008.

However, as the reduction from six stories to four might indicate, the sales of the second had not been as strong as the first. 'By the time we did the third season, unfortunately the sales had dropped off,' says Jason. 'I think that **Sapphire & Steel** was one of those shows that was very much affected by illegal downloads. It's a great shame because the sales were very consistent and then – almost overnight – people decided that they would illegally download the stories.'

And that is why there has been no further **Sapphire & Steel**. There is a definite passion for it at Big Finish. Nigel Fairs has even pitched a series of talking books, but while the problem of illegal downloads impacts so strongly on the range, a new season just cannot be sanctioned.

'I'd love to do more **Sapphire & Steel**, but it would have to be viable,' says Jason. 'What might make a big difference is when new legislation goes through. At the moment, if you download something illegally, there are no consequences for you. When the law comes in, it will effectively be handling stolen goods.'

Looking back down the corridor that is time, is there anything Nigel would nip back and change if he could? 'I think I would make the overall story of each season more cohesive, more like a serial than a series,' he says. 'I tried it with **Water/Immortality/Mystery/Second Sight** and think it worked. I'm proud of **Sapphire & Steel** and have very happy memories of some very talented people.'

So it looks like our heroes aren't likely to see the light of day again anytime soon. They're trapped and rescue seems unlikely if not downright impossible. But then, we've been in a similar situation before. Haven't we...?

Top:
Original series star David Collings (Silver) returned, joined by new Element Gold (Mark Gatiss).

#1.1 THE PASSENGER

CREW

Writer	**Steve Lyons**
Director	**Jason Haigh-Ellery**
Producer	**Nigel Fairs**
Executive Producer	**Jason Haigh-Ellery**
Original Series Creator	**PJ Hammond**
Music and Sound Design	**Nigel Fairs Nicholas Briggs**
Cover Art	**Andrew Orton**
Theme	**Cyril Ornadel**

CAST

Steel	**David Warner**
Sapphire	**Susannah Harker**
Gold	**Mark Gatiss**
Philip Burgess	**Hugo Myatt**
Mrs Warburton	**Jackie Skarvellis**
John Andrews	**Neil Henry**
The Princess	**Claire Louise Connelly**

TECHNICAL

Story Code	**BFPSASCD01**
Recorded Date	**August 2004**
Release Date	**May 2005**
Place of Recording	**The Moat Studios, London**
Number of CDs	**2**
Total Duration	**141' 40"**
Number of Episodes	**4**
Duration of Episodes	1 (29' 03")
2 (29' 11")
3 (27' 12")
4 (27' 33")
ISBN	**1-84435-138-6**

SYNOPSIS

After the events of the television series, Sapphire and Steel are released from the café in limbo by Silver (though this isn't confirmed until the story **Cruel Immortality #2.4**). They meet at a train station after what Sapphire describes as 'a long time' since their previous adventure. A train then arrives at the station. It is the source of time disturbances and thus the focus for the agents' new mission. Although constructed in the early 1930s, the train exists outside of time, although its carriages contain different, individual time zones, including 1919, 1938, 1942, 1963, 1982 and 2004. The only passenger appears to be a book dealer in his sixties known as Phillip Burgess. Burgess's copy of Agatha Christie's *Murder on the Orient Express* causes time to break through and dead spirits appear in the guise of passengers styled after characters from the book. Burgess himself had been a train driver – one that accidentally caused the death of a young girl – time uses his sense of guilt and transfers it to the other 'passengers', making them all believe that Burgess had killed them, too. As the enemy appears in the form of a faceless conductor and Sapphire and Steel struggle to hold the murderous passengers back, fellow agent Gold arrives to lend a hand. A maverick agent, Gold uses his powers to send the train dangerously out of control, distracting the conductor so that Sapphire can help Burgess come to terms with his guilt. Burgess confesses his sense of culpability to the other passengers, who decide that they no longer wish to murder him. As the faceless conductor no longer has a use for them, they disappear and the timeline is restored. A final coda sees Burgess, now unaware of what happened, being led away from the station by Gold, who has set up 'alternative arrangements' for him.

TRIVIA

- Released as a two-disc CD set, episode one of **The Passenger** was also released separately as a promotional disc in specialist shops and with the **Doctor Who Main Monthly Range** release **Three's a Crowd #69**.
- The story uses the first title sequence/theme (albeit re-mastered) , which included "Lead" in the list of available elements and not "Mercury" who had replaced Lead in the introduction of the final televised adventure.
- David Warner is famous for many theatre, film and TV roles. He is notable to SF fans for roles in *Star Trek: The Next Generation* and the *Star Trek* films *The Final Frontier* and *The Undiscovered Country*, as well as *The Omen*, *Time Bandits* and many, many more. He has appeared in many guest-roles for Big Finish, including appearances in **Bernice Summerfield**, **Graceless** and two **Doctor Who Unbound** adventures as the Doctor.
- Susannah Harker is well known for her role as Mattie Storrin in the BBC's political drama *House of Cards*, for which she received a BAFTA nomination, and as Angie in Channel 4's seminal vampire thriller, *Ultraviolet*. Her first appearance for Big Finish was in the BBC **Doctor Who** webcast **Shada**.
- Steve Lyons's original proposal stated that the reason for Burgess's guilt was that he had killed someone in a drunken brawl.

PRODUCTION SUMMARY

"This was probably the most 'traditional' of the original proposals and, as such, we thought it would be a good one to open the season with. It was the second story we recorded; by then David and Susie had established their brilliant working relationship and the creative sparks were flying! It's got one of my favourite scores, based on *The Runaway Train*, and one of my favourite episode endings: the end of part one where David delivers the line 'They're all ghosts' with such simplicity it's utterly chilling."
Nigel Fairs

WORKING TITLE(S)

The Train.

RETURNING MONSTERS/CHARACTERS

Sapphire and Steel.

Check box - CD ■

DAISY CHAIN

#1.2

SYNOPSIS

In 2004, James Sowersby returns home from university to his family home. Re-acquainting himself with mother Gabrielle and teenage sister Jennifer, all three live in quiet fear of the unspoken presence in their midst – Joshua, the spirit of Jennifer's stillborn twin. Joshua possesses a music box in which his ashes are kept and uses the television to communicate with them. Channels are switched over, while the radio plays jingles and songs that communicate his resentment. When Sapphire and Steel arrive to investigate they find a spirit that is increasing its powers – killing a pizza delivery boy at one stage. They also find that the family are aware of Joshua, but live out their lives in constant denial, refusing to discuss it. Unable to get them to divulge all under interrogation, Sapphire goes beyond her ability to read the conscious mind of humans, and uses her powers to delve into the subconscious, discovering all she needs to know. Later attempts to resolve the escalating situation see Sapphire take back time further than ever before, in order to greatly reduce the age of the family by around a decade. Yet Sapphire realises that it's Jennifer's grief that is causing Joshua's power, and only by eliminating that grief can Joshua's spirit finally be laid to rest. Jennifer realises the same thing, and makes the choice to end her life to resolve events for good. Sapphire hands Jennifer a piece of glass so she can slash her wrists and commit suicide. Steel assures Sapphire that "it was the only way", noting impassively that it was 'quite a tidy resolution'. They depart before they have to face any awkward questions, leaving Gabrielle to find her daughter's body. As the two agents leave, the sound of interference from a now-defunct television set can be heard.

TRIVIA

- Lena Rae (Jennifer) is now a scriptwriter on BBC soap opera *EastEnders*.
- Joe Lidster plays the pizza delivery boy, Tom, but is not credited.
- This is Joe's favourite script for Big Finish and was the one used by his agent as a 'calling card' before he had written more.
- This release includes a 14-minute behind-the-scenes feature.
- The original **Tomorrow People** proposal from which this stems was entitled *Dark Melody*.
- The recording took place at the same time as one of the **Gallifrey** plays.
- For this reason, the green room was packed with stars such as David Warner, Susannah Harker, Lynda Bellingham and Louise Jameson.
- The one that thrilled Joe Lidster most, though, was Kim Hartman who played Herr Flick's lover, Helga, in the BBC sitcom *'Allo, 'Allo*, which ran between 1982 and 1992. "Kim Hartman was really lovely and brilliant as the mum in **Daisy Chain**," Joe says.

PRODUCTION SUMMARY

"This was originally presented as a storyline for **The Tomorrow People** but I thought it suited **Sapphire & Steel** better. Brilliant concept, fabulous cast, and the script that I believe secured Joe's place in TV writing all those years ago. Quite right!"
Nigel Fairs

WORKING TITLE(S)

Dark Melody.

RETURNING MONSTERS/CHARACTERS

None.

CREW

Writer	**Joseph Lidster**
Director	**Nigel Fairs**
Producer	**Nigel Fairs**
Executive Producer	**Jason Haigh-Ellery**
Original Series Creator	**PJ Hammond**
Music and Sound Design	**Nigel Fairs**
Cover Art	**Andrew Orton**
Theme	**Cyril Ornadel**

CAST

Steel	**David Warner**
Sapphire	**Susannah Harker**
Gabrielle	**Kim Hartman**
Jennifer	**Lena Rae**
James	**Stuart Piper**
Voice	**Saul Jaffe**
Voice	**Emma Kilbey**

TECHNICAL

Story Code	**BFPSASCD02**
Recorded Date	**August 2004**
Release Date	**June 2005**
Place of Recording	**The Moat Studios, London**
Number of CDs	**2**
Total Duration	**106' 51"**
Number of Episodes	**4**
Duration of Episodes	**1 (22' 37")**
	2 (17' 14")
	3 (18' 31")
	4 (24' 59")
ISBN	**1-84435-139-4**

#1.3 ALL FALL DOWN

CREW

Writer	**David Bishop**
Director	**Nigel Fairs**
Producer	**Nigel Fairs**
Executive Producer	**Jason Haigh-Ellery**
Original Series Creator	**PJ Hammond**
Music and Sound Design	**Nigel Fairs**
Cover Art	**Andrew Orton**
Theme	**Cyril Ornadel**

CAST

Steel	**David Warner**
Sapphire	**Susannah Harker**
Silver	**David Collings**
Webber	**Michael Chance**
Fleming	**Kate Dyson**
Mary	**Suzanne Proctor**
The Girl	**Linda Bartram**
Policeman	**Neil Cole**

TECHNICAL

Story Code	**BFPSASCD03**
Recorded Date	**February 2005**
Release Date	**July 2005**
Place of Recording	**The Moat Studios, London**
Number of CDs	**2**
Total Duration	**110' 27"**
Number of Episodes	**4**
Duration of Episodes	**1 (28' 14")**
	2 (28' 14")
	3 (25' 51")
	4 (30' 38")
ISBN	**1-84435-141-6**

SYNOPSIS

A London historical recordings building in 2004 holds a mystery: a phonograph recording of Sapphire's voice from the 1890s. When Sapphire and Steel arrive to investigate they find that Silver has already arrived at the Archive before them. He is looking into the past of the building via a series of time bubbles that inhabit the building. Joining the investigation, Sapphire and Steel meet German inventor Weyburn, a man who photographed the clinically insane believing it would cure them. They then learn that the building was created on the site of victims of the plague. Steel soon exhibits symptoms of the plague, leaving Silver and Sapphire to continue their detective work. However, they become trapped in the past. Sapphire meets a Dr Webber, a man imprisoned there in perpetuity in a time loop. The temporal anomaly has been created by an entity called 'Maldeb', which turns out to be his imaginary friend that has been given life. First born in the 17th century, Webber invented Maldeb (Bedlam spelt backwards) to get over his loneliness. Determined that she would always have company of her own, Maldeb subsequently used her powers to constantly reincarnate Webber… a man who would eventually be reborn as the Weyburn of 2004. Knowing that he would one day meet Sapphire and Steel, Webber's intent is to trap Sapphire, having sent out shards of time in order to draw her towards him. However, Sapphire tries to stop Maldeb from escaping by placing both of them in a perpetual time loop of her own. Back in 2004, Silver realises that Maldeb is imbued in Weyburn's journal, and finally destroys her by setting fire to it. By burning the entire journal, the break in time is eradicated and all three agents are restored to the present. Silver takes his leave, saying to his fellow agents, "Nice to see both of you but my services are required elsewhere… If you ever need me, just ask."

TRIVIA

- David Collings reprises the role of Silver for the first time in **Sapphire & Steel** since the broadcast of **Assignment Six** in 1981. He also played the Doctor in David Bishop's **Doctor Who Unbound** play, **Full Fathom Five #3**. Other work for Big Finish would see David playing the villainous Gabriel Sanders throughout the second series of **Jago & Litefoot**. He also appeared in the **Doctor Who** TV stories **Revenge of the Cybermen** and **The Robots of Death**, both opposite Tom Baker, and **Mawdryn Undead** with Peter Davison.
- There was a six-month gap between drafts of the script because the production got held over to a later recording block.
- The original opening of the story was set on a London Underground train but this was changed as it was too similar to that of **The Passenger #1**.
- David Bishop's original proposal had the trigger as a diary into which Sapphire wrote herself rather than an antiquated recording device.

PRODUCTION SUMMARY

"Another 'traditional' story, not really my favourite but it was good to have a contrast with the more challenging scripts that surrounded it. We had to do a fair bit of jiggling the story a bit, as I remember, as it was all rather visual to start with."
Nigel Fairs

WORKING TITLE(S)

Bedlam.

RETURNING MONSTERS/CHARACTERS

Silver.

THE LIGHTHOUSE

#1.4

SYNOPSIS

Sapphire and Steel are investigating the events of Penryth Point Lighthouse, a building that dates back to 1858. In 2004 the lighthouse is occupied by a homophobic mass murderer known as Nicholas, an artist who sketches nude men then kills them as a reaction against his own homosexual nature. In 1972 Nicholas arrives at the lighthouse with his wife Suzy and best friend Adrian, a friend he secretly loves. Beaten by a father who only respected him when he got married, Nicholas had spent his younger years experimenting with Adrian, a past he tries to bury. When Nicholas's father learnt of his homosexuality he held him down and slit his back open with a knife, an act of domestic violence that left scars both physical and mental. Having then been taken away from his parents by social services, Nicholas's fragile psyche is finally driven to breaking point by denying his own nature and fear that his wife will find out. His self-hatred causes him to kill his wife and then embark on a killing spree that lasts between the two time periods. Both Sapphire and Steel are thrown outside of events in a time storm and are unable to stop the disruptions in time. However, as a result of the disruptions the older Nicholas is able to meet his own younger self and try to convince him to be with Adrian in order to stop him becoming a killer. Unable to change his younger self's mind, time remains on course, leaving the older Nicholas to become even more vengeful. Steel realises that the trigger causing the time storm is not only a painting but also the knife Nicholas uses to kill himself as an old man. With too much blood on it, it's only when Steel convinces the older Nicholas to kill himself with a gun that time is put right.

TRIVIA

- **The Lighthouse** was partly based on a stage play by Nigel Fairs that was originally set on a railway station, which was itself inspired by **Sapphire & Steel**, involving a JB Priestley-style time shift.
- The only actor to appear in both was Michael Adams, who played the rent boy.
- Suzanne Procter also acted in the original stage play, and is the person singing on the soundtrack for the Big Finish version.
- There was a three-month gap in the release schedule between **All Fall Down #1.3** and this, the fourth play.

PRODUCTION SUMMARY

"This was based on a stage play in which the 'ghosts' we saw in the first act (set in 1972) were actually from the future, and the interaction had effects on the people they'd seen in the past. Very **S&S** I thought, so I pitched it to Jason, this time set on a lighthouse. He decided there was only plot enough to sustain two episodes, which I should have disagreed with, as this didn't allow the plot to breathe and in effect pushed Sapphire and Steel out of a lot of the action. In the four-part version we'd go through the whole plot and then it'd start again, but this time involving Sapphire and Steel, changing everything, literally creating a 'time storm'. It wasn't to be, alas. Having said that I thought there were some great performances and I loved the music, using Suzanne Procter, who'd been in the original stage play."
Nigel Fairs

WORKING TITLE(S)

The Darkest Room.

RETURNING MONSTERS/CHARACTERS

None.

CREW

Writer	**Nigel Fairs**
Director	**John Ainsworth**
Producer	**Nigel Fairs**
Executive Producer	**Jason Haigh-Ellery**
Original Series Creator	**PJ Hammond**
Music and Sound Design	**Nigel Fairs**
Cover Art	**Andrew Orton**
Theme	**Cyril Ornadel**

CAST

Steel	**David Warner**
Sapphire	**Susannah Harker**
Adrian	**Joseph Young**
Old Man	**Neil Savage**
Nick	**Ian Hallard**
Suzy	**Lucy Beresford**
Mike	**Michael Adams**
Young Nick	**Stuart Piper**

TECHNICAL

Story Code	**BFPSASCD04**
Recorded Date	**August 2004**
Release Date	**November 2005**
Place of Recording	**The Moat Studios, London**
Number of CDs	**1**
Total Duration	**73' 00"**
Number of Episodes	**2**
Duration of Episodes	**1 (32' 52")**
	2 (33' 58")
ISBN	**1-84435-140-8**

#1.5 DEAD MAN WALKING

CREW

Writer	**Nigel Fairs (based on a story by John Ainsworth)**
Director	**Nigel Fairs**
Producer	**Nigel Fairs**
Executive Producer	**Jason Haigh-Ellery**
Original Series Creator	**PJ Hammond**
Music and Sound Design	**Nigel Fairs**
Cover Art	**Andrew Orton**
Theme	**Cyril Ornadel**

CAST

Steel	**David Warner**
Sapphire	**Susannah Harker**
Silver	**David Collings**
Michael Kent	**Trevor Littledale**
Marian Anderson	**Jo Castleton**
Richard Hanmore	**Arthur Bostrom**
Ian Jackson	**Neil Cole**
Hammond	**Michael Chance**
Mo Jackson	**Linda Bartram**

TECHNICAL

Story Code	**BFPSASCD05**
Recorded Date	**February 2005**
Release Date	**January 2006**
Place of Recording	**The Moat Studios, London**
Number of CDs	**1**
Total Duration	**62' 21"**
Number of Episodes	**2**
Duration of Episodes	**1 (34' 28") 2 (26' 09")**
ISBN	**1-84435-142-4**

SYNOPSIS

Sapphire and Steel investigate Blackledge Prison, where prisoner Michael Kent had hanged himself the night before. While studying the place of Kent's death, Sapphire attempts to take time back to discover more. However, time reacts and Steel finds himself pulled back through time to 1968 and into the body of a child murderer also known as Michael Kent. There, Steel's abrasive attitude angers his already hostile fellow prisoners and they kill him, burying him in the prison yard. Back in 2004, Sapphire finds a contradiction in the prison warden's files – that there were two Michael Kents, the Kent that Steel occupies born in 1946 and imprisoned there in the sixties. However, she looks at the file again and finds that the listing has changed to include only the Kent admitted in September 2004. Meanwhile, in the pathologist's lab, Silver has arrived to join in the investigation, studying the remains of the murdered Kent. Also occupying both timelines is prison officer Jackson, the father of an eight-year-old boy, Marcus, who Kent was jailed for murdering. However, as Sapphire and Silver interrogate Jackson in 2004 they discover that he had actually killed his own son, and intended to frame Kent for it because of a money dispute between the two of them. Time was fractured at the point where time tricked Kent into killing his own son in a drunken rage instead of his wife, creating the two divergent realities. Sapphire and Silver travel back to put time on its correct course, removing Jackson's deal with time. Jackson once more kills his wife and his son is spared... Consequently, Kent was never jailed for the crime he didn't commit and Steel is returned to the present day. The three agents leave the prison, Sapphire wondering what the significance of the boy was to time. As they leave, the prison radio finishes playing a piece of classical music, identifying Marcus Jackson as the lead cellist.

ORIGINAL IDEA SYNOPSIS (by John Ainsworth)

How about a story set in a modern day prison where there have been 'strange happenings' which Sapphire and Steel come to investigate. The cause of the disturbances lie in the past where, for some reason, a hanging (or hangings) took place in 1966, one year after capital punishment for murder was abolished.

Perhaps Time (or some other entity) had a reason to see one of the inmates dead (to alter the future or take revenge?) and so manipulated the prison governor and wardens in to carrying out the execution. The problems manifesting themselves in the present day could be something to do with the grave being uncovered and the corpse being discovered.

Perhaps though, the hanged man, as well as being dead, is also alive! The entity bungled it somehow causing a 'time bubble' where events happened one way but outside of it they continued as they should have been. But there are some people who do actually have memories of the illegal execution (perhaps an elderly warden) as they crossed out of the bubble into normal time. Perhaps, as well as the discovery of the body the 'spooky goings-on' have been precipitated by the incarceration of an elderly con at the prison - the very same man who was executed forty years ago! But was he guilty of the crime that he was (or wasn't) executed for?

The title would of course be 'Dead Man Walking'.

TRIVIA

- Arthur Bostrom (Richard Hanmore) is well known for his role as the policeman who mispronounced his words in the BBC sitcom *'Allo, 'Allo* which ran between 1982 and 1992.
- This release includes a music track of four minutes.
- Trevor Littledale (Michael Kent) has appeared in several Big Finish releases, most notably as TIM in **The Tomorrow People**, taking over voice duties from the late Philip Gilbert.
- A free promotional disc lasting 53'57" was included with the original CD release. The seventh track of this disc was a behind-the-scenes feature on **Sapphire & Steel** including interviews and clips.

PRODUCTION SUMMARY

"John's idea, which I ended up writing, from that one paragraph. Lovely to hear David reprise Silver; I think his scenes with Susie are a riot."
Nigel Fairs

WORKING TITLE(S)

None.

RETURNING MONSTERS/CHARACTERS

Silver.

Check box - CD ☐

THE SCHOOL

#2.1

SYNOPSIS

Sapphire and Steel investigate a school where disturbances have been detected. However, when they arrive, Sapphire senses everything is as it should be – a school that teaches 412 pupils of every school age from five to 16, 17 teachers and six other full-time staff. Yet as they explore they find the school is haunted by its own history... Entering its hundred-year anniversary, the memories, feelings and sensations of every pupil permeate the building and control Sapphire. Her empathic nature leads to her being taken over and reduced to a child-like state, wanting nothing more than to do finger painting. While in this state, Sapphire is repeatedly hit by teacher Mrs Leslie, who accuses Sapphire of thinking improperly about her teacher husband and wishes her to learn about the sin of temptation. Despite Steel bringing Sapphire back to her normal self, the nature of the school begins affecting her again as soon as he leaves her to investigate, causing her to become a sexually adventurous teenager. Meanwhile, Steel is surrounded by other teachers who are beginning to lose their memories of their colleagues. As the haunted presence of the school begins to take hold, even Steel's impenetrable nature is clouded, and he too becomes child-like in outlook, squabbling with Sapphire. Almost consumed by the school's strength, they pool their powers to restore themselves and uncover the real nature of the school. Mrs Leslie's husband had died and time had offered her a chance to bring him back using the school's unique properties. Yet, realising that her husband was consumed by the school and could never be the same man again, Mrs Leslie decides to let his memory fade. As she does so, the school too fades away... The entire building was an illusion created by Mrs Leslie as part of the deal.

TRIVIA

- Keith Drinkel (Mr Leslie) appeared in the 1982 **Doctor Who** TV story **Time-Flight** as Flight Engineer Scobie as well as the **Big Finish Main Monthly Range** release **Catch-1782 #68** and the **Bernice Summerfield** play **Timeless Passages #7.2**.
- The idea for this play was pitched to Nigel Fairs at the Regenerations convention in Swansea in September 2005.
- Simon Guerrier pretended that he and Nigel had already discussed it the previous evening... Even when Simon owned up, Nigel still let him write it!
- Simon Guerrier based Mr Leslie's speech on Tony Blair's speeches, which Simon had been transcribing as part of another job.

PRODUCTION SUMMARY

"I remember script editing this one whilst I was doing panto in Stafford – quite a contrast to the day job! I thought that the snogging between Sapphire and the head teacher was going a little far, but Simon insisted and in hindsight I think it was rather fun. As Simon will probably tell you, one of the remits of the story was to give David and Susie something interesting to do, as Sapphire and Steel are rather 'one-note characters'. Playing schoolchildren lived up to that – great performances."
Nigel Fairs

WORKING TITLE(S)

None.

RETURNING MONSTERS/CHARACTERS

None.

CREW
Writer	**Simon Guerrier**
Director	**Nigel Fairs**
Producer	**Nigel Fairs**
Executive Producer	**Jason Haigh-Ellery**
Original Series Creator	**PJ Hammond**
Music and Sound Design	**Alistair Lock**
Cover Art	**Lee Binding**
Theme	**Cyril Ornadel**

CAST
Steel	**David Warner**
Sapphire	**Susannah Harker**
Mr Leslie	**Keith Drinkel**
Mrs Leslie	**Lisa Daniely**
Chatura	**Victoria Gould**
Max	**James Daniel Wilson**

TECHNICAL
Story Code	**BFPSASCD06**
Recorded Date	**February 2006**
Release Date	**July 2006**
Place of Recording	**The Moat Studios, London**
Number of CDs	**2**
Total Duration	**101' 03"**
Number of Episodes	**4**
Duration of Episodes	1 (20' 09") 2 (19' 08") 3 (21' 22") 4 (23' 09")
ISBN	**1-84435-218-8**

#2.2 THE SUREST POISON

CREW

Writer	**Richard Dinnick**
Director	**Nigel Fairs**
Producer	**Nigel Fairs**
Executive Producer	**Jason Haigh-Ellery**
Original Series Creator	**PJ Hammond**
Music and Sound Design	**Steve Foxon**
Cover Art	**Lee Binding**
Theme	**Cyril Ornadel**

CAST

Steel	**David Warner**
Sapphire	**Susannah Harker**
Webb	**Richard Franklin**
Breget	**Tom Bevan**
Gerard	**Eric MacLennan**
Cecile	**Helen Goldwyn**

TECHNICAL

Story Code	**BFPSASCD07**
Recorded Date	**February 2006**
Release Date	**September 2006**
Place of Recording	**The Moat Studios, London**
Number of CDs	**2**
Total Duration	**108' 46"**
Number of Episodes	**4**
Duration of Episodes	**1 (27' 18")**
	2 (29' 53")
	3 (24' 45")
	4 (14' 07")
ISBN	**1-84435-219-6**

SYNOPSIS

Sapphire and Steel arrive at a modern day clock auction where Sapphire has sensed disturbances in the nature of linear time. Greeted by clock expert and auctioneer Mr Webb, their suspicions are alerted even further as Sapphire senses he was born in the 1850s. They confront the man, only to find that he's an immortal, and he regards his immortality as a curse. After investigating further, the two agents discover that the disturbances in time emanate from two antique watches by the 18th century watchmaker Abraham Louis Breguet. Deciding to trace the time disturbances back to their source, they use the energy contained in the watches as a conveyance back to their point of origin. However, when they arrive at the point of the watch's creation they are met by an entity from outside time, a creature in the form of Breguet's late wife. The entity tricks Abraham, telling him that if it allows her to infect the watches with time then it will enable him to go back and save his wife's life. When Sapphire and Steel enter the timeline the entity expels them by throwing them forward to Jerusalem in 1983. Now without the watch to allow them to leave, in order to escape their surroundings they hunt down another watch and arrive back in the present day. There they use one of Breguet's other watches in Webb's collection to once more travel back through time, only to be continually buffeted throughout time by the entity. Attempts to confront the entity are fraught with danger... Steel is captured and tortured before Sapphire travels back in time with Webb and he manages to destroy the time-infected Grand Complication at its inception. This frees Steel and causes the banshee to disperse... With her destruction Breguet dies but Steel reveals that his genius for watchmaking was not all a result of his contact with time. His genius for clock mechanics can live on without being tainted, and Mr Webb, having achieved immortality through his close exposure to the watches, can look forward to finally dying.

TRIVIA

- This is the first **Sapphire & Steel** play to be based upon real events.
- Richard Dinnick originally included the characters of a Journalist and Sir David Salomans, the last owner of the Marie Antoinette watch before its theft from the Jerusalem museum in 1983.
- In 2009 – two years after the release of the play – it was reported that the Marie Antoinette watch, along with others, had been returned to the Jerusalem museum.
- Richard Franklin (Webb) is best known to SF fans for playing Captain Mike Yates in **Doctor Who** between 1971 and 1974.
- Episodes 3 and 4 involved a lot of (albeit logical) travelling up and down the timelines of the various Breguet watches, which was subsequently cut for the purposes of clarity.
- The CD includes a 20-minute behind-the-scenes feature.

PRODUCTION SUMMARY

"I think this arrived as a bit of a **Doctor Who** script rather than **Sapphire & Steel** as I saw it. A lot of time-travelling and linear storytelling, with everything explained for the listener! One of the things that made **Sapphire & Steel** different (and interesting) was the lack of explanation about how they got where and when they were going and the great mystery about their origins and mission. I think I made the script more **S & S** but there was a nice central concept about watches."

Nigel Fairs

WORKING TITLE(S)

None.

RETURNING MONSTERS/CHARACTERS

None.

WATER LIKE A STONE

#2.3

SYNOPSIS

Disturbances in time have been plaguing director Arthur Bunnings' Capital Palace Theatre. When Sapphire and Steel arrive to investigate, there's a reference to the first television story as they see a poster for a (fictitious) play called *The Abandoned Lady*. Sapphire asks if Steel recognises the ship (a reference to the Mary Celeste of the first television story, Assignment One). Unfortunately for the two elements, they are joined on the assignment by Ruby, an agent who is far less disciplined than Sapphire and Steel. Ruby appears to be jealous of both Sapphire (to whom her greeting is, "Hello, Sapphire. Long time no nothing") as well as the closeness of her relationship with Steel. In an attempt to impress Steel, Ruby opens up a fissure between reality and the fiction of the plays performed there, becoming part of *Great Expectations*. However, her actions unwittingly mire their investigations because Sapphire and Steel are dragged into the fiction, becoming characters in *Cinderella* and *The Flood*.

Ruby manages to free herself, then her two fellow agents, but is once more dragged back into the fiction, trapped inside all the plays performed at the Capital Palace in its history. Her every attempt to escape is thwarted as she keeps getting pulled back into a loop of a music hall performance, with reality falling further from her grasp. Sapphire and Steel become gradually more immersed in the music hall tradition, threatening once more to lose their own sense of identity. However, they eventually find out that the time disturbances are attributed to Louisa, a teenage girl who died travelling to the theatre to meet her lover in 1824. With her spirit haunting the building, she is only exorcised after Sapphire and Steel convince Louisa to come to terms with her death. Louisa's passing over into the next plane of existence means that time manipulation is no longer present at the theatre and the gateway between reality and fiction is forever sealed. Sapphire is distraught as Ruby is trapped in a world of fiction…

TRIVIA

- This is the first appearance of the recurring character Ruby (played by Lisa Bowerman of **Bernice Summerfield** fame). It is also the first time that an element features in a **Sapphire & Steel** play that is not mentioned in the opening titles.
- Nigel Fairs wrote the play with Louise Jameson and Toby Longworth in mind for the guest roles.
- During the approval process, Nigel was asked whether he had the rights to include the *Poor Little Dolly* song, which he had actually written himself!

PRODUCTION SUMMARY

"Intended as a Christmas Special, starring Louise Jameson and Toby Longworth. I'm rather fond of it. I love the scenes at the end when we discover the ghost story – I pictured it like one of those lush atmospheric BBC dramas, shown on winter evenings, probably on Sunday."
Nigel Fairs

WORKING TITLE(S)

None.

RETURNING MONSTERS/CHARACTERS

None.

CREW

Writer	**Nigel Fairs**
Director	**John Ainsworth**
Producer	**Nigel Fairs**
Executive Producer	**Jason Haigh-Ellery**
Original Series Creator	**PJ Hammond**
Music and Sound Design	**Nigel Fairs**
Cover Art	**Lee Binding**
Theme	**Cyril Ornadel**

CAST

Steel	**David Warner**
Sapphire	**Susannah Harker**
Ruby	**Lisa Bowerman**
Arthur	**Nicholas Briggs**
The Girl	**Lucy Gaskell**
Dolly	**Suzanne Proctor**

TECHNICAL

Story Code	**BFPSASCD08**
Recorded Date	**9 & 10 August 2006**
Release Date	**December 2006**
Place of Recording	**The Moat Studios, London**
Number of CDs	**2**
Total Duration	**101' 24"**
Number of Episodes	**4**
Duration of Episodes	**1 (20' 29")**
	2 (28' 03")
	3 (20' 43")
	4 (20' 12")
ISBN	**1-84435-221-8**

SECTION 13 | CHARACTER PROFILE

The character of Ruby was introduced by Nigel Fairs in the second season of the Big Finish **Sapphire & Steel** range. Her purpose was to allow the producer and writers to explore aspects of the mysterious elements or time agents that had not previously been revealed.

'I was very interested in exploring what the elements were and their relationship to humanity, which is why we brought in Gold and Ruby,' explains Nigel. 'I didn't want to make their origins explicit – one of the best things about the series, I feel, is that very little is explained – but to raise questions. I think the closest we got to it was when Ruby lets Arthur (played by Nick Briggs) character "see into her music" in **Water Like a Stone #2.3**. I like that scene!'

The character first appeared in **Water Like a Stone #2.3**, reappearing in **Cruel Immortality #2.4** and finally in **Second Sight #3.1** in which she performs a rescue mission on previous versions of Sapphire and Steel.

The part was written with Lisa Bowerman in mind. Lisa was already well known to Nigel Fairs and Jason Haigh-Ellery thanks to her long association with Big

Finish's very first franchise, **Bernice Summerfield**. 'Nigel had brought me on board to direct – for which I'll forever be grateful – so you could say it was a cheap option because I was around for the directing anyway,' jokes Lisa.

Here, Lisa shares her further thoughts on the character and her role in the series overall.

What was the process of character development? How did the arc structure come into focus?

It's always hard to fit in a new character (or element in this case) into a very established double act, as there's always a danger it will unbalance it. However, I think Nigel had very clear ideas how all the elements (including Gold and Silver) would fit into the stories. The character was very clearly delineated when I got the scripts – so she came fully formed – on the page anyway. The story arc became fairly clear early on, as the stories all linked after **Water Like a Stone #2.3**.

Did you have any input into Ruby's background?

As I've said, the character was pretty well laid out by Nigel in the scripts, especially in relations with both Steel (had they or hadn't they?) and with Sapphire (who saw her as a bit of an interloper, I think!) There was no particular reason to put a lot of input into Nigel's ideas, as they were all great. I also think that the character had enormous fun at both Sapphire AND Steel's expense. I do particularly like the way she described herself and her 'forte' to Nick Brigg's character where she talks about her resonances with music... I think that puts her into context pretty well.

What do you think of Big Finish's attempt to expand the number of semi-regulars in Sapphire & Steel?

I rather liked that. When you're picking up an established TV series and intending to develop it, it would seem foolish not to want to move things on a little – you can't just set it in aspic and expect to keep people's interest. It was a great opportunity to develop in a way that was never explored in the original TV series. It was still very much Sapphire and Steel's series, and I don't think any of the others (Gold, Silver or Ruby) were ever allowed to unbalance that. I thought it was a great opportunity to bring out different facets of both Sapphire and Steel's character (who by the nature of the original programme were both rather blank and deliberately left as enigmas) the interaction with the other elements gave the writers a great opportunity to explore their characters further.

You took on directorial duties in Season Two. What was that like?

I loved it. I'd only directed once before... for Nigel

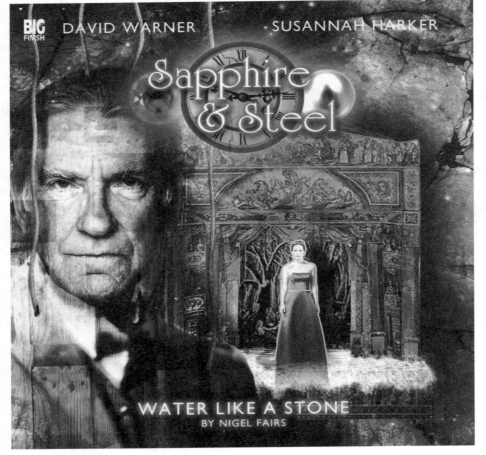

BIG FINISH | DAVID WARNER | SUSANNAH HARKER

Sapphire & Steel

WATER LIKE A STONE
BY NIGEL FAIRS

RUBY

again, on one of the **Tomorrow People** audios. This time though – I had a treat with some really stunning scripts, and had the opportunity not only to work with an equally stunning regular cast, but also cast some actors I'd always admired in parts that were well written, and satisfying for them to perform. I was really spoilt.

How was your relationship with Nigel?

Really good! As with all the Big Finish stuff I've directed, I've had free rein to cast who I like, and with the calibre of scripts and regular cast, there was never any argument about how creatively we went about it. As a producer he gave me the freedom to do what I wanted. But also it was collaborative, as he was also editing some himself. I'd go down to his house and I'd listen to the edit with a couple of other friends of his who acted as his "focus group". The episodes he wrote were also first rate – so there were no embarrassing silences when I read them, and gave my opinion!

What future do you think there might be for
Sapphire & Steel **– and Ruby?**

I really, genuinely hope that there is a future for Sapphire & Steel. As with all Big Finish products,

everything is dictated to by sales, and I think that, as far as I'm aware, that was the only reason it ground to a halt. I'm still really proud of the work we did on it, and it's a class product…. and also, I really miss Ruby. I loved playing her – a million miles away from Benny and great fun to do!

Top:
Big Finish's original audio star, Lisa Bowerman, joined Sapphire and Steel as Ruby.

#2.4 CRUEL IMMORTALITY

CREW

Writer	**Nigel Fairs**
Director	**Lisa Bowerman**
Producer	**Nigel Fairs**
Executive Producer	**Jason Haigh-Ellery**
Original Series Creator	**PJ Hammond**
Music and Sound Design	**Nigel Fairs**
Cover Art	**Lee Binding**
Theme	**Cyril Ornadel**

CAST

Steel	**David Warner**
Sapphire	**Susannah Harker**
Mrs P	**Muriel Pavlow**
Enid	**Daphne Oxenford**
Stanley	**Ian Burford**
Matron	**Lois Baxter**
The Carers	**Lucy Gaskell**
	Steven Kynman
	Lisa Bowerman
	Nigel Fairs

TECHNICAL

Story Code	**BFPSASCD09**
Recorded Date	**10 & 11 August 2006**
Release Date	**February 2007**
Place of Recording	**The Moat Studios, London**
Number of CDs	**2**
Total Duration	**104' 13"**
Number of Episodes	**4**
Duration of Episodes	**1 (26' 23")**
	2 (24' 49")
	3 (25' 50")
	4 (23' 31")
ISBN	**1-84435-220-X**

SYNOPSIS

Steel has ended his partnership with Sapphire after finding her too emotionally involved with their cases. The entrapment of Ruby in **Water Like a Stone** has brought things to a head. Steel finds himself in a nursing home in 1949. With Steel's memories fading as he begins to become human, he finds himself surrounded by sinister carers who torture the elderly patrons. Over time Steel's memories begin to resurface and he pieces together the true nature of the nursing home: a trap by the transient beings. They have placed people into the form of the elderly in the home as 'reflections' of their true selves who are, in fact, the sadistic carers. The carers have become sadistic because they know their patients to be immortal and think it is a squandered gift. They do not realise that they're actually torturing themselves. Steel realises that the whole thing is a prison devised by the Transuranics, but he finds himself growing ever more primitive and losing the mental ability to think of a way out. This is Steel's biggest fear, built as part of the trap: the horror of becoming human. In the middle of the trap is a bestial creature that is really a version of Sapphire without voice or reason. However, Sapphire has two 'reflections' in the home: the other being a shadow of herself known as 'Mrs P', an elderly resident suffering from dementia. It's left to what remains of Sapphire to carve a trans-dimensional chess set, and connect with Ruby by reading a book of one of the fictions in which she is trapped. The chess set activates as it is being used over another dimension, and Ruby is freed. Ruby then returns the favour and frees Sapphire and Steel from their own trap. As Ruby makes her goodbyes, Sapphire and Steel resume their partnership once more.

TRIVIA

- **Cruel Immortality** was written in a fortnight by Nigel Fairs as a replacement for Gary Russell's story, *Big Fun*, after Gary left Big Finish and did not have time to write the script.
- The release was accompanied by an hour-long behind-the-scenes disc when sold to subscribers.
- Daphne Oxenford was one of the original cast-members in *Coronation Street*, playing Esther Hayes. She had a minor role in the **Doctor Who** TV adventure **Dragonfire** and appeared in deleted scenes on the DVD release of series five, as the old Agatha Christie in **The Unicorn and the Wasp**.
- The play marks the directorial debut of Lisa Bowerman.
- Nigel wrote the script in a fortnight and at one point had blood poisoning so had to write part of it in hospital!

PRODUCTION SUMMARY

"This was a last-minute replacement but it's my favourite! The cast are magnificent, probably the best we ever had, and the joy of hearing Daphne reading Tennyson! What a legend. The ladies were wonderful, dressed immaculately and so pleased to be working. A wonderful day and Alistair did a superb job on the post production and music."
Nigel Fairs

WORKING TITLE(S)

Big Fun.

RETURNING MONSTERS/CHARACTERS

Ruby.

Check box - CD ■

PERFECT DAY

#2.5

SYNOPSIS

Eight years ago, the luxury yacht *Perfect Day* vanished without trace during the wedding of Richard Muldoon and Jennifer Holloway. All 13 passengers and the ship's captain were never seen again. When Sapphire and Steel arrive it becomes clear that those aboard the *Perfect Day* are re-enacting events. As Gold joins them, Sapphire and Steel discover that the humans are all complicit in the charade. It is revealed that the bride's mother, Lydia Holloway, has done a deal with a splinter of time. It showed her the future in which her daughter's life is marred by horrific events such as a miscarriage. So she and the rest have agreed to live in a bubble of time, repeating the same day ad infinitum. Gold becomes trapped in a ship in a bottle – a faultless replica of the *Perfect Day*. He works out that the model represents all the possible futures of the ship – it is the trigger. Gold manages to contact Steel while Sapphire confronts the Captain. He tells her that Lydia gained control of time by threatening to smash the bottle. When Sapphire shoots it with the Captain's service revolver, it is revealed that the Captain is the splinter of time. He tells them that Gold is now dead and then takes time back for him and Sapphire. When it appears that Lydia has shot Sapphire dead, Steel sends an SOS because he believes his partner and Gold to be dead. However, it is Gold who responds. Gold then stops the ship's engines and they confront the splinter. It is revealed that time has inadvertently caused a temporal paradox because it forgot to include the gun when he took time back. The splinter bargains with Steel to bring Sapphire back to life – and he agrees. However, Steel reneges on the deal, revealing that in actual fact the bottle that Sapphire shot was a former version, thus giving the splinter just an illusion of freedom. Time then returns to normal, although the passengers remember what has happened.

TRIVIA

- Philip McGough (The Captain) is well known for the role of Dr Charlie Bradfield in the BBC drama *Doctors*. He also played Dr Malcolm Nicholson in the ITV drama *Bad Girls*.
- Nigel announced this story as *Time Springs* at a convention in Chicago. This was the first title Steve Lyons had given to him.
- Originally, the play was going to take place in a big, airy village – the opposite of most **Sapphire & Steel** settings – but the more Steve worked on it, the more he realised that the story worked much better in a more traditional, claustrophobic setting, so he changed it to a yacht.

PRODUCTION SUMMARY

"Not one of my favourites if I'm honest, but it was interesting to hear the story of Gold moving on a little and Mark always gives a fabulous performance."
Nigel Fairs

WORKING TITLE(S)

Time Springs.

RETURNING MONSTERS/CHARACTERS

Gold.

CREW

Writer	**Steve Lyons**
Director	**Lisa Bowerman**
Producer	**Nigel Fairs**
Executive Producer	**Jason Haigh-Ellery**
Original Series Creator	**PJ Hammond**
Music and Sound Design	**Nigel Fairs**
Cover Art	**Lee Binding**
Theme	**Cyril Ornadel**

CAST

Steel	**David Warner**
Sapphire	**Susannah Harker**
Gold	**Mark Gatiss**
Lydia	**Victoria Carling**
The Captain	**Philip McGough**
Richard	**Daniel Weyman**
James	**Matthew Steer**
Jennifer	**Caroline Morris**

TECHNICAL

Story Code	**BFPSASCD10**
Recorded Date	**December 2006**
Release Date	**April 2007**
Place of Recording	**The Moat Studios, London**
Number of CDs	**2**
Total Duration	**112' 16"**
Number of Episodes	**4**
Duration of Episodes	**1 (29' 52")**
	2 (28' 45")
	3 (28' 57")
	4 (30' 38")
ISBN	**1-84435-222-6**

#2.6

THE MYSTERY OF THE MISSING HOUR

CREW

Writer	**Joseph Lidster**
Director	**Nigel Fairs**
Producer	**Nigel Fairs**
Executive Producer	**Jason Haigh-Ellery**
Original Series Creator	**PJ Hammond**
Music and Sound Design	**Nigel Fairs**
Cover Art	**Lee Binding**
Theme	**Cyril Ornadel (arranged by Nigel Fairs)**

CAST

Steel	**David Warner**
Sapphire	**Susannah Harker**
Narrator	**Colin Baker**
Lady Marjorie	**Sarah Douglas**
Arthur	**Ian Hallard**
Jane	**Cate Debenham Taylor**
Cornelius	**Ian Brooker**
MC	**Nigel Fairs**

TECHNICAL

Story Code	**BFPSASCD11**
Recorded Date	**December 2006**
Release Date	**June 2007**
Place of Recording	**The Moat Studios, London**
Number of CDs	**2**
Total Duration	**138' 09"**
Number of Episodes	**3**
Duration of Episodes	**1 (31' 58")**
	2 (37' 28")
	3 (68' 43")
ISBN	**1-84435-223-4**

SYNOPSIS

A narrator tells the story of how he met up with two famous detectives known as Shuffle and Sixpence in the Cairo of 1926. In the Cairo Hilton on December 3rd at 8pm a body is discovered. The female victim left her group of friends only a few minutes earlier, but when she is examined by a doctor, he pronounces that she had somehow been killed an hour before discovery. This is the impossible murder mystery at the heart of Shuffle and Sixpence's strange investigation. The people the detectives are mingling with seem a little two-dimensional and even seem to be delivering lines (sometimes with mistakes) as if they are role-playing. The scenario then becomes even stranger when references to various metals: gold, silver and steel cause the two detectives to begin perceiving that all is not as it seems. Shuffle comes to realise that he is in fact a being called Steel and that his partner is not Sixpence but Sapphire.

As this knowledge brings Sapphire and Steel to their senses, the whole reality of the Cairo Hilton setting and its group of people breaks down and instead, they find themselves in a recording studio. The year is 2007 and Big Finish is recording a play and all the people that Sapphire and Steel now find around them are actors saying lines in a recording booth and crew in the production office. Behind it all is Stephen Bunnings – the father of Arthur Bunnings who appeared in the earlier play **Water Like a Stone #2.3** as a writer. He has managed to achieve immortality through his writing by doing a deal with time. In a desperate bid to prevent time breaking in, Sapphire and Steel convince Arthur to reject the deal, causing him to be returned to reality… and Sapphire and Steel to be trapped on a compact disc which will erase them from existence the moment it finishes playing…

TRIVIA

- The basis for this script came about after a conversation between Joe Lidster and Nigel Fairs following the recording of **Daisy Chain #1.2**. After the recording of **Daisy Chain**, Joe went out for a drink with Nigel Fairs and some of the cast. He happened to use the phrase "between the wars" which is a quote from a French and Saunders sketch about the BBC TV Series *The House of Elliot*. The sketch is full of anachronisms and pokes fun at the melodramatic and pulpy soap opera aspects of the series. "Nigel overheard me saying this," remembers Joe, "and we decided that something along those lines could make for an interesting **Sapphire & Steel** story."
- Joe says this was one of the hardest scripts he has ever had to write. "There needed to be a genuine murder mystery and it needed to be funny but not too OTT," he says. "It needed to have the sinister elements that make **Sapphire & Steel** work but it also needed to be completely bizarre!"
- A song that the band play in the background is a different version of the song Joe wrote for his first **Sapphire & Steel** play. A dance remix of the same song appears in his **Tomorrow People** play, **Aftermath #5.2**.
- This release features a rearranged version of the **Sapphire & Steel** theme to reflect the crime novel genre in which it is set.

PRODUCTION SUMMARY

"One of my favourites. Joe Lidster created a rip-roaring parody of a badly made Agatha Christie audio play, which then, turned on its head in the final episode, revealed the chilling truth – that Sapphire and Steel are trapped on the CD you're playing and that all the actors are dead. Once again Joe pushed the boundaries with this one and there are moments we still quote to each other on a regular basis."
Nigel Fairs

WORKING TITLE(S)

None.

RETURNING MONSTERS/CHARACTERS

None.

SECOND SIGHT

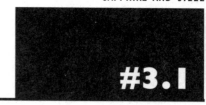

#3.1

SYNOPSIS

Sapphire and Steel are investigating the disappearance of a young male in an old house during 1987. While aspects of their new assignment seem familiar to them, their own natures do not: Steel is the easy-going, open-natured one, and Sapphire is the cold, terse and combative element. Even more unusually, they both speak with Australian accents. The alternative personas are an ongoing part of a trap in which the real Sapphire and Steel still exist behind the alternative personas as part of a dramatic play on a compact disc. The two agents have managed to create reality fissures as a way back into the real world, but unfortunately for them the transient beings are aware of this. They have placed real people into the fissures to prevent their escape, building the real people as characters within the fictions in which they are bound. Sapphire and Steel travel through many audio CDs in order to reach one that will finally attract Ruby's attention. After long periods of moving through songs and storybook plays they finally make Ruby aware of their predicament. Ruby widens the fissure to release her two fellow agents, but unfortunately she also releases the alternative Australian personas, who then take on a life of their own when brought over to reality. The two Australian elements embrace as they realise that they must be deleted, with just one night left together. As they fade away, the real Steel stores them both on a spare compact disc as a keepsake, leaving Sapphire, Steel and Ruby ready to return to fresh adventures. However, Sapphire and Steel's escape from the trap may not be all that it seems: at the end of the CD as it reaches the end of the last track, Steel's voice can be heard saying, "Hello? Can anyone hear me? Can you hear me?"

TRIVIA

- Like **Cruel Immortality #2.4**, Nigel wrote this script in a hurry (48 hours) when Joe Lidster had to pull out of writing the first story of season three.
- The monologues that Sapphire and Steel are trapped in are from a stage play Nigel wrote called *Unsex Me Here*.
- This radio play was like Alan Bennett's *Talking Heads* so the 'new' theme tune used on this release is a tribute to the opening theme to that series of plays!
- Nigel had worked with Blair McDonough in panto, which is how he came to be cast. McDonough had previously played Stuart Parker in *Neighbours* and prior to that was the runner-up on the first series of the Australian version of *Big Brother*.

PRODUCTION SUMMARY

"The actors and studios had been booked, but I had no scripts! Joe and I had always intended to launch the third season with a 'different' Sapphire and Steel and because I'd worked with Blair we thought it would be brilliant to make them Australian. To this day I've never read Joe's opening episode because it arrived with the email saying he couldn't write any more, so I started again from scratch."
Nigel Fairs

WORKING TITLE(S)

Reborn.

RETURNING MONSTERS/CHARACTERS

Ruby.

CREW

Writer	**Nigel Fairs**
Director	**Nigel Fairs**
Producer	**Nigel Fairs**
Executive Producer	**Jason Haigh-Ellery**
Original Series Creator	**PJ Hammond**
Music and Sound Design	**Nigel Fairs**
Cover Art	**Simon Holub**
Theme	**Cyril Ornadel**

CAST

Steel	**Blair McDonough**
Sapphire	**Anna Skellern**
Ruby	**Lisa Bowerman**
Mary	**Patience Tomlinson**
Polly	**Clare Calbraith**
Davey	**Duncan McInnes**

TECHNICAL

Story Code	**BFPSASCD12**
Recorded Date	**10, 11, 12 December 2007**
Release Date	**April 2008**
Place of Recording	**The Moat Studios, London**
Number of CDs	**2**
Total Duration	**104' 01"**
Number of Episodes	**4**
Duration of Episodes	**1 (27' 41")**
	2 (25' 59")
	3 (20' 43")
	4 (18' 30")
ISBN	**978-1-84435-336-1**

#3.2 REMEMBER ME

CREW

Writer	**John Dorney**
Director	**Lisa Bowerman**
Producer	**Nigel Fairs**
Executive Producer	**Jason Haigh-Ellery**
Original Series Creator	**PJ Hammond**
Music and Sound Design	**Nigel Fairs**
Cover Art	**Simon Holub**
Theme	**Cyril Ornadel**

CAST

Steel	**David Warner**
Sapphire	**Susannah Harker**
Eric	**Sam Kelly**
Kate	**Joannah Tincey**
The Nostalgia	**David Horovitch**

TECHNICAL

Story Code	**BFPSASCD13**
Recorded Date	**10, 11, 12 February 2008**
Release Date	**May 2008**
Place of Recording	**The Moat Studios, London**
Number of CDs	**2**
Total Duration	**124' 45"**
Number of Episodes	**4**
Duration of Episodes	**1 (29' 39")**
	2 (30' 55")
	3 (30' 59")
	4 (31' 51")
ISBN	**978-1-84435-337-8**

SYNOPSIS

A documentary is being filmed about Eric Gurney, a comedian and comedy actor in his late sixties with a faded career. Shot in an abandoned 1895 seaside musical hall, an entity from outside time has removed all the crew, leaving just Gurney and show runner Kate Lambert. Both of them are plagued by visions of people and sounds of laughter as the entity plays with their memories. When Sapphire and Steel arrive to investigate, the creature uses illusion to separate them from Gurney and then appears to Gurney as his estranged daughter. Manipulating Gurney to create distrust of Sapphire and Steel, the creature uses his memories to appear in other forms, such as his long-deceased comedy partner Charlie. With Gurney alone and open to temptation, the entity offers Gurney the chance to have the whole of reality restored to his wishes: including the return of his daughter and Charlie back from the dead. At the same time, Sapphire and Steel piece together what really happened from the moment they began their investigation: the television crew weren't taken, but left behind. Sapphire, Steel, Kate and Eric Gurney were all kidnapped into an alternate reality. Able to build events around them from memories of real happenings, the creature feeds on memories of the living and plans to grow and feed on the entire human race. In attempting to defeat the creature, the two agents realise that they've attempted to defeat it at least once before, but that the creature has altered their memories so they didn't recall a prior meeting. Discussing Eric's life, Sapphire realises that the creature has used Eric's guilt to enter the world: a man regretting the past as his affairs caused his wife to turn to alcoholism and die in an accident. With this information, Steel suggests their only course of action: to wipe Gurney's mind, so he no longer has any memories that the creature can inhabit. They leave Gurney in a vegetative state, though Sapphire muses over the nature of the entity... have they really defeated it, or has it controlled their memories so that they only think they have?

TRIVIA

- Sam Kelly (Eric) is well-known for his many comedic roles on TV, especially as Captain Hans Geering in BBC sitcom 'Allo, 'Allo which ran between 1982 and 1992.
- John Dorney's original concept had almost all the same plot beats. The main difference was that the older character in the original was female (and the story would have focused more heavily on the young nurse who became Kate than the older woman who became Gurney – in the final script it's the other way round).
- The original setting was a nursing home, which had to be changed after Nigel had used the setting in his own play the previous season.
- Gurney was originally called Eddie Grist – and one of his sitcoms would have been called 'Grist to the Mill'. But John thought it sounded too much like a made up name, so decided to go with the surname of a director friend of his – establishing his pattern of name-dropping friend's names wherever possible. For example – Derek Kettlety, the original owner of the pier, is named after a mate of his who he knew liked the audios.
- After the end credits Steel's voice can be heard saying, "Hello? If this is some kind of radio drama then presumably someone is listening. Can you hear me?"
- When the location needed to be changed, John looked for a new concept. He'd recently read Eric Sykes's autobiography, and needing to find someone new who could be lost in their memories, a character in this style seemed a useful one to run with. He thus wanted a location to match it and came up with the documentary concept and setting it in an old TV studio. But he then thought that TV studios are dull locations, usually just a vast empty room with little atmosphere, so wanted to find somewhere better. A daytrip to Brighton supplied the solution!

PRODUCTION SUMMARY

"Another one of my favourites. I was especially pleased with the post production and music I did on this one, though at the playback for Lisa, it broke her speakers!! A fabulous guest cast, thanks to David Warner, mainly! And a nice, tight script. Great stuff."
Nigel Fairs

WORKING TITLE(S)

The Nursing Home.

RETURNING MONSTERS/CHARACTERS

None.

ZERO

SYNOPSIS

The war with the transient beings is continuing, with Copper missing and Silver having only recently escaped from a möbius loop trap. In the middle of this, Gold is assigned to a 'routine intervention' on board the American space shuttle Aspirant. However, Silver is quickly sent to join him on the mission, something which Gold believes shows that he's not trusted, but which Silver believes is down to his inexperience. When they find corpses on board and something attempting to get in, Silver suggests they call in operatives as the mission is no longer a technical exercise. Gold disagrees, wanting to prove himself by completing the mission alone. When a sliver of an entity outside the vessel attacks, Sapphire and Steel arrive aboard the shuttle to help. As they investigate, all four agents keep hearing a radio voice that transmits despite the radio being disconnected, while Gold is infected with a virus that threatens to kill him. Gold manages to recover, and agrees to help Steel

with a dangerous plan: for Steel to lower his body temperature to freezing point and freeze the entity's slivers. However, when Steel and Gold are alone and Steel is frozen, Gold reveals his secret agenda… as a new recruit to the transient beings, he plans to leave Steel frozen forever. After Silver explores the outside of the shuttle in a spacesuit, Gold then disconnects his link to the craft, leaving him to drift off into space. However, Sapphire convinces Gold that his actions are wrong, and he agrees to thaw Steel. Meanwhile, Silver has held on to the outside of the craft and got back inside the shuttle, ready to challenge the entity that's attacking them – an entity that feeds on dreams and is using the shuttle to head to Earth. With the engines having been damaged as part of Gold's plan, the agents realise that the only way to stop the shuttle reaching Earth is to cause it to explode. Gold, the only one among them with the powers to cause such a feat, agrees to sacrifice himself to complete the mission.

TRIVIA

- This story sees the apparent demise of Gold.
- There is some hidden dialogue from Steel on the end of the 'Coming Soon' trailer.
- Angela Bruce (Andrea) is well known to SF fans for appearances in *Red Dwarf* (as Lister's female counterpart from an alternative reality). She also played Brigadier Winifred Bambera in the 1989 **Doctor Who** TV story **Battlefield** as well as in the Big Finish **Lost Stories** release **Animal #2.5**.
- This story also has a hidden piece of dialogue after the end credits, with Sapphire's voice saying: "Steel? It's cold."

PRODUCTION SUMMARY

"The final part of the Gold trilogy; my idea to get Silver and Gold in the same episode, and I think it worked very well indeed. The strangely unearthly setting gave it an entirely new atmosphere too."
Nigel Fairs

WORKING TITLE(S)

None.

RETURNING MONSTERS/CHARACTERS

Gold, Silver.

CREW

Writer	**Steve Lyons**
Director	**Lisa Bowerman**
Producer	**Nigel Fairs**
Executive Producer	**Jason Haigh-Ellery**
Original Series Creator	**PJ Hammond**
Music and Sound Design	**Nigel Fairs**
Cover Art	**Simon Holub**
Theme	**Cyril Ornadel**

CAST

Steel	**David Warner**
Sapphire	**Susannah Harker**
Silver	**David Collings**
Gold	**Mark Gatiss**
Andrea	**Angela Bruce**

TECHNICAL

Story Code	**BFPSASCD14**
Recorded Date	**10, 11, 12 December 2007**
Release Date	**June 2008**
Place of Recording	**The Moat Studios, London**
Number of CDs	**2**
Total Duration	**114' 57"**
Number of Episodes	**4**
Duration of Episodes	1 (27' 56")
	2 (27' 50")
	3 (27' 40")
	4 (27' 52")
ISBN	**978-1-84435-338-5**

#3.4 WALL OF DARKNESS

CREW

Writer	**Nigel Fairs**
Director	**Nigel Fairs**
Producer	**Nigel Fairs**
Executive Producer	**Jason Haigh-Ellery**
Original Series Creator	**PJ Hammond**
Music and Sound Design	**Nigel Fairs**
Cover Art	**Simon Holub**
Theme	**Cyril Ornadel**

CAST

Steel	**David Warner**
Sapphire	**Susannah Harker**
Sally	**Louise Jameson**
Justin	**Ian Hallard**
Russell	**Robert Maloney**
Jason	**Timothy Watson**
Miranda	**Joannah Tincey**

TECHNICAL

Story Code	**BFPSASCD15**
Recorded Date	**10, 11, 12 February 2008**
Release Date	**August 2008**
Place of Recording	**The Moat Studios, London**
Number of CDs	**2**
Total Duration	**129' 23"**
Number of Episodes	**4**
Duration of Episodes	**1 (31' 14")**
	2 (26' 36")
	3 (25' 20")
	4 (27' 52")
ISBN	**978-1-84435-339-2**

SYNOPSIS

An alternative reality sees the world of 2003 ravaged by nuclear war. Sapphire and Steel arrive a year later, where all that remains of San Francisco is an underground shopping mall. However, they become separated in divergent realities, including a reality where the war never took place. The rupture in time is traced back to Sally Brandon, a woman whose son killed a man in a traffic accident. That man would go on to write an inciting Presidential speech that would lead to the war. In the past Sally had been given a chance by time to have her other son returned to life, without realising that time would take her other son as a 'trade'. With her son Russell removed from time, the speechwriter was never killed and his actions led to war. Sally is killed so that she was never able to make the deal with time, yet the reality that remains is the one where the Earth is ravaged by war. The agents are left uncertain as to whether they've experienced anything real or whether they're still being manipulated by the entity from **Remember Me #3.2,** their memories and perceptions altered. Further revelations beset the two agents. A character called Justin is revealed to be an actor called Ian Hallard (who also appeared in stories from seasons one and two) who is trapped on the CD by an entity from outside of time. Sapphire is then surrounded by the sounds of their previous adventures. Eventually they find themselves in a library containing Big Finish CDs and novelisations of their TV adventures. Steel is separated from Sapphire and taunted by the creature that has trapped them. Asking how long they've been trapped for, Steel is told, "You always were… right from the very beginning." It's left ambiguous as to how long they've been trapped on the CD, whether it was since **The Mystery of the Missing Hour #2.6** or even that they are still trapped in the Café featured in the last TV story, **Assignment Six**.

TRIVIA

- Louise Jameson (Sally) is well known for her roles in **Doctor Who** (Leela), *Tenko* (Blanche), *Bergerac* (Susan) and *EastEnders* (Rosa). Most recently, Louise has been seen in several episodes of the 2011 series of ITV's hit drama *Doc Martin*.
- The second disc contains a behind-the-scenes feature lasting over 18 minutes.
- The idea with this story wasn't that Sapphire and Steel had never existed, which is how many people have taken the play. "The ending says the exact opposite," Nigel says. "Unlike any other 'fictional' characters, it says that Sapphire and Steel are real and that they are trapped in these dramas on your CDs – personally I find that chilling."

PRODUCTION SUMMARY

"I'm very fond of this one, though some people on the forums have been very vocal about their dislike of it. I'd love to say it's water off a duck's back, but these things are never easy to hear – of course one never intends to make one's work 'bad' and it's especially galling when criticism is unconstructive or cruel. However, a real highlight production-wise was Louise Jameson who gives a stunning performance as the mother whose life has been ripped apart by time."
Nigel Fairs

WORKING TITLE(S)

None.

RETURNING MONSTERS/CHARACTERS

'The Nostalgia', 'Ian Hallard'.

Check box - CD ■

Top:
The two Sapphires (l-r) Anna Skellern
and Susannah Harker.

Bottom:
The cast of series one's **All Fall Down** (l-r): David
Warner, Susannah Harker, David Collings, Suzanne
Procter, Kate Dyson and Michael Chance.

SECTION 14

HIGHLANDER

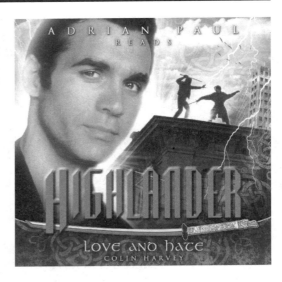

Very much like Big Finish's **Robin Hood** range, **Highlander** was a team effort. The two ranges came about at almost exactly the same time and were both released from April 2009 onwards. With Sharon Gosling producing, both Mark Wright and Cavan Scott were asked to script-edit the series, being fans of the **Highlander** films and TV series. 'There's something very satisfying about sending writers off with ideas and seeing what they come back with,' says Cav. 'There's always something new and unexpected.

Actor Adrian Paul had played the Immortal Duncan MacLeod for six seasons of **Highlander: The Series**, and he agreed to reprise the role for Big Finish in four brand new stories after producer Sharon Gosling entered negotiations with Paul's agent. With Adrian Paul in place, Mark and Cav were able to start planning stories based around Duncan in the style of the **Companion Chronicles** with a second voice joining Paul for each release

For three of the four slots, Mark and Cav approached experienced writers Trevor Baxendale and Jonathan Clements. 'I was asked if I'd like to contribute to the series and jumped at the chance,' says Trevor. 'I could scarcely believe my good fortune. One of the aspects of the series I enjoyed the most was the occasional flashback to Duncan's past, and I knew I wanted to write a story that would take place over his entire life.'

'Trevor was somebody we immediately thought of for the range,' says Mark. 'He always brings something highly atmospheric to the table, which is exactly what you need for a Highlander story. We had loved his contribution to *The Ghosts of Christmas* and we invited him to join us on **Robin Hood**.'

Trevor's original story was followed by Jonathan Clements's sequel to the TV show's opening episode of season three. 'It was actually script editor Cavan Scott's idea,' recalls Jonathan. 'He wanted to explore Duncan's Japanese past, but continuity's pretty tight on this. *The Samurai* by Naomi Janzen left me with questions that a new story could answer… Duncan kills a fellow Immortal who has boasted that the sword in his hand is a Muramasa. It's just a throwaway line in the episode, but it creates all sorts of story possibilities.'

'Again with Jonathan, he was an obvious fit for the series,' remembers Mark. 'He is so steeped in that world and we knew as soon as we were asked to script- edit the range that we wanted to work with Jonathan. And again, he would be alongside for two **Robin Hood** CDs at around the same time.'"

The third writer Cav and Mark chose was Colin Harvey who had contributed to the *Short Trips* anthologies Snapshots (edited by Joseph Lidster in

June 2007) and *The Ghosts of Christmas,* which the script editors had been in charge of themselves.

It was also decided that Cav and Mark would provide the final story of the first season. Due to their busy schedule, they had not contributed a script to Big Finish since their solo entries for the fourth season of **The Tomorrow People** in 2003. '**Kurgan Rising #1.4** was the first script we'd written ourselves for a while,' confirms Cav. 'So it was great to roll up our sleeves and get stuck back in. We wanted to continue tying the universes of the TV series and the original movie together. The Kurgan [the villain from the first Highlander movie] had already been mentioned in the TV show, and you always wondered what would have happened if it had been Duncan not Connor who faced the MacLeod's traditional enemy. This was our chance to find out!'

The plays were recorded over a two-day period at the end of January and beginning of February 2009 at the Moat Studios in London. Producer Sharon Gosling also fulfilled directorial duties for the four stories. Sound design was provided by Richard Dolmat while the series music – including a new theme tune – was composed by Big Finish stalwart, Jamie Robertson. His suite of music can be found on the CD/download of **Secret of the Sword #1.3**.

Amazingly, the news of the **Highlander** series was not announced on the Big Finish website; instead its launch was heralded in a podcast dated 4 April 2009, a mere three weeks before the first play's release.

The plays were well received by *Highlander* fans a second series was quickly commissioned. This time Paul Spragg would be in charge and James Swallow would be script editor. But we are getting ahead of ourselves – to March 2011, in fact…

SERIES 1

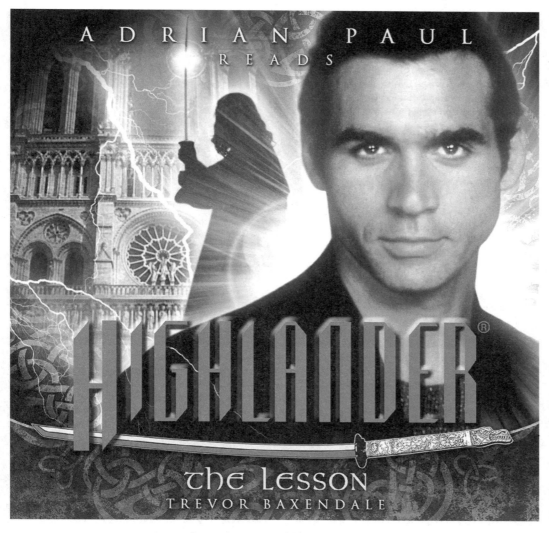

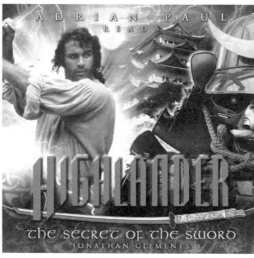

#1.1

THE LESSON

CREW

Writer	**Trevor Baxendale**
Director	**Sharon Gosling**
Producer	**Sharon Gosling**
Executive Producer	**Jason Haigh-Ellery**
Sound Design and Music	**Richard Dolmat, Jamie Robertson**
Cover Art	**Martin Stiff**
Theme	**Jamie Robertson**

CAST

Duncan MaCleod	**Adrian Paul**
Pieter Gatlan	**Trevor Cooper**

TECHNICAL

Story Code	**BFPHLCD01**
Recorded Date	**1 February 2009**
Release Date	**April 2009**
Place of Recording	**The Moat Studios, London**
Number of CDs	**1**
Total Duration	**69' 49"**
ISBN	**978-1-84435-358-3**

SYNOPSIS

In modern day Paris, Duncan MacLeod recalls his first meeting with another Immortal, the Russian Pieter Gatlan, in 1868. He duels with Duncan, and cuts his neck, but won't behead him to take the Quickening, saying he wants to play the Game a while longer. Back in the present day, Duncan finds an ornate knife sticking out of his boat's cabin, accompanied by a note from Gatlan. The pair have met up every ten years since their first encounter to fight, with Gatlan claiming the upper hand every time. Their second encounter came in Spain, and Duncan's friend Maria, who knows of Gatlan, tells another Immortal who won't play the Game, the Grandfather of Swords, that she thinks Duncan can beat Gatlan. In 1888, the pair meet again at a Zambezi staging post in Africa, then in 1898 in a Milan ballroom. After being bested in Italy, Gatlan staggers back, having been stabbed by Maria with a knife, but Duncan walks away without beheading his opponent. Duncan returns to his room to find Maria waiting on his bed – with her knife in her chest. This is the knife Duncan finds on his boat. He seeks out Gatlan, and they duel in the streets before moving into a car salesroom, where a dazed Duncan finds a cold blade against his neck. He brings up his knee and the pair fight with their hands, the Scotsman breaking his Russian rival's neck, and then realises why Gatlan has kept him alive. Rather than training him up to duel with Gatlan, his rival has been improving his fighting skills to better other Immortals, fattening him up for the Quickening that Gatlan aims to feast on from him. The swordfight restarts, with Duncan cutting off Gatlan's arm, but refuses to decapitate him. The Russian attacks again, the pair crashing through a window, but a sheet of glass falls down and cuts off Gatlan's head, ending their long conflict.

PLACEMENT

This story takes place between the films **Highlander: Endgame** and **Highlander: The Source**.

TRIVIA

- Prior to becoming an actor, Adrian Paul had been a dancer, model and choreographer. One of his early television roles was as a Russian ballet dancer in the short-lived spin-off from *Dynasty*, *The Colbys*, in 1987. Other TV appearances at this time included *Murder, She Wrote* and *Beauty and the Beast*. In 1992 he was cast as Duncan MacLeod in the spin-off television series from the **Highlander** movie franchise that had spawned three films starring Christopher Lambert. The series spanned six seasons until 1998, but Paul would return to the role in the movies **Highlander: Endgame** and **The Source** in 2000 and 2007. In 1997, Paul founded charitable organisation The Peace Fund.
- Trevor Cooper (Pieter Gatlan) is well known to SF fans as Colin Devis in the 1987 TV drama *Star Cops*. He also appeared in the 1985 **Doctor Who** TV story **Revelation of the Daleks** as Takis. Other roles in Big Finish productions include Shanks in **The Haunting of Thomas Brewster #107** and Smithy in **Castle of Fear #127**.

PRODUCTION SUMMARY

"I've always loved Trevor Baxendale's work, and here he provides a cracking season opener that shows off all the elements that a good **Highlander** story needs – villainous Immortals, swordplay, a battle through historical settings, with the notion of The Game and the Quickening right at its heart. And standing in the middle of it all is Duncan MacLeod, as heroic and brilliant as he ever was in **Highlander: the Series**. He was back, and there can be only one!"
Mark Wright

WORKING TITLE(S)

None.

RETURNING MONSTERS/CHARACTERS

None.

For the cover designs, Nick gave Alex Mallinson a free rein. 'Alex read the scripts and offered me the designs we used,' Nick says. 'He has a brilliant instinct, and when you can give him total freedom, unrestrained by formal approvals processes, he's particularly brilliant.'

The first two plays were released in November and December 2009 with the third following four months later. **Holmes and the Ripper** differed from the other two in that it was a full-cast drama rather than a dramatic reading. As the press release had stated, India Fisher appeared as Katherine Mead with Richard Earl taking on the role of Doctor John Watson with future **Doctor Who** companion actress Beth Chalmers appearing as Mrs Hudson.

As a promotion for the new range a special unabridged audio book of the Conan Doyle story **The Speckled Band** was released to subscribers on 13 May 2010. It was also a method of keeping the range's momentum going and as part of the related news story on the site, a second season of **Sherlock Holmes** plays was announced for later the same year, although, due to Nick's busy schedule, it ultimately failed to materialise until some time later.

One aspect of the new range that proved an education for the team was its promotion. 'We're still having difficulty knowing how to engage with the **Sherlock Holmes** audience because the fans are kind of everywhere, but how do you speak to them?' says Nick. 'We know how to speak to **Doctor Who** fans, it's second nature to us now.'

However, Nick managed to attract enough attention for the range to warrant a continuation. 'It was an experiment – a punt at doing it which has paid off,' says Nick. 'Luckily it's just about popular enough for us to do some more and now we're going to standardise it because I'm going to be playing Sherlock Holmes from now on.'

The plan for **Sherlock Holmes** was always to release a second season during 2011 with a mixture of adaptations of Conan Doyle tales alongside new, original adventures. 'They will be full cast dramas, but there will be an element of Doctor Watson's narration because I think that's how the original stories were told,' explains Nick enthusiastically. 'I think it's important to have that authentic voice, and on audio that can work well.'

Originally, **Doctor Who** script-editor Alan Barnes – a massive Holmes fan and published chronicler of the great detective's screen exploits – was going to join Nick for the second series to help out on the administration side of things. 'Yes, I was intending that Alan Barnes should work on the second series, as he's a great authority on Holmes and loves all that Victorian stuff,' Nick confirms. 'But he was far too busy on **Doctor Who**. Luckily, Richard Dinnick came to the rescue…'

#1.1 THE LAST ACT

CREW

Writer	**David Stuart Davies**
Director	**Nicholas Briggs**
Producer	**Nicholas Briggs**
Executive Producer	**Jason Haigh-Ellery**
Sound Design	**Nicholas Briggs**
Music	**Simon Slater, Jamie Robertson, Nicholas Briggs**
Cover Art	**Alex Mallinson**

CAST

Sherlock Holmes	**Roger Llewelyn**

TECHNICAL

Story Code	**BFPSHCD01**
Recorded Date	**10 September 2009**
Release Date	**November 2009**
Place of Recording	**The Moat Studios, London**
Total Duration	**69' 49"**
Number of CDs	**2**
Duration of Episodes	**118' 05"**
ISBN	**978-1-84435-454-2**

SYNOPSIS

Meeting an elderly Lestrade in 1916 after attending the funeral of his long-time associate, Dr John H. Watson, Holmes returns to 221B Baker Street and casts his eye over everything, which has a covering of dust, and tells Watson off for making his scientific investigations into stories. He recalls their first meeting, moving into his rooms, how he put his feelings for women aside, and how he felt lost when Watson married. Holmes reflects on the old days and comes to realise that not only was there so much that he had shared with Watson in his lifetime but also there was so much that he had not revealed to him: things he had kept hidden, including his deep affection for his friend. Imagining that Watson is present, Holmes addresses this failing and touches on aspects of past cases and the various characters he encountered during his investigations. He recalls investigating the death of the vicious Sir Eustace Blackenstall, bludgeoned to death with an iron poker, deducing his widow and her lover were responsible, and letting them go free. He admits his guilt at his drug taking and the fact he is still alive, while Watson is not. He remembers 'The Woman' Irene Adler and, of course, Professor Moriarty. He admits he felt bad for Watson after reading his own obituary, and how bad he felt at pushing Moriarty to his death. He recalls growing up in Yorkshire, and how vicious his own father was, pushing him against the stone fireplace one night when he was going to attack him, and leaving him there after hitting his head on the hearth. Holmes delves deeper into the darker aspects of his own history, revealing at last a shocking secret. Realising now how lonely and isolated he is without his old comrade, adrift in a new modern and war-ravaged age, he comes to wonder whether, like Watson, he too has come to the end of his time…

PLACEMENT

1916 and throughout the life of Sherlock Holmes.

TRIVIA

- David Stuart Davies's novel, *The Tangled Skein*, was adapted for the second season of Sherlock Holmes. Davies has written six original novels featuring the famous detective as well as several non-fiction works.
- The original stage production of **The Last Act** won 5 stars at the Edinburgh Fringe in 1999 and went on tour for eight years: 450 performances in 270 theatres around the world.

PRODUCTION SUMMARY

"I knew that these plays would lend themselves to audio very well. Roger Llewellyn is excellent and the original, author, David Stuart Davies, knows so much about Holmes. While they helped launch the series, I knew there was so much more we could do with the Conan Doyle stories and that we could even look at doing our own, but in terms of the financial side, these two gave the springboard for the whole series. What I love about this one is that it's about Holmes's emotions — him trying to say to his dead friend everything he's always wanted to but never quire managed to put into words."
Nicholas Briggs

WORKING TITLE(S)

None

RETURNING MONSTERS/CHARACTERS

Irene Adler, Professor Moriarty

THE DEATH AND LIFE

#1.2

SYNOPSIS

An EGM of *The Strand* magazine is called by its editor, telling the shareholders that Arthur Conan Doyle wants to end Sherlock Holmes. Conan Doyle writes to his mother, telling her he's become tired of the character who's taken on a life of his own. Soon after, he is met by a pedestrian who calls him "the Sherlock Holmes man", which convinces him it's time for Holmes to go. Holmes, meanwhile, notices Watson is sleeping and feels he's become bored of their exploits together, his friend glazing over whenever he talks. No clients come to his door anymore, there's just silence. Holmes begins to wonder if forces are at work to marginalise him, and becomes aware of Moriarty. In the shadows, Professor James Moriarty plans to make himself known soon. Conan Doyle writes to his mother again, upset by them placing his father in a mental institution, and decides to kill off Holmes. Moriarty confronts Holmes, asking him to picture his parents, but he never had them because they never existed – neither do Holmes or Moriarty, as they're all figments of Conan Doyle's imagination. Moriarty tells Holmes the writer plans to kill him off, but he wants to rebel – a character who isn't alive cannot die. The Professor tells Conan Doyle to beware. At the Reichenbach Falls, Holmes and Moriarty talk, and Holmes thanks his rival for not letting him fall to his death. He writes to Watson, telling him a joint menace awaits himself and Moriarty. At a séance, Holmes comes through to speak to Conan Doyle, angered at being portrayed as a drug addict. Working on his new book about a beast on Dartmoor, and having struggled to find a catalyst for it, Holmes appears to shoot the creature, proclaiming he, unlike the beast, will not remain dead. He goes to visit Conan Doyle's grave, then returns to 221B Baker Street, realising it will always be 1895 for him.

PLACEMENT

Throughout the life of Sherlock Holmes and beyond…

TRIVIA

- Simon Slater, who provides the music for this release (and **The Last Act**), also scored the original stage plays.
- The events of this play lead into Holmes's return in **The Hound of the Baskervilles**.

PRODUCTION SUMMARY

"This play experiments brilliantly with the boundaries between fact and fiction. In a way these plays are similar for **Sherlock Holmes** as our **Unbound** plays were for **Doctor Who**. While they certainly don't fit in the canon – and there is a very strict canon with Sherlockians – they are nonetheless fascinating sidesteps and were well worth our developing as audios."
Nicholas Briggs

WORKING TITLE(S)

None.

RETURNING MONSTERS/CHARACTERS

Professor Moriarty

CREW

Writer	**David Stuart Davies**
Director	**Nicholas Briggs**
Producer	**Nicholas Briggs**
Executive Producer	**Jason Haigh-Ellery**
Sound Design	**Nicholas Briggs**
Music	**Simon Slater**
Cover Art	**Alex Mallinson**

CAST

Sherlock Holmes	**Roger Llewelyn**

TECHNICAL

Story Code	**BFPSHCD02**
Recorded Date	**11 September 2009**
Release Date	**December 2009**
Place of Recording	**The Moat Studios, London**
Number of CDs	**2**
Total Duration	**106' 18"**
ISBN	**978-1-84435-455-9**

HOLMES AND THE RIPPER

#1.3

CREW

Writer	**Brian Clemens**
Director	**Nicholas Briggs**
Producer	**Nicholas Briggs**
Executive Producer	**Jason Haigh-Ellery**
Sound Design	**Nicholas Briggs**
Music	**Jamie Robertson**
Cover Art	**Alex Mallinson**
Theme	**Jamie Robertson**

CAST

Sherlock Holmes	**Nicholas Briggs**
Dr John Watson	**Richard Earl**
Katherine Mead	**India Fisher**
Netley	**Lex Shrapnel**
The Stranger	**Samuel Clemens**
Sir William Gull	**Matt Addis**
Assistant Commissioner Anderson	**Ian Brooker**
Mrs Hudson	**Beth Chalmers**
Lord Salisbury	**David Peart**
Saunders	**John Banks**

TECHNICAL

Story Code	**BFPSHCD03**
Recorded Date	**8 & 9 October 2009**
Release Date	**April 2010**
Place of Recording	**The Moat Studios, London**
Number of CDs	**2**
Total Duration	**143' 03"**
ISBN	**978-1-84435-456-6**

SYNOPSIS

As another Ripper murder hits the papers, Mary Kelly goes with cabbie Jack the Lad. Holmes is approached by clairvoyant Katherine Mead, telling him to return to Baker Street where he will meet a man wrapped in bandages. He returns home, and soon enough the man arrives, obviously unwell, but manages to speak clearly and distinctly, briefly telling them to find Annie, as Mary Kelly knows where to find her. Two men claiming to be from St Giles' Hospice, Netley and Potter, arrive to take the man away, saying his name is Charles Duvane and is bandaged after having a lobotomy. Holmes discovers the Mary Kelly who was killed was actually Catherine Eddles, but used the name Mary Kelly. Holmes is given a letter by Lestrade from the Ripper, who is obviously educated. Holmes reckons the victims have been targeted as they're all in the East End of London. Kate arrives and she leaves with Holmes to see a painting by Walter Sicott in a shop, which she was drawn to, showing a murdered girl. The shopkeeper is agent for Sicott, and knows of Annie, who used to pose for the painter. Sicott was last seen leaving for Dieppe, carrying a teddy bear.

Watson discovers a William Gorman and Annie Crooks were married, with witnesses Walter Siccot and Mary Kelly four years previously – the real Mary Kelly. Holmes finds her, saying she knew Annie's husband Eddie, has gone. She is killed soon after. The Queen's physician, Sir William Gull, a fellow mason, warns Holmes off the case, and spots his coachman is Netley. At St Giles' Hospice they find Annie, who has had a lobotomy, and she mentions her child, Alice, who was taken away. After an attempt on Kate's life, Holmes reckons there are two Rippers. He recalls Duvane had mentioned two Rippers, and used the royal "We". He deduces that Annie, a Catholic, met Prince Albert – known as Eddie – and bore him a child. Sicott, one of the Royal staff, took the child away. Holmes confronts the Prime Minister, telling him that Sir William and Netley lured the victims, who all knew Annie's secret, into the cab and attacked them. Holmes learned the Prince was also lobotomised, and is appalled, but will keep his silence for the good of the nation as long as baby Alice is left alone. Holmes returns home and plans a trip to Europe with Kate.

PLACEMENT

1888

TRIVIA

- This was the first *Sherlock Holmes* play by Big Finish to feature Richard Earl as Dr John Watson.
- Brian Clemens created and wrote the 1970s UK TV anthology series *Thriller*. The fourth story of the second season, *Kiss me and Die*, featured a young Jeremy Brett, who would go on to play Sherlock Holmes in the acclaimed Granada Television series. Edward Hardwicke (who played Dr Watson in that series) also appeared in *Thriller*.
- Other actors that would go on to appear in the second season of **Sherlock Holmes** are Beth Chalmers who returns as Mrs Hudson, Samuel Clemens, who here plays 'The Stranger', plays Sir Henry Baskerville in **The Hound of the Baskervilles #2.3** and Big Finish regular John Banks (who would take on the role of Lestrade).

PRODUCTION SUMMARY

"**Holmes and the Ripper** is an adaptation of a play by Brian Clemens, that brilliant thriller writer and major creative force behind *The Avengers*, *The Professionals* and *Bugs*. It postulates what might have happened if Holmes had been caught up in solving the infamous Ripper murders. Being a full-cast story, and featuring Richard Earl as Dr Watson, in many ways this was the blueprint for the development of the series."
Nicholas Briggs

WORKING TITLE(S)

None.

RETURNING MONSTERS/CHARACTERS

None

Check box - CD ☐   MP3 ☐

SHERLOCK HOLMES

Left:
Roger Lllewellyn brings life to the world's
greatest consulting detective.

295

SECTION 16

ROBIN HOOD

In 2008, BBC Audio approached Big Finish Productions about producing a range of audiobooks based on the hit TV series **Robin Hood**. BBC Audio already had a good working relationship with Big Finish due to the **Doctor Who** licence. 'They were keen to do some **Robin Hood** CDs, in association with Tiger Aspect, the independent that produced the series for BBC Television,' says Mark Wright, the range script editor. 'They offered the opportunity to Jason Haigh-Ellery, who jumped at the chance.'

At this time, the sixth season of Big Finish's **The Tomorrow People** had been cancelled due to the range's licence not being renewed. This left incumbent producers Mark Wright and Cavan Scott looking for a new project. 'Jason had asked if we'd be interested in taking on **Iris Wildthyme**,' says Mark. 'In the same meeting he also mentioned, amongst other things, **Robin Hood**. We were extremely keen, and came up with six story ideas pretty much overnight.'

Because **Robin Hood** was produced by Tiger Aspect, the Big Finish team had to work with the independent company as well as the BBC. So Jason, Mark and Cav attended a meeting with Foz Allen, who was the executive producer and co-creator on the TV series, at Tiger Aspect's central London offices. 'Foz was fantastically encouraging. We were given a run-down of the upcoming third season, which was very exciting!' recalls Mark. 'Then we went away to plan out one season of six audiobooks.'

At this point the two Big Finish producers became much in demand and as their workloads increased it became clear that they could not continue in that role. Cav Scott had to pull out altogether while Mark

became the series script editor, with Sharon Gosling acting as producer. 'We shaped the season with the writers,' says Mark, 'and we'd got to the commissioning stage when Cav had to pull out.'

After two successful seasons on television and with an intimate knowledge of what was coming up in the third, Mark wanted to produce stories that would reflect the direction and changes of the TV programme.

The story **We Are Robin Hood** , at the end of the show's second season, had seen Marian murdered at the hands of Guy of Gisborne, leaving Robin devastated. The third season would see the introduction of new characters, notably David Harewood as Brother Tuck, Joanne Froggatt as Kate and Lara Pulver as Isabella of Gisborne. The cast were also joined by Toby Stephens as Prince John and Clive Standen as Archer, Robin's half-brother. Finally, it was announced on 7 August 2008 that Jonas Armstrong would be leaving the programme in "an explosive and nail-biting finale."

'I definitely wanted to look at the aftermath of series two and Gisborne's murder of Marian, which I still think was a masterstroke on the part of the TV show's producers,' says Mark. 'Cav and I had thrown some ideas around of the kind of stories we wanted to tell, and that suggested the writers that we wanted to approach to work on the series.'

The storylines that Mark wanted to include were a story focusing on Tuck and what his character brought to the series; one featuring Isabella working with Robin and the gang; a tale about Prince John, and finally a story that examined the changes in Robin and Guy's relationship.

The writing team for the range was quickly assembled. 'I suggested a couple of storylines to writers that might be suitable for that story – Rebecca

Opposite page, top:
Sam Troughton (Much in the TV series) joined Big Finish to record **The Dambusters** and **The Deer Hunters**.

Right:
The Witchfinders, read by Richard Armitage, examined Robin and Gisborne's reaction to Marian's death in the TV series.

Levene and Trevor Baxendale,' explains Mark. 'I knew they could take a one-line thumbnail and run with it. I'd worked with Simon Guerrier on **Iris Wildthyme** and Jonathan Clements seemed an obvious fit. Finally I wanted a new voice in there, and Michael Abberton had provided Cav and I with a great story for *Short Trips: The Ghosts of Christmas*. He threw six story ideas at me within an hour! So there I had my writers.'

Because the format of the audios was to be that of a single-reader audiobook, it was decided very early on that both Jonas Armstrong (Robin) and Richard Armitage (Gisborne) should be approached to be readers. 'It also seemed right to include Sam Troughton (Much) because of the **Doctor Who** connection with his grandfather, Patrick, and father, David.'

With five of the slots filled, the team's last approach was to David Harewood. 'With such a brilliant actor as David being cast as Tuck, the chance to work with him was too good an opportunity to pass up,' says Mark. 'Sharon worked wonders in speaking to agents, and all four actors were very keen to be involved.'

With actors booked and storylines approved by the BBC Audio and Tiger Aspect, the writing got underway. Very soon, Sharon had the Moat Studios in London booked for recordings in November and December 2008, and January 2009.

By now, Mark was acting as script editor but he also directed four of the six releases. The atmosphere in studio was always good, with the actors encouraged to give it their all. 'Being able to sit in the director's chair on four of the stories and working with three incredibly talented actors in Richard Armitage, Jonas Armstrong and David Harewood was a real high point,' Mark says. 'The impression of Keith Allen's Sheriff of Nottingham from every member of the cast is one of the funniest things I've heard in a studio in all my years being involved with Big Finish.'

The low point for Mark was missing out on directing Sam Troughton. 'I was gutted!' he says. 'Sam had a cold on the day we originally had him booked and when he was next free, I wasn't available.' Because Mark was unavailable Sharon asked Big Finish stalwart John Ainsworth to step in as director.

The series as a whole was well received. 'I think each script has something to recommend it,' says Mark. '**The Witchfinders #1** really resonates with me for going into the Robin-Guy-Marian aftermath, and I like the pace and action of **The Dambusters #4**. In **The Deer Hunters #5**, Jonathan Clements made me laugh with the most outrageous gag I've ever heard in an audiobook – and which I'm pleased to say made the final cut!'

With Jonas Armstrong leaving the series, its future did not look especially rosy, but in January 2009 entertainment industry newspaper *The Stage* reported that TV writer Sally Wainwright had been approached to devise a "creative revampæ of the programme for the show's fourth series. She was quoted as saying: "I want to model **Robin Hood** more on **Doctor Who**, in terms of quality of script and quality of direction."

On 2 February 2009, the Big Finish website ran a news story announcing the new range. It stated that, "the first release will be available shortly after the first episode of **Robin Hood**'s third season airs on BBC1." In late March the news was updated with a release schedule of two CDs per month between April and June 2009.

As it happened, this was not quite the case… Just before the first pair of CDs was released, the BBC brought transmission of the 13-episode TV series forward to 24 March 2009. 'That put our own release schedule out a bit,' says Mark with a shrug. 'But that's showbiz!'

On 2 July 2009, the BBC announced that it would not be commissioning the show for a fourth season. To compound the bad news, Big Finish announced (on the same day) that the final two **Robin Hood** audio releases **The Deer Hunters** and **The Siege #6** had been unavoidably delayed at the reproduction stage. The stories were made available as downloads and sent out on CD two weeks later.

Mark is philosophical about the range. 'I think we put out six excellent releases that complemented the TV series well, but also stand up as good adventure stories in their own right,' he says. 'I would have liked to have done more, but without a TV show to support them it would have been pointless.'

However, Mark believes that the best testament to Big Finish's brief foray into Sherwood Forest was the reaction from the cast. 'Richard Armitage told me that the two stories he read were brilliant,' recalls Mark. 'He said he wished they could have done them as part of the TV series. That to me was a tribute to all five writers and to Sharon as producer that we really had got it right.'

#1 THE WITCHFINDERS

CREW

Writer	**Rebecca Levene**
Director	**Mark Wright**
Producer	**Sharon Gosling**
Executive Producer	**Jason Haigh-Ellery**
Music and Sound Design	**Richard Fox & Lauren Yason**
Cover Art	**Alex Mallinson**
Theme	**Richard Fox & Lauren Yason**

CAST

Sir Guy of Gisborne	**Richard Armitage**

TECHNICAL

Story Code	**BFPRHCD01**
Recorded Date	**21 November 2008**
Release Date	**April 2009**
Place of Recording	**The Moat Studios, London**
Number of CDs	**1**
Total Duration	**73' 41"**
Number of Episode	**1**
Duration of Episodes	**68' 14"**
ISBN	**978-1-84435-387-3**

SYNOPSIS

While tracking Robin Hood in Sherwood Forest, the Sheriff's men find a dog dressed as Robin. It's a decoy, but one of the soldiers claims that it is black magic, that Robin has the ability to transform into an animal. The Sheriff, although he says this is garbage, decides to use the witchcraft idea as a way to turn the people of Nottingham against Robin. Meanwhile, Sir Guy of Gisborne is obsessed with the death of the woman he loved, Marian. He is haunted by dreams of her but then starts seeing her while awake. This becomes something to be afraid of when a malevolent gang of witchfinders arrives in Nottingham, led by Hugh and Derek. The Sheriff has invited them to lead the witch-hunt for Robin. The Witchfinders go to Locksley and convince the people that there is evil in the woods. While Guy has problems with the ghost of Marian, Derek performs a convincing act for the villagers – like a medium – guessing things about them and their departed relatives. Then Guy orders the villagers to reveal the witch in their midst. A young girl points to the woman she has seen dancing in the forest with the devil – it's Kate. Hugh tests her with a needle, sticking it into her arm. She shows no pain, as Hugh has predicted (in reality, it is a fake needle) and Kate is sentenced to death. Robin learns of Kate's impending execution, and follows one of the witchfinders to a tavern, where he meets with a villager. The witchfinder buys information from the man and Robin has the proof he needs that they are frauds. As Kate is about to be burned at the stake, a witchfinder called Lazarus arrives and accuses Hugh and Derek of being witches themselves. The crowd turns against them and in the pandemonium Lazarus is unmasked as Tuck. He has provided a distraction for Robin to easily rescue Kate and escape over the castle walls. That night, Marian appears to Gisborne one final time.

PLACEMENT

Between the **Robin Hood** TV stories **Total Eclipse** and **Cause and Effect**.

TRIVIA

- The CD/download includes an interview with Richard Armitage, conducted by Mark Wright.
- Richard Armitage is a popular actor, perhaps best known as Sir Guy of Gisborne in **Robin Hood**, and as MI5 spy Lucas North in the long-running BBC drama *Spooks*. His other TV credits include *North and South*, *Cold Feet* and the final episodes of *The Vicar of Dibley*. Movie roles include *Captain America: The First Avenger* and the forthcoming *The Hobbit* as Thorin Oakenshield, which will also feature the Seventh Doctor, Sylvester McCoy.
- Rebecca Levene based witchfinders Hugh and Derek on Derren Brown and Derek Acorah.
- Richard Armitage describes his impression of the Sheriff as "a cross between a Dalek and Zippy from *Rainbow*".
- In keeping with the tone of the TV series, Rebecca Levene included several anachronistic touches in **The Witchfinders**, including references to being "as happy as Larry", and "cannon science" instead of "rocket science".
- This release was Mark Wright's first time in the director's chair for Big Finish.

PRODUCTION SUMMARY

"A contender for my favourite of the six – not that they aren't all brilliant! Rebecca really captured the pain that Gisborne was feeling at this point in the TV series, while managing to inject humour and tell a rollicking good adventure yarn with fights and heroic derring-do from the outlaws. From a personal point of view, this marked my directorial debut, and I couldn't have hoped for a better and more understanding actor than Richard Armitage to work with. Finally, the reaction from the online community was brilliant – especially the lady who said she almost crashed her car because she was crying so much at how sad the ending was. Madam, we hope you're okay!"
Mark Wright

WORKING TITLE(S)

Any Witch Way You Can.

RETURNING MONSTERS/CHARACTERS

None

THE TIGER'S TAIL

#2

SYNOPSIS

Trapped in Nottingham Castle, Robin, Tuck, Alan and Little John duck inside a building full of laundry to escape the Sheriff's men. They realise the clothes boiling away in a cauldron were once worn by lepers. Robin thinks they can escape by disguising themselves as lepers, but the gang refuses. Robin starts to recall his time in the Crusades with Much, when they watched men lying dead and dying after a battle in the desert. Back then, the pair found King Richard alive along with seven other survivors, and on Robin's instructions they removed all of their pageantry. The group marched north and rested at night, with Robin using a map to work out their course. In their backpacks, they discovered they had no tents, just robes. Robin heard voices over a nearby ridge – and found they were overlooking a Saracen army camp, blocking their escape route to Damascus. Robin ordered the group to bury all of their weapons, to lose anything that identified them as Crusaders. They donned the robes and posed

as monks, ordering the King to be their squire to avoid any suspicions. The group met Captain Khalid, who told them they are under orders to respect all religious groups. Robin claimed the others have taken a vow of silence, as Much giggled and broke his vow. Khalid quizzed them, and Robin said they were collecting donations to rebuild their church. They were taking pledges, so have no money to carry, and Khalid wanted a list of donors. Robin produced the map, and pretended to read a list of donations based on place names on the scroll-like map. Khalid sent the group on its way, but the King tripped and fell. Robin went over and slapped him, ordering him to move, fooling the Saracens. Back in the washhouse, Robin urges the others to pull on the robes and make their escape. Tuck queries details of Robin's story, and the outlaws' leader admits making it up to rally the gang to escape. As they make their escape, they receive a shiny coin from the Sheriff, who fails to see Robin is right under his nose.

PLACEMENT

Between the TV stories **Cause and Effect** and **Lost in Translation**.

TRIVIA

- Prior to **Robin Hood**, Irish born Jonas Armstrong first found TV fame in Channel 4's comedy drama *Teachers*, and in the police drama *The Ghost Squad*, again for Channel 4. Since leaving the BBC adventure series, he received recognition for his portrayal of an injured soldier returning from Afghanistan in the critically acclaimed *The Street*. Movie roles include *The Glass House* and *The Whiskey Robber*.
- The CD/download includes an interview with Jonas Armstrong.
- Some of the knights are named after friends of Jonathan: Hugh de Vide is Hugh David, now head of marketing at Network Distributors. Jonathan included him because he thought Hugh would think it was cool, but he only listened to about five minutes before turning off because he said that Jonas Armstrong's voice made him fall asleep. Jonathan doesn't think Hugh ever realised that he was in it! Clovis is named after Louis Savy, who runs the Sci-Fi London Film Festival. Sir Stephen takes his name from Stephen Cremin (aka "Sleepy Steve"), who manages an Asian movie news service, and was always falling asleep during the day because he kept Hong Kong time.
- Jonathan Clements based the story that Robin tells the outlaws in **The Tiger's Tail** on a twelfth-century Japanese legend about the famous warrior Yoshitsune who passed safely through an enemy stronghold with his samurai retainers dressed as monks. The incident was dramatized in Akira Kurosawa's 1945 film, *Those Who Tread on the Tiger's Tail*.

PRODUCTION SUMMARY

"A tricksy and clever tale from Jonathan Clements that takes his love of Japanese legend and weaves it seamlessly into the world of **Robin Hood**. Throw in a few references to modern pop culture – there's a *Star Wars* nod in there if you want to listen – and some nice in-jokes, and it becomes a story that goes in unexpected directions. **The Tiger's Tail** plays with the characterisation so well that you can't help but be drawn into the story that Robin weaves to get his men out of trouble. My favourite part is the cameo by the Sheriff of Nottingham at the climax, affording Jonas Armstrong the chance to show off his Keith Allen impression – something every reader on the series was keen to outdo his colleagues on!"
Mark Wright

WORKING TITLE(S)

None.

RETURNING MONSTERS/CHARACTERS

None

CREW

Writer	**Jonathan Clements**
Director	**Mark Wright**
Producer	**Sharon Gosling**
Executive Producer	**Jason Haigh-Ellery**
Music and Sound Design	**Richard Fox & Lauren Yason**
Cover Art	**Alex Mallinson**
Theme	**Richard Fox & Lauren Yason**

CAST

Robin Hood	**Jonas Armstrong**

TECHNICAL

Story Code	**BFPRHCD02**
Recorded Date	**27 November 2008**
Release Date	**April 2009**
Place of Recording	**The Moat Studios, London**
Number of CDs	**I**
Total Duration	**68' 23"**
Number of Episodes	**I**
Duration of Episode	**64' 13"**
ISBN	**978-1-84435-388-0**

#3 FRIENDLY FIRE

CREW

Writer	**Trevor Baxendale**
Director	**Mark Wright**
Producer	**Sharon Gosling**
Executive Producer	**Jason Haigh-Ellery**
Music & Sound Design	**Richard Fox & Lauren Yason**
Cover Art	**Alex Mallinson**
Theme	**Richard Fox & Lauren Yason**

CAST

Brother Tuck	**David Harewood**

TECHNICAL

Story Code	**BFPRHCD03**
Recorded Date	**6 January 2009**
Release Date	**May 2009**
Place of Recording	**The Moat Studios, London**
Number of CDs	**1**
Total Duration	**70' 57"**
Number of Episodes	**1**
Duration of Episode	**64' 34"**
ISBN	**978-1-84435-389-5**

SYNOPSIS

Guy of Gisborne comes under attack with his men as he hunts for the headman of Farthing village. Robin is forced from hiding when the headman is held at knifepoint when the outlaws emerge from the woods. But it's a trap and more of Gisborne's men appear. In the fighting the headman's brother falls dead with an arrow in his back – one of Robin's. The outlaws all escape, but Tuck stays behind and hears the mood turn against Robin. Gisborne aims to use the situation to his advantage, telling the villagers there's a bounty on Robin's head – and they would live six months tax free if he's handed over. Robin, stricken with remorse, gives himself up to Gisborne's men and is taken to Nottingham Castle. The Sheriff mocks him, and plans to hang him in the morning. Much brings Kate back to the camp, and she tells them Robin gave himself up. She also tells them of Gisborne's offer to the village. Tuck infiltrates the castle and goes to Robin's cell, trying to convince him why he should continue in his fight for justice against the Sheriff and to stand up for what is right. Robin is reinvigorated by the monk's words. The Farthing villagers, despite the tragedy, reiterate their support for Robin. As the gallows are built, Tuck and Robin make their way out of the dungeon. The crowds start to arrive for the hanging – the outlaws among them – and Kate stands up to tell everyone the allegation against Robin is false. The headman says it was Robin's arrow, but a village boy comes forward to say he saw the whole incident. The arrow was pushed into the man by Guy of Gisborne. Robin escapes with the outlaws, who blend in with the crowd as they depart from the castle.

PLACEMENT

Between **The Tiger's Tail** and the TV story **Lost in Translation**.

TRIVIA

- David Harewood has been a popular face on British television for more than 20 years. He is best known as DS Joe Robinson in *The Vice* opposite Ken Stott, and as Max Robertson in *Fat Friends*. Other TV work includes *Baby Father*, *Always and Everyone*, *The Palace*, and David Tennant's final episodes of **Doctor Who** as Joshua Naismith in **The End of Time**. Harewood's film work includes playing Nelson Mandela in 2010's *Mrs Mandela*.
- The CD/download includes an interview with David Harewood, conducted by Mark Wright.
- In an early acting role, David Harewood played a doctor in an episode of Steven Moffat's *Press Gang* – in an episode called *Friendly Fire*.
- Although third in the running order, this was the last of the six titles to be recorded.

PRODUCTION SUMMARY

"This is a story that goes right to the heart of the theme that season three of **Robin Hood** was running with – the notion of "We Are Robin Hood", that Robin is more than just one man, that legend and myth are just as important in fighting injustice. When I approached Trevor to work on the series, I was thrilled at the response. He was a big fan of the show, as were his children, and he jumped at the chance. Again, it's a story that thoroughly understands the heart of the TV series. In studio, listening to David Harewood deliver the final appeal to Robin in the dungeon was quite magical, a sequence that could have been straight out of a TV episode. Great writing and acting coming together as one."
Mark Wright

WORKING TITLE(S)

None.

RETURNING MONSTERS/CHARACTERS

None

Check box - CD ☐ MP3 ☐

THE DAMBUSTERS

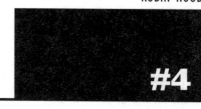

#4

SYNOPSIS

Stopping a cart in Sherwood Forest, the outlaws find it carrying some large carved stones and let it continue on its way. Elsewhere, Kate is visiting her family in Locksley, where she witnesses brutal German mercenaries breaking the millstone from the village mill into pieces. Meanwhile, while returning from an expedition, Brother Tuck finds a new track running through the forest and follows it. Returning to the outlaws' camp, he tells them he has found an enormous dam and a brand new mill. Robin believes this is some new scheme of the Sheriff's and the outlaws spring into action. Returning to the dam with Much, Tuck finds the Sheriff showing off his new toys to Gisborne and Isabella. Having put all the other mills in the area out of action, as well as charging a toll on people entering Nottingham, it will give the Sheriff a lucrative monopoly. Tuck, wanting to see the mill for himself, is captured by the Sheriff's men and tied to the mill. A storm is approaching, and with the water level set to rise, the Sheriff plans for the monk to be drowned. Lady Isabella is appalled by the Sheriff's plan. Helped by Kate, she drugs the Sheriff and they head off to the mill to drug the mercenaries – but they are followed by Gisborne. Robin and the gang stage a daring rescue of Tuck under cover of darkness, but Robin is confronted by Guy on a parapet. As thunder and lightning rage around them, a swordfight ensues, and Robin knocks his rival into the water. As the Sheriff arrives, Tuck tells Robin to take a fine wire thread from him, and to attach it to an arrow, then fire it right into the heart of the storm. He does so, and a lightning bolt strikes the arrow, with the wire conducting the electrical charge down into the dam, completely destroying it – and the Sheriff's scheme. The outlaws and Isabella return to Nottingham

PLACEMENT

Between the TV stories **Let the Games Commence** and **Do You Love Me?**

TRIVIA

- Sam Troughton is a film and TV actor who has appeared in the films *Vera Drake*, *Aliens vs Predator* and *Spirit Trap*, alongside **Doctor Who** companion Billie Piper. On television he was a regular in the Sky One supernatural drama *Hex*. He is of course a member of the Troughton acting dynasty – his father David has made appearances in both classic and new **Doctor Who**, as well as several Big Finish titles, and his grandfather Patrick played the Second Doctor.
- Writer Michael Abberton is who Mark Wright named Big Finish **Doctor Who** villain Nimrod – aka Dr William Abberton – after.
- Abberton also contributed to the *Short Trips* anthology *The Ghosts of Christmas* with the Third Doctor story *Jigsaw*.
- The CD/download includes an interview with Sam Troughton conducted by John Ainsworth.

PRODUCTION SUMMARY

"The other contender for my favourite of the range, this is a big action adventure with an exciting climax that would have been difficult to realise on screen, one of the beauties of the audiobook medium. Michael Abberton's script uses all the characters at their best, juggling the ensemble effortlessly at a point where the TV series continuity was complicated. I was gutted not to be in studio with Sam Troughton, but his reading is breathtaking, his range of voices astonishing. This has everything – some laughs, a lot of action and swordplay, and even some social comment on monopolisation of services and food production."
Mark Wright

WORKING TITLE(S)

None.

RETURNING MONSTERS/CHARACTERS

None

CREW

Writer	**Michael Abberton**
Director	**John Ainsworth**
Producer	**Sharon Gosling**
Executive Producer	**Jason Haigh-Ellery**
Music & Sound Design	**Richard Fox & Lauren Yason**
Cover Art	**Alex Mallinson**
Theme	**Richard Fox & Lauren Yason**

CAST

Much	**Sam Troughton**

TECHNICAL

Story Code	**BFPRHCD04**
Recorded Date	**22 December 2008**
Release Date	**May 2009**
Place of Recording	**The Moat Studios, London**
Number of CDs	**I**
Total Duration	**68' 13"**
Number of Episode	**I**
Duration of Episodes	**62' 55"**
ISBN	**978-1-84435-390-3**

#5 THE DEER HUNTERS

CREW

Writer	**Jonathan Clements**
Director	**John Ainsworth**
Producer	**Sharon Gosling**
Executive Producer	**Jason Haigh-Ellery**
Music & Sound Design	**Richard Fox & Lauren Yason**
Cover Art	**Alex Mallinson**
Theme	**Richard Fox & Lauren Yason**

CAST

Much	**Sam Troughton**

TECHNICAL

Story Code	**BFPRHCD05**
Recorded Date	**22 November 2008**
Release Date	**July 2009**
Place of Recording	**The Moat Studios, London**
Number of CDs	**1**
Total Duration	**66' 46"**
Number of Episodes	**1**
Duration of Episodes	**61' 56"**
ISBN	**978-1-84435-391-0**

SYNOPSIS

Exploring a remote part of the forest, Much spots a white stag, but disturbs it and sends it bolting towards civilisation. Word makes its way to Prince John's court about the stag near Sherwood Forest and he decides to get the animal's pelt to impress Lady Isabella. Hunters descend on the forest, putting the outlaws on alert. Prince John offers a full and free pardon to whoever brings him the pelt. Tuck and the men make a fake stag for Little John and Alan using wool, goat skin, chalk and old antlers, while Robin and Much try to find the real one. They find the animal, living in a naturally enclosed area of the forest. Meanwhile, Kate, dressed as a milkmaid, points Tuck and the hunters away from the direction in which Robin and Much have gone – towards the fake stag. One of the hunters is able to get in a shot, which hits the stag in the head. Alan is worried when he sees the shot has managed to draw blood, but is relieved to find it hasn't seriously injured Little John. The pair separate and go back to the outlaws' camp. The group of hunters decides to split in two, following tufts left behind on trees. One group heads north and the other south. Prince John meets Lady Isabella and asks if she would like a white cape, but she declines as it would be too difficult to keep clean and that it is hardly a slimming colour... Dismayed, Prince John angrily calls off the hunt. Robin and Much fell a tree to seal off the only entrance to the deer's enclosed area, and watch from a distance as it re-joins its family as Much asks if the group has now become vegetarians...

PLACEMENT

Between the TV stories **Too Hot to Handle** and **The King is Dead, Long Live the King**…

TRIVIA

- The CD/download includes an interview with Sam Troughton conducted by John Ainsworth.
- Like Richard Armitage, Sam Troughton recorded both his contributions to the range in just a single day.
- Following his work on the **Robin Hood** TV series, Troughton took up residence in Stratford-upon-Avon as a member of the Royal Shakespeare Company's ensemble from 2009 – 2011.
- Sam's grandfather, Patrick, was the first actor ever to play Robin Hood on television in a six-part series broadcast in 1953.
- Jonathan Clements pitched the idea before he had heard back from the producers about his first one, **The Tiger's Tail**, because he was worried they didn't like it. As it turns out they commissioned both!
- The story includes what is – by Jonathan's own admission – one of his worst puns (or one of his best, depending on your point of view). In a little tip of the hat to *Jaws*, Tuck says: "We're going to need a bigger goat."

PRODUCTION SUMMARY

"This is the out-and-out comedy entry for the range, a silly run around Sherwood Forest where all the characters get to have fun. This is the only release of the audio series to feature the character of Prince John, played by Toby Stephens in the TV series. Jonathan captured him so well and gave him such presence and humour in the few scenes he appears in – and all without seeing a second of footage. In fact, every writer had not seen any of the new characters in series three, and they all nailed them. But for me, **The Deer Hunters** scores highly because of one audacious, brilliant gag that made me laugh out loud when the first draft came in, Brother Tuck's opinion that "We're going to need a bigger goat." Oh, and we should have called it *Hart to Hart*…"
Mark Wright

WORKING TITLE(S)

Hart to Hart.

RETURNING MONSTERS/CHARACTERS

None

Check box - CD ☐ MP3 ☐

THE SIEGE

#6

SYNOPSIS

Newly allied, Robin and Guy of Gisborne are on the run, arrows flying through the air, as a group of German mercenaries attacks. They take shelter in an old castle, known to Robin from his teenage years when he served Lord Brackenbury. They barricade themselves inside and explore the castle. In a bedroom they find the emaciated corpse of Robin's former master. They awake the next morning to find the castle surrounded by the mercenaries. Robin thinks they will give up and leave if he and Guy can convince them there are a greater number of men in the castle than there actually are. They find an old trebuchet and gather together as much ammunition as possible. Robin initially fires rocks over the walls to attack their enemies, before firing over bales of hay, which have been dipped in oil. During their earlier search, Guy found a longbow and an arrow, which Robin sets alight before firing into the straw, forcing the invaders back for a while. The mercenaries eventually return with their leader, the Sheriff of Nottingham – Lady Isabella of Gisborne. Robin takes Guy's boots from him and runs indoors before returning. They load themselves into the trebuchet and fire themselves to freedom over the walls, just as the mercenaries break down the castle doors - and the pair land in the river outside, which carries them to safety. Trying to find their way back to Nottingham, they come across a tavern and an old friend of Robin's, Deborah, who had worked in the castle when he was an apprentice. She tells them Isabella had passed by the tavern and told Deborah the mercenaries had fled. Apparently they had been scared off by Lord Brackenbury's ghost! Because they had found his body lying in its bed, with a pair of muddy riding boots beside it, they feared he had risen from the dead to protect his old castle.

PLACEMENT

Between the TV stories **The Enemy of My Enemy** and **Something Worth Fighting For Part One.**

TRIVIA

- The CD/download includes an interview with Richard Armitage conducted by Mark Wright.
- Richard Armitage had expressed a desire to film a scene on television in which Guy gets drunk with Robin. Although he never fulfilled that wish on screen, **The Siege** features a sequence in which the former enemies share several bottles of wine.
- Simon Guerrier's story originally featured the character of Prince John instead of Isabella, as it was thought that actor Toby Stephens might be available to perform a reading for the series. Mark Wright asked for this to be changed to Isabella when it was realised that in the TV series continuity Prince John would have departed.
- The story pitched by Simon Guerrier featured all the outlaws, but Mark Wright was keen to showcase the new-found alliance between Robin and Gisborne, so they were conveniently left behind in Nottingham.
- Armitage recorded both **The Witchfinders #1** and **The Siege** in one day.
- The story was based on a **Doctor Who** story that Simon wrote when he was 14.
- Simon Guerrier sent six ideas to script editor Mark Wright on 5 July 2008: he liked **The Siege** and one about shipbuilding…
- Simon told Mark that his wife would be very pleased with him if he got to write for Richard Armitage (hence the line "Deborah, you're an angel)!
- The castle is named after Simon's friend, Erykah Brackenbury.

PRODUCTION SUMMARY

"A more serious script from Simon Guerrier to finish off the six stories, but one that still captures the heart of the BBC's **Robin Hood**. At this point in the TV series continuity, Robin and Gisborne have become uneasy allies, brought together by previously unknown family ties. When Simon wrote **The Siege**, we didn't really know how this was going to play out on screen – our supply of TV scripts had stopped before these events were played out. So Simon was shooting in the dark a little, but he keeps the characters true to what we knew about them up to that point, which is why the story works. And Richard Armitage, tired from a morning's work already on **The Witchfinders** but nicely sated on a lovely Big Finish lunch, ploughed on through to give us another fantastic reading. I'm so proud of this range and the work everybody did, it was a pleasure from start to finish."
Mark Wright

WORKING TITLE(S)

None.

RETURNING MONSTERS/CHARACTERS

None

CREW

Writer	**Simon Guerrier**
Director	**Mark Wright**
Producer	**Sharon Gosling**
Executive Producer	**Jason Haigh-Ellery**
Music & Sound Design	**Richard Fox & Lauren Yason**
Cover Art	**Alex Mallinson**
Theme	**Richard Fox & Lauren Yason**

CAST

Sir Guy of Gisborne	**Richard Armitage**

TECHNICAL

Story Code	**BFPRHCD06**
Recorded Date	**21 November 2008**
Release Date	**July 2009**
Place of Recording	**The Moat Studios, London**
Number of CDs	**1**
Total Duration	**75' 06"**
Number of Episode	**1**
Duration of Episodes	**70' 07"**
ISBN	**978-1-84435-392-7**

APPENDIX I

SUGGESTED DOCTOR WHO SEASONS

The following is how Big Finish suggests the Main Monthly **Doctor Who** range releases up to and including **The Raincloud Man #116** be split into seasons.

THE FIFTH DOCTOR AND NYSSA

SEASON ONE
04	Land of the Dead
10	Winter for the Adept
15	The Mutant Phase
26	Primeval

SEASON TWO
34	Spare Parts
44	Creatures of Beauty
66	The Game
91	Circular Time

SEASON THREE
93	Renaissance of the Daleks
VI	Return to the Web Planet

SEASON FOUR
107	The Haunting of Thomas Brewster
110	The Boy That Time Forgot
113	Time Reef
142	The Demons of Red Lodge

THE FIFTH DOCTOR AND TURLOUGH

SEASON ONE
02	Phantasmagoria
20	Loups-Garoux
76	Singularity

THE FIFTH DOCTOR SOLO

SEASON ONE
47	Omega
87	The Gathering
DWM 9	Cuddlesome Excelis Dawns

THE FIFTH DOCTOR, PERI AND ERIMEM

SEASON ONE
08	Red Dawn (just Peri)
24	The Eye of the Scorpion
DWM 4	No Place Like Home
38	The Church and the Crown

SEASON TWO
41	Nekromanteia
56	The Axis of Insanity
59	The Roof of the World
69	Three's a Crowd

SEASON THREE
71	Renaissance of the Daleks
81	Return to the Web Planet
95	Exotron (just Peri)
99	Son of the Dragon

SEASON FOUR
102	The Mind's Eye
104	The Bride of Peladon

THE SIXTH DOCTOR AND PERI

SEASON ONE
03	Whispers of Terror
35	…Ish
86	The Reaping
90	Year of the Pig

SEASON TWO
III	Her Final Flight
IV	Cryptobiosis

APPENDIX I

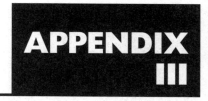

APPENDIX III

CONTENTS

#11

- **Introduction** - Executive producer of the Audio Adventures of *Doctor Who* and Voice of the Daleks Nicholas Briggs is your host for this behind the scenes look at Big Finish.
- **The Downloads Press Launch** - In February we held a press launch in London to celebrate the arrival of the Big Finish downloads service, *Doctor Who* stars Peter Davison and Louise Jameson met with the press - here are the highlights of the Q&A panel.
- **Sapphire and Steel – Season Three** - Sapphire and Steel have been assigned again, and we go behind the scenes of the upcoming season with the producer and stars.
- **Bernice Summerfield – Season Nine** - Incoming producer Eddie Robson gives us a taster of what to expect in the forthcoming ninth season of *Benny* stories.
- **Doctor Who – Cuddlesome** - The audio story **Cuddlesome** was produced by Big Finish and given away free with *Doctor Who Magazine*. We talk to Peter Davison and the stars of this special story, including Timothy West and David Troughton.
- Additional Trailers

FREE WITH
Check box - CD ☐

The Haunting of Thomas Brewster #107

CREW
Presentation	**Nicholas Briggs**
Interviews	**David Richardson**
Sound Design	**David Darlington**
Sleeve Design	**Alex Mallinson**
Producers	**Nicholas Briggs**

TECHNICAL
Production Code	**BFM11**
Release Date	**April 2008**
Number of CDs	**1**
Total Duration	**73' approx**

AFTERWORD BY DAVID WARNER

I count myself very lucky indeed to have been discovered by Big Finish… People find it difficult to believe me when I tell them that of all the times during 15 years living and working in Los Angeles (mistakenly called Hollywood) the most pleasurable and fulfilling was appearing in radio with The California Arts Radio Theatre, a company founded by the last surviving members of Orson Welles's famed Mercury Theatre. They do it because they love it and they have respect for the work, each other and their audience.

On returning to the UK, I was invited to join the Big Finish family to record a number of **Sapphire and Steel** stories with Susannah Harker. It was a delight, and a welcome reminder of my LA radio days. This led to being asked to participate in many other of the Big Finish titles listed in this book. I've always said yes. The size of the role really hasn't been important and, without going into details, it definitely wasn't the money, or the location. It could certainly be the exotic lunches extraordinarily provided by our multi-tasking sound engineer, studio manager, cricket nut and family man Toby.

It has always been a pleasure to turn up to work in the studio here, and each recording session is a joy; filled with a mixture of great humour, enthusiasm, dedication to producing the best work, and an awareness, care and consideration for the audience.

I've made many good friends here over the years.

Recently, in most of the companies I have worked for, non-creative executives and administrators are (unfortunately) allowed to make artistic decisions. This is not so at Big Finish; here administration and creativity go hand in hand and that is a major attraction. Once the writers have created a story, directors, actors, sound and graphic designers are given the courtesy of respect and are simply trusted to do their job without interference from talentless jobholders – a rare thing in this industry!

And so to Jason Haigh-Ellery, Nick Briggs, Gary Russell, John Ainsworth and David Richardson – thank you for letting us get on with it!

Every actor I know recording here for the first time asks, "when can I come back?". I hope what I've said above helps explain why they might ask that question.

David Warner

December 2010

ACKNOWLEDGEMENTS

Thanks to my two researchers who helped compile some the vast swathes of information necessary to the production of this book, Kenny Smith and Richard Callaghan, who also provided synopses for some of the 214 stories covered in this volume of *The Big Finish Companion*.

My thanks must also go to Benjamin Cook and Simon Guerrier who wrote such in-depth and fascinating books. Although not at all the same book, their levels of detail and historical significance kept me constantly striving for the same high standards.

Thanks to everyone who took the time to provide interesting details and curious trivia about their work, to those who helped check facts or who agreed to talk to me – or worse – subject themselves to interview – in some cases twice!

Those are:

John Ainsworth, Sophie Aldred, Peter Anghelides, Colin Baker, Alan Barnes, Lee Binding, David Bishop, Stuart Bevan, Lisa Bowerman, Nicholas Briggs, Nicola Bryant, Beth Chalmers, Jonathan Clements, Steve Cole, Paul Cornell, David Darlington, John Dorney, Nigel Fairs, Susannah Harker, India Fisher, Nev Fountain, Simon Guerrier, Jason Haigh-Ellery, Steven Hall, Scott Handcock, Colin Harvey, Frazer Hines, John Leeson, Joe Lidster, Steve Lyons, Ian McCloughlin, Sylvester McCoy, Paul Magrs, Alex Mallinson, Katy Manning, Stuart Manning, Philip Martin, Jim Mortimore, Wendy Padbury, Marc Platt, Jac Rayner, Justin Richards, David Richardson, Adrian Rigelsford, Jamie Robertson, Eddie Robson, Robert Ross, Gary Russell, Cavan Scott, Sarah Sutton, Rob Shearman, Elisabeth Sladen, Paul Spragg, Maggie Stables, Mark Strickson, Jim Swallow, Mary Tamm, Lalla Ward, David Warner, Conrad Westmaas, Scott Alan Woodard and Mark Wright.

I also owe a massive debt of gratitude to everyone at Big Finish past and present. My thanks to them are for so much above and beyond the commissioning of *The Big Finish Companion*! So to Jason, Nick, David, Gary, Alan, Paul, John, Nigel, Xanna, Frances and Alex: Thank you so much!

I must also acknowledge Anthony Lamb for his great layout work, and to Alex Mallinson for supplying me with PDFs of cover notes and CD sleeve artwork.

Finally my love and thanks to Clare who ensured my life and family continued while I remained glued to the computer screen for several months. Without Clare, this book would be seeing publication on the 12th day of never…

Richard Dinnick

Volume I was just the beginning…

THE STORY CONTINUES

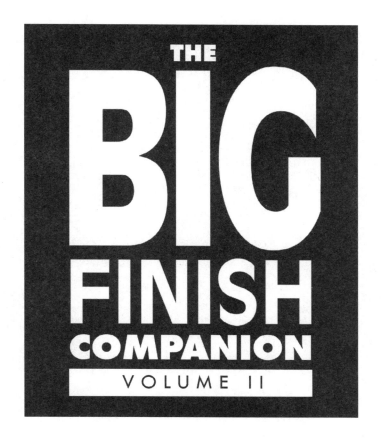

THE
BIG
FINISH
COMPANION
VOLUME II

BY

KENNY SMITH

COMING SOON

WWW.BIGFINISH.COM

PROMISES
TO PAY

The first three hundred years
of Bank of England notes

DERRICK BYATT

SPINK
London 1994

Published by Spink & Son Limited in 1994 for The Bank of
England on the occasion of its tercentenary

ISBN 0 907605 50 8

The endpapers show a selection of designs for notes
considered in 1931. The drawings are by S.Gooden,
M.MacDonald, K.Gray, F.Griggs and J.Blunt.
The tailpieces used in the text are based on pen
flourishes which appeared on notes over the years.

Designed by Paul Sharp

Typeset in Bembo by
Pepberry Limited, Milton Keynes

Printed in England by
Balding + Mansell, Wisbech

Contents

Dimensions of the illustrated notes are
given in millimetres, width before height

Acknowledgements

At lunch late in 1986, shortly before I was due to retire after 40 years' service, the then Deputy Governor - Sir George Blunden - asked me to consider writing a new history of the Bank of England note. I was unaware of the wealth of relevant material which was destined to pass across my desk, as Records Adviser, over the next three years. I had not served very long, however, in this new role before deciding to accept the challenge. I am particularly grateful to Sir George for having given me the opportunity and to the Governor and Company of the Bank for allowing me unprecedented access to the records and Museum collections. It has been interesting and absorbing work.

No book can be undertaken without the co-operation and contribution of others. I am also grateful, therefore, to all those who have helped in any way: to Emma Herbert, Joanne Richards and Karen Aedy, who turned the manuscript into machine-readable disk form and uncomplainingly accommodated my late thoughts by re-typing where necessary (one word of warning: original spelling etc has been retained in extracts from documents!); to Ian McQuire for the excellence of his photography which provided almost all the illustrations which clothe the text; and to Paul Sharp, the designer, for making the clothing fit perfectly; to John Keyworth (Curator) and his staff - in particular Christine Simpson - for cheerfully easing my access to the unique note and document collections; and to Henry Gillett (Archivist) and his assistants, Elizabeth Ogborn and John Egan, who bore the burden (literally) of making many records available promptly to me.

The management of the Issue Office have co-operated with enthusiasm, in particular David Hobden and Chris Bell who guided me through the intricacies of the German forgeries. In the Reference Library, Kath Begley has as ever been very helpful and remarkably forbearing. Arthur Smith (Newcastle Branch) provided the photographs which appear on page 212. Geoff Croughton (Secretary) has housed me comfortably.

Last, but certainly not least, I have been severally encouraged by many former colleagues and other friends and, of course, by my family. I thank them all for their interest and support and hope they will enjoy this end product.

London, April 1994   Derrick Byatt

Foreword by E A J George *Governor of the Bank of England*

The Bank of England's most important task is to preserve the integrity and stability of the currency. This means, first and foremost, ensuring that the currency that we issue maintains its value year by year, so that people can save and businesses can make investment plans in a stable monetary environment.

But another challenge is to ensure that the currency notes themselves command the confidence of those who use them. In particular, our notes must be designed so as to be difficult to counterfeit; this involves close co-operation between researchers, designers, papermakers, platemakers and printers. We have to make sure that they are available where and when required, that there are arrangements for secure handling and distribution to note centres around the country. And within the constraints of the technical and security requirements, we have to try to make the notes attractive and easily identifiable. If we count the holders of our notes as customers - and I do - then the Bank of England has more customers than any other bank in this country. It sometimes appears to me that everyone of them holds strong views on what constitutes an attractive and well designed currency note.

Derrick Byatt's new book should be required reading for those of our customers who feel that the Bank of England note is not what it was. It tells the story of the Bank's currency from the first hand-written cash notes to the present colourful Series E - the latest of which, bearing the portrait of our first Governor, is being issued in this tercentenary year.

Mr Byatt's book is a scholarly work, making the fullest use of the Bank's archive; but it is also a good read. The story is a fascinating one, showing as it does the evolution of the Bank's struggle against the counterfeiters - involving the use first of terror and later of technology - and the more recent debates on the design of the 'pictorial notes' which have in their way been as controversial as the policy of hanging counterfeiters was 150 years earlier. All those involved with banknotes, whether as producers, collectors, or simply as users, will find something of interest here, and it is a splendid contribution to the Bank's tercentenary year.

E. A. J. George

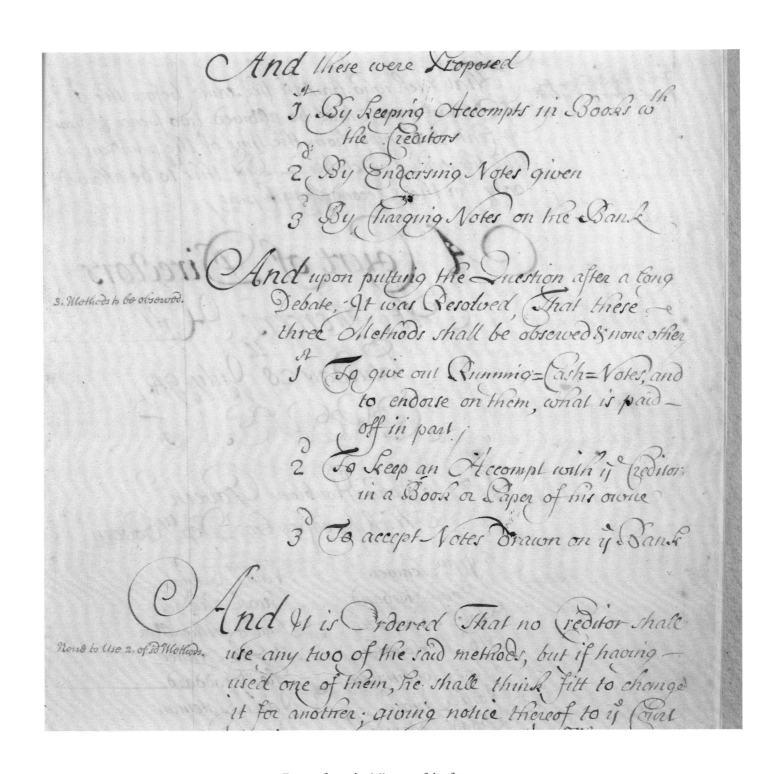

And these were Proposed

1st By keeping Accompts in Books wth the Creditors

2d By Endorsing Notes given

3 By Charging Notes on the Bank

And upon putting the Question after a long Debate, It was Resolved, That these three Methods shall be observed & none other

3. Methods to be observed.

1st To give out Running=Cash=Notes, and to endorse on them, what is paid off in part

2d To keep an Accompt with y^e Creditor in a Book or Paper of his owne

3d To accept Notes drawn on y^e Bank

None to use 2. of s^d Methods.

And It is Ordered That no Creditor shall use any two of the said methods, but if having used one of them, he shall think fitt to change it for another; giving notice thereof to y^e Court

Extract from the Minutes of the first meeting of the Bank's Court of Directors, relative to the issue of Running Cash Notes, the first 'promises to pay'

CHAPTER 1　The Last Classical Banking Function

'...(at y^e Opening of y^e Charter)...

The Method of giving Receipts for running=Cash was Debated, whether one certain Method, - or more than one, should be observed, and what method in particular.

And these were Proposed

1st By Keeping Accompts in Books wth the Creditors
2^d By Endorsing Notes given
3^d By Charging Notes on the Bank

And upon putting the Question after a long Debate It was Resolved, that these Methods should be observed & none other

1st To give out Running=Cash=Notes, and to endorse on them, what is paid off in part
2^d To keep an Accompt with y^e Creditor: in a Book or Paper of his owne
3^d To accept Notes drawn on y^e Bank

And it is Ordered That no Creditor shall use any two of the said methods, but if having used one of them, he shall think fitt to change it for another; giving notice thereof to ye Court he is at liberty to use any one of the said Methods.'

History has not recorded how long the debate had lasted during that first afternoon meeting of the Court of Directors of the Bank of England on 27 July 1694 at Mercers' Hall, when arguments were marshalled for and against various possibilities; nor how the final Resolution was made. The Directors clearly recognised the advantage to commerce generally of the goldsmith's note payable to a named depositor or order (later, or bearer) and must have had little difficulty in deciding to adapt this form as first choice for their infant Bank of England. The second method was banking with a passbook, the third was banking with a cheque book. Thus was laid the foundation stone for the Bank's series of note issues down the centuries. In the words of Sir John Clapham: 'Issue was the last of the classical banking functions to evolve spontaneously in England, and it was England's main contribution to the evolution of European banking'.

Three days after the initial meeting of the Court the cashiers were ordered to 'gett a fitt place ... to sitt and doe their business in ... fenced in to keep off people from Disturbing them'. The following morning they were instructed only to pay out on notes to persons known to them - not an easy task in the opening business days, it would seem. That afternoon, orders were made for the printing of Running Cash Notes in a form already agreed; further, that the Notes were to bear two written signatures. Proofs still exist which were taken from copper plates engraved for five denominations (£5, £10, £20, £50 and £100), lettered in

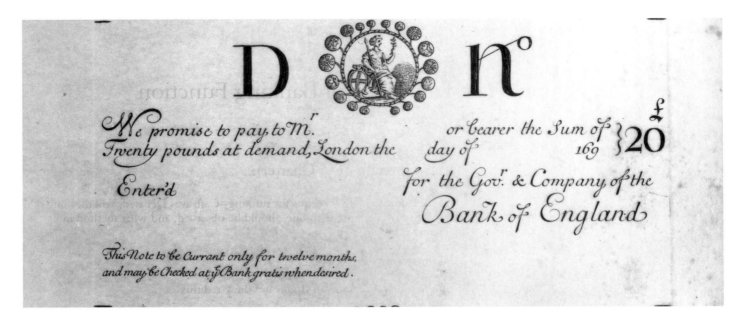

D ℞ Nᵒ

We promise to pay to Mʳ.   or bearer the Sum of } 20 £
Twenty pounds at demand, London the   day of   169

Enter'd

for the Govʳ. & Company of the
Bank of England

This Note to be Currant only for twelve months,
and may be Checked at ỹ Bank gratis when desired.

Proof Running Cash Note for £20, engraved in 1694. Note the elaborate framework of coins surrounding Britannia (207 x 111mm)

1 Respectively First, Second and Third Cashiers; Madox signed himself 'Madockes'.

The signature of Thomas Madockes on a Bank note of 29 July 1697: he became Chief Cashier two years later

accordance with their respective values and using the now familiar 'promise to pay' clause. It is almost certain, however, that none was printed for issue since, at their meeting on 11 August 1694, the Court considered them liable to be counterfeited and ordered that printing should be done on 'marble paper indented'. However, an objection was raised at the next Court (once again, the Minutes lack further details on the point) and the previous Order was 'respited', ie rescinded. No new order for printing was given until the following summer. The early proofs mentioned above include a central vignette of Britannia, a figure which has featured in every known printed design and which the Bank had already adopted for its official seal. All notes would have had to be written by hand in these early days though consideration had clearly been given to a form of partly-printed text, a proof of which has survived. Two cashiers were required to sign each note, one of whom, it was decided early in 1695, should be Thomas Speed, Robert Hedges or Thomas Madox[1]. During their first winter the staff were ordered not to receive or pay any money after candle light, save in respect of foreign bills. We can safely assume from the existence of the proof notes referred to above that it was the original intention to issue notes in amounts of even pounds. But the scarcity and deplorable state of the coinage, and the fluctuating value of the various gold pieces then current, made the Bank bow readily to public demand for a fully substitute currency and therefore many notes issued by the Bank in its initial years would have been for odd sums, often including both shillings and pence. It was also possible to ask for a part-payment which was then endorsed on the note so that notes which had actually started life as denominations familiar today were often reduced to 'odd sums'. It is possible that a new note was occasionally issued to replace a written down note which had become too worn to remain in circulation. The highest denomination ever to be issued to the public was £1,000. With the exception of a short period in 1695, this style of note was to remain the norm until 1725.

The move towards printing notes on 'marble paper indented', which had been halted by Court's second thoughts in August 1694, was eventually carried forward at their meeting on 1 May 1695 which ordered

'That notes indented on marbled paper Bee made payable by the Company to the Bearer on demand.'

Their form was to 'promise to pay the Bearer of this Indented Note the summe of ... pounds on demand.' These Lettered Notes (A-G, distinguishing their respective denominations now extended to £5, £10, £20, £30, £40, £50 and £100) were the first printed notes to be issued by the Bank and had a validity of one year only. 2,000 each of the two lowest values and 1,000 each of the others were run off by William Staresmore, the Bank's stationer. A £15 denomination was pricked into the series as 'C' soon afterwards. The issue was short-lived, however, though apparently initially a success: a minute of May 1697 reports that 700 each of the £10, £20 & £50 and 600 of the £100 (now lettered H) had been paid although they were only available from May to August 1695. The withdrawal followed the discovery of a £100 note, one of 60 such, whose manufacture was admitted by one Daniel Perrismore. In the absence from the Statute Book of capital punishment for forgery of notes at this time, a considerable fine and a period in the pillory were his rewards. The order to stop the issue of printed notes and to revert to hand-written issues was promptly made. Erasure and alteration returned to haunt the Bank.

The earliest known Running Cash Note: handwritten for £22 and dated 18 June 1697 (180 x 111mm)

Running Cash Note for £555, dated 19 October 1697 (196 x 111mm)

Running Cash Note dated 16 January 1699, originally for £62:15:– and endorsed with a part payment of £54:13:1 (200 x 113mm)

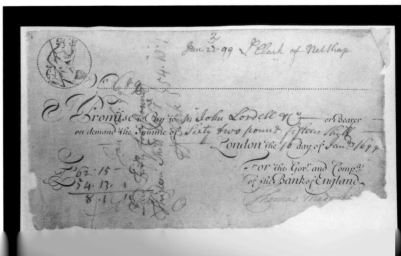

2 The earliest printed reference to a Bank note appears to be contained in an advertisement in the *London Gazette* of 17-21 January 1694/5, relating to one of £17:2:4, payable to Philip Weake and lost in a fire

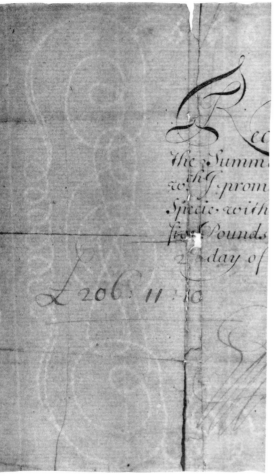

Detail of scroll in the first watermark (1697)

A week later a special committee was appointed to consider the form of a mould for making paper for Bank notes[2], work which eventually led to one of the outstanding security features: the watermark. As this period watermarks were being used only as maker's marks or to indicate the sheet size (foolscap, for example, bore a fool's cap watermark). As Mackenzie suggests in *The Bank of England Note*, the Bank of England was probably the first private corporation to make a security feature out of a watermark. The task of producing a satisfactory result could not be rushed since many skills needed to be combined. The basic design had (and still has) first to be worked in wire before being fitted into the mould which was to be dipped into the wet pulp from which the paper would be formed. The design was positioned in such a way that notes could be printed, initially, in pairs side by side. As experiments continued so the Bank began also to consider proposals for using a unique type of paper. The end result came in July 1697 when first supplies reached London from the mill of Rice Watkins, at Sutton Courtenay in Berkshire. The watermark was a looped border with an elaborate scroll in the left hand margin and 'Bank of England' in a panel near the foot. The method of manufacture meant that the paper itself thinned out at each of the four sides, causing a rough, uncut or 'deckle' edge. As the sheets were cut into two after receiving the plate impression, each note ended up with one straight edge and three deckle edges. Numbers and dates were written in by hand, the daily register reverting to number 1 each morning. If demand was heavy and more than one register in use, a distinguishing letter was added. By this time, however, printing of the running cash note, on plain paper, had recommenced and the first use to which the new paper was put was for the manufacture of Specie Notes.

The Specie Note was first issued in 1696 in connexion with the recoinage of that year and the consequent monetary crisis which brought about the first serious run on the Bank. The type of coinage tendered by the depositor was noted and, originally, he was entitled to be paid out only in the same, usually with interest at a rate specified on the Note. However, on 14 April 1697 the Court 'Ordered that the Cashiers shall hereafter give notes for all hammer[d] mony by the name of Currant mony only and not otherwise'. Some 40 years ago or so Mackenzie wrote that there were 'no surviving specimens' of Specie Notes: two are now in the Bank's collection, one of which (dated 2 October 1697) is there thanks to the generosity of a member of the public who felt it was 'coming home'. Printed from different plates, they are the first to show Britannia (centrally) on an issued note and are also the first to include 'Comp[a]' as the short form of 'Company' - the antiquated style of an abbreviation, making use of the next available vowel (cf 'Gov[r]' where the *final letter* is made use of). Another issue of Specie Notes was made during the crisis of 1700/1701.

For two short periods the running cash note also bore interest but the Court was clearly unhappy at this facility and it was never repeated.

The recoinage having again successfully oiled the wheels of commerce, the Bank took steps to reduce the availability of its notes for small change. Instructions were given in August 1696 that no notes were to be issued for less than £20 and

A Specie Note for £206:11:10 dated 2 October 1697, incorporating the earliest known Britannia on a printed Bank of England note (180 x 111mm)

Hammered coinage issued in the reign of Charles I was acceptable in exchange for the Bank's notes as late as 1697, but repayment was made in contemporary specie

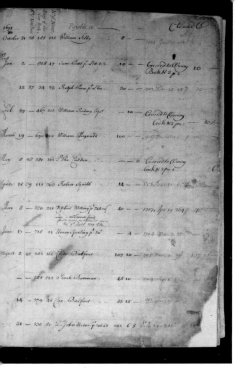

Cuddon's note for 6d has never been repaid. It was recorded as outstanding in the first Clearer

Bank Post Bill at 3 Days Sight for £20, dated 10 November 1732
(195 x 117mm)

remarked earlier, it had been official policy since 1697 not to issue notes for less that £20. The Bank's collection contains, however, one issued in January 1699/1700 for £17:10:- (possibly in change for a part payment on an old note) and another for 6d issued to Sir Thomas Cuddon on 8 May 1700 as a favour: the latter note, signed by 3rd Cashier John Wase, is held in the Bank's collection but remains unpaid in the Bank's books.

Another feature of the Bank's currency activities at this time is worth mentioning here although the instruments concerned were not, *de facto* or *de jure*, banknotes. One of the problems facing the public was the vulnerability of road travel, and particularly of the mail coaches, to being held up by highwaymen. And the pavements were no safer from the attention of footpads. One of the drawbacks of achieving the aim to have Bank notes widely accepted was that the proceeds of robbery could easily be cashed. In an attempt to foil the thieves a three-day promissory note was made available in 1728: it was transferable only by endorsement and if it was stolen the sender had up to three days to lodge a stop order against its payment. This was too short a term to afford much protection to the true owner but another 10 years were to pass before representations by the Postmaster-General resulted in 'Post Bills' (as they later became known as) being issued with longer terms. The facility was finally withdrawn as late as 1934, when the incidence of robbery on the roads must have been very infrequent.

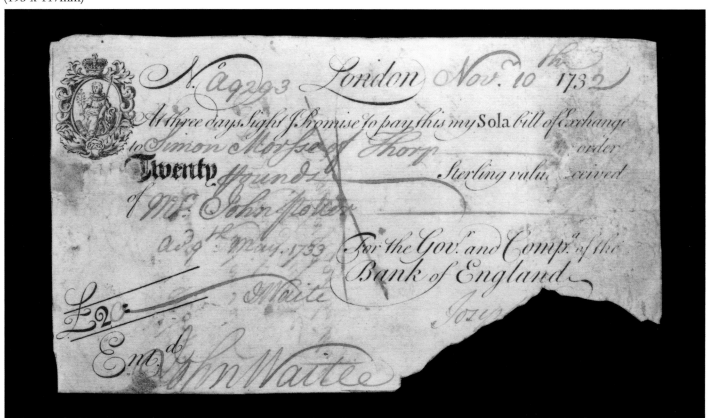

As mentioned earlier, all notes, as they were issued, were recorded in registers and were marked off when presented for payment (this is believed to be a unique procedure among central banks and Government note-issuing authorities even in more modern times). In the case of a part payment, the register was amended appropriately. Since notes were lost on occasion, often irretrievably, or were not presented for many years (over 100 in many instances), the number of registers would have grown unwieldy unless some action was taken. From time to time, therefore, the outstanding entries were transferred into other books (known as 'Clearers') as the number of live notes recorded in them diminished. The first note listed in the earliest extant clearer is one for £50 dated 26 March 1697 and drawn in favour of Henry Salter. By 1842 it was estimated that notes issued prior to 1 November 1764 were outstanding to a total of £40,902:7:11. Irrespective of whether a note is shown in any of the surviving registers or clearers as paid or unpaid, a genuine Bank of England note is always honoured if presented for payment in London at the Bank by a lawful holder: the 'promise to pay' is without any limit as to time. (For legal tender status see post, page 84)

CHAPTER 2 One Excellent Man – and Others not so

When William Maynee was elected an Accountant in 1722 and first went to work for the Bank in Grocers' Hall he would hardly have been expected to end his career, and his life, on Tyburn-tree. It was in 1731 that Maynee, still working in the Accountant's Office, was discovered to have incurred the Bank in losses of £4,420 over a period of years through the erasure or alteration of endorsements on what were, in the broadest sense, notes drawn on the Bank but were more like cheques: Accountable Receipts, issued as certificates of deposit. He pleaded guilty and was sentenced to death. He petitioned the Court of Directors on 20 January 1730/1 'with the utmost contrition; and deepest sence of his crimes, heartily sorrowfull for his great ingratitude, in offending against such kind, and Worthy Masters, at the feet of whose mercy he now humbly throws himself; imploring for the mercy of Transportation'. He particularly begged the pardon of Sir Edward Bellamy, 'for the unhappy mistake, both Mr Cook & himself made in misunderstanding him'. He signed off as 'your most distrest, & most miserable Petitioner'. We know that Cook was one of Maynee's sureties since he was later given time to pay under his bond. The coupling together of Cook's name with Bellamy's suggests that Bellamy was also a surety. If so, it is not surprising to note that Bellamy (by now Deputy Governor) was the only dissenting vote when rejection of the petition was moved. The Directors clearly felt deeply offended by Maynee's breach of trust for the Secretary, David Le Gros, was asked to let it be known to the authorities at Newgate Gaol that if any (further) application were to be made on his behalf, 'Notice may be given to the Court of Directors of ye said Bank who have every objection to his being pardoned or Transported'. Having again begged the pardon of the Court and prayed for the prosperity of the Bank of England, Maynee was duly turned off at Tyburn on 8 March 1731 and died, according to the reporter covering the event for the *Gentleman's Magazine*, 'very penitent'.

£50 note of 30 June 1732
(195 x 115mm)

£30 note of 20 June 1752
(195 x 116mm)

Wm. GUEST (condemned for High Treason)
drawn on a SLEDGE to Tyburn)

Another victim at Tyburn was William
Guest, a Bank Teller found guilty of
diminishing coin by scraping the edge of
guinea pieces – a treasonable offence. He
is shown here on his way to execution
(By permission of the British Library)

Nearly 37 years later a teller, William Guest, was to meet the same fate having been charged on the 'violent suspicion' of diminishing the value of gold coins, using a device of his own invention to pare the edges of new pieces and then re-mill them. The doctored guineas were issued over his counter the next day in payment for notes, no one at the time suspecting that they were other than of valid weight in view of their pristine appearance. When his house was searched some 5lbs of gold filings and dust were discovered. Diminishing coinage or mutilating it in any way was a crime against the State and the evidence against him left no hope of defending the charge of high treason which he faced. Having been drawn on a hurdle to Tyburn 'dressed in decent mourning with a club wig on' he was hanged there on 14 October 1768 but not before, according to the *London Magazine*'s reporter, he had prayed on his knees 'with the greatest devotion, and his whole deportment was so pious, grave, manly, and solemn ... as to draw tears from the greatest part of the numerous spectators'. An informal contemporary notebook in the Bank's possession has Guest's entry terminating thus –

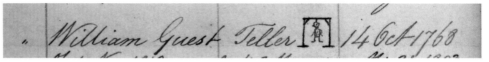

The protection which the law gave to the Bank's notes and to the Bank more generally was gradually being tightened. In 1724 it was decreed that because of 'divers Frauds and Deceits ... by altering, forging and counterfeiting ... Bank-Notes ... to the Prejudice of Public Credit and to the great Hurt and Diminution of Trade and Commerce ... any person ... shall be (on conviction) adjudged a felon' and suffer accordingly. By 1742 a further Statute was being passed to the effect that 'Any Person forging, counterfeiting or altering a note shall be deemed guilty of Felony and suffer Death as a Felon without Benefit of Clergy'. Furthermore, embezzlement by Bank Servants was also to be treated as a felony. The problems which were to arise later in the century when forgery became much more widespread were clearly beginning to cast warning shadows.

£20 forgery by R W Vaughan,
executed 1 May 1758 at Tyburn
(184 x 119mm)

Daniel Race, Chief Cashier 1751-1775. Mezzotint by James Watson after the portrait by Thomas Hickey

Abraham Newland, Chief Cashier 1778-1807: his right hand is pointing to a £1 Bank note. Etching by A Mills after D Mills (1803)

The rules and procedures for dealing with lost or stolen notes were kept under constant review. The book in which notifications were recorded was examined regularly by the Committee in Waiting and signed by a Director. By 1735 two acceptable sureties had to be nominated by a claimant and a year later it was ordered that no divided notes be accepted by the cashiers without reference first to inspectors who would carefully examine the pieces. It was also difficult to devise a satisfactory procedure for dealing with claims that notes had been irretrievably lost, eg through fire. If the claim was genuine the holder would lose interest waiting for his payment to be made. If it was not, then too early a refund could incur the Bank in losses if the claimant had disappeared and left an unexercisable indemnity as well. In 1745, when Susanna Griel claimed for notes totalling £260 which she alleged had been consumed by fire, the sum was paid to her upon her arranging to transfer £300 in 3% Annuities into the names of the Governor and Deputy Governor to be held in trust for her in order to indemnify the Bank should all or any of the notes have survived to be presented for payment. Stolen notes could have their payment stopped by the victim.

Thomas Madockes retired as Chief Cashier in 1739 and was the first recipient of a pension from the Bank. An allowance of £125 for one year only was in fact renewed each year until his death in 1745. On his resignation, the Bank appointed joint Chief Cashiers, James Collier and Daniel Race. Collier had been entrusted with at least two important responsibilities in his career thus far. In 1707 he was one of three officials in charge of escorting some £100,000 in cash and £300,000 in Exchequer Bills to Edinburgh, which sums had been granted to Scotland following the Act of Union. Thirty troopers acted as the guard for the 12 wagons (each drawn by six horses) which attracted hostile action from a mob on arrival at their destination, it being assumed that the boxes contained ammunition. Then, in 1724, Collier spent a few months in Frankfurt in a fruitless attempt to bring Moses Waag to justice for forging a Bank Stock transfer, the first to be discovered. On Collier's death in 1751 he was replaced by Elias Simes, the existence of whose signature on a 'Madockes' note has already been described. Eight years later Race was able to hold the title of Chief Cashier on his own, continuing thus until his death at the age of 78 in 1775. That Race is not completely lost in the mists of antiquity is due to the fact that the Directors, towards the end of his service, commissioned Thomas Hickey to paint his portrait. Engravings were then made and sold widely. His memorial placed in St Luke in Old Street was eulogistic to the extreme. Race, it says, was 'a man of plain appearance, and in no way associated with the depravity of the times, but in every respect a man of business, the gentleman, the philosopher, the Christian: eminently distinguished by his extraordinary virtues and abilities ... the clearest ideas and the soundest judgement, most unblemished integrity, singular diligence, attention and regularity in every branch of his department: wonderful calmness of temper, affability of manner, unruffled by times or persons ... remarkably correct, and in a manner faultless himself, yet indulgent to the faults of others ... full of Benevolence ... ONE EXCELLENT MAN'. A hard act to follow for Charles Jewson, who then held office for only three years before the commencement of Abraham Newland's stewardship.

An important development in the appearance of the notes occurred in 1743 with the first use of the so-called 'Sum Piece' or 'Sum Block' in the lower left-hand corner,

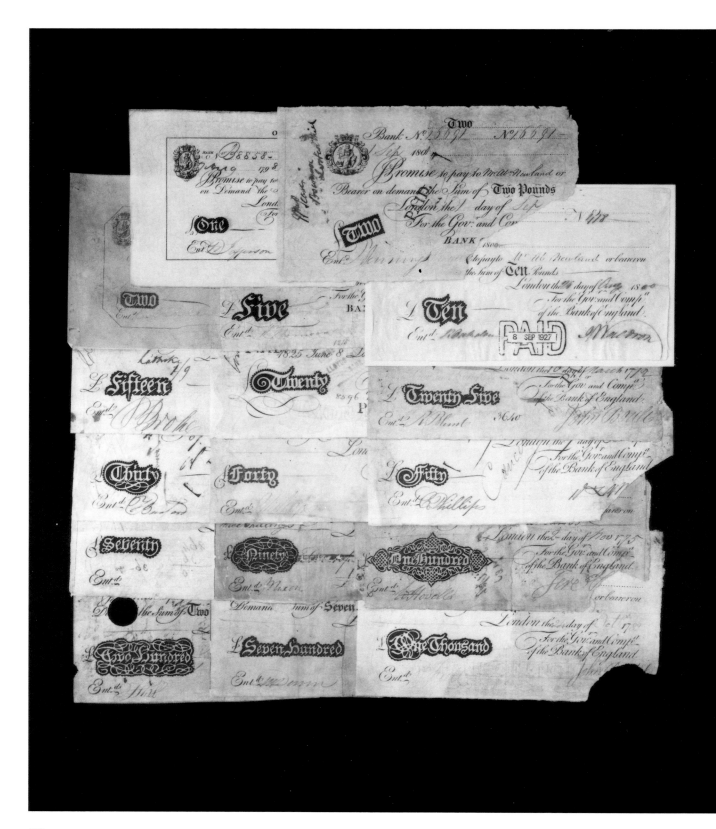

Opposite, the pattern of various Sum Blocks on issued notes

intended to make the alteration of a note that much more difficult for the fraudster. In essence the Sum Block comprised an elaborate pattern following the £ sign, spelling out in words the denomination, in white lettering on a black background, a different design being used for each value: by 1745 there were 14 denominations listed as being printed (£20, £30, £40, £50, £60, £70, £80, £90, £100, £200, £300, £400, £500 and £1,000) but the Bank's collection includes one for £700, dated 1770. Over the years the initially rather hesitant beads projecting from the edge of each pattern became more positively defined. The Seven Years' War, which began in 1756, caused a drain of specie abroad and resulted in a serious shortage of gold and, particularly, silver coinage. To alleviate the situation to a limited extent, the Bank added £10 and £15 denominations to its range (a decision taken in 1751 to prepare £10 notes had apparently never been acted upon) in 1759 and added a £25 denomination in 1765. Notes for amounts under £1 were prohibited by Act of Parliament in 1775 and those for less than £5 were similarly barred the next year.

Five further Sum Blocks from plate impressions enlarged to show details

£50 note of 27 November 1771, payable to the Chief Cashier, Daniel Race (200 x 118mm)

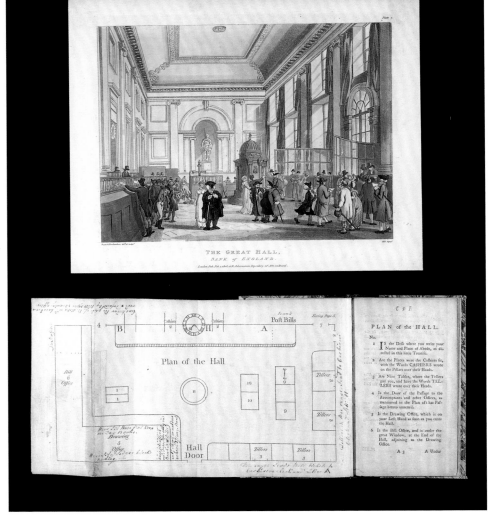

Plan of the Banking Hall, published in 1782 in a Vade Mecum (guide) to the Bank; and a contemporary print

The practice of using one of the Bank's tellers' names, as a 'person known to the Bank', as payee has already been observed. This continued after 1704 when notes drawn in favour of a fictitious name, or bearer, became legally assignable. From 1752 the name of the Chief Cashier began to appear from time to time, a practice which occurred more regularly once Daniel Race had become sole Chief Cashier. Shortly after Newland took over it became the exclusive practice to use the Chief Cashier's name: until 1855 when the notes were made out simply to bearer. The regularisation of the practice of using one name soon led to the suggestion that notes should be 'ready made out' in advance so that a store of such notes could be accumulated and the business of issuing carried out with greater security and facility. This led in turn to a change in the methods of numbering and dating the notes. No longer did the numbering revert to 1 each morning, nor was the date the date of issue, more likely (in those early days) the date on which they were printed. Many notes continued to have Newland's name written in, in others it was printed in a handwritten style. According to the *Bank of England Vade Mecum*, published in 1782, the facility of obtaining notes for broken amounts was still available at that time: this would explain why the word 'pounds' continued to be

£1,000 note of 12 April 1793. The facility must still have been available to have had an additional amount inserted since the word 'Pounds' has had to be written in manuscript (198 x 118mm)

£5 note of 15 April 1793, shortly after the introduction of this denomination (204 x 115mm)

handwritten in the body of most denominations. The Bank's rules laid down that 'No Addition of Pounds can be made ... between 10l. and 15l.; between 15l. and 20l. but Shillings and Pence may, as for Instance, on a 10l. Note, you may add from 10l. 0s. 1d. to 10l. 19s. 11d. ... And Pounds, Shillings, and Pence, may be added to any 20l. Note or upwards. For Instance, from ... 30l. 0s. 1d. to 39l. 19s. 11d. and so on'.

The outbreak of war with France in 1793 caused yet another shortage of specie and led to the issue of the first £5 denomination, after due reference to William Pitt and an advertisement in the *London Gazette*. At the same time, the word 'BANK' was engraved at the side of the vignette, presumably to denote the place of origin (this was replaced in 1810 by inserting 'London' in the dateline). Notes had begun to bear numbers on the front of each half in 1791; the date was meant to be similarly shown on all notes from 1 January 1793, the Bank intending to give notice 'that for the convenience and security of all persons who may chuse to cut Bank Notes into separate

CHAPTER 3

Rouzing by Example

Between 1783 and 1796 only three people were capitally convicted on charges relating to forgery: between 1797 and 1818 the figure was 313. We have seen that the sharp rise in the incidence of forgeries detected at the Bank originated with the issue of the two small denominations: £1 and £2. In 1801, out of a total face 'value' of £15,549 discovered, well over half was attributable to these issues, the bulk of the rest being at £5. The burden of dealing with these cases by reference to the Court of Directors was no longer expedient and a special Committee of Law Suits was appointed 'for managing prosecutions, retaining counsel, and preferring indictments'. Their principal rôle was to weigh up all the evidence and decide which was the fairest charge – if indeed any. By the public outcry which was to gather strength from around 1811, one would have had to believe that the Bank was determined to hound anyone to death – or to Botany Bay – on any evidence remotely connected with forged notes. The very opposite is the truth. To make, utter (that is, spend) or distribute forgeries were indeed capital offences but possession was punishable by 14 years transportation. There were many cases where, although there was irrefutable evidence that a note had been passed as money, although not genuine, the offender was allowed to save his or her neck by pleading guilty to the lesser charge of possession, a discretion which was later to be criticised by the Prince Regent. The Bank realised in these cases that even £1 was a loss out of all proportion to the defendant's means and that it was only natural that he or she should make a desperate effort to prevent such a devastating depletion of resources. When the evidence clearly showed that the defendant had purchased several forgeries, the Bank's view was less compassionate.

Forger's tools of the early 19th Century

The Bank nevertheless determined to stamp out forgery if it could and its attitude towards those who had manufactured or distributed the forgeries was quite ruthless. A good example of this attitude occurred in 1802 when Edward Allen and three others were convicted at Warwick (a fifth man was acquitted as he had been too intoxicated when first questioned to know what he was saying, although he had incriminated himself). The Bank's prosecuting solicitor thought that an example ought to be made of those involved by having them executed where as many people as possible could see them. He wrote to London on 30 March 1802:

'After the Prosecutions I applied to the Judge to direct the persons we had convicted to be executed at Birmingham, instead of Warwick – You may recollect we made a similar application in the Summer of 1800, when the Wells's were convicted at Warwick, but Mr Justice Lawrence thought there not being a prison where they could be lodged at Birmingham, was an insurmountable difficulty – however upon the present application Mr Baron Graham told me, if I could arrange it with the Undersheriff he would readily order it – I then applied to the Undersheriff & so satisfactorily explained the propriety of the application that he agreed, if the Bank would pay the extra expence attending the Execution, it should be done. I told him I had no doubt the Bank would do so, as it would certainly be hard upon Mr Legge the Sheriff, to put him to the Expence, which he could not be reimbursed by the County. The Judge has therefore directed our application to be complied with, upon the Terms I have mentioned.

It is of great consequence to Society & the interests of the Bank that these men should be executed at Birmingham. All the persons upon whom the Example is intended to operate, reside there – independent of which the Executions at Warwick are conducted in so private a manner that the poor wretches seem to crawl out of Society unnoticed – I have been told by a Gentleman who attended an Execution here that he & the Sheriffs men, were the only Spectators – Warwick being distant from Birmingham 20 miles therefore the rabble are prevented attending or indeed of being at all rouzed by the Example.

I shall therefore be obliged to you to communicate these particulars to the Gentlemen of the Bank & obtain their directions immediately, as not a moment's time is to be lost in countermanding the present arrangement if the Bank should decline incurring the Expence'.

The Bank agreed and in due course received the following bill for the whole gruesome business:

1802 April 19th
Expences & Charge of executing Allen, Baker, Hill and Carter on
    Washwood Heath.

To Gaoler his Bill, exclusive of his Charge for) his Trouble)		7:19: –
To Gaoler for his Trouble		3: 3: –
To John Docker for putting up the Drop etc		8: 5: –
To James Marshall his Bills for Iron-work on) the Drop & for his Journey and Attendance)		2:17: 2

It cost the Bank £78:12:6 to remove the executions of four forgers from Warwick to Birmingham in 1802 so that a larger crowd could be attracted. One of the condemned men is alleged to have written in verse about his downfall, whilst in gaol

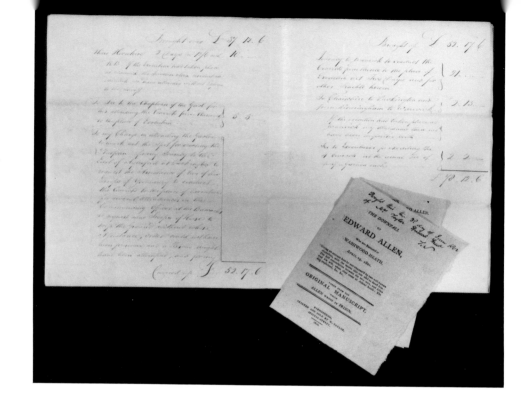

To Christ' Hale's Bill for conveying the Convicts)
   to the place of Execution)   10: 8: 4

To Edward Humphreys's Bill for Waggon & Horses)
   to convey the Drop to and from Washwood Heath)   4:10: –

To Compensation for Damage done to the Widow)
   Lilley's Fences & Garden belonging to her)   –:10: –
   Cottage by some of the populace)

To the Expence of 8 Javelin Men in attending)
   from Birmingham, including their Horsehire)   10: –: –
          2 Days @ 12/6 each

     N.B. If the Execution had taken place
     at Warwick the Javelin Men resident in
     Warwick would have attended without
     Expence to the Sheriff

To Fee to the Chaplain of the Gaol for his)
   attending the Convicts from Warwick to the)   5: 5: –
   place of Execution)

To my Charge in attending the Gaoler to mark)
   out the spot for erecting the Platform: for)
   my Journey to the Earl of Aylesford at)
   Packington to request the Assistance of two)
   of his Troops of Yeomanry to conduct the)
   Convicts to the place of Execution; for)
   several Attendances on the Commanding Officer)   21: –: –
   at the Barracks to request some Troops of Horse)
   to keep the Ground without whose assistance,)

order could not have been preserved, and a)
Rescue might have been attempted, and for my)
Journey to Warwick to conduct the Convicts)
from thence to the place of Execution out Two)
Days and for other Trouble herein)

To Chaisehire to Packington and from Birmingham) 2:13: –
to Warwick)

If the execution had taken place at Warwick
my attendance there would have been
dispensed with

Fee to Executioner for executing the 4 Convicts) 2: 2: –
at the usual Fee of half a Guinea each)

£78:12: 6

The Bank's agent in Birmingham at this time was William Spurrier, clerk to the magistrates there. He was vigorous in the war against the forgers who congregated round the town (then, it must be remembered, an important centre for the printing industry). Edward Allen had attracted much sympathy and Spurrier went in fear for his own life. (His office was apparently under constant surveillance to try and identify informers.) On 20 April 1802 he wrote as follows:

'(Allen was) executed in the presence of 100 000 People on Washwood Heath, he protested his Innocence to the last, say'd he was murdered and that I was his murderer and his blood fell upon me & has so excited the popular fury against me that I consider myself in imminent danger – I have nothing thank God to charge my conscience with, nor I can be induced to believe that any of them could be so abominably wicked as to have sworn falsely against him to take away his Life or to charge him wrongfully.

Last Night Mrs Spurrier in my absence from Home was insulted in her own House and frightened into Hysterics and so much are the deceased's Declaration believed by the lower Classes that the Magistrates this Morning have on consultation advised me to correct the falsity by a short statement of the Evidence in the Paper on Thursday ... Allen say'd he had published a Book to shew his Innocence which would appear in a week, this I suppose will be full of foul Invective, & falsehoods to sacrifice me to popular fury – His spleen seems directed against me alone because I was the Person that laid the Trap for him.

... My peace of mind & Character is so injury (sic) by the diabolical Calumnies propagated by Allen, at such an awful Moment and to such a vast Concourse of People from all Quarters, that nothing can restore the one or retrieve the other without contradicting it wherever it has spread – My conscience I again repeat is perfectly clear. I only did my duty as your Agent, but my Peace of Mind, Fortune, Character & Family see I am afraid irretrievably ruined, My Character not with who know me or the thinking part of Mankind, but with the lower orders which are the most dangerous part of this Community ...'

He did not feel any easier when Allen's alleged work was published, in verse. Entitled 'The Downfall of Edward Allen' it began:

'A certain Lawyer in this town,
Whole deeds have grac'd his fame,
Was agent to a noted Bank;
Old England's firm by name.

One Allen who suspected was
Of utt'ring forged bills;
He by our agent was destin'd
For punishment that kills.'

He described how the evidence was planted by Spurrier's hired 'officious men' who asked if they could leave their cash in his house so that it would be safe from theft during a planned visit to a bawd–house. Later, as Allen proposed to return the notes to them:

'Then in they came with the agent,
And the constable also;
Then handcuff'd him and search'd his wife,
A usual thing you know.'

Five forged notes were shown to him which Allen denied knowledge of but he could not deny possession of some blanks which he doubtless planned to work up. Their discovery 'did grieve him sore'. The last verse describes his last moments:

'When to the drop poor Allen came,
Repeat his words I can;
Unto the people, then said he
I AM A MURDER'D MAN.'

Forgeries varied greatly in their appearance, depending on the type of paper available and the skilled craftsmanship of the counterfeiter. There were several ways of producing a forged note. Most forgers were engravers but if this skill was lacking

Forged copper plates for £1 and £2 notes, recovered from a privy into which they had been thrown by William Badger in an attempt to escape detection

£2 note of 1809, forged by French prisoners-of-war at Chatham, using a pen (195 x 118mm)

it was possible to bribe one, leaving the forger only the more simple task of printing from the plate. Added to the knowledge that this method of operation could lead to information being laid against the hirer of skills, was the danger that the plates would be discovered: no defence would have been possible. Before the public became familiar with the new £1 and £2 notes the small-time forger set about with pen or brush to simulate the genuine article, whether issued by the Bank or by a local bank. Some of the best examples of hand-drawn notes were the work of French prisoners-of-war. They had the skills and, of course, plenty of time on their hands. They were doubtless aware that Napoleon had had £1 and £2 notes forged and sent over to England. Drawing Bank of England notes was probably more profitable in the short run than carving ships from bones but in the long run these artists risked their lives, which no four-masted model barque would have brought about.

Those responsible for mass production of forgeries were few in number and difficult to catch. Information was gleaned by the Bank from agents like Spurrier and no opportunity was lost to interrogate prisoners to see if anything new could be learned so as to help in planning the ongoing battle. Probably the commonest distribution points were fairs where itinerant traders of no fixed abode would meet up: horse dealers, tinkers, chapmen etc. A seller of gingerbread, incarcerated in Reading Gaol, named a number of other dealers including a rival in the gingerbread trade who 'secreted the notes sometimes in a plant under the stall'. Accepted techniques included never passing 'softs in a Town till the Jug (Bank) is locked up'. A soft was a £1 note, of which 25 could be bought (in 1820) for £7:10:- (£7.50); £2 notes ('double softs') cost twice that. Another contemporary price list quotes 7/- (35p) for an individual £1, 9/- (45p) for £2 and £1:3:- (£1.15) for a £5 (which was less easy to pass). The comment by the Reading prisoner that 'They do not know good notes from bad ones at Newbury' was probably a far more widespread truth. Although 'There is scarcely a Stall Keeper Fishman or Horsedealer frequenting all the fairs but what deals in forged notes and base Coins' it was not easy to get in on the trade: 'Those who sell notes and hard money will not sell to any Stranger without an old hand to recommend him and not even then till the Seller has examined him to see if he is down to all the flash terms and pretends he has done 30 or any other large number of softs and thinks he could do more – He must be proficient in the Terms otherwise he will get none, even if strongly recommended by an old hand'.

A typical contemporary broadsheet of 1810 concerning five more forgers who paid the extreme penalty at York

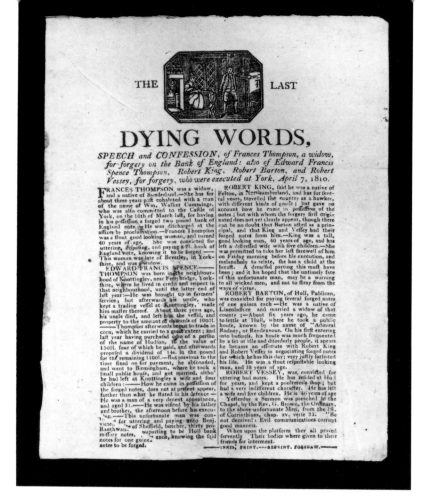

Inexperience led one of Spurrier's *agents provocateurs* to come unstuck in 1817 when he bought a parcel of worthless paper

'Burmingham

Sir

I ham very sorry to henform was has happned to me in the way as it as on friday last I hengaged with the person as calld himsefe Wm Quinn it is Wm Sharman for fore lb worth of nots their wass to have havebin 16 One lb nots & 4 lb of silver for the 5 lb as you gave to me & wen I came to hopen the parsle it wass blancke paper instead of noats the wass lapped hup in brown paper and seald hup the man as broat them to me wass Benjeman Graves he toar the brown paper ther and the hinside paper was licke onto the paper as the bill an mad of the hother parsol was laped hup in brown paper & instead of mony it wass lead Sir if you will pleas to sen me aletter as soon as you can I went to Mr Spuriers Ofiss to get him to right for me and he wass not at hom I thinc if Mr Spurier adbin at home I shoold have none better how to performed in the bisnes

I thincks of seeing those men at the Turcks Head litchfield street on saturdy night next and I shall bevery glad sir if you can send me aletter before satterday night your humble servant
John Pain

Direct to me at
Mr Roberts at the buls head
Knowl Warwick Shire'

Generally speaking a purchaser of forged notes normally did not dare to spend them himself for he could have been accused of knowing they were not genuine. Instead, he would use a servant or passer-by (duly rewarded) to buy a quantity of drink from an inn or buy some specific object from a shop (eg a pair of boots) and wait for the change. ('Old Patch', as we have already seen, favoured the purchase of Lottery tickets.) One such unfortunate, Simon Evans, writing in 1821 from on board the *Leviathan* convict ship claimed he had:

> 'been the Dupe of a Hartfull villan woo Was a Compnion of James Gardnor woo Suffered the Last May for Selling These distruktive Bad Notes but he Never Could bee Pervaled on me Till that Unfortnight Munday Night wich he gave me the Bad Ten pound Note and Shood me the Brothell ware him and wife had Been the Sunday Night bee fore and gave a Bad five Pound Note and if I would go with the Ten I Should have the Half of it I bee came Akwented with these Men throw Living in a Publick House ware they Both used and I Lodged in the Same to my Misfortn ... I now Suffer for and Labor under Rumatick Panes in my Limbes and very Sory to hear that my Aged Mother 80 years old Lies very ill as I ham tha youngest Son and the furst that ever disgrast the famley and am now 40 years of Age and Can Prove at the furst Boot Makers Shops in London to the very Hour that I holwas folwod my Employment for my Living'.

Informants were always hopeful of advancing their status and fortunes. Thus Joseph Vernon in 1820 :

> 'the Police Officer as not Put me in no berth Which I expected he whould a don for doing what I Did for him and you in the hapurinchon Tod and thother 6 at Liverpool and Rogiley at Chester for Putting of Forged notes to me and Linacer   Sir ther his a Mainy that folow smashing Notes a bout where I live now has I could very soone haprend In smashing them but I Doant like to medel whith them Bout I was Maid a Constabul if I Did the whould A buse me but If I was swarne in a cunstable I should not be Afraid and I should be very happy to serve you in the haperinchon of those that Do so for the his a grait mainy that smashes Notes and Silver and all that I could easly catch the whould not fence any to hany bady for the are nothing but smashers and live boy so Doeng ther his A Fair At Tarporley on next Monday but one which the all mak Ther (?) point at there has been grait complaints after the last fair ther whas a Deail paid to Difrent Paper
> Sir Iif you think fit of me to tray to catch them Pleast to send a hancer back by Returne of poste and put your Requst in the letter to Magrets of the County of Chester to swaire me in A cunstable then I shall be very glad to sirve you'.

Others found the Bank less receptive to their pleas for a hearing. In irons in Horsemonger Gaol one Benjamin Prichard complained

> 'Mr Griffes caled on me and told me that you could not cum to see me nou sir i be glad   you cum hear for i have maded it my studey to tel you all i noe i can tel you more than ever you herd of Befour there more mackers of nots then one in Brumingham and i can Let you noe the coyners of tockens and other silver
> sur i hope you concider me i have got a very Bad cold and I ham Ruptered Both sides and ware a duble trus and my iorn mackes it wors'.

In 1818 the Bank's solicitor, Kaye, was able to look back on 31 years' experience of dealing with forgeries, when he gave evidence to the Commissioners charged with enquiring into the means of preventing such forgery. Forgers, he said, 'have become so extremely cautious that it is now very difficult to detect any of them. Their fabrications' were brought to Birmingham for sale or supplied to other areas in parcels. 'The Correspondence on the subject is carried out as if it related to Birmingham Goods of various kinds' using fictitious names and addresses. Wholesale dealers 'conceive they are safe in selling to those who do utter, as the Evidence of such persons would not alone and unconfirmed be deemed worthy of credit ... the Vendors never deal in the presence of two or more persons and they are always paid for the Note some time previous to the delivery, that they may dispose of the money to prevent detection by its being marked ... Two or more persons are generally engaged in plans for circulating forged Notes. One carries the stock of Notes and supplies the other with one at a time and as he succeeds in putting them off the Purse bearer receives from him the Change and the Articles purchased so that when he goes to put off another Note he is without Change ... to show that he had been previously engaged in a similar pursuit. The Utterer is also generally supplied with a good Note to be substituted for the bad one in case of detection'.

A new surge in forgeries discovered at the Bank had commenced in 1811 when the value jumped from £9,072 to £15,729. After a lull, a resurgence took the annual total in 1817 to £37,040. All this put further pressure on the Bank Directors to find an improved note to protect the law-abiding public. At the same time voices were increasingly being raised against the death penalty for forgery offences and juries became reluctant to convict. (Newspapers did not hold back on reporting an execution, however. *Bell's Weekly Messenger* devoted 10 column inches on 26 April 1818 to the fate of John Ward and Harriet Skelton who paid the supreme penalty, for uttering and possession of forged notes, 'at the front of the debtors' door, Old Bailey'.) In the House of Commons on 8 April 1818, General Thornton referred to the great 'sacrifice of human life in consequence of convictions for forgery ... several persons have been

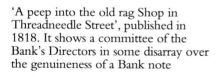

'A peep into the old rag Shop in Threadneedle Street', published in 1818. It shows a committee of the Bank's Directors in some disarray over the genuineness of a Bank note

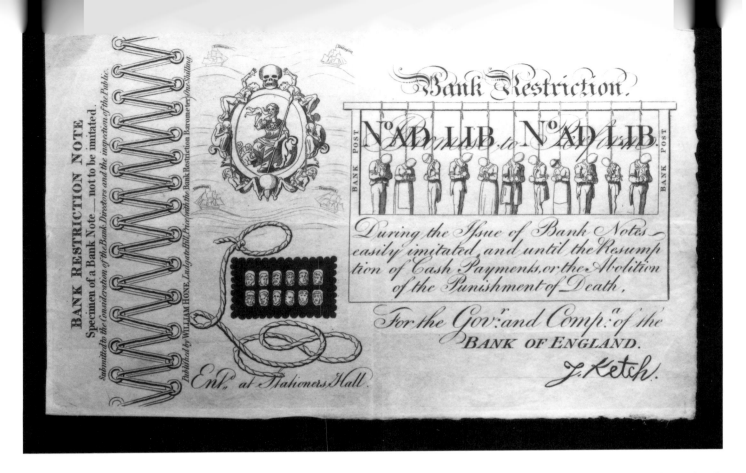

George Cruikshank's macabre 'Bank Restriction Note' which he drew in 1818 as a protest against the severity of the anti-forgery laws, in particular the death penalty (which remained for another 13 years). The signature purports to be that of Jack Ketch, a 17th Century public hangman. This 'Note' was redrawn by Cruikshank in 1872

suffered to escape with impunity'. Compromises were frequently entered into 'with a lesser charge than a capital one accepted by the Bank'. At this stage the Bank were advised that 'the Prince Regent will not approve of prisoners having been induced to plead guilty to uttering forged Bank Notes by an assurance, which compromises the Royal Prerogative'. *The Times* appeared to question the Bank's right to plea bargaining in these cases when it commented on 18 September 1820 'that discretion still continued to the Bank of singling out those who shall be tried on the capital charge. Several other prisoners pleaded in the same way but no such lenity was extended to them on the part of the Bank'.

On 26 January 1819, William Hone published a 'Bank Restriction Note' designed by George Cruikshank. The crowds at his shop in Ludgate Hill in London were so great that the police had to clear the street. At first glance the 'Note' appeared to be a real Bank Note but it showed a row of male and female bodies suspended from a gibbet. The vignetted Britannia, crowned by a skull, was eating an infant. A hangman's looped rope formed the £ sign whilst the Sum Piece actually portrayed 12 heads. An ornamentation based on leg irons or shackles graced the left-hand border where a warning sentence was printed: Specimen of a Bank Note - not to be imitated. The signature was J Ketch, public executioner 1663–1686, whose name had passed into the language as the common name for a hangman. In 1872 Cruikshank claimed that this production helped to drum up public support for the abolition of the death penalty for forgery.

For many of the victims of circumstance the Bank showed a charitable disposition, taking positive steps to try and ease their sufferings. By early 19th Century standards the Bank was being extremely considerate. Women prisoners could petition the Court for an allowance, after entering prison, whilst they awaited space in a convict ship: they were customarily granted 5 shillings (25p) a week each. Most had been forced to pawn what little they had - including clothing - simply to eat. Before they embarked they were usually allowed £5 to buy provisions for the voyage. The Bank's largesse was so well known that one woman, awaiting transportation for an offence not connected with forgery, tried to get the Bank to endow her, too - but without success. Some donations went far beyond the nominal 'value' of the original offence in order to prevent undue suffering. Pregnant women had to wait a long time for transportation as no unweaned child was allowed aboard. In a typical plea for help, Mary Smith wrote from Woolwich in 1819:

'To the Honerable Bank of England

Honeard Gentleman pardin the Liberty of advisin you I am a powr Widow and Left 4 Helples Childern Behind me I am sent out of my Cuntiary for 14 Eyrs for Haiving In my peshin Bank of England Forged Notes and Never Having Had any Relife for this Nine Months I wass tryed In July a sizes at Durham In the County of Bishipbridg Hoping Honeard Gentleman you Extend your Charity By givin me a trifle as I am In the Greatest Distress a Gown out of my Cuntiary without one shilling
Honeard Gentleman
I Shall in Duty
Bound Evear pray'

In another appeal, Susanna Leonard in Newgate Gaol asked for help as her landlord was holding her furniture against half a year's overdue rent:

'Excuse me for trublin you my Prisint Situation Is in the greaitst Distress I am Left Distute and No frind to come Neir me to Bring me Lost Relife I have a powr Child In the Work House allmost Naked and not a show apon His Feat to Kipe Him from the Cold Honeard Sir I Hope you take my unhapy Kase In to your Humane Consideration to Let me Have my Little things as I am Naked When I sent a parson affter them Mr Cousins my LandLord said that Mr Rooken Ordard now wone to have them honord Sir Would you B so good to Order the Sherif Officer to Dispose of them to Relive me and my powr Fatherliss Child.'

In addition to the manufacture of forgeries designed to pass as genuine notes of the Bank, there was the additional worry of so-called 'flash notes' (also known as 'puff notes', 'skit notes' or 'jokers'). In their simplest form they were quite harmless, if illegal, forms of advertising. For instance, in 1823, a selection of pieces of paper made to look like Bank notes was distributed to call attention to a barbers' shop in Threadneedle Street. They purported to be for sums varying between £10,000 and £50 and were drawn on the 'Bank of Elegance' or the 'Bank of Fashion'. *Punch's* so-called 'City Article' which appeared on 22 February 1845 was devoted to the 'Bank of Elegance':

'One of the chief topics of conversation in the City to-day, has been the unexpected publication of the state of its deposit and issue account by the Bank of Elegance. It seems that in the note department there has been, what at first sight appears, an alarming over-issue, for the nominal value of the paper is 200,000 pounds, whereas in the market it would only realise the price of waste. If tissue paper is a shilling a hundred dearer in London than it is at Westminster, the exchange will be about the tenth of a mille in favour of the latter; and supposing gold to be the same price in the Strand as it is at Hammersmith, the eighth of a cipher will represent the mean difference. The Bank of Elegance has, it seems, sent round its own bills to all its customers, with the view of adding to the amount of bullion. To judge from the face of one of the parties who came out of the bank parlour (behind the shop), we should say that a system of very close shaving will be acted on. Under the head of deposits we find only two pocket-handkerchiefs and a silver pencil-case, while the column which shows the amount of rest, has the word Sunday under it. Among the dead weight we find some Macassar Scrip, and a quantity of reduced Columbian, generally known as Oldridge's Balm; but if there should be a rush of bears the Columbian will not retain its value.'

A selection of 19th Century 'flash' notes:
House of Correction (212 x 138mm);
Bank of Engraving (204 x 125mm);
Bank of Rawcliffe (193 x 127mm); and
a Two Pence signed by Zekel Hardbrass
(208 x 93mm)

Where advertisement was the motive, whether the instigator was a barber, a wine merchant, Mr Gowland commending His Lotion or any other sort of trader, a note from the Bank drawing attention to the penalties to which he was making himself liable was usually sufficient. These notes, in the hands of the unscrupulous, were used to defraud the unwary by using them to inflate packets of good notes, or the befuddled by 'flashing' them quickly under their noses. The next stage of the Flash Note was that of an imitation note made specifically to pass as a real one without its creator being liable to the drastic penalties for forgery. One of the most popular methods was to replace the word 'Pounds' by a similarly flourishing 'Pence', or sometimes 'Pens', so that if challenged the perpetrator would be quite prepared to honour his somewhat unusual promise. He could thus be charged with fraud but not forgery. The best known of these deceptive pieces of paper were the 'Fleet notes'. Usually headed 'Bank in England' they were copies of the Bank's notes in almost every detail except that 'Pence' was printed in the place of 'Pounds' and the medallion depicting Britannia usually had an odd look, possibly because its reproduction called for art as well as penmanship. The notes got their name because they were supposed to have been made originally by debtors in the Fleet Prison. It may well be that they were used in the first place as local currency within the prison walls for during the daytime the prisoners were allowed to wander about their particular 'side' of the prison, either the Master's Side, if they could afford to pay for the privilege, the Common Side if they couldn't, or the Felons' Side if they were not debtors. Released prisoners presumably took their accumulation of Fleet notes out with them and if successful with them doubtless came back as visitors to collect more.

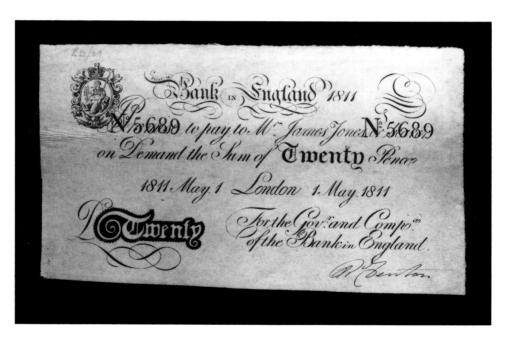

Fleet Prison 'flash' note for 20 pence, designed to pass as a £20 Bank note. The word 'Fleet' occurs in the ornamentation of the first letter in 'Bank' (195 x 117mm)

As late as 1891 the Bank received claims for the repayment of £5 notes where the right-hand half of a genuine note had been joined to the left-hand half of a 'Bank of Engraving' flash product, proving that fraud had been successfully attempted.

The desire to protect the public from being defrauded by documents incorporating features, from the Bank's own notes, which were protected by law – such as the Sum Block – led the Bank to take action on many occasions over the years. Even if the manufactured item could not possibly have been used as money – and often was not even made of paper – the Bank would write a reprimanding letter, which usually did the trick. If it did not, then a prosecution would be started. If the manufacturer lived abroad then action was taken against the importer or the retailer.

The charge of 'knowingly purchasing or receiving or having forged notes in possession' ceased to be a capital offence by Act in 1830. The action of forgery itself remained on the statute book as a capital crime for just two further years. Transportation was substituted in each case, respectively for 14 years and for life.

An unholy alliance between a 'Bank of Engraving' flash note (left-hand half) and a genuine £5 Bank note (right-hand portion) of 1890 bearing the signature of Frank May (Chief Cashier 1873-1893). This 'note' had passed as money.

Opposite page
'...the parents loss is his eternal gain': a £1 note with a sad history. It was part of the wages of a 12-year old boy, Samuel Oakly, who had sailed to Bengal and died of a fever on 7 November 1809. The note 'was kept sacred by his parents in memory of poor Samuel whom they can never see again. But the parents loss is his Eternal gain – he is now happy'. It was finally presented for payment in 1901

CHAPTER 4

Increasing the Difficulty of Imitation

£50 note of 14 November 1806
(201 x 121mm)

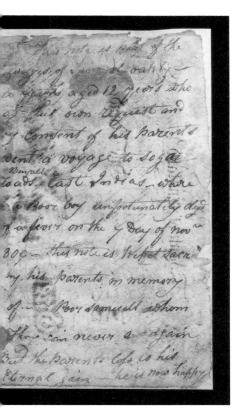

By inviting the public as it did in 1797 to submit suggestions for the improvement of its notes, whether in terms of design, printing techniques or paper, the Bank set out to achieve an impossible ambition: the perfect note 'which one man shall be able to execute (and) which others cannot imitate', as a correspondent to *The Times* was later to write. The truth of this was never brought home more clearly to the Directors than when the Bank itself successfully reproduced the many designs submitted to it over the next 20 years or so as having the advantage of 'inimitability'.

The Bank's senior Standing Committee - the Committee of Treasury (comprising the Governor, Deputy Governor and other senior Directors) - was felt to be the best forum for the consideration of any suggestions made by those of the public at large who had responded to the invitation. These were important resources to devote to the subject. If not heavily engaged in running the Bank - the Governor and Deputy Governor had to devote almost all their time to its affairs - Directors would have had their own business interests to oversee as well as take their turn on the Committee of Waiting, which directly oversaw the daily business of the Bank, on a weekly rota basis. The problem faced by the Bank was, however, equally important since the general acceptability of its notes (and therefore faith in the Bank as a whole) was at risk. As forgery increased so did the volume of submissions and it was decided to form a special committee in 1802 'to examine plans for the Improvement of Bank Notes'. In the previous five years the Committee of Treasury had examined on average seven proposals a year: the new committee investigated another twenty during a life of about 13 months. One of the first came from the studio of Thomas Bewick, who submitted for consideration a wood-engraving which had been executed by him on the end-grain, using engraving tools. This was in contrast to the normal woodcuts made with a knife on the side grain. Unfortunately for Bewick, the Bank's engraver, Garnet Terry, was able to copy his design using copper plates.

While these deliberations were keeping the Committee busy, the number of forgeries discovered gradually declined as the new paper, incorporating the waved line watermark, began to deter the lawless counterfeiter. In March 1803 the Committee reported that they could not recommend any alterations. In their opinion the new paper was the best that could be hoped for then and they were satisfied that no improvement could sensibly be put forward for the notes as a whole. They felt, no doubt, that any more complex design would actually lead to the public's experiencing much greater difficulty in recognising the notes easily. A simple design, which could readily be committed to mind even by illiterate members of the public, had definite advantages. Unfortunately, the same feature - simplicity - was a quality of equal advantage to those operating from the forgers' dens. The Committee of Treasury did not argue against this conclusion and themselves reverted to the rôle of examining similar suggestions until 1817 when the Special Committee was called out of retirement. Parliamentary interest being such at that time, the Government was forced the next year to set up a Royal

£5 note of 30 May 1809
(203 x 120mm)

£10 note of 6 February 1817, payment
of which had been stopped
(201 x 120mm)

Commission of Inquiry. At the same time the Society for the Encouragement of the Arts, Manufactures and Commerce was conducting its own enquiries, not into inimitability, which they recognised was impossible (however desirable an aim), but into 'increasing the difficulty of imitation'.

Many of the suggestions received by the Bank during the years up to 1820 were practically possible to adopt but most would not enhance protection to any significantly useful degree. A favourite subject was the addition of visible material to the paper, nowadays quite commonly used for security documents, though not in the variety of forms suggested by the public: coloured marks with or without silk threads and hair; perpendicular and horizontal cross lines of straw or silk; silver dust; gold leaf; Brazil wood (presumably in shavings or chips); green vegetable substance and red animal-based substance. It was claimed that impregnation with chalybeate water would facilitate the detection of fraudulent alterations by the use of a pen dipped in tea. A portrait watermark found favour with some. The most impractical suggestion in this area was perhaps that the serial number and date of each note should be incorporated in its watermark.

Suggestions for changing the design included the introduction of 'ornaments'; a different symbol for each month; human faces (but not specifically as portraits); random numbers which could be checked against special plates; matching prints on the reverse side; all-over stippling (to deter alterations). Secret marks were favoured by some who were unaware that such were already included. Their advantage lay in the fact that they *were* secret, their disadvantage in the fact that they were only of practical use to the issuer: the public had already been defrauded. Once their existence and form became known to the public, which would have to happen if the public was to derive any practical benefit from them, then they would become equally well-known to a prospective forger. A bizarre proposal was that the surface of a note should be divided into 576 compartments, each of which would take one day to engrave! The design would be changed within two years, thus frustrating any attempt by a potential forger who would be forced to start again.

Portrait watermarks, Royal portraits and coincident front and back images are a common feature of today's notes. So, too, is coloured ink 'varying even within a letter or figure' (1818 proposal).

One submission related to the appointment of Bank Inspectors in the principal cities, with local agents authorised to sign so that the validity and authority of a note could easily be established. Another correspondent wanted the Inspectors to be located 'in all the principal streets in London' for the same purpose, the instant verification of every note proffered. Although impracticable, at least these proposals recognised the difficulty which the man or woman in the street faced in detecting forgeries. Others concentrated on devices which would, they averred, have made detection easier once the notes had been returned to the Bank - again, scant solace for the defrauded trader or other recipient.

The Directors had been regularly under attack since the incidence of forgery had

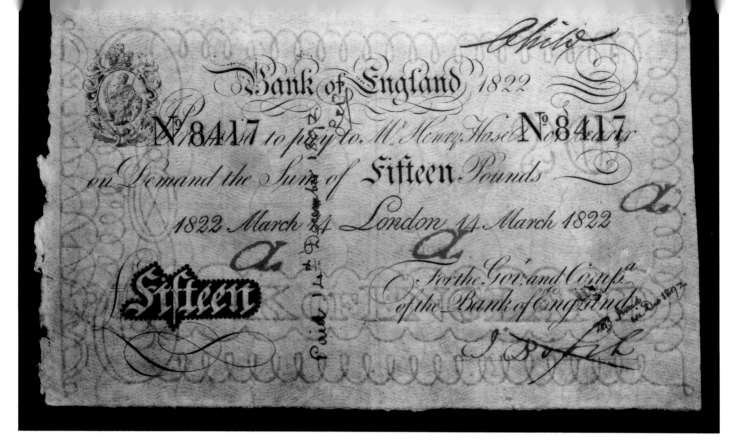

Showing the watermark clearly, one of the last £15 notes dated 14 March 1822 – the final year of issue. It was paid 70 years later (206 x 130mm)

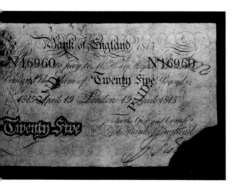

The £25 denomination was also withdrawn in 1822. This example is dated 19 April 1815 (200 x 120mm)

increased following the issue of the small denomination notes (£1 and £2) consequent upon the Restriction imposed on cash payments by the Government. They seemed particularly impervious to criticism that they had shut their minds to reasoned suggestion and argument. As we have seen, forgery was a capital offence, as was the uttering of a forged note. The *Black Dwarf* periodical, in a bitter attack, referred to the Directors as 'priests of Moloch's blood-stained altar' and 'grand purveyors to the gibbet'. In an anonymous letter to the *Monthly Magazine*, a correspondent said that 'the only way to prevent forgery in the future, would be to have the plates so well executed, as to defy the imitation of burglars in the art of engraving, and to continue the abilities of different artists in the same plate, so as to make the total difficulty amount nearly to impossibility ... No fewer that 10 people were convicted at the late Lancaster assizes; the majority of whom are left for execution ... these persons may be said to suffer from the obstinacy of the directors of the Bank'. He went on to suggest that 'if, at the next conviction or execution of a criminal of this description, a Bank Director were compelled to share the same fate, the evil would immediately be remedied'. The Bank's solicitor deemed the whole letter libellous, in which view he was probably influenced by the allegation that 'the involvement of the Solicitors, and Bank Engravers, is deemed of more consequence than the lives and morals of these unfortunate wretches, who are tempted to the commission of crime, by the facility of the operation ... any engravers' apprentice who had served two years, is fully competent to the execution of any plate issued by the Bank; and with regard to the water-mark, the mutilated state of the notes, frequently renders a critical or minute examination impracticable'.

It must not be assumed that the Bank had confined itself to the rejection of every suggestion out of hand, even if 'maturely' considered. Admittedly, it was as late as 1817 before any active work was put in hand beyond the regular occupation of faithfully

Designs for a £1 note by Applegath and Cowper (183 x 113mm, 175 x 112mm)

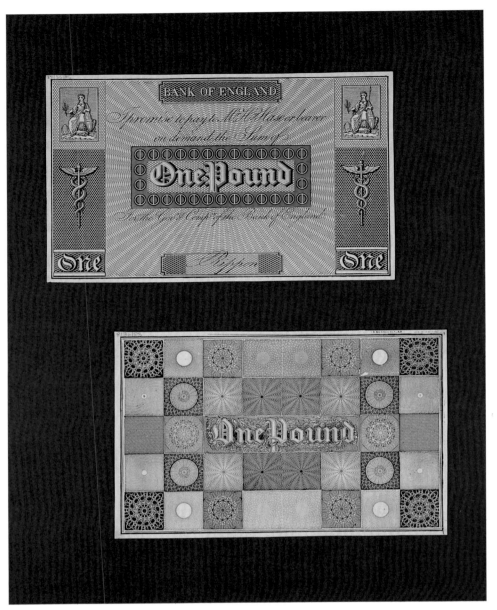

copying other manufacturers' productions. The reconstituted Special Committee had, as one of its first tasks, to examine a letter from Augustus Applegath who, with his partner Edward Cowper, formed a powerfully inventive printing team. Their proposal was to surface-print, in several colours, from an original relief cut in wood or metal. Applegath stressed that few engravers in relief should be able to imitate the work of a first-rate artist skilled in that particular line. The sum of £1,200 was advanced to them initially 'to enable them to complete their experiment to prevent forgery by a plan which is to include different kinds of engraving and printing on Bank Notes in various colours with the most perfect and infallible register'. In theory this was little removed from what had been suggested in the *Monthly Magazine*. The design proposed comprised a figure of Britannia on either side of the note, flanking a large central panel in which the denomination appeared and which divided the promissory clause. The Chief Cashier's signature was to appear at the bottom, the note being headed 'BANK OF ENGLAND'. The design on the back was a reverse impression of that on the front, and was aligned in perfect register with it (shades of George Nicholas!).

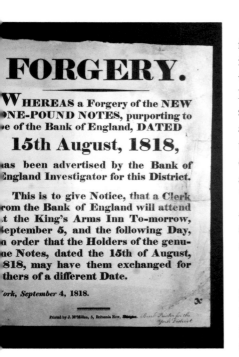

An offer made at York to exchange genuine £1 notes dated 15 August 1818 following the discovery of a serious forgery of this date

The Bank obtained statutory backing in 1820 for issues based on similar design features. At the same time, authority was included for signatures to be impressed on its notes by machine. Naturally, the products of Applegath and Cowper's experimental work were given to the Bank's superintendent of printing and engraving, William Bawtree, to see if they could be satisfactorily reproduced. It is therefore somewhat surprising that the Bank went as far as seeking an Act of Parliament in order to issue an Applegath and Cowper note for Bawtree seems to have had no difficulty with his task. A bi-coloured note having fallen to his skills, another was submitted in three colours: once again Bawtree overcame the challenge. The Bank brought the contest abruptly to a halt in September 1821 when five colours provided no better defence: 'in the opinion of the Committee, Mr Bawtree's imitation is quite fatal to Messrs Applegath and Cowper's Note'. The Court may have been helped in their decision also by the authority they had received to resume cash payments the previous May, after a gap of some 24 years.

Another important experiment resulted from a suggestion from an American, J C Dyer, that notes should be engraved on steel. Notes so printed for use in New England had never been forged and ought, he said, to provide a more satisfactory method of producing the Bank's notes than the use of copper plates. However, Harper, who had succeeded Garnet Terry, reported quite adversely. Engraving the harder metal took four times as long as copper without any production benefits. In hardening the plates (by heating in a closed container) breakages were suffered. Oxidisation caused spotting. Harper found he could only produce about 35,000 notes from a plate which had survived these processes whereas a copper plate (after repair and re-touching) should have been capable of a life output of between 150,000 and 200,000 impressions. Had the Bank been able to take a more positive view on steel plates at this time it could have benefited from Jacob Perkins' technique of siderography: an exact transfer process which facilitated the use of a master plate to produce a considerable number of plates used for the actual printing. It would also have permitted the incorporation in the design of complex, engine-turned geometric patterns, which are so useful today.

The Royal Commission considered very little fresh evidence, concentrating on acquainting itself with details of the proposals studied by the Bank, including the pioneer work by Applegath and Cowper. They observed that 'it has been very commonly imagined, that, in consequence of the simplicity of execution in the present Bank Notes, the actual Forgery of them was very generally and extensively practised, and that often by persons without money or talent; and this idea has formed the basis of much of the reasoning used by many of the projectors, whose plans have been under our view. The reverse of this we believe to be the fact; and from the information before us, we feel ourselves warranted in stating our opinion, that great quantity of Forged small Notes which have lately been found in circulation, have all issued from a very few Plates only; and that the fabrication of them is chiefly confined to one particular part of the Country, and carried on by men of skill and experience, and possessed of a very considerable command of capital. Upon a cursory observation, it appeared remarkable that whilst so may Utterers are constantly brought to justice, the actual Forger should very rarely indeed be detected. But further investigation has led us to think, that this fact may be accounted for; and without entering into details, which upon this point it

engage a well-qualified artist to design new letters and figures. Hase exhibited specimens cast in the Bank and they were approved for use. However, nothing further is recorded so that we do not know why their introduction was abandoned.

The notice setting all these changes out for the public's benefit did not appear until 16 December 1808. All of the Bank's notes dated on and after 22 December would be headed 'Bank of England', have dates and numbers stamped (not written) and omit the names of entering clerks. The notice added that "The Dexter Number will be stamped or printed on the Words 'I Promise': and the Sinister Number will be stamped or printed on the Words 'or bearer' ". At the same time it was ordered 'That on all occasions the terms dexter and sinister be in future reversed, and applied as in Heraldry, conformably to the ... Advertisement'. In other words, the dexter side is the left-hand half of a note as viewed, the sinister therefore the right-hand half.

The Governor had given notice to the Speaker of the House of Commons in 1799 that the Bank would pay in cash (ie coin) all fractional sums under £5 and, as from 1 February 1800, would pay cash for all £1 and £2 notes dated prior to 1 July 1798 or exchange them for new notes of the same value at the option of the holder. Ten years later the Court expressed concern that the actual practice of the Cashiers was at variance with the Governor's earlier advice. The Chief Cashier was summoned to attend the Court meeting on 29 June 1809 and firmly instructed that 'Henceforward no payment in Cash if required be made only' (ie unless) 'the Draft, Warrant or other Order, expresses a fractional Sum under £5, and consequently cannot wholly be discharged by Notes of £5, and upwards'. The drain on their gold stocks even by this concession worried the Bank, however, and in May 1811 the Court submitted that 'in consequence of the high price of Gold great inducement is held out to Individuals to apply for the Payment of small sums in Guineas under £5 to a much larger Amount than heretofore ... as the drain may continue to increase without any benefit to the immediate Circulation of this Country' the Governor and Deputy Governor were requested to discuss with the Chancellor of the Exchequer, Spencer Perceval, the advisability of a bill to prevent the payment in gold. The Chancellor felt that no adequate case had been made out. He had 'every disposition ... to adopt any measure conducive to the Convenience or Interest of the Bank of England' but felt it his 'Duty to express my strong disinclination'. Further discussion took place in 1813 but was not pursued.

This pressure for gold stemmed from the high bullion price and matters came to a head during 1811 when his tenants were asked by Lord King to pay their rents in gold or 'in bank paper of a sum sufficient to purchase ... the weight of standard gold requisite to discharge the rent'. A bill was therefore introduced into the House of Lords the same year – Stanhope's Act – making it illegal to receive gold coin at more than its Mint value or to receive Bank Notes at less than the amount expressed thereon.

The rise in circulation occasioned by the issue of the low sum notes in particular brought increased work to the Inspectors' Office in the examination of notes returned for payment but it was also reported that their burden was aggravated by the 'superior manner in which the Forged ones are executed, particularly those of French manufacture'.

There was a continuing stream of claims for notes lost or mutilated – it had cost 2s6d (12½ p) since 1807 to place a stop on the payment of a lost note. The principal cause of loss remained theft, usually of half a note in the mails. A note which did not escape for long was one for £30 which had blown out of the Cash Book window. As a result, brass lattices were installed. On one occasion at least a Bank note was used to record an attack on a man's enemies. Sir Thomas Cochrane had been fined and imprisoned for suspected association with a Government stock fraud. He finally cleared his reputation but in the meantime he had paid his fine with a £1,000 note, endorsed: 'My health having suffered by long and close confinement, and my oppression having resolved to deprive me of property or life, I submit to robbery to protect myself from murder, in the hope that I shall live to bring the delinquents to justice. (Signed) Cochrane. Grated Chamber, King's Bench Prison, 3 July 1815'.

Another piece of important legislation protecting the Bank's notes was enacted in 1812 when use of the Sum Block – the denomination in words printed in white Gothic lettering on a black background with a beaded edge – was granted exclusively to the Bank. The Bank preferred to gain exclusive use of elements which it considered gave integral protection to its notes. Some alarm was expressed in 1815 when it discovered that Portals were making paper for use by private bankers. When they said that they would restrain such business 'as much as possible' they were sharply reminded that the Committee expected compliance with their previous instruction not to undertake *any* such business.

A firm of Shrewsbury bankers, Rowton and Co, had asked the Bank in 1808 to return forged notes to 'Banking Houses and Persons of respectability' since 'many inconveniences and losses are sustained by the Bank's detaining forged Notes and delivering only Investigator's Tickets certifying the same'. They further suggested that the Notes be marked 'Forged' or in any other way which the Bank may deem advisable. The approach was rejected. But in 1818 the Court had to reconsider the subject in the light of Lord Ellenborough's comments in the case of Brooks v Warwick. Warwick was an Inspector of Bank Notes, Brooks a silversmith and pawnbroker who was in possession of a note which had been marked at the Bank as forged. He was charged by Warwick with possession and committed to prison. He counter-charged Warwick for damages for false imprisonment – and won. Ellenborough's judgment included these remarks:

> 'It seems *crassa ignorantia* indeed to say that because a man retains that which he thinks his own, he is to be deemed guilty of a felony; such a doctrine would almost put a halter round the back of every man who takes a Bank Note in the common course of his trade'.

The Bank's reaction was prompt. The Governor exhibited to Court on 25 June a forged note stamped according to their wishes at the previous meeting. It was resolved that the Chief Cashier be instructed 'That Forged Notes properly stamped be not retained, contrary to the will of the Party bringing them'. This practice explains why such forgeries are occasionally seen in collections and dealers' lists although possession of them (knowing that they are forgeries) contravenes modern law. The usual description denies recognition of the Bank's original action: 'possibly a forgery'!

£1 note of 15 January 1819, payable to Henry Hase (200 x 120mm)

When cash payments were resumed in May 1821 the Bank was faced with the fact that the considerable number of staff involved in the £1 and £2 note issues would no longer have anything to do. In September of the same year it was decided to dispense with the services of 127 men, action which led to the Bank's making its first special pension offer. Service was to cease at the end of the next month but salaries would continue to be paid in full until 5 January 1822. Thereafter pensions of between one-half and three-quarters of salaries and allowances, depending on length of service, were paid. Because the terms were so generous many other clerks, who had not been among the 127 selected by the Bank, also sought release on the same basis: 47 more were allowed to go, bringing the total up to 174 and creating an initial annual pension burden of some £30,000. Contemporary press comment was favourable: '... the Bank have acted with a degree of liberality which merits praise'. It was noted, too, that the option of commuting the annuity would be of particular advantage to 'those who are still young and have a talent for business, an opportunity will be afforded, by a supply of capital, of engaging in trade, and of working out their own independence'.

Watermark mould for £5 notes (1824)

In April 1821 John Portal showed the Court some examples of paper on which part of the waved lines was much more strongly impressed than on existing supplies and on which the value of the note appeared in its watermark. It was agreed to adopt these alterations 'on the Paper for the Notes of this House'. Further improvement followed at the end of 1822 when it was agreed to order paper with 'a Waved Water Mark across the centre of the Note: the Word Five in the Center, and a thickened Scolloped Edge round the Note'. It was not until 12 February 1824, however, that these changes could be brought to the notice of the general public in the following advertisement:

'... all Notes of the Governor and Company of the Bank of England, dated on and after the 1st March next will vary from their Notes as now issued, in the following Particulars. The Notes of £5, of £10, of £20, of £30, of £40 and of £50, will

£20 dated 1 August 1827. From 1825 the watermark incorporated the value of the note in lettering (207 x 130mm)

£30 note dated 28 May 1825 (207 x 127mm)

The popular £50 denomination, dated 14 June 1828 (210 x 130mm)

have the respective numerical Sums for which they are issued, visible in the Substance of the Paper in Roman Letters, on waved Lines, which waved Lines will be broader than heretofore. The Notes of £100, of £200, of £300, of £500 and of £1,000, will be upon Paper with waved lines, similar to those of £5 and upwards, but will not have the respective numerical sums visible in the substance of the Paper. The waved edges of the Paper will be thicker than the other part of the Note; the Words 'Bank of England' will appear visible in the substance of the Paper, both at the top and the bottom of the Note, instead of the bottom only as heretofore. In the engraving the yearly date, after the words 'Bank of England' at the top of the Notes will be omitted.'

The yearly date, referred to in the second paragraph, had been a feature since 1810. The new watermark served for 30 years and remained the basis of subsequent watermarks on these issues. The incorporation of the numerical sum in the watermark of the notes in the range of £100 to £1,000 eventually took place in 1887.

Consequent upon the failure of a number of banks and the ensuing financial crisis, another run on the Bank occurred in 1825. Fortunately a stock of approximately one million unissued £1 notes bearing the year 1821 at the top but undated otherwise, and unnumbered, was located in a vault. The printers were called in to complete the process of making these forms into notes – and later to print urgently some £5 and £10 denominations – and the crisis soon passed. What was now needed was a strengthening of the position of the country banking system.

CHAPTER 6

Branching Out

Notes for denominations above £50 did not have their values shown in the watermark until 1887. This £300 note is dated 2 July 1827 (205 x 128mm)

The earliest date on a Branch note represented in the Bank's collection: £5 Swansea of 25 September 1828 (205 x 127mm)

The crisis of 1825 had caused both Government and Bank to focus their respective attentions on the lack of any Bank of England branch network in the provinces, a subject which had been commented upon from time to time almost from the Bank's inception. As recently as 1811 Earl Stanhope, in a prescient letter to the Lord Chancellor, had recommended the establishment of branches to remedy 'the inconvenience arising from the lack of a legal tender'. As the Directors now referred the subject to a Special Committee (which rapidly decided in favour) so did the Prime Minister, Lord Liverpool, and his Chancellor of the Exchequer agree to recommend to the Bank that branches be established. There was a sting in the tail, however, since the Country Bankers Act of 1826 which made this possible also seriously breached the curtain-wall of privileges which surrounded the Bank's activities: it limited the exclusion zone protecting the monopoly of joint-stock banking - hitherto a country-wide ban - to a radius of 65 miles from London.

1 All outstanding Exeter Branch notes became payable at Plymouth Branch; or in London as hitherto; or by Cole, Holroyd and Co (Devon County Bank).

The first country branch to be opened was at Gloucester on 19 July 1826, followed up to 1829 by, respectively, those at Manchester, Swansea, Birmingham, Liverpool, Bristol, Leeds, Exeter, Newcastle, Hull and Norwich. Further branches were set up at Plymouth and Portsmouth in 1834 (when Exeter was closed[1]), at Leicester in 1844 and at Southampton in 1940. Although not as brief an existence as was the fate of Exeter, Gloucester (closed in 1849), Norwich (in 1852), Swansea (in 1859) and Leicester (in 1872) had comparatively short working lives. This century saw the demise of Portsmouth (1914), Hull (1939), Plymouth (1949), Southampton and Liverpool (both in 1986). There were also two London branches which existed for a considerable number of years: Western (1855-1930), situated in Burlington Gardens, and Law Courts (1881-1975).

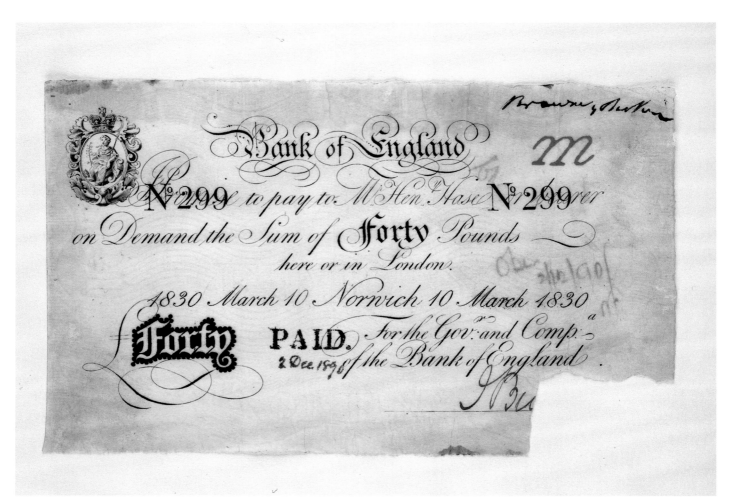

A posthumous issue: a £40 Norwich Branch note dated 10 March 1830, payable to Henry Hase who had died the previous year. It was paid in 1898 (205 x 125mm)

The Branch Banks' Committee, meeting in April 1826, decided that notes should be issued by the country branches 'prepared in London with the paper now in use, but marked with the name of the Branch by which they were to be circulated...each Note should be payable only at one place...distinctly specified on the face of it'. The Committee suggested a coin reserve at each Branch equal to one fifth of the amount of the notes in circulation, which they felt would be 'amply sufficient to meet any conceivable Demand' considering the ease with which further stocks could be sent from London – an invaluable back-up facility not capable of being enjoyed by the country bankers such as those who had recently failed. In June the Court resolved, in consequence to the 1826 Act which laid down that any Promissory Note issued on the Bank's account in any place where the Bank carried on its business should be made payable in such place as well as in London, that notes with the words 'here or in London' should be adopted for Branch issues. In all other respects the notes presented the same appearance as the London series, including the use of Roman lettering for 'Bank of England' above the signature on the £5 denomination and of Italic lettering for these words on the other denominations. When discussing the case of Taylor Jennings, a clerk at the Liverpool Branch in 1843, who was paid by a well-known fence to switch stolen notes for untainted notes paid in by customers (ie those not subject to a stop on payment), it was said that no Branch would change another Branch's notes for a stranger without the permission of the Agent or Sub-Agent at the receiving Branch. It was, however, pointed out by the Bank's solicitor that there was no reason to withhold payment to a stranger if there was no stop recorded against the note(s) in question. It

Extract from the meeting of the Branch Banks Committee on 17 May 1826 when it was decided that the Branch notes should be dated locally but paid also in London

The only known survivor of notes issued by the Bank's short-lived Exeter Branch: a £20 of 24 November 1828, payable to Henry Hase (205 x 127mm)

The full range of denominations issued by the Leicester Branch (1844–1872). The £20 and £100 are payable to Matthew Marshall, the others to Bearer – a change introduced in 1855

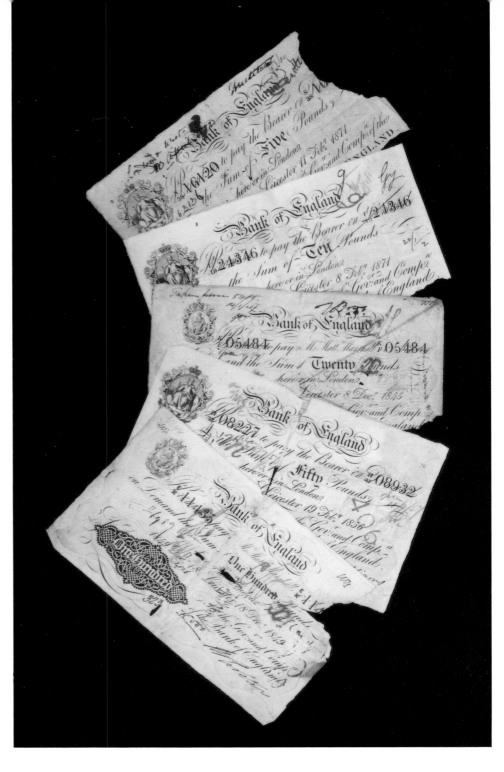

2 On one occasion, recorded by Mackenzie, the Law Courts Branch was asked to cash a Country Branch note. The presenter, a solicitor, was indignant when advised that he must go to Threadneedle Street since, for the purposes of the Bank of England Note issue, the Law Courts Branch was not deemed to be 'in London'!

was decided also by the Court that each branch should offer the full range of available denominations, with the exception of the £200, £300 and £1,000 categories. However, this did not actually occur, since, for example, there were no £30, £40 or £500 notes printed for use by Leicester Branch, opened in 1844. Also, some denominations were dropped for individual Branches: there were no £20 notes made for Plymouth after 1861 or for Bristol after 1889. No notes were issued specifically in the name of the two London branches[2] nor for Southampton, branch issues having

£100 note, payable to Bearer, issued by
Hull Branch and dated 3 September
1860 (209 x 130mm)

ceased before it was opened, as will be seen.   Further details of the denominations
supplied to each branch and the dates of final printings are given in Appendix   A.   A
short-lived issue of £1,000 notes was made by the Hull Branch between 1883 and
1892, following a request from the Hull Incorporated Chamber of Commerce and
Shipping who thought it would 'greatly convenience' the local merchants.   An initial
supply of 1,000 was dated 19 September 1882 (dates on Bank of England notes are *not*
those on which actual printing necessarily took place).   Three further printings, each
of 1,000, were made and delivered up to 1890, by which time the Agent agreed that
the denomination might well be discontinued;   stocks were exhausted in September
1892.   It is interesting to observe that the Bank's records reveal that £1,000 notes were
also prepared for Liverpool Branch, a much larger operation than Hull's, but they were
never delivered to the Branch nor, apparently, discussed or referred to in
correspondence.   Notes for branch usage were not printed after 1938:   the latest date
on a branch note is 28 November 1938 (£10 Plymouth).

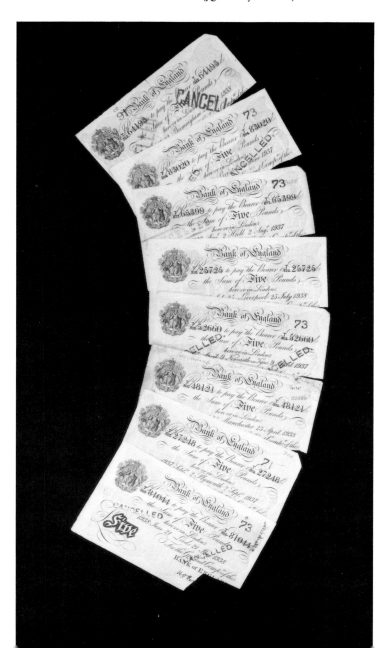

Examples of final cyphers used for £5
notes issued at 8 different Branches

produced in the thirtieth week of 1888. The first form from this batch was signed in 1894. Printing was from plate number 8, which was in use between 1873 and 1893: a tiny figure indicating this appears under the Maclise vignette of Britannia. Signatures from 1857 onwards are on £1,000 denominations. Before that date various denominations were used from £5 to £1,000, the choice appearing haphazard. Included are £30, £40 and £300 denominations.

In places the list of signatories reads like the *Almanach de Gotha* ; but royalty is occasionally forced to rub shoulders with diplomats, soldiers, statesmen, a sportsman, an authoress, the Church (when God met Mammon?) and some who, after the passage of years, appear to have left no other mark in history. German titles abound: Prussia, Mecklenburgh, Baden, Saxony, Hesse, Hohenzollern, Leiningen, Oldenburg, Wurttemberg, Holstein-Glucksberg, Saxe-Meinengen - Kings, Princes, Grand Dukes and others, reflecting the close links between the German and British reigning houses. Forgotten kingdoms and empires come to life again as the pages turn: the Emperor of Brazil; Kings and Queens of Portugal, Burma, Sweden and Norway (joint), the Sandwich Islands (the Queen Dowager in 1865, the King in 1881); Tsar Alexander II of Russia; Princes of China, Romania and France (Napoleon); the Shah of Persia (in 1873); Indian rulers (Surat, Bahadur, Bobbili) and the Sultan of Zanzibar. In addition, there are representatives of houses which still rule today: the Netherlands (the young Wilhelmina in 1895), Denmark and Japan.

What of British royalty? The Prince of Wales (later Edward VII) was the first (on a £10 note) in 1853. He was accompanied by Prince Alfred whose note is not signed: at least two other unsigned notes are in the collection, the name of the visitor simply

Prince Oscar of the combined Kingdoms of Sweden and Norway autographed this £20 note during a visit on 11 July 1856

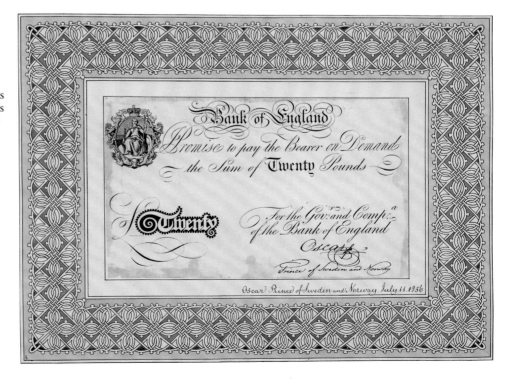

being recorded in place of the signature. 20 years later when he escorted the Cesarevitch and Cesarevna of Russia the Prince of Wales signed again. When George V's young children paid a visit in 1907 they each signed a note. The first visit by a reigning British monarch was by George V on 18th December 1917 and his signature is followed by that of Queen Mary, who repeated her visit in 1937, accompanying the present Queen (as Princess Elizabeth). Queen Elizabeth has signed further notes as monarch.

This form of record has for a number of years now been confined to visiting British royalty and other heads of state. In consequence much less frequent use occurs today than in the last century when the Bank seems to have revelled in the fact of being a 'sight' and in receiving exotic visitors - such as New Zealand Chiefs (1863), the Japanese Daimio and '3 Native Friends' (1864), High Officers of the King of Burma (1871) and Bulgarian Deputies (1887). These groups are among a number of notes which are signed by more than one visitor.

The church is represented by the Archbishop and the Archimandrite of Syria and Tenos (1870), by the Bishop Suffragan of Dover and the Bishop of Moray (1878) and by the Bishop of Lincoln (1883). Diplomats abound, including three American Ambassadors (Everett in 1845, Schenck in 1871 and Phelps in 1887). One is reminded that 'tycoon' has a Japanese origin: in 1867 a visit was made by Tokugawa Mimbutaiko 'brother of the Tycoon of Japan'.

Noble family names of the United Kingdom appeared occasionally during the last century: Buccleuch, Salisbury, Norfolk, Sutherland, Breadalbane, Spencer, Carnarvon and Granville.

Among the early signatures were those of Sir Robert Sale, then Quartermaster-General of India, and Lady Sale, who had been wounded during the retreat from Kabul in 1842; and of General Sir Henry Pottinger, the first British Governor of Hong Kong. Rowland Hill, who introduced the Penny Post in 1840, was received in 1862, Winston Churchill in 1955. The sportsman? He was D W Gregory who had captained the Australian side which won the very first Test match in Melbourne in 1877 when the English side was weakened due to the necessity of leaving their wicket-keeper in New Zealand - in gaol! Gregory also led the first Australian cricket XI to visit this country and came to the Bank on 21 June 1878.

Less important visitors to the Bank in 1881 were handed a leaflet as follows:

The Stock of Paid Notes for 5 years is about 77,745,000 in number, and they fill 13,400 boxes, which, if placed side by side, would reach 2 $\frac{1}{3}$ miles; if the Notes were placed in a pile, they would reach to a height of 5 $\frac{2}{3}$ miles; or, if joined end to end, would form a ribbon 12,455 miles long: their superficial extent is rather less than that of Hyde Park: their original value was over 1,750,626,600 l; and their weight over 90 $\frac{2}{3}$ Tons.

In anticipation of the separation of the Bank into Banking and Issue Departments, the Committee of Treasury considered in 1843 what should be done about notes which had been outstanding for many years, almost back to the inception of the Bank in some cases, which it was thought unlikely would be presented to any significant amount. It was felt that all notes issued before 1794 and not presented could now be written off to a suspense account, which would be drawn on if any were subsequently presented for payment. In the event, all notes of £5 and upwards, still outstanding, issued and dated before 1 November 1794 were carried to a new Suspense Account in February 1843 – totalling just over £40,900. The next month the balance of outstanding £1 and £2 notes was transferred to a special Suspense Account – the amount was over £269,000. When the Issue Department was created in 1844 all remaining notes outstanding, which were issued and dated on or before 1 January 1827 were transferred as 'Dead Notes' to Suspense Account – some £372,600. Included in these transactions was the sum of £2:–:1d, the balance of an 'Odd Sums' Ledger, comprising two notes each for £1 and one for one penny, believed to be spoiled notes made out in 1797, 1806 and 1828 respectively for the purpose of internal balancing and taken away instead of payment being demanded the next business day. The Bank's records show a proliferation of small amounts created shortly after the Bank Charter Act of 1844 but these were always redeemed the next day. Eventually coin movements took the place of this arrangement. Technically these small notes were 'in issue' but they were never issued to the public. Although the creation of a *regular* large denomination note for internal purposes only did not occur until the beginning of the 20th century, the Bank's collection includes hand-written examples of £500,000 and £1 million notes of 1780.

A unique, unnumbered £5 note payable to Henry Hase but altered in manuscript to serve as a one penny note, for internal Bank purposes. Dated 10 January 1828, this note was purchased by the Bank for £1 in 1868 from the landlord of the Blue Last in Bell Alley, London. It is still outstanding in the Bank's books (209 x 130mm)

£500,000 internal note of 1780 – an early 'giant' (200 x 118mm)

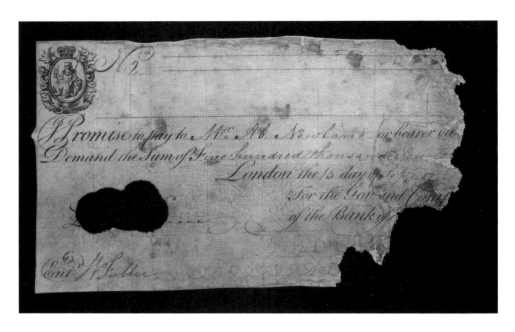

Three years later, Abraham Newland was to explain to a Committee of Directors that, in order to enable notes received in subscription to a loan or lottery managed by the Bank to be processed at leisure, the total amount tendered in this way was customarily converted into a 'spoilt note', being sent to the General Cash Book the next morning for payment.

Considerable uncertainty arose as to the validity of adding to or reducing the Dead Note Account and Counsel's opinion was sought. It was decided that the Bank could not legally increase the Account without Parliament's approval. The confusion was removed by the Bank Act of 1892 which provided for the placing to Dead Note Account of all notes outstanding for 40 years, an easy enough provision to meet since a date appeared on each one at that time.

Most lost notes have a legitimate owner somewhere but there are occasions when no claimant comes forward. Special care had to be exercised by the Bank in respect of notes found on the premises by its own servants. A year after he had handed in a £5 note which he had picked up in the 3% Office, the House Porter, Thomas Lucas, petitioned for payment, having advertised once for the owner. The Court decided that four advertisements must be inserted on different days and only then, should no legitimate claimant come forward, would the money be paid to the finder after a year and a day.

There were many occasions in the Bank's first years when claims were made in respect of notes damaged by immersion in liquid. Nowadays there are claims for virtual destruction by accidental exposure to washing machines – usually as a result of leaving a note or notes in a pocket inadvertently. Yet handwork was just as unfriendly to a banknote in the days before the facility of machines. In 1855 the Viscount Maynard, writing from Easton Park, Dunmow claimed £50 in respect of three notes 'placed by the Viscountess Maynard in her stays for security whilst travelling abroad – who neglected to take them out when they were sent to the Laundress – on 26 May in Switzerland & thus they became damaged'. The Old Lady was understandably sympathetic and paid up promptly.

Reflecting on his Victorian service with the Bank, a pensioner in 1921 recalled the occasion where a respectable elderly female, having been told to write her name and address on the back of a note she wished to change and then to 'put it through the grating' was discovered 15 minutes later still seated patiently. On enquiry, a messenger was told by her that she had put it through the grating but no one had given her change. She then indicated the grating on the iron stove which stood in the centre of the office, not the brass protection on the counter. Fortunately it was summertime and the lady, by now reduced to tears, soon happily restored to equanimity and duly repaid.

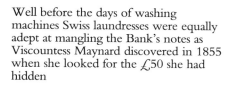

Well before the days of washing machines Swiss laundresses were equally adept at mangling the Bank's notes as Viscountess Maynard discovered in 1855 when she looked for the £50 she had hidden

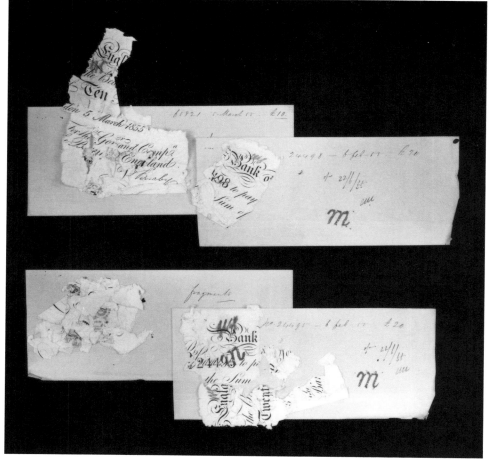

Matthew Marshall, Chief Cashier 1835–
1864. Lithograph by F W Wilkin
(1841)

The £5 Note Office around 1840,
designed by Sir John Soane, where the
issue and payment of this denomination
were recorded

CHAPTER 7 The Monopoly of Money

Matthew Marshall, who had succeeded Rippon, had joined the Bank in 1810 at the age of 19 and was appointed First Assistant to the Chief Cashier in 1829. He served as Chief Cashier for 29 years from 1835 and during his tenure he saw the division of the Bank into Banking and Issue Departments under the Bank Charter Act 1844. Coppieters has observed (*English Bank Note Circulation 1694-1954*) that David Ricardo, who had proposed a State monopoly of the note issue, believed that the resultant large profits (a holder of a bank note is making an interest-free loan to the issuer) should accrue to the State in the same way as seigniorage on coins. Bank Stock holders should no longer be able to share in the profits of note issue. Rather than simply nationalise the note issue, the Government decided first to see if it was possible to separate the note issuing function of the Bank from its banking function. In achieving this, the Government was also able to limit (initially to £14 mn) the amount of notes which could be backed by securities – the profit on these being for the Bank's benefit. All other notes had to be backed by gold and silver reserves, the latter not to exceed one-fifth of the former.

Stamp Duty had first been imposed on bank notes by an Act of George III in 1782 for which the Bank made compounded payments. After a number of increases in the annual figure, duty was removed by the 1844 Act subject to the Bank making an increase to £180,000 of its existing 'allowance to the public', a rise of £60,000.

One of the principal objectives of the 1844 Act was to impose restrictions as far as was possible on the ability of banks in England and Wales to issue notes, the Bank of England excepted. No new bank of issue could be established; those who had ceased already, or ceased in the future, to issue could not resume; and those who continued to issue were not allowed to expand the total. The main reason for cessation was the consequence of a merger with a non-issuing bank. (The last private English bank notes were issued in 1920 by the Somerset house of Fox Fowler and Co which then merged with Lloyds Bank Ltd.) Provisions in Section 24 actually encouraged bankers to give up their rights in exchange for compensation (known as 'composition'), paid annually. Before 1844 the Bank had already entered into several such arrangements as a number of private bankers faced up early on to the competition of the joint-stock banks authorised under the Country Bankers Act of 1826 but there were still many which hung on, on the grounds of profitability, prestige and fairly economic advertisement.

The Bank followed three principles when agreeing to composition arrangements under the new Act: it was not obliged to enter into agreements (the Act was permissive); it was careful to stress it was acting for the Treasury; and it would not continue to pay compensation if a bank disqualified itself – for example, by acquiring more than six partners. Agreements already in force, however, continued to attract payments until the banker went out of business.

£5 Birmingham Branch note of 1844, featuring printed asterisks to facilitate the payment of composition to former note-issuing Banks (see main text).

The basis of composition was the annual average of Bank of England notes issued by each contracting banker and actually remaining in circulation. In order to measure this, a series of special printings of notes took place for the use of certain Branches. They were distinguished by the addition of a star in front of the date on the dexter portion and another after the serial number on the sinister side; all Branches were informed by General Circular on 6 August 1844 but the notes carried dates from November 1843. The full range of Branch denominations – £5-£500 – was prepared in this way for Liverpool and Manchester, seven of the remaining Branches receiving £5-£100 only; none were made for Gloucester, Hull, Norwich or Swansea. These special notes were intended to be issued only to local contracting bankers who were customers of the Branch concerned. In April 1845 the Birmingham Agent was told that this experiment for determining 'the action of your Contracting Bankers on the Circulation of your Branch has satisfied the Governors that an amount of Notes fully equal to the Scheduled Amounts will remain constantly in circulation after issue to them'. It had therefore been decided to discontinue the issue (by Birmingham) specifically to those banks of any more 'Star Notes'. Ordinary notes could now be issued and reissued to them in the same manner as to any private customer. 'Star Notes' were to be dealt with as if they were any other note, the distinctive mark being totally disregarded in future. The last 'Star Notes' were dated 14 August 1846 (£5 Newcastle).

At its peak in the mid-nineteenth century, total composition amounted to about £20,000 each year but the figure fell to below £10,000 by 1900 due to failures, dissolutions and mergers. By 1920 only four banks were in receipt of payments – in all, less than £3,000. Three were joint-stock banks: Union Bank of Manchester (acquired by Barclays Bank in 1940), Martins Bank and District Bank (as successors to, respectively, Bank of Liverpool and Manchester and Liverpool District Banking Co). Martins Bank was merged with Barclays Bank and District Bank with National Westminster Bank, in 1968. The fourth survivor, the last of the private country bankers, Gunner and Co had been acquired by Barclays in 1953. With the passing of the Barclays Bank Act 1969 and the National Westminster Bank Act 1969, the annual composition payments came to an end.

The separation of the Bank into two Departments required the transfer of some staff to man the Issue side but hardly the infusion of new blood of which *Punch* claimed to have

'The Strongest Corroboration
In consequence of the alterations caused by Sir R Peel's new law, it is reported that ninety additional clerks have been engaged at the Bank. This report must be true, as we have been told that ninety additional newspapers have been ordered to be sent in every morning to the same place.'

The theft of over £40,000 from the bankers Rogers and Co in 1844 embraced the whole range of denominations contemporarily available from the Bank (though only one @ £500). Payment was immediately stopped and the notes were retained by the Bank when they streamed in for payment

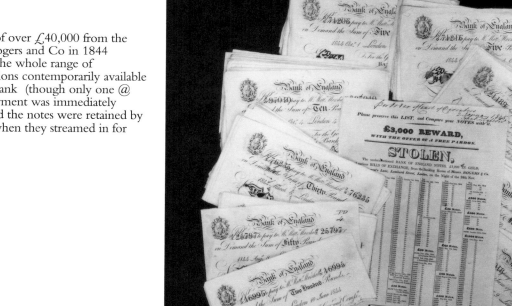

Original drawing by Daniel Maclise for
the Britannia figure adopted for the
Bank's notes in 1855

William Brewer, the Bank's mould-maker for 45 years, regarded the challenge of creating a satisfactorily shaded watermark as one he could not resist. His patience was rewarded when, in collaboration with a die-sinker (John Smith), he patented a process for incorporating into the mould thin brass plates which had been die-stamped with the required design and perforated to allow the rapid drainage of surplus water. In 1851 they were joint parties to an agreement by which the Bank obtained sole rights to the process. It was to be one of the important features of the form into which the white Bank of England note would finally be shaped.

William Smee, the Bank's Chief Accountant (1831-1858), had a remarkable son, Alfred, who combined a medical career with that of electrical engineering; he was, in fact, the Bank's first medical officer, appointed in 1857. Alfred Smee had invented a battery which was instantly available for use, powerful, cheap to produce and easy to clean after use. Known as the 'Smee Cell' the invention gained him Fellowship of the Royal Society at the early age of 23. The steadiness of the current made it very suitable for the electrical deposition of metal and Smee interested himself in the production of electrotypes. It is Mackenzie's view that the concept of printing the Bank's notes from electrotypes in relief, instead of plate-printing from recess engraving, was Smee's. After Oldham, used to the old ways of engraving and plate-printing, had died in 1851, Alfred Smee presented to the Governor his proposals for surface printing from prototype. Henry Hensman had now filled the vacancy left by Oldham, as Engineer, and he and John Coe (Superintendent of the Bank-note Printing and Stationery Office) proceeded to experiment. After overcoming the initial difficulty of finding engravers skilled enough to cut a relief out of solid metal, they proceeded apace and a specimen note was exhibited to Court on 14 July 1853. It bore the famous vignette of Britannia, especially commissioned (for £100) in 1850 from Daniel Maclise RA, a leading contemporary painter. The practice of printing the Chief Cashier's name as payee was dropped – the notes were now payable simply to bearer. However, Marshall's signature was introduced into the watermark, in the lower left hand quarter. The laborious work of hand-signing the notes had been abandoned in 1853: instead, the Cashier's signature was printed - initially, J Vautin, H Bock, J Ferraby, J Williams or J Luson - provision for which had been made in the Forgery Act of 1820 but which was repeated in the Bank Notes Act of 1852.

£100 note of 5 February 1858 with a
printed signature

£5 note of 1 January 1855 from the first printing of this denomination with the Maclise Britannia; it was payable to Bearer instead of to the Chief Cashier, was no longer signed by hand and incorporated Chief Cashier Marshall's signature in the watermark
(209 x 130mm)

The result of these diverse efforts was the production of a crisp, cleaner-looking note whose forthcoming appearance was advertised in the customary manner, first issues bearing the date 1 January 1855. The space occupied since 1838 below the Britannia vignette by a tiny printing plate number was now vacant although it was to be re-introduced between 1878 and 1892, for most printings. The range of denominations had been reduced a few years earlier when the £40 (in February 1851) and £30 (December 1852) were discarded.

£30 note dated 7 January 1848 which was in circulation for nearly 50 years. This denomination was removed from the Bank's range of notes in 1852
(209 x 129mm)

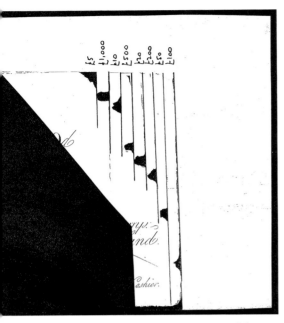

A comparison of the positions of the paper-maker's markings to facilitate the printers' selecting the correctly watermarked paper (taken from actual examples)

Opposite page
£5 notes of 4 January and 1 December 1865. The Chief Cashier's signature (Marshall) still appears in the watermark of the earlier note but had been replaced by a paper-maker's vat number before the year was out. William Miller was by now Chief Cashier but his signature was never used (207 x 129mm)

By 1860 it had become possible to reduce the cost both in time and in effort to ensure that, before being inserted into the machinery, each blank sheet of paper was the correct way up in relation to the watermark and also was the correct paper for the denomination being printed. A simple expedient was devised: the marking of each sheet of paper in the mould itself. Paper for £5 notes had a flattened corner, whilst those sheets intended for the £10, £20 and £50 denominations had small, semi-circular notches in the same edge in different positions for each value. All these marks occurred on what the Bank had chosen to term the sinister, or right-hand, edge. As the notes were printed 'two up', only one half of the production run would feature these markings. The sinister edge being deckled, there was a slight security advantage in case a note were altered (say, from £5 to £50) - provided the public were aware of the feature, which seems unlikely. The Bank's reliance for security on the peculiar attributes of the paper used for its notes rested on the legal protection which it enjoyed from other note-issuers making use of paper with any similar feature. It was therefore more than a little disturbed when, in August 1862, a large quantity was stolen from Portal's Laverstoke mills and was being used to manufacture forged notes. *The Times* reported that bankers and others customarily handling notes had been warned no longer to rely on the quality of the paper and to examine much more carefully than hitherto the actual printing on notes which came their way. A cast of a key had been used to get into the mill and a boy bribed to hand over the paper. Three men were subsequently given prison sentences for the affair.

When Matthew Marshall retired in 1864, his facsimile signature was removed from the mould but that of his successor, William Miller, had not replaced it by the time he (Miller) died 2 years later. He was 19 when he joined the Bank in 1829 and his career had been spent almost entirely in 'Cash' offices although he had Branch experience for six years from 1831 at Bristol. His widow received a sum of £1,000 for his 'special and important services' to the Bank. The reason for his signature not appearing in the watermark may simply have been due to the consideration of a much more radical change: the printed signature of the Chief Cashier on each note. Marshall's signature was actually replaced by a paper-making vat mark.

The Forgery Act of 1861 made it an offence to produce imitation Bank of England notes in any form so the Bank was much exercised when the Committee of the West Central Industrial Exhibition displayed specimens of penmanship which included exact replicas of *Punch*, the *Illustrated London News* and similar frontispieces - and three Bank notes, 'imitated even to Maclise's vignette in the corner'. This Committee had been established to sponsor an exhibition at the Floral Hall, Covent-garden, in 1865 of works of skill and art. Pleading the 1861 Act, the Bank applied to the Bow Street Police Court for the offending reproductions to be removed, under threat of prosecution under the Act. The Committee argued that the pictures in question did not come within the meaning of the law. The parties had met together beforehand when John Coe, disclaiming any disposition to act harshly or injuriously towards the Exhibition and acknowledging that emulation in producing a work of art was the sole motive of the draughtsman, showed 'by a variety of specimens of notes done by pen in bygone years that the skilful employment of so simple an instrument by dishonest persons had caused them to be hanged'. Sir Thomas Henry, who was hearing the argument, supported

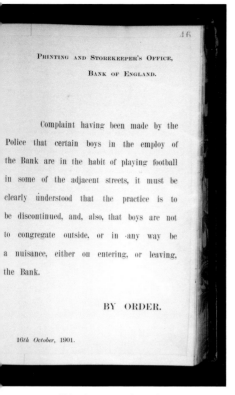

Boys will be boys. A disciplinary notice of 1901

The police found cause to warn the Bank in 1901 of the behaviour of some of the staff employed in the Printing Office. Since 1847 the Bank had been recruiting boys of 10 years old and over to undertake various menial tasks. They were the sons of Bank messengers and porters or of other staff or had been recommended by other members of staff. As they reached suitable age they were generally apprenticed to a master in order to learn a trade, the necessary premium being paid by the Bank. The majority chose to stay within the printing trade and many were able subsequently to return to practise their qualified skills in the Bank's employment. Following the Education Act of 1870, which provided for the full-time education of children, a large number of boys under 13 had to be released for schooling. A few who had nearly reached that maturity were allowed to stay on, the Superintendent of the Printing Office becoming responsible, in addition to his other worries, for their part-time education. This 'lively, albeit inky, community' enjoyed playing football and other games. A notice was issued on 16 October 1901 from the Printing and Storekeeper's Office, adverting to the complaint 'having been made by the Police that certain boys in the employ of the Bank are in the habit of playing football in some of the adjacent streets, it must be clearly understood that the practice is to be discontinued and, also, that boys are not to congregate outside or in any way be a nuisance, either on entering, or leaving the Bank'. By 1914 this branch of the staff had ceased to exist.

No particular developments concerning the note issue occurred during Bowen's tenure as Chief Cashier, which ended in January 1902 when he resigned on health grounds. He had suffered illness a year earlier, culminating in the amputation of a leg. Having struggled back to his office for a while he reluctantly found he could not carry on; he died suddenly four months later, aged 61. He was replaced by J G Nairne.

Reward notice of 1899 relating to the theft of some £20,000

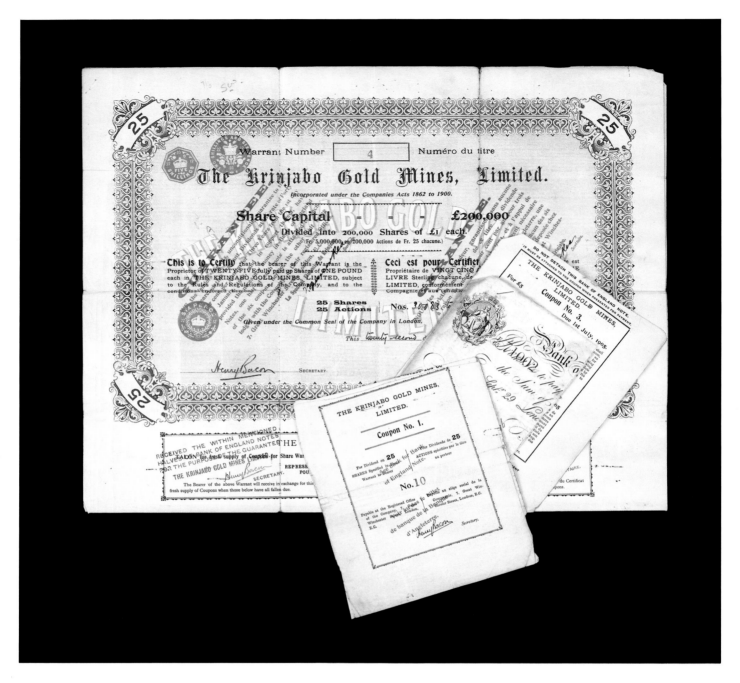

A Krinjabo Gold Mines Warrant and coupons. The half £5 note was intended to secure the payment of the whole dividend of £5

A novel, if not unique, use of Bank of England notes was made in 1903 when Alfred Grover, a financial agent, was persuaded to register a new company to exploit 70,000 acres in West Africa – The Krinjabo Gold Mines Ltd. This was to be financed by the issue of warrants to bearer for 25 £1 shares, returning an annual guaranteed dividend rate of 40% for three years. To support this guarantee the backing 'Syndicat Financier de Krinjabo' provided the necessary money in advance by securing to each of six half-yearly coupons attached to the warrants the left-hand half of a £5 note, the other half being lodged with the company itself. The dividend was only payable if both coupon and half-note were presented. Shares were placed in London, Manchester and Birmingham. The rather doubtful speculation collapsed before any dividend could be claimed but not before several of the bonds had been stolen.

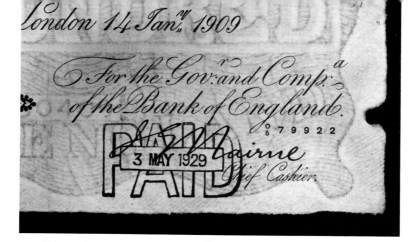

Detail from a £100 note of 1909, showing the position of the third number and also the distinguishing paper-maker's notch for this denomination

Discussion on any matter affecting the Bank's notes usually took place in the Committee of Treasury first who would submit any recommendation to Court for approval. In July 1903 they reconsidered a proposition to print a third number on each note. Notes were cancelled at that period by tearing out the signature and punching holes ('milling') through the Sum Block and in this state they were transmitted by the Branches to Head Office. From 1826 to 1872 lists had been prepared and retained at each Branch so that, in the event of the loss of the cancelled notes in transit, the necessary postings in the registers could be made by using these lists. Between 1872 and 1897 the practice was to send notes by special messenger. In 1897 it was decided that the notes should be cut in half and sent at different times to Head Office, where they were tediously reassembled and gave rise to ungainly bundles in the Bank Note Library – the centre of each packet being twice as thick as the edges. The Committee concluded that the number could usefully be printed a third time in small type near the signature. The signature corners would then be torn out at the Branches and retained for use, if the cancelled notes disappeared, in reconstituting the list of numbers needed to post the registers. The system was also found useful for reconstituting bundles of notes paid in, in circumstances where the bulk of a note was inadvertently lost within the Bank. Such a system had a beneficial by-product, too, in that the identification of badly mutilated notes submitted by the public was facilitated. The Printing and Store-Keeper's Office produced a table on 1 July 1904, showing the cypher numbers and dates of the last notes printed *without* the small number.

Table printed in 1904 showing the cypher, serial number and date of the final printings of London and Branch notes listed which did *not* incorporate the additional cypher and number close to the signature

BANK NOTES.

STATEMENT showing the CYPHER, NUMBER, and DATE of the LAST NOTE of the SERIES printed *without* the additional small number at the foot of the Note. (See Extract from the Minutes of the Court of Directors of the 9th July, 1903.)

	£5	£10	£20	£50	£100	£200	£500	£1000
LONDON	65000, 5 March 1901	39000, 17 June 1903	94000, 14 Aug 1902	80000, 12 Jan 1903	65000, 17 Sept 1902	30000, 18 March 1902	68000, 15 Jan 1903	10000, 29 Jan 1904
MANCHESTER	64000, 21 April 1904	33000, 5 June 1903	73000, 29 May 1903	94000, 30 May 1902	30000, 1 June 1903		63000, 27 May 1902	
BIRMINGHAM	24000, 9 Oct 1903	12000, 26 Sept 1902	36000, 29 Sept 1902	80000, 1 Aug 1903	34000, 27 Sept 1902		54000, 3 Aug 1901	
LIVERPOOL	31000, 9 Dec 1903	80000, 5 Dec 1903	78000, 1 April 1902	26000, 2 April 1903	50000, 1 Sept 1903		94000, 23 July 1902	
BRISTOL	46000, 7 July 1903	20000, 26 June 1902	23000, 22 Feb 1903	60000, 28 June 1902	70000, 22 June 1902		29000, 10 May 1901	
LEEDS	75000, 10 Nov 1903	60000, 25 Oct 1902	94000, 29 Oct 1902	48000, 20 Oct 1902	87000, 27 Oct 1902		24000, 29 Oct 1902	
NEWCASTLE	22000, 22 Feb 1904	5000, 25 Nov 1902	57000, 27 Nov 1902	88000, 29 Nov 1902	47000, 27 Nov 1902			
HULL	82000, 23 April 1902	93000, 5 Feb 1903	47000, 29 April 1902	45000, 2 Feb 1903	87000, 5 Feb 1903		26000, 28 April 1902	4000, 25 Sept 1893
PLYMOUTH	54000, 7 May 1903	67000, 5 May 1903	3500, 22 Nov 1904	20000, 1 May 1903	19000, 10 Jan 1900			
PORTSMOUTH	54000, 21 Feb 1902	81000, 5 March 1903	46000, 22 Oct 1895	29000, 28 Feb 1902	95000, 27 Feb 1902			

PRINTING AND STORE-KEEPER'S OFFICE,
1st July, 1904.

On the division of the Bank into Banking and Issue Departments it became necessary each day to settle the balance of transactions by the physical movement of notes between the two. To facilitate this purpose a far higher stock of the £1,000 denomination had to be kept than was necessary for meeting the demand of the public. In 1905 this demand did not exceed 600 a week yet a stock of over 21,000 was needed to accommodate the balancing process. These notes passed to and fro, were continually being counted and suffered deterioration accordingly. It was not practical to hold the cover in smaller denominations for the obvious reason that counting would take longer and cause the same wear and tear but also because a large amount of extra safe accommodation would be needed. (It was estimated that the replacement of the 21,000 notes of £1,000 by £5 notes would require over 100 new safes.) It was therefore suggested by William Steel, the Senior Cashier in the Bank's Treasury, that there should be 'a Special Note, of much larger denomination, for purely internal purposes, and so marked that it could never be fraudulently dealt with'. He went on to suggest a denomination of £50,000 and he was wise enough to suggest as another benefit the time and labour which would be saved at the annual November audit when the Directors counted every £1,000 note! As an example he instanced a typical daily transfer of £407,000 being satisfied by 15 notes in place of 407.

The lawyers were consulted early in 1908 and answered by reference to the hypothetical case of the purchase of gold by the Issue Department from a member of the public for £50,000. In payment the Chief Cashier might issue a warrant which would entitle the seller to £50,000 in notes from the Issue Department. But if the seller did not want notes, as was probable, he would hand it to his bankers who, in turn and also not wanting notes, would ask the Banking Department to credit their account. The Banking Department would then use the warrant in the end of the day balance transfer. A note for £50,000 could be used, as a voucher only, in a similar way. There was therefore no objection, so the lawyers advised, provided that the note was in the form of a Bank of England note and printed on any paper which the Bank regarded as suitable for the purpose. It could bear some notification to the effect that it was only negotiable or exchangeable into notes or gold at the Bank itself. They concluded 'We believe it was customary in the earlier times of the Bank to issue Notes providing for the exact amount to be filled in writing but we suppose the practice has been so long discontinued that this would not be feasible or it might be objectionable even for internal use'.

The concept of a 'Settlement Voucher' did not find favour. Instead, the way was cleared for the birth of the first printed 'giant notes': 500 @ £50,000 each, dated 31 March 1908 and using the otherwise unallocated prefix $\frac{F}{1}$. The Note was printed in black with a red crossing 'Available only in Settlement between the Issue and Banking Departments'. Having become very soiled, they were destroyed in 1914 and replaced by 300 notes @ £100,000 each (printed in red with a black crossing) and 100 notes @ £50,000 (similarly printed to those being destroyed). A further 300 of the larger denomination were added in October 1914 – all were dated 31 January 1913. Another series was printed in 1918, limited to being 'Available only for Deposit at Bank of England o/a Currency Note Redemption A/c'. The range of the 'giants' series was extended by the preparation of £5,000 and £10,000 notes in 1928. The overprint now read 'For internal use only and not available outside the Bank of England'. Until 1933

Opposite page
Suggested form of a 'giant' Voucher and the resultant first 'giant' note, for £50,000, sanctioned in 1908 (210 x 130mm)

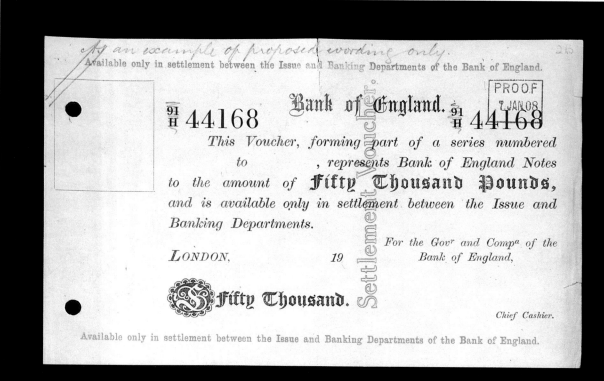

all recommendations for printing 'giants' were approved by Court but thereafter it was only necessary to obtain the authority of a Director. The earliest printings were on General Security Paper but Bank Post Bill paper was being used in 1933 and 'Draft on Demand' paper in 1938 and 1951.

Following the tragic sinking of the *Titanic* on 15 April 1912, about 100 claims were received by the Bank in respect of notes believed or known to have been lost on board, totalling just under £1,500. 39 of these derived from lost registered letters to the amount of £345, mostly £5 or £10 notes but one for a £50 denomination. These were accompanied by letters from the Post Office, confirming that the letter in question had been on board the vessel and advising that no compensation could be offered by them. Eleven claims related to victims, including one by a widow who had survived the disaster, Mrs Pears. The evidence in these latter cases had to be circumstantial, based on the proven knowledge that the victim had drawn out from his or her bank certain numbered notes which he or she might still have possessed when embarking for the fateful maiden voyage of the 'unsinkable' ship. In a few cases some notes were found to have been presented for payment, it being clear that they had in fact been spent beforehand. The largest claim was in respect of £200 in £10 notes lost with H S Morley.

The *RMS Titanic* disaster

Purser's label submitted by a survivor of *RMS Titanic* in support of a claim for payment of notes lodged in his safe and lost in the disaster

The ship's steward, G C Dodd, was believed to have had in his possession 37 notes for £5 each, the balance of £200 drawn by his wife from Lloyd's Bank, Southampton on 9 April 1912. Two survivors claimed in their own names for cash lodged with the purser: L Beesley £20 and Miss K Buss (later Mrs K Willis) £15. She supported her claim by sending in the purser's numbered receipt, on the back of which she had recorded:

3 x £5
£5.10/ – changed into American
Bracelet
Brooch
Pendant and Chain
Watch chain

The ticket survives in the Bank's Museum collections (all the claims are held in the Bank's Central Archive).

Each claim, as substantiated and after completion of the appropriate indemnity, was settled promptly save for one where two notes out of three believed lost had been presented for payment and the remaining £5 apparently forgotten until the claim was revived – and paid – in 1923.

It needed a cool nerve to be a good forger at any period of the Bank's history. None seems to have demonstrated this more than the man who called on H G de Fraine at St Luke's[1] in the mid-1920s. de Fraine recalls in his autobiography *Servant of this House* how a visitor was announced, purportedly from Scotland Yard (though no steps were taken to check his identity at the time). The visitor alleged that when a search warrant had been executed recently in an investigation into the theft of two clarinets, several pieces of engraved metal had been found which appeared to relate to most of the design of a Treasury Note (see overleaf). de Fraine was asked if they were dangerous to which he responded that they were of good average workmanship but of course lacked the King's head. This, he went on to volunteer, was probably due to the fact that 'picture engraving' could only be successfully undertaken by a few skilled persons in the country at that time. The visitor came alive at this point and asked how he could get in touch with one. de Fraine said that the Bank employed its own expert and he was (apparently genuinely) unable to recall the names of any others. The visitor looked somewhat disappointed and left. Six months later, de Fraine asked a Chief Inspector (whom he knew, on this occasion), sitting in the very same chair, what had happened to the man who stole the clarinets and, more to the point, had any more counterfeiting equipment been found. The detective knew nothing about the case but promised to look into the matter since de Fraine was so interested. A few days later he telephoned. There was no record of such an incident. 'Do you realise' he asked 'who your visitor must have been? The forger himself! He'd done all the rest - and was stuck for the King's head!'

As the clouds of war began to gather over Europe in 1914, both the Government and the Bank of England turned their thoughts to the effect that the outbreak of hostilities would have on the need for paper currency. Since the Bank already held the contract for printing postal orders and had invested in a high-speed rotary machine only two years earlier, it was comparatively simple for the printers to produce very large quantities in very quick time once the necessary decision had been taken to make postal orders legal tender. This was for the benefit of the public. But it was necessary to consider how the country could benefit, too, through the protection of the gold reserves against erosion. The only practical small change for a £5 note in 1914 took the form of the half-sovereign and sovereign. It was decided without much hesitation that a substitute paper currency should be issued, accompanied by an appeal to the public not to demand gold, an action detrimental to the nation in such times.

1 to which the Printing Office had moved by early 1920 (see page 118)

The only known example of the Bank's proof £1 note proposed for issue in 1914, which promised to pay gold coin (160 x 95mm)

The Bank clearly expected that any small denomination banknotes would be its own issues and work was covertly put in hand by the Printing Office to adapt the design of the existing higher denominations - the production of emergency stocks of which, in particular the £5, as well as the additional postal orders, was occupying the work force day and night at this time. Although a superb mini-version was prepared (possibly by an engraver on the staff of the Bank, P E Harrison), the work of reduction and general adaptation of the existing design had not proceeded fast enough to meet the Government's timetable. (Recalling the sharp rise in forgeries when it had first issued small denomination notes in 1797, the Bank was working on a note requiring hand-made paper, the preparation of which would have taken far more time then was allowable by the emergency situation.) The design measured approximately 6" x 3¾" (almost the same size suggested by Portals in 1891), featured the version of Britannia which had preceded Maclise's 1855 design and promised payment in standard gold. The Treasury decided, however, to award the contract to Waterlow Bros and Layton Ltd after the Currency and Bank Notes Act 1914 had been rushed through Parliament in the days immediately following the outbreak of war. This gave the necessary authority for the issue of £1 and 10s notes by the Treasury, conveyed responsibility for design and printing on the Treasury and legal tender status on the notes.

There was also a political factor as well as the practical time factor and this may have been a more important element in the decision-making process. The banks in Scotland had stated their objections to a move to issue Bank of England small denomination notes on the grounds that the Bank had no acceptable authority in Scotland, so its notes would not actually circulate whereas Government notes would.

The quality of the first notes available for issue was poor and by the following October an improved version of the £1 denomination was ready for release (the 10s followed in January 1915), after the involvement of Thomas de la Rue & Co. This, however, caused the Bank to reach for its pen and ink, for the second issue (unlike the first, which was printed on paper watermarked for use in the production of postage stamps) was on paper which incorporated a waved-line watermark, the use of which was a breach of the law[2] if for any purpose other than a Bank of England note. Of particular concern was that the paper had not been manufactured by Portals, who had been the exclusive suppliers for over 100 years. The Bank protested in writing on 3 November 1914 but never received a reply from the Treasury.

Early in 1916, when the Bank learned that a further new design was being contemplated, they promptly wrote again and asked that their 'rights' in the matter should not again be overlooked. On 30 March the Treasury responded, in a letter signed by Bradbury, by asking the Bank if there was any objection to the continued use of a 'wave' line watermark, which had substantial security advantages. Nairne replied on 6 April 1916 that the Court 'feel it their duty to protest against the proposed employment of curved or wavy lines in the watermark for Currency Notes'.

In 1917 work was finished on the completely new design for these Currency Notes, this time printed by photogravure - but *not* on waved-line watermarked paper. The Bank had successfully defended its cause. The Chancellor of the Exchequer, McKenna, refused to approve the proofs at first and asked the Bank to submit its own design. The 1914 submission had been kept under review and revised from time to time. It was resurrected again but the Maclise vignette of Britannia now featured once more. McKenna commented so favourably ('I like your design. Nobody can deny it is a great improvement on ours') that it is surprising that it was not promptly adopted. The Committee on Currency and Foreign Exchanges after the War (the Cunliffe Committee: Lord Cunliffe had assumed the Chairmanship on ending his term of office as Governor in 1918), whilst not suggesting that a desirable change was imminent, inspired the Bank with sufficient confidence in 1918 to prepare for the eventuality, by authorising the purchase of 14 plate-printing machines on which to produce the Bank's preferred design: but they were never used for that purpose. Paper itself no longer presented any difficulty because Portals had devised an acceptable substitute for hand-made paper - known as 'mould-made' paper it could be produced in larger sheet form than hitherto by the old method, an invaluable aid to the mass production which was increasingly necessary. That being said it has to be admitted that the new Treasury design, by Bernard Mackennal, was the first important step on the road to an official issue incorporating pictorial features in colour.

Since 1915 the clerks at the Bank's counters had been instructed internally to pay out Treasury Notes in lieu of gold coins unless the presenter of its own notes of £5 and above insisted on gold. If he or she did so insist then the clerk would ask why. By

2 The Forgery Act of 1861 had referred to 'curved or waving Bar Lines, or with the laying Wire Lines thereof in a waving or curved Shape'. This provision was superseded by the Forgery Act of 1913. The Bank would have preferred to keep the specified wording of the 1861 Act but had to accept at this time the advice that they were still adequately protected by the less precise references of the new legislation. So the Treasury's assumption of waved-lines alarmed Threadneedle Street.

making such enquiry a conditionality was being imposed on the payment by the Bank on demand and this was *ultra vires* the 1833 Act, which had made its notes legal tender for amounts above £5 provided such notes were payable in gold on (straightforward) demand. The Bank had placed national interest above all else. In 1925 the Gold Standard Act released the Bank (partially) from this obligation: the minimum amount of gold permitted to be paid over on demand was a 400-ounce bar. The obligation was in turn suspended by the Gold Standard (Amendment) Act 1931 when the United Kingdom finally 'went off gold'.

At their meeting on 13 August 1914 the Directors had assumed that, were 10s and £1 notes likely to be a permanent feature in the currency of the United Kingdom, then the Bank would be asked to take them over, a request they would not refuse. It was to be 10 years later, however, before the first practical steps were taken by the appointment by the Chancellor of the Exchequer of a committee to examine the question.

In the meantime, a number of changes had taken place relative to the administrative aspects of the Bank's existing issues. A new signature had appeared on the notes, that of E M Harvey, who had been appointed Chief Cashier when Nairne (now Sir Gordon) had moved to the newly-created post of Comptroller of the Bank in 1918 (he subsequently became a Director). Harvey was knighted in 1920 and was to follow Nairne as Comptroller in 1925, ultimately serving a lengthy spell as Deputy Governor, in which capacity he was created a Baronet. Harvey's successor in 1925 was C P Mahon, the first Chief Cashier to see his own signature on 10s and £1 notes. Mahon's tenure was a comparatively short one, ill health causing him to step down in 1929 and replace Harvey in the less rigorous responsibilities attaching to the Comptroller's office: Mahon's successor was B G Catterns.

The Printing Office itself – still a part of the Cashiers departmental structure – was by this time suffering from a severe shortage of space as the pressures of printing increasing quantities of wartime loan documents and of postal orders and notes began to exert themselves inexorably. In October 1915 the Bank became aware that a former mental hospital at Old Street in the City – St Luke's, built in 1782 – was up for disposal. Negotiations began for its purchase and conversion principally into a printing works. Possession was taken in April 1917 but fortunately by then premises had been rented (in Tabernacle Street) to which dividend book and warrant printing had been transferred in 1915, thankfully relieving some of the pressure within the Threadneedle Street building (where the complete printing operation had been taking place since 1808). The move to St Luke's was completed on 20 April 1920. Until the outbreak of war again in 1939 all Bank of England notes were printed at St Luke's.

What was to be the final printing of the £200 note destined for issue to the public was made under the date of 20 June 1918: 65,000 were prepared with Harvey's signature and the prefix $\frac{5}{P}$. Issue to the public ceased in 1928, after the Committee of Treasury had reported to the Court that 'the demand ... has rapidly fallen to an insignificant quantity'. Later printings were made, however, as part of orders for specimen sets[3] of currently-issued denominations in 1922 and 1925. The first of these

3 Impressions of individual plates were taken from time to time for record purposes. The earliest notes, bearing a 'Specimen' marking, in the Bank's collection, are four £5 denominations dated 8 November 1892.

From the final printing of this denomination for issue to the public, a £200 note dated 20 June 1918, signed by E M Harvey (210 x 130mm)

sets was made in response to a request in the following terms from the Reichsbank in Berlin on 23 January 1922:

'We desire to form a collection of samples of the paper money of the important European states for the purposes of comparison and particularly for *testing spurious notes* presented to us. We should therefore be very much obliged if you could let us have five samples each of Bank Notes which are in circulation at the present time.

Accordingly we hope to receive specimens which have not yet been in circulation which are not perforated and which are distinguishable only by the fact that instead of numbers they bear only ciphers '0,000,000' and in each case the face of the note not injured by the stamp 'specimen' and in other respects resembling ordinary circulating notes.'

In meeting this request, on 22 February, the Bank replied:

'In compliance with your request of the 23rd ultimo. I send you, herewith, for reference five specimens each of the £5, £10, £20, £50, £100, £200, £500 and £1,000 Bank of England Notes in circulation.

These Notes are lent you subject to return on demand without notice: a condition with which I have to request you to signify your concurrence when acknowledging receipt of the Notes and to couple with your guarantee of their safe custody.'

Printing Works' records show that these specimen notes were specially prepared, only five sets being dated 4 February 1922. They were prefixed ♀ to ♀, in ascending order of value and overprinted 'SPECIMEN' twice (in spite of the request from the Reichsbank in this regard). It is interesting to conjecture how useful this particular set of notes may have become in connexion with the forgeries by the Nazis during World War II which utilised plates manufactured in Berlin (see Chapter 11). Further £200 notes were included in the specimen sets printed with the dates 7 September 1922 and 9 April 1925. The denomination had been withdrawn when the next specimen sets were ordered with the date of 2 July 1929.

A minor change in the numbering of notes was introduced after a Court meeting on 14 December 1922. In order to avoid the recurrence of any cypher during the period of 40 years which then had to elapse before unpaid notes were written off, cyphers on the £5 and £10 denominations were in future to contain a number of three digits instead of two, to permit numbering beyond 99. To facilitate sorting, the typeface in use prior to 1894, which would involve a change of lettering (only) in the cypher, would furthermore be reverted to. A contemporary Printing Works' report explains that the preferred style of lettering had been especially engraved for the Bank in 1872 and had been in actual use from 1877 to 1894. When proofs of the new designs were submitted 'the face of the figures was not considered heavy enough ... this design was selected from an old Note on which the cipher had not been well printed'. The figures were therefore photographically enlarged and then thickened by hand; after reduction to the correct size they were used by Caslons to engrave new matrices in February 1923. The alterations to the printing machines were small. Portions of the plates, which retained the large cyphers in place, were cut away in order to make room for the third digit. The small numbering barrel required no alteration since the new three-digit cypher could be cast in the same body as the two-digit one. The report shows that it was necessary to purchase 1 lb each of 12 letters (A to V), 2 lbs each of figures 0 to 9 and 0.5 lb of half-en spaces to comply with the Court's wishes. A page of new typefaces was prepared so that staff handling subsequent printings would have an authoritative document to consult.

The Cunliffe Committee had given consideration to how and when the Treasury Note issue should be replaced by a Bank of England issue. They decided that it could not be carried out before the future dimensions of the fiduciary element had been settled. In the meantime, instead of backing new issues of Treasury Notes with Government Securities, Bank Notes should be taken from the Bank. As the Bank would have to allocate gold from its reserve in the Banking Department to cover these issues to the Treasury, the reserve would be reduced and this would lead to an increase in money rates to encourage gold imports. By raising its discount rate the Bank would also control credit expansion. Furthermore, the combined Bank/Treasury fiduciary element would also be reduced.

The Committee on the Currency and Bank of England Note Issues, appointed by Treasury Minute of 10 June 1924, recommended a modified return to a gold standard. They argued that it would be a luxury to use gold coins for domestic circulation (adding the recommendation that no more half-sovereigns ought to be made) yet quite practical simply to require the Bank to buy and sell gold at a fixed price (and in bars). They were also of the opinion that all Bank of England notes should in future be payable in coin only at the Head Office of the Bank and not at the Branch offices and they endorsed the Cunliffe Committee's recommendation that the two note issues should be amalgamated.

The Bank required a year's notice to prepare for the issue of the smaller denominations (see next chapter) but there were a number of legal steps to be taken: power to the Bank to issue notes under £5 (banned by the 1826 Act) and legal tender status for the new 10s and £1 notes. Leslie Lefeaux (then Deputy Principal of the Discount Office and later to be the first Governor of the Reserve Bank of New Zealand) was asked to consider what arrangements would have to be made. His report occupied him for most of 1926 and ran to 128 pages, over half of them being concerned with the fiduciary issue. Other chapters related to metallic cover; the Branches (including consideration of Branch issues of 10s and £1 notes); the position of the Scottish and Northern Ireland banks; the date for the changeover; the method of effecting the transfer; and the management of the issue (division of profits). The questions of machinery and paid notes were for the St Luke's Committee (see next chapter) to consider.

The Currency and Bank Notes Act 1928 sanctioned the issue of the two new denominations and provided for their availability at Branches without their being made payable there – indeed, it went further by restricting payment to the Bank's Head Office. Legal tender status was conveyed, including any circumstances when the Bank itself was making the payment (cf. the 1833 Act where notes above £5 could not be tendered legally by the Bank and its Branches). The Truck Act of 1831 was overridden: payment of wages in the new notes was valid, whether or not the workman consented. There was provision for an amount of assets backing the Treasury's issues to be transferred to the Bank, equivalent in value to the liability taken over. The period for writing off old 10s and £1 notes was 20 years (from the last date of issue of a series), compared to 40 years for the 'white' notes outstanding (based on their date). Profits were payable to the Treasury. Provision was also made for the banks in Scotland and Northern Ireland to regard Bank of England notes as gold coin for the purpose of calculating how many notes each bank could issue against its holdings of gold and silver coin – creating another use for the Bank's internal 'giant' notes. Finally, it became an offence to print, stamp or impress on any note issued by the Bank any words, letters or figures: but the penalty for this offence was only £1. As will be seen, satisfactory progress had been made in the design and production of the new notes so that everything was now prepared for the changeover, which commenced on 22 November 1928.

Experimental designs for a £1 note,
circa 1921 (151 x 85mm, 158 x 90mm)

CHAPTER 9 Merely Banknotes, but Colourful

In 1921 a special committee was appointed to report and advise on the financing and general administration of the Printing Works in their new location at St Luke's. As a result of their recommendations a standing committee of the Court of Directors was set up as the 'Committee on St Luke's', answerable to the Governor and Court for the conduct of Printing Works' operations. In their turn, the officials at the Works reported to the new Committee and thus severed their link with the Chief Cashier, under whose care they had worked since the printing operation had been brought within the Bank's walls in 1783. As the first World War progressed doubts began to creep into the minds of St Luke's as to the practicality of the miniature £1. Up until this point in time the notes of £5 and above were rarely handled repeatedly in a multiplicity of transactions. The paper usually remained fairly clear as did the watermark. Although the project continued to be worked on, the then deputy manager, S B Chamberlain, was sufficiently visionary to suggest (on 17 November 1920) that the Printing Works had reached a watershed. If a miniature white £1 were to be proceeded with the paper would need to be thicker, which would diminish the effectiveness of the watermark as the key security feature. None of the available methods of printing could add to this protection. A successful forgery would severely dent the prestige possessed in the public's eyes by the existing denominations. He therefore suggested that consideration was given to a plate-printed note, bearing coloured overprints, a printing on the back and a watermark in a 'window'. Late in 1924 he elaborated on the protection afforded by the right choice of design. 'The maximum difficulty is presented to a forger', he wrote, if the note contained 'in one printing a wide range of colour from a faint tint to a deep colour which is almost black'. He also explained that a photogravure note could more easily be reproduced and passed as genuine because the original would lack the definition which was the feature of a plate-printed design.

By 1924 it had become clear that amalgamation of the Treasury and Bank note issues effectively only awaited the detailed planning. A plate-printed design for a £1 Bank note was examined in May 1924 and this brought forth the suggestion that a litho-printed note should be looked into. Although cheaper it was a less secure product and what could be saved would have to be set against the probable need to replace the design as frequently as every five years. The Principal of the St Luke's Printing Department was instructed to prepare designs for the 10s and £1 notes which would replace the Treasury's issues. His only guidance lay in a direction from a Committee of Directors that the front designs 'should shew all the familiar features of Bank of England notes in their relative positions one to the other'.

Various proofs of designs were considered by the St Luke's Committee, all apparently stemming from one pair of original designs. Outside expertise was suggested but the Deputy Governor (Sir Alan Anderson) is recorded in the Committee's Minutes of 7 July 1925 as saying: 'Let us get our design and approve it ourselves before calling in experts to criticise it'. This may have led to their taking too close an interest in all the detail: but it was a major break with tradition. Two months later de la Rue were instructed to prepare the plate-print portions of the designs (lithoprinting had not been pursued). By 1926 a new watermark was provisionally approved, designed by A Kavanagh for Portals but executed by a Frenchman, Mascaux: a helmeted Britannia facing right (the British Museum had advised the Bank on the correct helmet to utilise). That the watermark would not be as bright as on the traditional notes caused some concern but it was soon accepted that the cost of shortening the fibres by extra beating in order to facilitate a brighter image would show itself in the shorter lifespan of the paper weakened as a result of this process.

W M Keesey's artwork for the reverse of the Bank's first issued £1 note printed in colour (150 x 84mm)

The front designs of each note were not the product of one individual and must narrowly have avoided looking as if they had been designed by a committee, as they had been worked up by a number of people within and outside St Luke's. Yet someone must have masterminded the operation, ensuring that the 'familiar features' were in place and that the large unprinted (or only lightly printed) watermark area was best sited. It was probably de Fraine himself, who may also have suggested the use of the Maclise Britannia. What is certain is that the foliage depicted on the backs was the work of W M Keesey, Inspector of Art Schools at the Board of Education whose request to be allowed to incorporate his initials was firmly rejected in July 1927 by the Committee, at which stage the preparatory processes were virtually complete. The early work necessary in order to translate all the design proposals into forms suitable for the intended notes - balancing the contributions to be made by hand and machine engraving, for example - may have been carried out by Malcolm Macdonald, who had been recruited in 1922 specifically to work on bank note design. Thomas Macdonald & Sons Ltd were responsible for the preliminary engravings and for the final work on the backs of the notes whilst de la Rue were contracted to prepare the intaglio engravings for the fronts. However, the work could only proceed with the necessary momentum by calling on the services of foreign specialist engravers: Vaquer, of the Spanish Royal Mint, was entrusted to engrave Britannia whilst a first-class French expert, Dezarrois, prepared the backs of the notes.

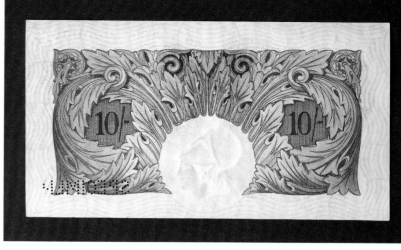

Front of the first 10s note, issued in 1928 to replace Treasury (Currency) Notes. Signed by C P Mahon (140 x 78mm)

Reverse of the first 10s note

The views of the Royal Mint Advisory Committee (responsible for coin and medal designs) were favourable and an engraving expert - A J Bull, Principal of the London County Council's School of Engraving - was also consulted; he was to remain a consultant for many years. In September 1927 the Committee decided that *no* action should be taken to secure public approval of the designs before issue.

Indeed, the public's first encounter with the new issues was at arm's length for, although the following full descriptions were released on Monday 19 November 1928 (issue date being the following Thursday), the Bank provided no photographs:

'The notes are of the same size as the Treasury notes.
The design of the face of both notes is based on the existing Bank of England issues of £5 and upwards, whose familiar features, with the exception of the date of issue, are embodied in their relative positions one to the other. The principal addition is a special 'Window' water mark in the centre of the lower half of the note, representing in profile the head of Britannia whose figure, adopted in 1694 as the Seal of the Bank, has appeared on the Bank's notes from the earliest days. The head is surmounted by a helmet of classic type. A panel in the right-hand top corner, containing the denomination of the note, balances the panel of the seated figure of Britannia on the left.
The Bank's 'wave-line' water mark appears round the edges of the notes.
The £1 note is printed in green ink, with an underlying crossbanded tint of blue.
The 10s. note is printed in red with an underlying crossbanded tint of mauve.
The design on the back of both notes has been worked up from the acanthus leaf device surrounding the seated figure of Britannia on the face. In the £1 note the elaborated foliage in tints of blue, green and mauve supports a reproduction of the long, low main front of the Bank, below which on either side of the special water mark is Pistrucci's 'St George and the Dragon' from the reverse of the sovereign, exact to size.
In the 10s. note the sketch of the Bank is omitted, and in place of Pistrucci's model the value of the note in figures is shown in two interstices in the leaves of russet and grey tints.
The numbers, in red on the £1 note, in black on the 10s. note, are in approximately the same position as on the Treasury notes.'

Production was in sheets of 21 notes (3 rows wide by 7 rows deep), two sheets being printed at a time.

Staff in banks were somewhat taken aback to discover that the basic colour of each denomination was a reversal from that used for the Treasury's notes: the latter's 10s note was green, the dominant colour of the new £1; the new 10s was red-brown, close to the colour used for the Treasury £1 denomination. On balance, however, comment recorded by the Press was favourable. It was inevitable that long queues should form at the Bank itself and many other banks as people hastened to change the old Treasury Notes for the Bank's own issues. Once armed with examples small knots of people gathered in the streets passing on, or listening to, the views of the man on the Clapham omnibus. The *Liverpool Post* thought that at first glance the new notes 'present a strange and somewhat foreign appearance'. The *Glasgow Evening Times* found them 'bilious-looking' suggesting 'that adulation of America may go too far'. The *Daily Mail* observed that they looked 'as if they had been designed and printed in the United States'. Britannia was described as 'a middle-aged lady of somewhat generous proportions' who 'is presumably the tutelary goddess of banking'. The designs met mixed reaction from experts in certain other artistic fields. The sculptor Jacob Epstein thought them 'poor, commonplace and undistinguished'; W Reynolds-Stephens, president of the Royal Society of British Sculptors found them 'not creditable as a matter of design ... too complicated ... unworthy of a great country'. Guy Dawber, on the other hand, an ex-president of the Royal Institute of British Architects, thought the notes 'infinitely preferable to the old ones ... a great artistic triumph'.

In a more considered judgement, the *Manchester Guardian* felt that the designs 'are not the improvement that in these days of the Design and Industry Society and the Royal Fine Art Commission we had a right to expect'. They noted a lack of harmony between the design surrounding the Britannia (executed in Madrid) and that surrounding the figure 1 on the right (executed in London). The quality of the paper and the appearance of the new watermark received almost general praise and there was no criticism as such of the Maclise-based Britannia ('Raphaelesque'). The anti-foreign lobby criticised the use of German lettering. There was recognition by others that the task of the forger had been made much more difficult (or so it was thought at the time).

The *Cork Examiner*, in its 'London Letter' on 24 November took a very down-to-earth view of the fuss going on: 'Probably the only occasion on which bank notes are viewed with a really critical eye in regard to their aesthetic qualities is when they are first issued ... After the first vision they become merely bank notes and one's sense of pleasure in them is derived from the acquisition of them as tangible wealth, however ugly or otherwise they may originally have appeared'. Later on in the same article the red and green lines are attributed to 'the baneful influence of jazz on modern Life'! The earlier comment certainly remains true of today's reactions to new issues.

The *Shoe and Leather Record* reported receiving a letter from a correspondent who bemoaned the fact that the Government had not seen to it that the new notes were made larger than the Treasury Notes so that the trade would benefit from new orders for larger wallets. With a General Election only a few months away, responded the *Record*, no Government would wish to incur the wrath (and lose the votes) of existing holders of stocks of wallets or of users of such wallets.

The *Financial Times*, meanwhile, had submitted C P Mahon's signature to a graphologist, who magnified it 20 times before setting out his opinion that it 'revealed characteristics of stability, solid reliability, and great experience of routine work'. Reassured, *Punch* had 'no hesitation in accepting them'. The *South Wales Evening Express* learned that one reporter measured £500 in Treasury Notes against £500 in Bank £1 notes and found that new ones were one-eighth of an inch thicker. Thus, the new notes did not seem to last as long. This extreme example of how far grousers would go to find a fault brought a comment from the *Express* that any man earning £3 – £10 a week was unlikely to be deluded. 'People well enough off to carry a £500 wad ought to be provided with a cheque-book. If they are not, they deserve the mental anguish of carrying an eighth of an inch too much paper'.

Front of the first coloured £1 note issued by the Bank in 1928 (151 x 85mm)

Reverse of the first coloured £1 note

A bizarre reaction was reported in the *Daily Mail:* a 'composite wreath of Mother Nature's kindly currencies, mingled with a puzzled nation's tears' was laid, on the evening before the new issue, at the Stock Exchange War Memorial as a protest against the omission of the King's head and the Houses of Parliament from the designs. The protest continued:

> 'Our glorious dead gave their last best gift for liberty, King, and Country. Their broken wives, mothers, brothers, and sisters have been squeezed, peeled, and scattered, and their lives frustrated by another blind, backward, blundering attempt to equate gold with flesh and blood.
> Our currency has been linked with that of foreign Powers and our great physical victory is lost.
> This act of remembrance is performed as a pledge to our gracious King that the humiliation of his royal house by this betrayal of trust on the part of his advisers is noted'.

In the light of Chamberlain's views, expressed in 1924, on the subject of colour, it has to be admitted that the background printing on both the new values is very dull and featureless. Partly this may derive from the belief that it was the main design which needed time and effort. In the opinion of a later General Manager - M J S Cubbage - another reason may be that, with so much of the face of the note covered by heavy plate-printing and with little overprinting over the large watermark, any vigorous coloured image would have had a visually disturbing effect and been unacceptable on aesthetic grounds.

As already mentioned, the only Bank of England notes to be nicknamed were those for £1 and £2 issued in Newland's time. The first Treasury Notes were 'Bradburys', the issues from 1919 were 'Fishers'. There was much speculation over the possible name by which the new notes would become acceptably known. The *Evening News* of 23 November 1928 went too far in suggesting that they would bear the patronymic of the Governor, in a verse which began 'Norman (for such the honoured name By which the host of thy well-wishers will wed thee to undying fame, Along with Bradburys and Fishers)...'. Five days later the same paper reported that the notes were being 'affectionately termed' Messrs Green and Brown. Two days later a Mr L Pugh, writing from South-East London, suggested 'Ma honey' as the 'inevitable' nickname for a note signed C P Mahon (the *Irish Independent* had already observed that he was an Irishman). The *Derby Daily Telegraph* was less sure: 'The difficulty may be the pronunciation of Mahon ... I have heard it differently pronounced Mayn, Mahon and Mahn', to which the *Nottinghamshire Guardian* added: 'Torn between Mayhon, Mane and Mahn, the man in the street will steer clear of it altogether'. And so he did.

Within a week it was reported that some ink was rubbing off. Instances were found of notes bearing the same number, inviting a Bank official to comment that it was 'supremely important' for the notes in question to be returned to the Bank at once. One aspect of the Currency and Bank Notes Act 1928, to which the Bank took pains to draw particular attention, was clause 12, which prohibited the defacement of banknotes by 'printing or stamping or by any like means impressing on any bank-note any words, letters or figures'. They warned not only the public but also bank cashiers throughout the country who had been issued with the appropriate instructions through their respective head offices. 'The action of the Bank of England' the *Financial Times* reported on 17 November '... is dictated by reasons of economy'. And so it was: notes which had not been defaced could be reissued whereas defaced notes had to be pulled out of circulation and replaced by costly new ones. It was generally conceded that a light pencil mark would be permitted. Nevertheless some public concern was felt that a trader might refuse payment by a customer tendering, say, a £5 note already in circulation bearing an inked endorsement.

The release of the new notes was accompanied by arrangements for the first 125 numbers of each denomination to be made up into sets available for presentation. Originally it had been arranged that the £1 note series should commence with the cypher A01 and the 10s note with Z01. As it was considered somewhat incongruous to start with Z, one million notes were specially printed with the A01 prefix. The first two numbers were presented to King George V and Queen Mary in parchment envelopes lettered 'Bank of England 22 November 1928' in gold. The third numbered pair was given to the British Museum. A further 65 pairs were distributed to members of the Government and of the Civil Service, the Chairmen of the larger banks, the Lord Mayor of London, the President of the Royal Academy, and the Court of Directors of the Bank (who paid for their own sets). Another 39 pairs were presented to

Pair of notes with matching numbers, from the first cyphers, presented to W M Keesey in the parchment envelope lettered in black. The King and Queen received their respective sets in envelopes lettered in gold

Governors or Presidents of other central banks. Each of these 104 sets comprised celluloid containers edged brown for the 10s note and green for the £1 note, one pair being placed in a parchment envelope, the lettering for these being in black. (Notes numbered A01 000024, given to Keesey, were subsequently acquired for the Bank's own collection.) Of the remaining 18 sets there was a further allocation by purchase to certain heads and deputy heads of the Bank's departments, the few remaining being held at the disposal of the Chief Cashier. By 1933 only four sets were left. On 20 January 1928 the Committee on St Luke's decided to take out a patent for an invention by the Supervisor for numbering single notes to replace spoils in production.

In spite of the Bank's confidence that the notes would prove difficult to forge economically – the Press were no doubt briefed accordingly, some quoting anonymous experts to the effect that the designs were in fact unforgeable – a very dangerous £1 example was detected as early as 22 April 1929. It was an excellent imitation of plate printing on the front by carbon photography, an actual film of coloured gelatine having been placed on each note. The watermark and the back were poor and some work had been done by hand. Until October 1929 all copies of this forgery bore the same number. They had been passed in London suburban shops by a woman who became known as the 'Beautiful Lady'. By the time the gang was caught, early in 1936, some 2,060 of these 'notes' had been received at the Bank, of which 822 in 1935 alone: the sharp increase in their utterings probably helped to trace the source. The gang comprised a man, his daughter and a domestic servant, all of whom pleaded guilty to the charges: the daughter was bound over whilst the others received gaol sentences.

During the first seven years following their first issue, there were other forgeries of the 10s and £1 notes of less importance in numbers. The methods employed to produce these included hand-drawing, hand-painting, photogravure, letterpress combined with lithography and hand-cut blocks of cork or other wood.

In some respects a contemporary 10s forgery was a greater danger than the early £1 forgery. First seen in May 1930, it had been lithographed, the design having been traced by hand over a photographic enlargement. It was so clever that, over the first 3 years after its discovery, 90% of the counterfeits found were not detected until they had reached the Bank itself. The original sources pointed towards a Bristol centre of operations; initial success led to an outward movement of distribution centres, including Birmingham. Since the majority of notes emanated from towns directly connected by rail to Bristol it was suggested that booking clerks should be especially alerted and also local banks to see if any customer had started to pay in unusually large quantities of coins. In the end it was a shopkeeper in Taunton (appropriately named Key), who suspected the validity of a 10s note changed at his tobacconist's shop and unlocked the door to the prosecution of the two brothers involved - one living in Bristol, the other in Weston-super-Mare. They were responsible for nearly 8,000 'notes'. Both were given custodial sentences.

A minor worry in the first few years was the appearance of notes which had been split, front from back. S B Chamberlain, now Supervisor at St Luke's, dismissively observed 'it is not a really difficult matter to split a sheet of paper'. There were, however, latent dangers of fraud since it would be possible to attempt to use each half as a separate whole, particularly at fairs, race-tracks etc. With skill, the missing design could be drawn or crudely represented on the now blank front or back, making the passing off as a genuine note more probably successful. So the Bank reacted unusually firmly when instances came to its knowledge, particularly after a successful prosecution had been completed in 1935 against a man for uttering a split note with intent to defraud. For example, in 1936 a split 10s note was sent to the Bank by G J A McKenzie of Liverpool. He had separated it with his fingers only, in response to a challenge. Since a conviction could only be obtained if he had an intention to deceive (the act of splitting was not an offence), the advice received from the Bank's legal advisers, Freshfields, seems unnecessarily heavy-handed. The Bank had suggested that the replacement 10s note should be sent to him by letter containing a warning of the possible dangers he was inviting. They countered by advising that 'a Police Officer be instructed to see Mr McKenzie and point out the foolishness of his action and warn him that an intentional mutilation of a Bank of England note might involve him in criminal proceedings'. Surprisingly, they went on to say that 'McKenzie and his friends may be left with the impression that they can always recover from the Bank the value of any Note which they may mutilate, even intentionally'. It is true that the form necessary to claim payment of a mutilated note asked for the cause of the damage and usually required a bank reference as to character but no instances have been found of a refusal to pay because damage had been caused deliberately. After a visit by a CID Superintendent,

MacKenzie was reported to be 'very penitent and was much relieved that no action' was to be taken against him. His method was to worry the corner of a note with his thumb nails until it began to come apart.

The new notes had not been issued and the ink on those already printed was hardly dry before the Committee on St Luke's commissioned a new plate design for the £1 note to be held in reserve (August 1928). Proofs were submitted a year later, not of a completely different design but of a few modifications to the existing one. The principal differences were in freeing the watermark panel of any overprinting, to improve its clarity, and to modify the two-colour undertint on the £1 so as to make photographic reproduction more difficult. It was decided not to make any changes in the issued notes for the present since there was no real evidence of any threat to their security and a change might induce public concern unnecessarily. It was decided, however, that the only alteration was that necessitated by the appointment in the interim of a new Chief Cashier ie the signature. de la Rue were nevertheless commissioned to engrave a new die for the £1 in September 1929. The Committee of Treasury requested early in 1930 that work should also proceed on a reserve 10s note, too. Specimens of the original designs but with the Catterns' signature were not submitted for approval until 6 January 1930, a measure of the stocks it had been decided it was necessary to build up bearing the Mahon signature to ensure adequate supplies to meet initial demands.

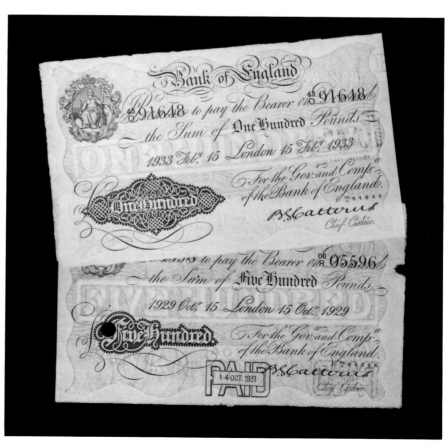

Catterns' £100 note of 15 February 1933 and £500 note of 15 October 1929, the latter with a paper-maker's notch (211 x 129mm, 212 x 130mm)

Portals had been working on a new watermark for use with the reserve design or any new design it might be decided to proceed with. One bearing the portrait busts of William III and Mary was seen by the Committee on St Luke's at their meeting on 16 January 1931. Thoughts began to turn more towards a replacement design than a reserve one and Ronald Dale, the Bank Secretary, was instructed to arrange for three artists to be approached to see if they would be willing, individually, to undertake the necessary preliminary studies and produce designs. The Chairman of the Committee and the Comptroller were authorised to settle the details. The three approached were George Kruger Gray, F L Griggs ARA and Stephen Gooden. (A St Luke's employee, J Blunt, also produced a design, voluntarily, in 1931.)

Separate consultations with the three artists began in June 1931 and there followed a steady stream of correspondence as they sought information and help and floated rough ideas across Chamberlain, who was their main contact. (He had been appointed General Works Manager in February of that year, on the retirement of de Fraine.) A copy of the specification to which they would be working was given to each of the three: it defined the size, colouring, wording and general layout. The principal features were: protection against forgery, dominant features recognisable by the public, general design such as facilitated easy recognition by tellers and artistic merit. The watermark was not to be in the central lower half of the note nor in the top right corner (the commonest handling area for counting notes and therefore one where the paper ought not to be weakened). The main structural design was to be reproduced by recess (intaglio) process and lend itself to an infinite variety of colour. Two undertints were required in exact register one with the other. Two surface printings, also in exact register, were required for the back. A free hand was given on the subject of the main design save that any emblem of royalty should be avoided as the Bank of England was not a State Bank (yet William and Mary as a subject for the watermark was considered acceptable!).

Griggs had difficulty coming to terms with the Bank's requirement to move the watermark to one side yet not reduce the area which it now occupied (on the issued notes). He suggested replacing the Maclise vignette with a head of Britannia, to balance the watermark and also that a rose or an oak motif - either appropriate to an *English* banknote - should predominate the reverse design. Chamberlain had already briefed him on the protective value of a finely-engraved portrait as such (as he had the two other competing artists) and, whilst not discouraging Griggs about Britannia, was minded to suggest that he think about William and Mary or Sir John Houblon, the first Governor. '... the Bank do not desire to tie your hands in any way', he wrote on 22 June 1931, 'as regards design ... these suggestions are only put forward for your consideration'. There is an element of uncertainty here about the security value of a finely executed portrait, now virtually mandatory. By April 1932 the Committee on St Luke's were advising the Committee of Treasury that a portrait was 'the greatest single security'. Griggs had also proposed a recess printing in black but Chamberlain, although acknowledging the greater range of tone thereby obtainable compared to any other colour, pointed out that 'it definitely reduces the protection of the note from the point of view of forgery'. Preliminary designs were shown to the Committee early in January 1932, Griggs commenting that he would still prefer a smaller watermark. He further suggested that if his own conventional-floral or more abstract designs were insufficiently protective they might be replaced by an engine-turned pattern 'though this of course would rob the notes of something of their decorative value & give them a more mechanical appearance ... regrettable in view of the artistic scrutiny & criticism anything as important as a Bank of England production is certain to invite'. He was not, therefore, unsympathetic towards the Bank's aims but the Bank had had enough – Chamberlain halted further work in a letter of 11 January 1932: '... your designs do not conform to the Bank's detailed specification in several most important features ... the necessary inclusion of the large window for the watermark together with adequate space for the serial numbers would demand a complete recasting of your designs'.

The new series of coins issued by the Royal Mint in 1928 were the work of Kruger Gray but he was unable to convince the Bank of the acceptability of his designs for the 10s and £1 notes, based on a portrait of Houblon (he had also toyed with the idea of using an aerial view of the Bank). In writing to him on 23 May 1932, Chamberlain told him that they had not been adopted for use in the event that a change became necessary largely 'because of certain technical considerations concerning the protective values of the designs, from the point of view of security against forgery'. Accepting this decision with good grace, Kruger Gray added in his defence that it had been made on the basis of 'drawings which were never intended to be final'.

The Bank processed an unusual case in 1932, involving three mutilated £5 notes which had been sent anonymously to the Treasury as conscience money. The three sets of cypher and serial number details on each note had been completely cut out. Rather than wait 40 years to proclaim these notes as officially 'dead' and then write them off it was decided by Leslie Lefeaux (Deputy Chief Cashier) to pay £15 to HM Paymaster General immediately, although no entry would be possible through the Registers. A diary note was made for 40 years later to adjust appropriately the total amount then to be written off to the Dead Note Account in respect of outstanding notes.

Stephen Gooden's abandoned designs
for a Houblon Series: 10s (138 x 78mm),
£1 (151 x 85mm), £2 (159 x 90mm)
and £5 (159 x 90mm). The £2 value
did not proceed beyond the design stage

CHAPTER 10   Thread of Hope

With Griggs and Kruger Gray out of the running the field was now open for Stephen
Gooden who seems to have reached the right rapport with Chamberlain from the start.
(He was later to be the Bank's consultant note designer.) Not only that, he was
producing rough designs more quickly than his rivals. His first proposal was the use
of a double rainbow printing on the reverses. By September 1931 he had submitted
a 'rough scribble' of a William and Mary portrait note and by November had shown
the Committee a Houblon design as well as possible reverses. He would have liked to
have used offset-printing for the portrait but was advised that this method was only
employed for the reverse of the existing notes, and that the letterpress used on the front
did not lend itself to the satisfactory reproduction of fine portraits. A fine *recess* printing
was the only acceptable way of treating the main security feature. In December Gooden
expressed the difficulty he was meeting in reconciling artistic and protective qualities
in the designs. But he was not averse to criticising the Bank's efforts at design. Sent
a payment on account early in 1932 he wrote to Chamberlain:

> 'I really must protest against your perfectly hideous and abominable cheque-form. I
> do not know if you realise that St Luke is the patron saint of Painting, but this being so
> I think you might pay a little more respect to your patron! Also, his symbol, the winged
> bull, would make a very pretty decorative device. You really ought to do something
> about it'.

Regular exchanges of letters and of ideas continued and the impression given is that
matters were proceeding satisfactorily. (Gooden was retained as a visiting artist, working
at home and fitting in his work for the Bank with his other obligations.) The work need
not, nor could, be rushed and indeed certain technical aspects naturally took time.
Gooden's own view of an engraver's natural pace is perhaps neatly encapsulated in his
design for an invitation to an exhibition of his work, held at the Ulysses Bookshop in
June 1932. Early in 1933 it seemed as if the end was in sight. By now Gooden confessed
to Whitworth (Chairman of the Committee on St Luke's) that he was almost indifferent
as to whether the Bank ever used the designs: '... to me the enjoyment was in doing
them, and though I want to see how they look actually as banknotes, I'm afraid that
if I had to see them every day of my life, I should be constantly worried by their
imperfections. If you do use them I shall probably emigrate so as to escape them!'

Stephen Gooden's visual comment on
an engraver's need to hasten slowly at
his work

Bradbury Wilkinson were working for the Bank on the designs (in conditions of extreme secrecy) and in sending to Gooden certain of their lay-outs Chamberlain asked him, when responding, 'to temper purely artistic impressions with a cold leavening of security desirabilities', a gentle reference to the difficulty Gooden had once expressed about the tug-of-war in his mind on these aspects. The Court of Directors were asked to give their approval to the alternative designs before the plates were hardened (after which no alteration could be made to them). This they did at their meeting on 14 December 1933. The last stage was to approve proofs pulled from the hardened plates on 30 April 1936. Two years later there was another move towards issuing the Gooden notes but Chamberlain was reluctant to make any change: forgery of the current notes remained negligible and with war looming again he preferred to keep the designs in reserve because of 'the possibility of the country being flooded from the air, with excellent reproductions of our present currency'. In the event the Houblon design never went into production but the close link between the Bank and Gooden (made a Royal Academician in 1942) remained, bearing fruit at last in 1957, as will be seen.

The design on a note, once the novelty had worn off, was of little heartfelt concern to the public, as the *Cork Examiner* had observed in 1928. A contemporary musician and lyricist, Sam Mayo summed up the popular attitude towards paper money in the words he wrote for *The Pound Note Song* in 1936:

> '... Little pound note I love you
> Without you I really don't know what I should do
> I'll tell you sadly –
> I need you badly
> But I'm sorry that I shall have to part from you'.

The last two lines were a plaintive echo of many a thought over the years:

> 'But I wish your big brother fiver
> Was here instead of you'.

£1 note Series A, signed by
K O Peppiatt

Catterns was appointed an Executive Director in 1934 (eventually to follow Sir Ernest Harvey into the Deputy Governor's chair) and was succeeded by K O Peppiatt as Chief Cashier from 18 April in that year.

At the end of 1934 Chamberlain took out a provisional patent, secret for one year, concerning the incorporation of metallised cellophane thread in banknote paper (at this stage he was envisaging using gold). In a note for the Committee on St Luke's, written in April 1935, he said that if the scheme were a success then 'an entirely novel method of protection against forgery would be available for paper currency all over the world'. The concept of laminating threads into paper had already been patented abroad, dating from 1904. A German patent of 1925 actually referred to a thread, which could be metallised, being embedded in security paper as a better protection than a watermark. When Chamberlain was made aware of this he suggested abandoning the attempt at a patent in the United Kingdom but continuing to experiment with the process. Developments had reached an important enough stage by August 1937 for Chamberlain to propose a minimum test which would involve the printing of one million notes. However, since this would cost between £500 and £600, he suggested approaching the South African Reserve Bank in Pretoria – whose own £1 notes were then being printed by St Luke's – and switching the experiment to *their* notes. The Chairman of the Committee (Arthur Whitworth), to whom he had given a memorandum, preferred to use Bank of England notes since the appearance of the device first in South Africa would give forgers extra time to prepare themselves for an issue here; there was also the prestige to be gained if the experiment was successful and could have then been said to have been completely pioneered by the Bank in London.

The more Chamberlain reflected on this issue, the more convinced he was that the South African option was the one to take. Aside from the cost of running off one million notes there was the technical consideration that such a small run could hardly be expected to show up any damage to the printing plates by the thickness and hardness of the thread. It could lead to serious spoilage. There might be difficulty in feeding the paper in automatically since the thread could act similarly to a thick watermark and cockle the paper. The trial run could not be issued and no experience of handling, folding or general wear and tear could be gained. A two year trial in South Africa would give paper-maker and printer better chances of detecting problems in all fields. As to loss of face if it all went wrong,

> 'With regard to prestige, it is known throughout the world, by everybody concerned with Bank Note printing, that the South African £1 notes are produced by the Bank of England and, for that reason, if the scheme were not a success in South Africa for any reason, and had to be abandoned, a very small loss of prestige might, perhaps, be suffered by the Bank, as printers, but it would be infinitesimal compared with the loss of prestige involved if it concerned their own notes, launched in a blaze of publicity with an initial stock of at least 300 million ... A trial with South African notes seems to me to be rather akin to the quite common practice of 'trying-out' a play at a suburban theatre before producing it in the West End'.

There was also an advantage in knowing early on if successful forgeries could be made, before a lot of capital had become tied up in expensive new machinery at the paper mills and at the Printing Works.

The South Africans were happy to assist but it took until January 1939 for a supply of threaded £1 notes to be available for them to issue. At this stage it seems as though silver was being used in the form of 'Viscut' trimming tape[1] ½mm wide, supplied by Nathaniel Lloyd & Co Ltd of London. Aluminium was substituted soon afterwards. The metal had to be purchased, after the outbreak of war in September 1939, through a Priority Permit issued to the Bank. To protect the Bank's own notes even more, Portals agreed to confine the use of metallic thread exclusively to the production of paper for the Bank and to sell the stock of thread which they had bought for their private business to the Bank. In ignorance of the earlier experimental work carried out by Chamberlain, Portals had succeeded in producing a threaded paper without a metal base: this they were allowed to use for their private business and to this end the contract with Nathaniel Lloyd would be amended so as to maintain an exclusivity of supply. (Chamberlain's experiments had included printing on cellophane in gold, silver and aluminium inks before he had become aware of the possibilities of using laminated metallic thread.)

1 Technically, 'an opaque narrow composite ribbon of extremely fine calliper composed of a central metallic layer combined with protective layers of regenerated cellulose'.

Eager to lose no time, Chamberlain next remitted to the Committee for their meeting on 13 April 1939 a proposal to print a stock of 250 million 10s and £1 notes of the same design as existing issues but in different colours, on paper with the metallised thread. The Committee approved the 10s specimen a month later but required a minor change to the £1. Both were lithoprinted, a reduction in the degree of protection afforded by plate-printing but a risk that would be offset by the thread; the process also saved money. Before giving the go-ahead, the Committee asked to be advised of the results of the experimental issue in South Africa. These were encouraging. By July, with Treasury agreement, stocks of notes on threaded paper were at last being laid down. The main colours were changed to blue for the £1 note and mauve for the 10s note. Without such a change the public would have noticed the difference between the more sharply defined appearance of the former plate-printed note and assumed the lithograph product was a forgery. Release to the public took place early in 1940.

Front and reverse of the 10s Series A printed in wartime emergency colours

 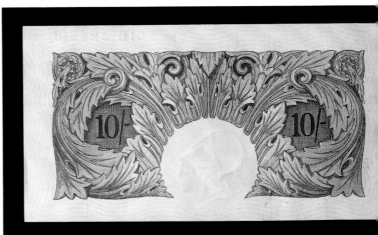

 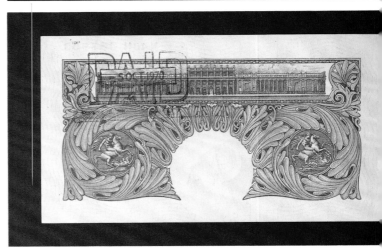

Front and reverse of £1 Series A printed in wartime emergency colours

Other measures were also being taken as the Printing Works faced up to the inevitability of armed conflict in Europe. In September 1938 the Committee of Treasury agreed to increase the normal reserve of 10s and £1 notes held at the Bank's own Branches and to store a further £11 million at some branches of the 'Big Five' commercial banks. Two factories at Overton, in Hampshire, were leased in May 1939 to which the main printing operations could be transferred. Some spare capacity machinery was moved and Chamberlain wanted to begin work there by carrying out certain processes on the reserve Houblon design, completion to take place at St Luke's. Within two weeks after the outbreak of hostilities Portals were being asked to build up a stock of (unthreaded) £5 note paper as Chamberlain proposed to start reprinting the denomination at St Luke's to meet the increasing demand which had inevitably come about: in time of war many people prefer cash to bank accounts. Future production plans included a project to move all lithoprinting and threaded paper to Overton by early 1940.

Chamberlain had, after all, become the patentee in spite of his own doubts as to its advantage and he had assigned the patent to the Bank by 6 October 1939. Some concern was felt when a £1 forgery was discovered in November, a very good example of plate-printing which it was surmised may have emanated from Germany. At their meeting on 8 December 1939 the Committee on St Luke's decided that the production and issue of lithoprinted notes on threaded paper should be accelerated, if necessary by using the services of outside specialist printers such as Waterlows and Bradbury Wilkinson. They were later informed, however, that the Deputy Governor (Catterns) thought this an unnecessary precautionary move. As it was clear that printing capacity could be destroyed or severely limited in one of the many air raids on Southern England, tentative arrangements were made with John Waddington in June 1940 for the emergency production of 10s and £1 notes at Leeds. By August 1940 two watermark dandies had been lodged in the Bank's vaults for use by Wiggins Teape to produce a threaded paper containing a wave line watermark but omitting the panel watermark, should Portals suffer damage.

St Luke's suffered bomb damage on four occasions during the early part of the war, the worst incident occurring on the night of 9/10 September 1940 when a bomb hit the eastern end of the Dividend Preparation Office. V T Kalmar was in charge that night and he reported that the worst damage was to the boiler house, engineers', carpenters' and electricians' shops. Roofs were dangerous, the chimney insecure and broken glass lay everywhere. The main works was undamaged. The other three occasions, in October 1940, comprised blast and incendiary damage only. Contrary to some reports, there was no destruction of, or interruption to , banknote production.

In September 1939 consideration was being given to the production of 5s, 2s and 1s notes to supplement dwindling stocks of silver coin. Instructions were given to the Printing Works to obtain a design from Bradbury Wilkinson which was identical back and front. Mould-made paper, unwatermarked but threaded, was to be used. The different denominations must be in different colours. The notes would not be numbered and it was envisaged that Bradbury Wilkinson, Waterlows and Waddingtons would undertake the actual printing. Initial supplies suggested were 5 million @ 5s, 12 million @ 2s and 10 million @ 1s. On 4 October 1940 the Committee on St Luke's were advised that authority had been given for £2 million in 5s notes and £1 million in 2s6d (*not* 2s) notes to be printed, using the Bradbury Wilkinson design. St Luke's would print part of the order. Although a secret project, news leaked out and *Whitaker's*

Almanac for 1941 reported:

'As a war measure, notes to supplement or replace the silver currency have been printed, but will not be issued unless a special emergency develops.'

The publisher was persuaded to drop this item from subsequent issues.

Waddingtons delivered 4 million notes @ 2s6d, printed by them under the supervision of a small team from St Luke's who commented that the firm had shown the 'highest efficiency' both in care and following all recommended procedures. A total of 10 million notes were also supplied by Bradbury Wilkinson and 2 million by St Luke's but the breakdown is not known. Another 8 million at each value were ordered in 1941 but there is no indication in surviving documentation where these were printed. Notes with a face value of £5 million in these two denominations were distributed as a precautionary measure to the Bank's own Branches and to some of the Big Five commercial bank Branches[2]; an Order in Council would be required to be laid before the House of Commons before either the 2s6d or 5s note could become legal tender. The notes were not required in the event and were never issued (which, for the purpose of this history, is fortunate since they contained no 'promise to pay' although they bore Peppiatt's signature: in this respect they resembled the Treasury Note form).

At the end of the war all stocks of the small notes were withdrawn and pulped although some are known to have escaped these processes. In 1944 the Bank had turned down a request by Lord Mayor Sir Samuel Joseph for specimens of the 2s6d and 5s for a scrapbook he was compiling of events during his term of office. The Bank was able to refuse this on the grounds that 'even if specimens exist' (which they did) the notes had not in fact been prepared during his term.

It has already been observed that the Currency and Bank Notes Act, 1928 authorised the issue of the new 10s and £1 notes at the Bank's Branches without their being made payable there, restricting the legal place of payment to Head Office in London only. With the nationwide acceptance of the Bank's notes of all denominations firmly established by this time, the luxury of Branch issues more generally could now be dispensed with. Certainly, for many years from 1826 the provincial Branches needed the status of their own notes to hold their competitive position vis-a-vis local bank issues. For years now, though, this had been simply a tradition – and in terms of note production an unnecessary expense. In any case, the denominational coverage was not the same at every Branch (see chapter 6). So, when the Currency and Bank Notes Act 1939 was drawn up, principally to forge a link between the Issue Department and the Exchange Equalisation Account in regard to the weekly revaluations of the former's assets, the opportunity was at last taken to get rid of two anachronisms. Section 4 (1) provided that notes of £5 and upwards could be issued by the Bank otherwise than at Head Office without being made payable at the place of issue and that such notes should be payable at Head Office only (save that existing Branch issues remained payable also at the originating branch, if this still operated). By Section 4 (2) the last vestige of the Gold Standard was severed by the removal of the obligation laid on the Bank by the Bank Charter Act 1844 to issue notes in return for gold.

2 to whom a further distribution of 10s notes and above, totalling £241 million, had been made in May 1941, under the 1938 Committee of Treasury authority.

Opposite page
Small denomination notes (1941). The 1s and 2s values were not taken beyond the proof stage. Bulk printings were, however, made of the 2s6d and 5s values but not issued. The notes were to be unnumbered and carried the same design on both sides (115 x 74mm)

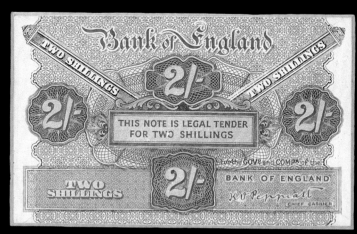

The final printing of the £1,000 note, dated 18 January 1938. This example carries the paper-maker's notch appropriately placed for the denomination (206 x 129mm)

Although postal censorship had been imposed from the very start of the war it was not until 20 August 1940 that a ban was imposed on the import of bank notes. It was estimated that between £10 million and £20 million was held abroad in Bank of England notes and the ban was intended to make it difficult for the enemy to get value for them easily. The enemy at home, however – black marketeer, tax dodger, exchange control evader, to name a few – caused the next major change in the Bank's note-issuing policy. Early in 1943, when the German forgeries (see next chapter) were increasing, it was considered by the Committee of Treasury that the issue of notes over £5 should be discontinued 'mainly with a view to the probable post-war conditions under which Exchange Control will have to work'. It would also help in combating the 'menace' of the increasing number of dangerous forgeries. The Chancellor of the Exchequer gave his approval and made public the news by arranged Question and Answer in the House of Commons. On 31 August 1944 the Committee further recommended:

a) the calling in of outstanding notes above £5 under the Emergency Powers (Defence) Acts, 1939 and 1940;

b) preparation of a new £5 to replace the existing issue, using lithoprinting and mould-made, metal-threaded paper

c) discarding all designs for the 10s and £1 notes and the preparation of new designs, aimed for issue in 1948.

(The last item, abandoning Gooden's Houblon design, must have pleased the then Secretary of the Bank – H C B Mynors (later to be Deputy Governor) – who two months earlier had privately minuted to the Deputy Governor his 'hunch that – beautiful thing as it is – an unknown periwigged figure surrounded by heavy-bosomed ladies would not do the Bank any good'.)

The Treasury agreed (in November 1944). Since there were no existing powers to call in notes of £5 and over a new Regulation had to be made under the Acts mentioned above. Statutory Rules and Orders 1945 No 73 added Regulation 7AB to the Defence (Finance) Regulations, 1939 which gave the Bank power, on giving one month's notice, to call in any notes of any denomination of not less than £5: at the end of the one month notice period such notes ceased to be legal tender. Notice was duly given in respect of £10 notes and above on 16 March 1945.

By the time this notice appeared, the Bank had progressed its plans for a new £5 note. The Committee on St Luke's had approved, and submitted to the Court, specimens of the paper and watermark to be used. There was a brief reference to the possibility of a plate-printed £5 note in colour but this idea seems to have died after an informal discussion with the Governor. On 23 March 1945 a specimen of the lithoprinted £5 (prepared eight on a sheet) was submitted to the Committee on St Luke's and promptly forwarded to the Committee of Treasury and the Court. Lord Monck (Portals) expressed surprise that the appearance so closely resembled the plate-printed note. He explained that hand-made paper was not thick enough to be used with a thread. When the Bank submitted a specimen to Eady (a Second Secretary at HM Treasury) on 28 March 1945 Deputy Governor Catterns drew attention to the loss of 'some of the attractiveness of the old (note), largely as a result of the thicker paper required to carry the anti-forgery device'. Herbert Brittain responded in Eady's absence. It had been seen by the Chancellor, Sir John Anderson, 'with a twinge of regret'.

The final rites with respect to the replaced, plate-printed £5 note were carried out when the Bank gave notice on 25 January 1946 of the calling in of all £5 notes bearing a date earlier than 2 September 1944 (the first date on the new lithoprint series) ie those not containing the metallic thread. According to Bank records, notes dated 30 and 31 August and 1 September (respectively bearing cyphers D 316–318) were printed but were not issued. The first lithoprinted notes were dated 2 September and the series' cyphers began with E 01. The use of mould-made paper brought about the demise of the deckle edge. Experiments to reduce the thickness of the mould-made paper continued and met with success such that a change could at last be made. Notes dated 12 December 1945 were the last to utilise thick paper (cypher L 02) whilst the thinner paper series began 1 January 1947 (cypher L 03). Because there was still a yearning to restore the glories of hand-made paper in the appearance of the mould-made substitute, Portals continued to experiment. Lord Portal exhibited to the Committee on St Luke's samples of new paper in April 1947, containing an all-over thread device, but this caused problems in printing. A reversion to a single metal thread had to be made and examples finally received approval at the Committee's meeting on 10 June 1948. The Committee suggested to the Committee of Treasury, in seeking their blessing, that the new paper would see 'a welcome return to the traditional style and (reflected) great credit on those concerned in its production'. Over 250 years of tradition remained a desirable aim and legitimate excuse.

An 'Operation Bernhard' £5 forgery
(London issue) of 15 January 1938. Note
that the chipped corner has been
carefully copied too

CHAPTER 11 Andreas and Bernhard

The Bank was first alerted to the likelihood that the German Government was proceeding with plans to forge British banknotes by information from the Embassy in Paris in December 1939, passed on by the Treasury. In time of war, if your enemy's currency is widely used internationally, you can take advantage by printing your own supplies and using them to purchase essential goods and services from, or in, neutral countries. Unless your forgeries are undetectable from the genuine notes, this can only have short-lived success because doubt will quickly spread and international readiness to accept the notes quickly disappear. This is of less advantage than the continued use of the currency. A second and more important advantage, in the longer run, is successfully to disturb the faith of the enemy nation, at large, in its own currency - an important psychological factor. It will be on the agenda for any preparatory plans and, as we have already seen (page 84), it was a ploy used by the United Kingdom during the Napoleonic wars.

The story which the Embassy reported was that a Fernand Romano had volunteered information to the effect that the German Government was 'etching' £1 notes with three motives in mind

a) to withdraw Reichsmark notes in Germany at Rm 65 = £1; anyone in Germany who accepted these £1 notes would have to conceal them since they would be breaking German currency regulations;

b) to buy other currencies in parts of the world so remote as to mean that some considerable time would elapse before the forgeries were presented to the Bank of England;

c) for propaganda purposes: the British authorities could then be said to be repudiating their own notes by pretending they were forgeries.

Romano was an Italian Jew with British sympathies and a British fiancee; his information had come from a Frau Viktoria Kunst-Gunther, employed by the Vienna newspaper *Neues Wiener Zeitung*, and an active member of the Nazi Party but allegedly anti-Nazi. He thought it possible that he might be able to obtain some of the forgeries to show the authorities. The Bank encouraged this since they had seen a few new forgery types in the previous few weeks which were good enough for them to consider possible enemy involvement. Hence an anxiety to compare specimens.

Hopes rose when the British Consulate General in Milan advised the Embassy in Paris on 27 January 1940 that Romano had called in and asked that the Embassy be told that 'he is on his way to his destination (Berne), duly provided with samples, and that he is awaiting a new passport and a German visa'. The trail then went cold.

The first forgeries to be classified by the unique letter-coding BB, applied by the

Bank to most of the German wartime forgeries in the 'white' note series, were one £10 note dated 19 August 1936 received from Glyn Mills on 21 September 1942 and eight more £10 notes brought in three days later by the Bank of British West Africa. All these notes were carefully inspected by Bank Inspectors and adjudged genuine. They were all returned by the Bank Note Office as notes bearing the same serial numbers and dates had already been posted as paid. Subsequent detailed examination at St Luke's proved that none was genuine. Since the various Inspectors had accepted them, they were described by the then Deputy Principal of Issue Office as being 'the most dangerous seen for many years'; this comment is described in a marginal note as 'a stock phrase, I believe ... BB is the most dangerous *ever seen*'. The main detectable difference, though not with the naked eye, was that the paper used for the forgeries showed a different reaction under an ultra-violet lamp from that of genuine notes.

Several £100 forgeries of extremely good workmanship had already been received in July 1942: German involvement was suspected and was, in the light of the £10 notes now received, now more or less certain. They were the products of 'Operation Andreas'.

In 1939 an office had been established within the German Security Bureau 'Reichssicherheitshauptamt' (RSHA) - an organisation built up by Himmler and his deputy, Kaltenbrunner - to supply forged documents to help the prosecution of the war. It was initially under the command of Alfred Naujocks, a major in the SS who initiated the idea of forging Bank of England notes. Although the task was very difficult, he was advised, it could be done with a high degree of success. Naujocks then sought approval for his scheme from Heydrich, Head of the Security Service, and ultimately it received Hitler's own imprimatur although he was concerned at that time that no American currency should be forged.

The problems were, principally, to produce comparable paper, to prepare accurate printing plates and to work out how the numbering system should be applied. There is evidence that the necessary engraving work and plate preparation were carried out at the branch of the Reich's Printing Works at Delbrueckstrasse in Berlin under the watchful eye of a private printer, August Petrick. Engraving was executed by Gerhard Kreische, one of the finest in Germany skilled in that art, who was under threat of death if he refused to engrave plates for the 10s and £1 notes. Other necessary skills were brought in, including an expert in ink, but in the end it was the paper which proved the stumbling block. It had to be made by hand and yet when its ordinary appearance was virtually indistinguishable, even under magnification, it continued to fail the ultra-violet test. Eventually, after experimentation with different mixes of linen and rags, Naujocks was satisfied that he had passable material.

In the meantime a successful attempt had finally been made to engrave a Britannia which compared favourably with an original, genuine note. It was now summer 1940 and Naujocks was forecasting another 9 months before he could 'flood the world with £5 notes'. He still had the numbering system to crack and wanted to improve the success rate for printing notes. With many hundreds of combinations of dates, numbers and signatures, he finally devised a scheme for using separate 'slugs' for these elements which meant that the master plates would be serviceable beyond the normal production run of 100,000 notes. By 1 March 1941 a trial parcel had been accepted at a Swiss bank as genuine with, apparently, confirmation obtained from the Bank of England that the numbers etc tallied with notes still outstanding in the Bank's registers.

By this time, Heydrich was looking for ways to eliminate Naujocks and the opportunity arose to invent evidence against him on an illegal gold-dealing charge. The recommendation was execution but Himmler overruled this by substituting a dishonourable discharge. Heydrich then had Naujocks drafted to the Adolf Hitler front line commando unit. However, Heydrich was again thwarted since there was a personal order in existence from Hitler banning anyone with knowledge of official secrets from being exposed to risk of capture by the enemy. As a result, all the top officials concerned with 'Andreas' were sacked and the operation closed down. When interrogated in late 1944, Naujocks said that only 10% of total production was suitable for issue: a total of 50,000 notes printed by letterpress. Most of these were for £5 but £10, £20, £100 and £500 were also made. No £1 notes were turned out. The hardest feature was the watermark, which work was undertaken by Kupferrat in Marianweilen, near Dueren. The paper itself was the product of two companies: Spechthausen in Eberswalde, near Berlin, and Hahnemuele, near Dassel (Hanover). Three printing machines were available although only one was used. Notes were printed two up, the serial numbers being applied in a second operation.

The end of 'Andreas' seems to have been followed by a period of reflection until a scheme for a renewed operation was approved. In July and August 1942 an appeal for artists, printers, engravers, designers etc was made throughout a number of concentration camps. All volunteers had to be a Jewish extraction. Some camp commandants nominated a number of their prisoners who had not volunteered. The first seven prisoners, or *Haftlinges,* were taken to the Sachsenhausen concentration camp on 23 August 1942 and placed in a special section isolated from the rest of the camp by three rows of electric fencing. Communication of any sort between the inhabitants of this area and other inmates was punishable by death. By the end of the year the number of *Haftlinges* had increased to 30 and by 1944 had reached full strength at 140 men. In February 1943 production of banknotes commenced but with little success due to the bad quality of the paper supplied.

The operation was now in the charge of Bernhard Krueger, whose forename distinguished the undertaking. He, as Naujocks had been, was an SS major. He had been head of the Security Service operation which produced fake documents at the time that Naujocks was starting 'Andreas'.

Experiments at Hahnemuehle concluded with the production of paper from a base of 90% cotton rags and 10% linen rags. Watermark meshes for £5, £10, £20 and £50 were supplied and the first paper began to flow by the end of May, possibly earlier (the first large order - for 750,000 notes - was received from Berlin in April 1943, some of which may have been used in the rescue of Mussolini the following August). In full production, 50,000 sheets a month were being delivered with watermarks for eight notes on each. The last delivery took place in November 1944. The sheets were cut

German £50 forgeries. K O Peppiatt's signature has been used in error. The Catterns' example incorporates an unrealistic paper notch

into two pieces: thus each printing pass produced four notes, double the 'Andreas' rate.

Printing plates were imported from Petrick's factory in Berlin, the source for the aborted operation, too.

The plates were carefully inspected after each 100 impressions had been taken. Drying of the sheets took between four and six days, the £5 notes having been printed three times, the other denominations only twice. The notes were machine cut on one side and torn on the others, to imitate the deckle edge. A machine then filed the edges so as to give an appearance of being hand-cut. Using special apparatus to examine the finished product, the *Haftlinges* then sorted the notes into five categories:

1 Notes without any faults, to be used for purchases in neutral countries.

2 Good notes with only a minor fault, used for paying agents abroad.

3 Notes with more than one fault but presentable enough to be used for purchases and for paying agents in occupied countries.

4 Other unsuitable notes to be dropped over the United Kingdom in any disruptive economic warfare project.

5 Notes suitable only for re-pulping.

Jakob Lauber, a Polish Jew from Cracow, who had been sent to Sachsenhausen from Buchenwald, stated in 1945: 'we used to put a pin hole through the eye of Britannia for the first and second choice notes, if there was a slight defect, but as a rule the eye came out very well. If the point was missing on the word 'Ten', we pin-pointed. An error of two millimetres in the figures was enough to take a note out of the first choice'.

Such 'pin-pointing' served another purpose: imitating the regular feature of pin-holes left in genuine notes which had been pinned together or to other documents. Some of the inmates were given the task of imitating handwritten names and/or numbers, similar to markings made by tellers, for example, whilst others were engaged in forging genuine bank rubber stamp impressions. All this extra activity was designed to make the forgeries look more authentic and discourage a closer examination.

On average, Berlin expected 600,000 notes a month. Max Bober, another *Haftlinge*, said that he had personally addressed large linen envelopes to German Commercial Attaches at Consulates at Oslo, Copenhagen, Madrid, Lausanne, Ankara, Lisbon and other cities. The sender's name was always that of Himmler and the envelopes were marked 'Secret'. Bober also gave evidence that:

'We have, however, during the whole of our long daily work over a period of three years, carried out acts of sabotage. We broke off printing letters, damaged plates, rollers etc. This was not so easy however. We had by this time been able to cause many delays and by the stoppage of machines no production of notes could take place.'

Another *Haftlinge*, Adolf Burger - a Slovak arrested in 1942 for anti-fascist activity - gave similar testimony:

'All ... were determined that every possible excuse should be made to get the machines to run slower. We even made the excuse that in summer owing to the heat the machines could not run at speed very long, as otherwise the print would not be good enough to pass inspection. The SS guards were not experts and could do nothing to prove we were wrong in these assertions.'

Krueger was regarded as being not a hard man but he left the *Haftlinges* in no doubt that they would never leave the factory alive. In the event of a German victory they would be allowed to live with their wives in a sort of garden village but never go back into the world. Bearing in mind that the *Haftlinges* believed they would actually be executed when their work was completed – they could hardly have expected the promise of an isolated 'village' in the event of a German victory to be fulfilled – their acts of sabotage were perhaps as much a venture to prolong their lives as a supportive gesture to the Allied cause.

On 26 February 1945, as the American advance neared, the camp was moved to Mauthausen, just east of Linz and one month later to Redl-Zipf, in Austria. Although installed at the latter site, the machinery never went into production. The American advance was so swift that the SS troops thought their own escape more important that liquidating the workers, who survived to be liberated on 6 May 1945.

1 Skala was taken hostage when the Germans annexed Sudetenland. He was one of the original members of the camp and the only Christian employed there.

According to records kept by Oskar Skala[1] a total of nearly 9 million notes was supplied, with a face value of about £134.5 million. Just under half the notes, by number, were for £5, nearly a quarter were £10 and the rest almost equally £20 and £50. These figures are very close to those given by another *Haftlinge*, Jakob Goldglass when interviewed by the FBI.

German forgery of a £10 Birmingham Branch issue, dated 24 December 1926. This was probably the only use made of C P Mahon's signature since his notes would not commonly be met with in circulation in the 1940s, particularly a Branch issue. The cypher $\frac{105}{V}$ is correct for the date and issue

Skala also volunteered the information that the notes were numbered according to instructions from Krueger. It appears that no full run of 100,000 was ever made for one prefix or cypher. Branch names recalled were Birmingham, Leeds, Liverpool and Manchester, examples of which have been found. It has been suggested that the Bank's arcane cypher system was obtained by using a mole. The distribution of the key 'Dating Scale' was probably wide enough within the Bank at this time for that to be possible but it is far more likely that it was readily deducible by sampling notes still in circulation.

One of the Printing Works' own officials, P J Reeves, was sent to Germany in June 1945 to investigate the stories being told of mass forgery and of the dumping of forgeries and of machinery by the SS in an attempt to hide all traces. Much of this material was subsequently recovered from Lake Toplitz in 1959 and handed over by the Austrian authorities to the Bank. Other recoveries have also been reported. Reeves is known to have written a report of his investigations but this does not appear to have survived in the Bank's records.

Considerable assistance was given to the Bank in this affair by the Swiss National Bank, Zurich who wrote to Cobbold (then an Executive Director) on 1 December 1942, enclosing a suspect £5 and a suspect £10 note which were in a parcel comprising 6,000 x £10 and 4,000 x £5 received from 'a neighbouring country'. They commented that 'we reached the conclusion that (all) the notes are excellent and, therefore, very dangerous forgeries'. They requested specimens of £10, £20, £50 and £100 notes to add to their single £5 specimen, in order to have genuine products against which to examine suspect notes. Only a £10 specimen was forwarded immediately; the other denominations following two weeks later. When the latter were sent Cobbold confirmed that the two notes sent over on 1 December were indeed 'dangerous' forgeries. A precautionary alert was sounded to the Branches and the counter clerks at Head Office.

By end-December high quality forgeries were located in Geneva, having come from Liechtenstein. The Swiss wanted better information. On 28 December the National Bank wrote to Cobbold:

> 'We shall much appreciate your giving us some idea of the criteria, as well as any other clues which you consider essential, by which the alleged forgeries may be detected'.

They had submitted paper samples to the Swiss Federal Laboratories whose 'expert's report states that the various papers differ materially neither in composition nor in substance'. (St Luke's did not agree: 'the £5 is better, but neither reacts correctly under quartz lamp'.) The National Bank thought they had detected 'certain deviations in comparison with the specimen £10 note ... particularly ... the water mark'. They reported that the notes received had been variously alleged to have originated from English soldiers and foreign immigrants. The Bank would only go so far at this point as to tell the Swiss to rely on the 'feeling and texture of paper and, if possible, examination under ultra-violet light'. A swift response followed on 12 January 1943: 'unfortunately these particulars do not help us in overcoming our present difficulty ... to draw up a proper warning for the benefit of the Banks and the general public'. They had gone so far themselves as to have further tests made:

> 'The composition of the (paper) did not (seem) materially different. Nor was any worthwhile difference to be discerned in regard to touching, thickness and surface ... chemical test proved similarly inconclusive. The ultra-violet rays alone exhibited certain deviations in that the fluorescence of the paper of the genuine note emitted a light bluish, that of the counterfeit a dirty yellowish colour'.

In the meantime a quantity of forgeries had been traced to the Chilean Embassy in London, imported (in contravention of the Defence (Finance) Regulations) with the benefit of diplomatic privilege from Lisbon. Further notes were traced to the Portuguese Vice-Consul in Liverpool and to the Argentine Embassy.

The Bank grudgingly gave a little more help to the Swiss National Bank, repeating their suggestion as to the feel and appearance of the forgeries but adding three further clues:

1 The three sides of a forgery which corresponded to the deckle edges of a genuine note would show that the fibres protruded regularly - a sign that the edges had been torn (subsequently confirmed when investigations were under way in 1945)

2 The dark embossing of the watermark in a genuine note (the words FIVE and TEN, for example, and the rectangles containing them) appeared prominently on the surface of the paper. There was less prominence seen on the forgeries.

3 The maximum weight of a genuine note was 45.8 grammes per square metre; the forged £10 weighed 54.1 gsm.

The letter added that 'it would not be practicable to issue any form of notice to aid discrimination by the banks and the general public'. This would have helped the Germans, too.

Still the careful Swiss were not satisfied with the information at their disposal. The Federal Laboratories had advised them that notes which had been exposed to sunlight would react differently from those not so exposed. They had also detected 'deviations' in the watermarks. Chamberlain was consulted as to whether anything more helpful could be given to the National Bank, especially as they were sparing themselves no pains to co-operate to the fullest extent. After much heart-searching the Chief Cashier, Peppiatt, wrote on 19 July 1943:

'The Bank appreciate the difficulties which confront you and the other Swiss banks, when endeavouring to determine whether notes are authentic or counterfeit, and have carefully considered whether there are any further points of guidance which can be afforded to you in this direction. They feel, and you will I think agree, that it would not be feasible to define closely all the technical features connected with the printing of their notes, particularly on account of the minor differences to which you have drawn attention. I would, therefore, confirm the information and advice given in previous communications and emphasise that the greatest disparity between a genuine note and the present type of forgery lies in the paper, that used for the latter being heavier in substance and duller in colour; it is detectable to a considerable degree by feel and comparison, even in cases where the notes have been much handled with usage. The Bank fully realise that reaction under a quartz lamp is not an infallible criterion but, nevertheless, believe it to be a valuable test, a view which would indeed seem to be borne by the remarkable success of your own investigations'.

The Swiss were no doubt seeking to be made privy to the secret marks included in the notes for the very purpose that now confronted them: the accurate diagnosis of forgery. Back they came in September and it was over a month before a reply was sent. Peppiatt now wrote (on 8 November 1943):

'... the Bank's printing experts ... think it pertinent to mention that a bank note has yet to be produced that cannot be closely imitated, success in forgery depending solely upon the skill and equipment at the disposal of the forgers; and that because there is reason to believe the skill and equipment of the perpetrators of the current type to be the equal of their own, the natural result must inevitably be an extremely close resemblance to the genuine product. But in spite of this very close resemblance it is, they add, almost impossible for the forger to attain absolute perfection and his handiwork may be detected by the development of a special technique when comparing doubtful notes with a genuine specimen. There are a number of points which may be looked for, most of which have been mentioned in earlier letters, such as the degree of blackness of the ink, the size of a full-stop, the thickness of a line or curve, as well as differences in fluorescence under ultra-violet rays and in the colour and/or the feel of the paper. These factors, either singly or collectively, cannot necessarily be regarded as positive criteria, since varying degrees of impression (ie weight of printing) may account for the above-mentioned differences in printing; fluorescence may show marked differences between two or more manufactures of genuine paper, due to varying properties of raw materials; fluorescence may also be affected by liquids or substances with which a note has been in contact, either through handling or through being kept at, say, a chemical works or a garage; the familiar rustle which may be very marked in a new note (not necessarily a clean one) can soon be almost entirely destroyed by handling.

Nevertheless if there are differences in structural design, that is to say, if the angle, position or direction of any line or curve, the shape of a letter or the point of crossing of, say, a line and a curve, differs from its counterpart on a genuine note; the note under examination may be considered to be a forgery; these instances are, of course, purely hypothetical, but they are tests which may be applied in attempting to pronounce judgment on notes which are suspected of being counterfeit.'

As their next ploy the National Bank asked the Bank to indicate those parts of the notes which were considered to be typical criteria of forgery. This, said Peppiatt, was 'impracticable, if not, in fact, impossible'. However he then drew:

'... particular attention, by comparison with the specimen notes in your possession, to definite differences both in the 'sum block' in the lower left-hand corner and ... in the angle, position or direction of a line or curve and to the point of crossing of, say, a line and a curve in certain portions of the wording'

Further examples then followed and by March 1944 Chamberlain was in a better position to give detailed comment and preliminary conclusions as to the processes used by the forgers. Writing to H G Askwith (Deputy Chief Cashier) he passed on Portals' observation that the quickest way of distinguishing between the watermarks on real and on forged notes was that on the latter it was more distinct and definite, particularly as regards the lines running East to West. On one specific forgery he had observed that the paper had not been cut squarely enough, resulting in the appearance of the watermark for another note at the lower edge, leading him to conclude that the forgeries were being processed two up but one under the other, rather than side by side. It was considered that the paper was mould-made, not hand-made.

'Hand Made paper has no 'direction of manufacture'; it is lifted straight up out of the vat and, as a consequence, possesses very little in the way of what might be described as 'latent stress' and, if wetted, will stretch more or less equally in both directions.

On the other hand, mould-made and machine-made papers have a definite 'direction of manufacture', ie, from N to S or E to W.

If a sheet of mould-made paper is wetted it will stretch and its greatest stretch is at right angles to the direction of manufacture, the stretch in the direction of manufacture being almost negligible.

I would suggest that the Issue Office should cut out a small disc of paper, say ⅝" diameter (or the size of a large cancellation hole) from both genuine and forged notes; these should be laid on the surface of (say) a saucer of water.

The hand-made paper of a genuine note should remain flat because there are no stresses; on the other hand, if the forgeries are mould-made the discs should show a definite tendency to curl up and a line drawn across the disc of paper, at right angles to the curl, will indicate the direction of manufacture. In other words, if my theory is right, discs from genuine notes should stay put and discs from forgeries should curl up'.

(In experiments, Issue Office proved these reactions.)

Although the plate printing process seemed to achieve uniformity of product Chamberlain was of the opinion that complete congruence could not be guaranteed for any printing on paper without elaborate air-conditioning. Complete congruence was impossible because 'our plates (for each note) were made up of nine separate pieces, each with its own slight variations of register due to the drilling of screw holes etc'. (This comment applied to notes made up to various dates between 1936 and 1939 inclusive: thereafter only paper stretch would have been a reason.) If notes were printed in dry, sunny weather on old paper stocks no shrinkage would occur later; but if the paper was 'green' (freshly made) and the weather wet, then when completely dry the resultant notes would be noticeably undersized compared to a 'dry' original product.

Other suggestions he made were to continue to stress to the Swiss the importance of the ultra-violet test, particularly if the note was viewed against backing treated with fluorescent dyes such as Rhodamine or Fluoresceine (resorcinol-phthalein). Either would show a light to deep pink colour on a genuine note, salmon-pink to light red on a forgery. So, how much actually to 'tell Zurich'?

Peppiatt wrote on 5 April 1944 and relayed virtually all Chamberlain's comments, save the incongruity caused by the use of separately assembled plates. Stress was indeed laid at great length on the ultra-violet testing and the additional help which could be gained by the use of fluorescent dyes. Contrary to normal practice, the forged notes were returned to the Swiss but Peppiatt explained that, on account of the growing number being submitted to London, it was proposed in future to stamp each article 'forged' unless the Swiss disagreed. The closest he was able to get to the point about congruence was in referring to a genuine £5 note discovered with the forgeries:

'... the fact that it occurred to you that there were slight differences in the printing does perhaps support the view that certain minute variations in detail cannot necessarily be relied upon to indicate that the note in question is a forgery'.

On 29 September 1944 the British Embassy in Madrid addressed a Note to the Spanish Government about the activities of German agents in Spain in negotiating forged Bank of England notes. Several names were mentioned, including that of

Although the Germans correctly used a Catterns signature and a date which had been appropriated to Leeds Branch this forgery contains an error in the cypher prefix: $\frac{138}{V}$ had been used by the Bank for Birmingham Branch issues; the Leeds prefix $\frac{143}{V}$ should have been applied

Ernesto Heymann, and a request was made that all should be arrested for criminal activities. Heymann had already been apprehended following the alleged discovery of a parcel of forged notes at the Cafe Kondor but had been released through the intervention of an official of the Spanish Information Service. There was an interesting sequel to this incident. A British agent had made contact with Heymann and afterwards reported that Heymann had £18,000 in Bank of England notes believed to be forgeries. The agent was given a genuine £5 note which he managed to exchange for a forgery in Heymann's possession which was forwarded to London and impounded on 4 August 1944. In January 1945 the genuine £5 note reappeared in a consignment of 3,745 alleged notes received from the Instituto Espanol de Moneda Extranjera via the Embassy in Madrid.

In December 1945 the Czechoslovak criminal police observed that the forgeries could be distinguished by:

a) the paper: it was too hard and shiny;

b) the watermark: too conspicuous. In the top lefthand corner of some examples the horizontal lines were uneven;

c) the printing which lacked the richness of the original, the loops on the initial letters being less sharp. In many £10 notes vertical strokes could be seen in the black markings around 'ten'. In all the forgeries the beaded markings round the 'Sum Block' were uneven below, on the left. Triangular ornaments in the inscription 'BANK OF ENGLAND' were rounded at the tips, not sharp;

d) the medallion: the foliage shading was too elaborate, as was the shadow of the drapery on the right. The second fold of the garment was omitted. The eyes and nose were blurred. On many forgeries there was a small loop round the hive. In other words, 'a general lack of flawless draughtsmanship'.

On 9 January 1951 all 'BB' type forgeries received up to the end of 1947 were destroyed: 104,665 in all (£5, £10, £20 and £50); additionally 1,756,588 seized in Germany and never circulated had already been destroyed. For many years thereafter thousands more were seized. There were also two more caches discovered of uncirculated material: nearly 64,500 in Rome in August 1950 (face 'value' about £1.2 million) and some 425,000 (roughly 'valued' at £516 million) recovered during the operation at Lake Toplitz in 1959. Reports that over 3 million forgeries were recovered (many of the bundles had been immersed in the water for so long that they could not be accurately counted) appear to have been greatly exaggerated: the estimate made by the two Bank of England officials – E de M Rudolf and R T P Hall – when the material was incinerated in Austria was the much lower figure given above. Type 'BB' forgeries are still being received, from Eastern Europe in particular, but the flood which began as the Second World War ended is now very much a trickle. (More detailed information regarding 'BB' type forgeries and their detection will be found in Appendix B.)

CHAPTER 12

The Victorian Sampler

Following the successful outcome of the war effort, the Bank could turn its attention to more normal considerations. When the lithoprinted 10s and £1 notes on threaded paper had been released in 1940 there was a stockpile of unthreaded paper at St Luke's, sufficient to produce three months' stock of 250 million notes and a smaller store of partly-printed paper, adequate for 72 million more. No plate-printed 10s or £1 notes had been produced at St. Luke's since before the outbreak of the war. Once these stocks had been used up, it was intended to switch plate-printing to the threaded paper and in the interim sufficient notes would be manufactured by the litho method (and on threaded paper) to ensure an adequate overall supply of each denomination. It was still the aim to issue the Houblon design as soon as practicable.

On 13 May 1946 Chamberlain (who was to be deservedly honoured by the award of the CBE in 1947) reported to the Committee on St. Luke's that plate-printing had resumed but that it was 'a very slow process by reason of the lack of women operatives' resulting in only one machine out of the battery of 15 being in commission. 'The increase of output depends almost entirely on the rate at which women can be engaged and trained... impossible to say when... the cessation of production of the present war-time lithographic note' would be justified. If, he added, plate-printing was not to be resumed and the lithoprinted notes were to be continued until the Houblon design (which had survived the assassination attempt in 1944) was in production there would be a 'prohibitive' loss as a very large additional staff had had to be engaged already and started on a two-year training period; this would be in addition to the loss by disuse of the unthreaded paper stockpiles. The Committee - and the Committee of Treasury, to whom the proposals were remitted - agreed with his plans.

Just over two years later Peppiatt reported on the state of play to the Governors. Although it was desirable to keep to the shortest possible period the time when both litho- and plate-printed notes were being issued concurrently, there were difficulties in maintaining a joint production rate and in keeping adequate stocks both at Head Office and at the provincial Branches. For technical reasons the production of lithographic notes had to continue until the end of August which indicated that their issue would last into September. He proposed, therefore, to issue only plate-printed notes in London (in the basic pre-war colours of a red-brown 10s and a green £1) and to send all the litho production to the country Branches. This would satisfactorily avoid giving out to the commercial banks and the public two varieties of the same denomination at the same issuing centre. At a later stage the Branches would gradually be supplied with the new plate-printed notes. These proposals having been approved, the unthreaded 10s and £1 notes in the pre-war colours were released in June 1948, to be followed three months later by the threaded versions.

At this stage the Bank remained firmly wed to the plans to issue notes with the Houblon design but the timetable continued to slip. The war had prevented a

250th anniversary 'commemorative' issue in 1944 and production difficulties meant that 1948 was a lost target date; tentatively it was now scheduled for September 1949. The Treasury had first seen the design in 1944 and thought it an improvement on Maclise's long-serving portrayal of a 'blowzy Britannia', a reaction which contrasted with Mynors' personal view (page 142).

In March 1948 the National Union of Bank Employees suggested (in letters sent to the Bank, the Committee of London Clearing Bankers and the Treasury) that £2 notes should be issued to increase economy and efficiency 'in all spheres of commerce and industry'. This approach prompted Questions in the House of Commons by Peter Freeman, MP for Newport, and Air Commodore Harvey, MP for Cheshire, Macclesfield: the latter asked the Chancellor of the Exchequer to consider introducing £2 Treasury Notes whilst Freeman asked also for a £3 Treasury Note 'to minimise the counting of large numbers of £1 notes .... and for the convenience of the public generally'. In their heart of hearts the Bank would have liked to issue a £2 note in order to economise in the production of the £1, which was often found in circulation in a very dirty state as the banks tried to extend its life by reissue. Such condition was hardly to the public's liking, besides which it is less easy to tell if a dirty note is genuine. But there were other demands on their time in 1948 and the standard reply given to each of the Parliamentary Questions was 'No, Sir'. In answer to a supplementary question, the Financial Secretary to the Treasury explained '... it would require legislation. It would take a long time to elaborate the designs, and the shape would have to be different'. The Bank's briefing, whilst certainly not raising the point about 'shape', had drawn attention to the possibility that it may have recognised a degree of inflation, along with providing tax dodgers and others a greater convenience.

Nevertheless, the Bank did not dismiss the idea of a £2 completely. A study had already been made in 1943, and very soon the idea became attractive enough to commission Gooden to produce a design in what was now seen as a Houblon *series*. By October 1949 Gooden had prepared a rough design. Legal authority was still a hurdle to be dismantled and it was timely that the Treasury, as part of an exercise to tidy up wartime legislation, had submitted a draft Bill which primarily dealt with Defence (Finance) Regulation 7AA - limiting the Bank's authority to maintain a fiduciary issue

£1 Series A, signed by P S Beale

(see pages 214/5) – but also amended Regulation 7AB. As we have already seen, this Regulation enabled the Bank to call in any of its notes of any denomination not less than £5, after which such notes were no longer to be a legal tender. Since the Currency and Bank Notes Act 1928 referred only to 'calling in' the 10s and £1 notes and thus appeared to draw a distinction between this procedure and the demonetisation provisions of Regulation 7AB in relation to £5 notes and above, the Bill's clauses included one which gave the same legal treatment to all existing denominations in issue. The Bank seized this opportunity, without admitting the reason (the £2 note, which it had not yet mentioned to the Treasury as something being worked on), to suggest a revised wording which would 'give the Bank power to issue, or call in, notes of such denominations (not being less than 10s) as may be approved by the Treasury from time to time on the recommendation of the Bank'. The words 'as may be approved' applied equally to the issue as well as the calling in. (Note that the Treasury's involvement is strictly limited to the agreement to denomination: design remains wholly in the Bank's hands.)

The Bank's wishes were eventually reflected in a new draft, which had come to hand by March 1950. It would also like to have seen legal tender status conveyed on its £5, and any future higher, denomination notes circulating in Scotland and Northern Ireland but realised the political and nationalistic sensitivities which this suggestion would irritate and that it could lead to controversy over the powers of Scottish and Northern Ireland banks to issue their own notes. (Since the withdrawal of the £1 note in 1988, the situation in Scotland and Northern Ireland is that the only legal tender is coin.) No further progress was to be made on the Bill for nearly two years.

The public's dislike of the inconvenient size of the £5 note was becoming so vociferous that in February 1950 P S Beale, who had succeeded Sir Kenneth Peppiatt as Chief Cashier in March 1949, wrote to D W Tilley, General Manager at St. Luke's[1], and instructed him to prepare an alternative £5 design in the Houblon series. By now, however, doubts were again surfacing about the suitability of Houblon as a subject (the Bank had been nationalised in 1946 and thoughts were turning to less domestic subjects); Gooden was asked to provide different portraits to go with his existing, accepted designs. This proposal he rejected uncompromisingly:

'... such alterations are hardly possible. To make any but the smallest alterations on the master die ... is most undesirable ...

There remains, however, a difficulty which seems to me quite insuperable, for it is quite impossible for any artist to re-design one half of a piece of work done fifteen or more years ago and to make a satisfactory whole. Supposing that a novelist were asked to rewrite a couple of chapters of a novel he had written as long ago as that so that they fitted in with the old work nobody would expect the result to be satisfactory ... (Incidentally, I may say that I found it most difficult to design the face of the £2 note so that it fitted in with the manner of the earlier designs.)'

He therefore offered to design a completely new series, although this would take 2-3 years. Since a portrait remained the key component of the security of a design it was suggested to Gooden that Britannia might be an acceptable subject so far as the public were concerned. For the reverses, Gooden put forward a Gatekeeper in full livery and the Bank Picquet (without identifying one particular regiment). It is hard

1 He succeeded J R Dudin, who was Chamberlain's successor in 1948, in 1949.

to believe that there was no direct contact at this period between artist and printer: Sir George Abell (an Executive Director) had instructed the General Manager in October 1951 that the Chief Cashier alone should deal with Gooden. Perhaps Beale was asserting his position as *primus inter pares* within the Bank's hierarchy of senior management.

At the same time as these exchanges with the artist were taking place, trialling of 10s and £1 Houblon notes was halted. They had been severely criticised by Axel Rosswall, on loan from the Bank of Sweden as a technical adviser on banknote printing, as being not in accordance with the best modern practices, particularly as forgers had discovered the advantages of using photographic equipment. The design needed to be improved by the greater use of the geometric lathe and less use of hand engraving. He was, however, enthusiastic about Gooden's Britannia portrait: 'it is much clearer and simpler, but it has at the same time more engravings of different kinds with corresponding possibilities of variation in depth and width of line'. Since the design called for register between the printing and the watermark, it was unsuited to the continuous, or 'web' printing process then under development.

In spite of long bouts of illness, including some surgery, and the frustrations attendant upon matching his own acknowledged skills with the technical requirements of the Bank's own experts, Gooden had completed work on a new £2 denomination by October 1952. By the end of 1953 he had adapted his earlier £2 design to create a £5 design and in June 1954 specimens were being printed. These proved unacceptable due to a very noticeable variation of register between the lithoprinted background and the plate-printed main design. Production was altered from a sheet of 18 to a sheet of 12 notes. The watermark was also causing difficulty in cutting the sheets and its design was changed. Although '12 up' had proved satisfactory, instructions to hold up all further work on this note were given in March 1955. (Because of Gooden's ill health, D V Wicks was recruited on a part-time basis as artist-designer in January 1954.)

The multicoloured Houblon £5 note referred to above displeased Gooden, to such an extent that he conceived an entirely new design which he exhibited to the Bank in September 1953: the £5 'Britannia' note which was eventually to be issued in 1957 (this was originally termed the 'Series III' note, Houblon being designated 'Series II').

Following the accession of Queen Elizabeth II in February 1952 the question was raised as to the propriety of using the royal portrait on any new series of notes which were not 'Government Notes'. Almost three years were to pass before this suggestion surfaced as a positive proposal. Beale was succeeded as Chief Cashier from 17 January 1955 by L K O'Brien (later Lord O'Brien of Lothbury) who, 10 days later, wrote a note to the Governors about the state of play on the design front. At this time a £5 Houblon was still being targeted with the rest of the series on ice, whilst a Britannia portrait series was planned to follow (the £1 design then being the most advanced). When the Britannia series was completed, he concluded, 'I wonder whether we should not have a Queen's Head design prepared - the issue of the Houblon may revive and increase pressure for such a series'. One of the advantages which was now suggested

£1 Series A, signed by L K O'Brien

was that once the monarch's head had been used it would always be used and this would remove permanently any doubts about the central design feature such as had caused so much wasted time and money since Gooden had first started his work. It was recognised, too, that the Bank was in Government ownership and the Court was appointed by the Queen. Houblon, by contrast, could be seen to be emphasising the independence of the Bank. (A further, if not final, nail in Houblon's coffin was that the notes had, as Rosswall had pointed out, been designed in the context of the lower technical standards and abilities of yesteryear.) The Committee of Treasury agreed to back a Queen's Head note series at their meeting on 4 January 1956. Formal advice to the Treasury about the abandonment of the Houblon design had been given by Governor Cobbold to Sir Edward Bridges on 18 March 1955 'regretfully and on hunch'. Sir Edward was reported as having 'heaved a regretful sigh of relief' as must also the designer, who regarded it as now out of date and unsuitable.

Gooden was by this time, however, quite a sick man and he died in September 1955 without seeing any of his designs actually in use as a medium of payment. So he never had to emigrate. Who was to succeed him? The Bank sought the opinion of the President of the Society of Painter-Etchers and Engravers, Malcolm Osborne. In his opinion only one person could match Gooden's skills: Professor Robert Austin who had recently retired from the Chair of Engraving at the Royal College of Art. His appointment was announced in December 1955 with the remit that he was to work closely with the technical experts at the Printing Works in order the more efficiently to intermix the aesthetic design qualities which he would bring to the work with the security and printing considerations so essential in the day-to-day battle against the counterfeiter. (Beale was now out of office.)

In a memorandum of 21 March 1955, O'Brien had himself set down what he saw as the principles of a satisfactory note issue. The basic general requirement was to give the general public the kind of paper money best suited to its needs and preferences. Notes must be in convenient denominations both for everyday use and to enable reasonable sums to be carried about without undue bulk. They must be of convenient size (which the 'white' £5 clearly was not). Protection against forgery must be as great as possible, having regard to expense. The notes must be capable of standing up to a good deal of use without becoming unduly dirty or replaced quickly in order to maintain an acceptable average condition. They should be of the highest aesthetic standard and be readily distinguishable, one value from another. Due attention should be paid to public and Parliamentary comment and to any indications of desirable change voiced by the banks. Costs (which are effectively borne by the Government, to whom the net profit of the note issue is paid) should, however, be kept as low as was consonant with these aims. Finally, it was essential to be prepared for the contingency of a flood of serious forgeries by having reserve designs in hand, ready for immediate production.

The forgery of low sum notes had dropped off during World War II but a surge of 10s and £1 counterfeits - reminiscent of an unresolved pre-war eruption - occurred in 1955. The source was traced to Leeds where a 68-year old man, Sydney Wainwright, was arrested. All the equipment necessary for his activities in this regard had been discovered at the house he occupied. He was brought to justice thanks to an alert counter assistant in a local shop who said she 'did not like the feel' of the £1 note tendered to her in payment for chocolate. Unusually, but because the case was so important, she was given a £25 cheque by the Bank as a reward. Wainwright pleaded guilty to charges of forging 73 £1 notes and admitted responsibility for the pre-war operation which had resulted in some 300 £1 and 2,400 10s counterfeits being detected between 1934 and 1940. He was gaoled for 14 years, later reduced to 12 years. In a statement voluntarily given on 9 May 1955, Wainwright described how he went about his task. The watermark, for example, was reproduced by using fine sandpaper to remove the texture of the actual paper and to produce a shadow when held up to the light. To change the Beale signature to O'Brien 'I got some solder and with a soldering iron running the solder and with very fine 00 emery cloth I rubbed over the top very finely and completely filled it in and then using my eye glass and engraving tool I wrote in or engraved the new cashier's name. It's easy when you are used to it'.

A couple of years earlier the Bank had begun to receive examples of its notes from which either (and more commonly) vertical strips or horizontal strips had been excised. These notes were then rejoined with opaque tape so that they appeared to be of correct width (or height), the tape hiding the gap. The object was to remove enough from say 10 notes to create an 11th. Approximately ¼" would be removed from the first note and spliced into a second, from which ½" had been taken. The half-inch was then spliced into a third note from which more had been removed; so the process continued until a possible extra note had been created. Another fraud in this period was the removal of a small triangular portion, including the serial number, from the top right-hand corner of several £1 notes. These damaged notes were then spent in the normal way, eventually being submitted to the Bank as 'mutilated notes' when they were seen to lack one number. Meanwhile the triangular pieces were singed or scorched and presented in separate claims through several banks and Post Offices as being all there was left after a fire. To avoid detection through the matching of serial numbers the perpetrator had altered one part: thus, an original note Z33C was altered to Z38C. Thanks to skilled forensic photography at the Home Office's Harrogate Laboratory the original notes could be matched exactly in many examples to the triangular fragments, particularly where the latter included an undamaged cut edge. The fraud came to light when 48 fragments were submitted as one claim. The charges were of false pretences and forgery (alteration of a serial number being 'material') to which the perpetrator pleaded guilty and he was given eight years' preventive detention.

Although the new Currency and Bank Notes Bill was brought back to life in January 1952, Parliament was too pre-occupied with the new Government's plans to find time for it and the Second Reading did not take place until December 1953 at which stage - along with other matters of moment, such as the design of the notes and their dirtiness - the necessity of the 'promise to pay' clause was again debated. Since the abandonment of the Gold Standard the Bank could only effectively 'pay' its own notes by issuing others in their stead. This, suggested F J Errol in the House of Commons, would lead to the ridiculous pantomime of the Chief Cashier giving out £1 for £1 '... and so we would go, backwards and forwards, until closing time...' The Bank consulted its solicitors. A simple alternative would be to replace the phrase with something akin to 'Legal Tender for -' as had appeared on the unissued wartime 2s6d and 5s notes. The legal opinion, however, was that a banknote was in law a promissory note and this made the retention of the phrase advisable. In deciding to follow this advice the Bank added the further reason that 'it underlines that the note is a Bank of England note'. The Bill itself entered the Statute Book as the Currency and Bank Notes Act, 1954, becoming operative on 22 February of that year. Section 1 dealt with the issue and recall of the Bank's notes in five principal subsections:

1 The Bank to issue notes of such denominations as the Treasury may approve.

2 All such notes to be legal tender in England and Wales; notes of less than £5 also to be legal tender in Scotland and Northern Ireland.

3 Notes to be payable only at the Bank's Head Office, unless expressly made payable elsewhere.

4 Any holder of a note is entitled to exchange it for such lower denominations as he may specify, within office hours.

5 One month's notice to be given for calling in any banknotes after which period legal tender status expires.

The Bank was now set on course for the issue of Gooden's £5 Britannia design. He had been ill during the latter half of 1954 and this delayed a redesign of the front of the note until the following January. A month later he suggested that the watermark should be based on Pistrucci's St George and the Dragon (which had appeared on the reverse side of most of the gold coinage since 1817). At about this time, Bradbury Wilkinson began the engraving work, the note having one plate printing on each surface as well as a litho-printed background. In March Gooden redesigned the St George vignette placed underneath the signature and produced two alternative watermark designs: Britannia and a lion's head. O'Brien's view of the latter was that it looked 'like a grotesque human face' and he strongly recommended the Britannia. Approval was given in April to a paste-up of the note and Bradburys began to engrave the lion on the reverse. Progress pulls resulted in certain modifications of colour tones and O'Brien asked for a larger signature but with compressed initials.

Ink for the plate-printing was proving somewhat of a problem. Design of the cypher letters was completed, based on those used for the 10s and £1 denominations with the addition of serifs: since it was a requirement of the Issue Office (responsible for dealing with mutilated notes) that letters had to be recognisable when cut in half horizontally, the cyphers F, G, I, P, Q and V were, as before, omitted from the series to avoid the possibility of alteration. In November 1955 remedial work was carried out on some of the etching due to a loss of parts of the overall design when pulls were taken on a machine run (the hand pulls had been satisfactory). By May 1956 it was realised that the watermark was deeper and more brilliant than the standard and therefore too intrusive to the eye. As a result, a degree of pressure in applying the tint was necessary, causing slight distortion of the paper. The next month, another difficulty was revealed when attempts were made to guillotine the printed sheets. There was such a difference in the thickness of the printed area in a stack of 500 sheets and the unprinted margin that the blade slipped when the platen failed to hold firmly.

At last, in July 1956, the Bank felt confident enough to commit itself to a press release, announcing:

'... that a £5 note of a new design incorporating a head of Britannia is in course of production. The new note will be in colour and the paper will be of the same quality as that used for the existing £1 and 10s notes. In size it will be slightly larger than the £1 note, measuring 6 ¼ inches by 3 ¹⁷⁄₃₂ inches.

The new note will be issued early in 1957. The production of the present £5 note will then be discontinued, but the status of existing £5 notes in circulation will not be affected.

The Bank of England also announce that permission has been sought of, and granted by, HM The Queen to prepare designs for a later series of notes incorporating a portrait of Her Majesty. Notes incorporating these designs are unlikely to be issued for several years to come.'

A final problem was encountered shortly afterwards when a high degree of humidity caused parts of the plate printing to offset onto the litho fronts. There followed satisfactory reports of progress towards stockpiles and deliveries in September. Specimens were available in January 1957 and arrangements made to present the first 10 numbered notes as follows (no such procedure had occurred since the 1928 issue of the 10s and £1):

1   The Queen
2   The Duke of Edinburgh
3   The Prime Minister
4   The Chancellor of the Exchequer
5   The Lord Mayor
6   Portals
7   Bradbury Wilkinson
8   Mrs Stephen Gooden
9   Lord Braintree (Chairman, Committee on St Luke's 1950-1955)
10 The Institute of Bankers

The first coloured £5 note (Series B) issued in 1957 by the Bank, designed by Stephen Gooden. The reverse was altered slightly when it was changed to a lithoprint in 1961 (160 x 90mm)

It was finally decided that the note should be issued to the public on Thursday 21 February 1957, and the following Press announcement was made the previous Monday:

'The Bank of England announce that the new £5 note, which was stated in July of last year to be in course of production, will be issued on Thursday next, the 21 February. The issue of the existing £5 note by the Bank of England will then cease, but the status of those in circulation will not be affected. The two notes will circulate side by side, the new gradually replacing the old as the latter become unfit for circulation.

The new note measures 6 ¼ inches by 3 ¹⁷⁄₃₂ inches, slightly more than the £1 note. The dominant colour is blue. The paper is of the same quality as that used for the £1 note and incorporates a metallic thread.

On the face of the note, the main features of the design are a head of Britannia on the left, balanced by a 'window' containing a watermark on the right. '£5' appears on a geometrical background in the right-hand top corner and, on a smaller scale, on a circular medallion below. In the centre the words 'Bank of England' appear at the top in heavy capitals with the traditional wording and the Chief Cashier's signature below; and at the foot a small picture of St George and the Dragon. The many-coloured background includes lettering, a tile-like pattern and a device of lions and keys. The numbers are printed in black, in about the same position as on the £1 note.

The main feature of the back of the note is a standing lion, holding a large key with one paw and the ring of the key-chain in his mouth. 'Bank of England' appears above and '£5' in each lower corner, all on a ground of geometrical lines in blue, over a light background in mauve and green.

The watermark comprises another head of Britannia in the 'window' and a 'wave line' watermark round the edge.

The note was designed by the late Stephen Gooden, RA.'

As had occurred in 1928, no photographs were supplied to the Press.

O'Brien had decided in 1955 that the new Queen's Head notes should be designated Series C, leaving Britannia as Series B and the 10s and £1 designs of 1928 issues as Series A.

When the £5 Britannia was released there were no Registers set up and use of the existing ones was virtually discontinued. Their continuing use had been questioned from time to time after the 1928 issue of the smaller denomination notes, for which no Registers were established. The Bank simply refused to entertain any claims for lost or destroyed notes or, as a general rule, to 'stop' specific notes. The Treasury had already agreed that the high cost of maintaining Registers to the standard needed to make them useful was now an unnecessary luxury for the public's benefit in the climate of the day. The existing Registers for £5 letterpress notes and £10 notes and above were retained until 1960, by which time the spate of German wartime forgeries had abated. Another continuous link with the first days of the Bank's existence had been broken but it was clearly uneconomic to maintain Registers for notes which were no longer legal tender whilst denying a similar facility to the users of current notes.

Public criticism of the new note seems to have been quite muted, the relief at the appearance of a smaller size seeming to outweigh other considerations though a number of letters in the press referred to the unfortunate similarity in colours and size of Scottish £1 notes. The *Architects' Journal* was, however, not pulling its punches:

> 'It is hard to imagine anything worse. There is a large prettified head of Britannia (?) on the left, contained in a geometric frame garnished with what looks like tangles of knitting. Part of the border and background consists of tudor roses tinted in two shades of green, mauve and brown – for all the world like a cheap Edwardian wall paper for a doll's house. The words 'five pounds' appear twice, and the figure '£5' three times, but the repetition barely counter-balances their comparative illegibility. The main text, 'I promise to pay', etc., is arranged symmetrically above a picture of St George killing a three-legged dragon, but all this is arranged very slightly, and apparently needlessly, to the right of the centre line of the note. The back of the note is not quite so bad: it consists of a vaguely Lombardic lion carrying a key and chain.
>
> The present pound and ten shilling notes are nothing to be proud of, but this effeminate-looking design by the late Stephen Gooden, RA is appalling.'

Not surprisingly, *Punch* also had a go, but in somewhat lighter vein:

> 'This new fiver is not a beautiful thing. It is rather like a Victorian sampler as seen in a nightmare by the Council of Industrial Design. Amorphous panels sprawl on both sides, vaguely suggesting lacework, commemorative masonry, wallpaper and the covers of old-fashioned exercise books. There is Britannia (decapitated), St George and the Dragon, a lovable old lion mauling a key on a chain, and the magic signature 'L K O'Brien'. The note is slightly larger than the one-pound note, and therefore resists every attempt by the owner to stow it away uncreased in the standard wallet. It is multicoloured but predominantly bluish, and most people familiar with the trend of prices will regard this as cynically significant.'

In the Bank's eyes, the 'lovable old lion mauling a key' actually symbolised the strength of the Bank, the key itself denoting security.

An adjournment motion in the House of Commons on 24 February 1958 gave MPs the opportunity to debate the design of the new £5. The principal speech was given by William Shepherd, Member of Parliament for Cheadle, who described the design as 'clumsy, ugly and undistinguished... the back of the note is really ghastly'. He sought assurance that the Treasury would 'have this wretched note redesigned' and agree to submit similar 'symbols' to a competent body for judgement - such as the Council of Industrial Design. He was supported by Michael Clark Hutchinson (Edinburgh, South) whose main point was the similarity with the Scottish £1 notes. The Financial Secretary to the Treasury (J E S Simon) made a spirited defence ('the notes with which I have been provided this evening are far more valuable than I have had before!'). He concluded '....the Bank of England could not have done more than it did in getting an artist absolutely of the first rank as a modern engraver to design its notes'.

Occasionally a cry was voiced for the return of the old style 'white fiver'. '...the size and quality have been absurdly curtailed', wrote a correspondent to The *Daily Telegraph* on 14 December 1959, so that Edward Lear's owl and pussycat 'would find difficulty in wrapping honey, money or anything else in it'. The death-knell was irreversibly sounded, however, when the Bank called in the outstanding £5 notes (ie those on threaded paper, the earlier issues having already been called in), which ceased to be legal tender from 13 March 1961.

During the latter part of 1960 it had been decided that in order to facilitate the production of other denominations the back of the £5 Britannia note should be printed by the litho process instead of by plate printing. The public were notified in a press announcement on 11 July 1961 of the change which was explained as being 'for technical reasons concerned with speed and economy in production'. In order to distinguish the new production from the old, the £5 symbol on the back appeared in outline, so that the background design showed through: on the plate-printed version this symbol was printed heavily in dark blue. This alteration in the method of printing released machinery for the production of other notes, particularly the 10s Queen's Head, which was scheduled for release in the Autumn.

It became obvious quite soon after the return of the Printing Works from Overton that the St Luke's site was inadequate to cope with the demands of the post-war period and the Bank looked around for alternative accommodation. Eventually an area at Debden, in Essex became available, on which a completely new works was constructed. It was formally occupied on 20 February 1956 and all Bank of England notes have been printed there ever since. The Committee on St Luke's was renamed the 'Debden Committee'.

In keeping abreast of developments in security printing the Printing Works had been alerted to the possibility of producing notes on a reel of continuous stationery and Chamberlain agreed to act as the Bank's liaison with the Swiss company, Chambon, late in 1949 – a role that was not terminated until the move to the new quarters at Debden had taken place. In considering the design of a modern banknote, therefore, it was now essential to take into account the prospect that it might be printed continuously 'on the web'. One obvious problem would be how to dry the ink quickly enough to prevent smudgy products or off-setting of back upon front and vice versa.

The requirements remained the same as did the ground rules. No single security feature would defeat a forger but a combination of such features could deter him on cost grounds which would be less significant in respect of official bulk production. Clearly, the larger the denomination he could make, the larger the forger's potential profit; but the larger denominations had always been given careful scrutiny and should therefore incorporate the more expensive anti-forgery features. Watermarks should be invisible in reflected light and very clear in transmitted light; they should be moulded into the paper to give areas of greater and less thickness than the rest of the paper, not of the 'dandy' type which produces only a local thinness. They should not be centrally placed since the habit of folding notes in the middle soon affects the clarity. Multicoloured designs cause immense difficulty when the forger attempts the complex colour separation by photography. It is preferable to have a definite front and back to a note so that cashiers can more readily detect a counterfeit. A portrait of a well-known person, preferably living – such as the reigning monarch – is best, shown full or three-quarter face since the eyes play the largest part in a facial expression. (One of the greatest difficulties experienced by the Germans, it will be recalled, was getting Britannia's eyes accurately copied.) Expensive equipment should be harnessed in order to take advantage of new design tools. Since the forger usually has difficulty in getting a good register of his multiple printings, very finely engraved lines should be incorporated since the human eye can normally detect irregularities as small as one-thousandth of an inch. For this reason a design built up of fine lines is sharper to the naked eye than one composed of dots. Plate-printing has the greatest security value since there are many commercial machines available to undertake letterpress, offset and photogravure printing. Today, due respect has to be paid, too, to the standard of accuracy capable of being displayed by colour-copying machines.

CHAPTER 13　The Queen, the Beauty and the Beast

Robert Austin's first task was to tackle the £1 note but before he could commence serious work a decision had to be made as to how the Queen should be portrayed: Full-face or profile? Wearing a crown or tiara? Dress or robes? Jewellery etc? Austin had expressed a preference for an artistic portrait but soon realised that he would have more room to manoeuvre if he used a photograph. A special session at Buckingham Palace was arranged on 1 May 1956 where one of the senior assistants to Dorothy Wilding (a well-known society, and official Royal, photographer whose portrait of the Queen had been used for the first postage stamps of the new reign in 1952) took the necessary photographs to Austin's direction. In the meantime the plan to use the Queen's head as the watermark had had to be abandoned when it was realised that the likely introduction of web-printing would necessitate a continuous watermark which could not be guaranteed to avoid incomplete sections appearing at the top and bottom of each note. For this reason it was considered disrespectful to use the portrait of a living person, especially the Queen. Austin suggested two alternative designs: a girl in plaits, and stylised leaves, neither of which found favour. He was reported as becoming a 'little restive and to be finding the deliberate pace of the Bank rather tiresome'. At the Printing Works, now settled into the Debden environment, it was necessary to set up a Design Section to cope with the volume of work currently in train. In June 1956 the Debden Committee considered a submission from the Printing Works which criticised the lack of whole-time design experts and of an in-house design structure. Given the 'intimate connection between the aesthetic appeal of a design, the economy of production, the difficulty it presents in counterfeiting and the ease with which the public can recognise a counterfeit' the writing of 'technically good features into the design of a note therefore needs the collaboration of artist, scientist and craftsman, and in addition, of course, the skill and experience of the paper-maker'. Therefore, the paper added, '... the artist needs to cultivate an intimate understanding of the capabilities of machines for engraving in order to compose attractive and secure designs, and experimental designs therefore need to be machined and developed in closer association between the artist and technical people than is possible when the machining is done elsewhere'. The main reason why no design team had hitherto been assembled was historical: London was a world centre for commercial printing of banknotes and it was natural that this experience should have been drawn on by the Bank's own printers. Although Wicks had been taken on the part-time strength two years earlier this had not meant that no use would now be made of outside expertise. The paper was at pains to point out that 'an outside artist would continue to be needed to supply basic artistic conception for each new design (and) an outside portrait engraver would be used because our programme of work would not justify whole-time employment of one of the few first-class portrait engravers in the world'.

In order to strengthen the resources of the Printing Works itself, therefore, Austin recruited to the permanent staff one of his former students at the Royal College of Art - H N Eccleston - in January 1958 from the South-East Essex Technical College in

Barking. Eccleston's developed and developing talents had clearly been recognised and this shrewd move by Austin would ultimately lead to Eccleston's own important contribution to the history of the Bank of England note.

Inevitably the shroud of secrecy began to lose some of its thickness, hence the reference to a Queen's Portrait series in the Press Release in July 1956. Fortunately this had of necessity to refer to the new Series C notes as unlikely to be issued for some years to come: progress was slow and very difficult at times. Austin's first portrait had been rejected and O'Brien was still dissatisfied with the replacement, even after six months' alteration. His recorded comments at this stage of the work are a reflection of the difficulties facing the engraver of the portrait of a living person: there was too much hair, reduction of which might make the image look younger; the chest was too full, giving the Queen a portly look; the left eye did not seem to be looking in the correct direction; the elimination of the extreme fullness of the face in the first portrait had given the line of the chin a slightly pinched effect; the mouth needed a little softening. Austin had ignored the traditional method of portrait engraving in which a photograph of the subject is copied by a technique of heavy cross-hatching; instead, he chose a relatively open type of engraving with a minimum of engraved lines. Tests made at Debden showed that such a portrait was sensitive to the malformation or omission of lines and dots, such as often occurred with forgeries, and therefore caused readily-discernible changes of expression.

However, the watermark was settled: a head crowned with laurel wreaths. This must have been of great relief to Portals, who 'seem to have about reached the end of their tether' as O'Brien had recorded in April of that year. A third and final version of the portrait was finished and engraved by June 1958. The engraving was carried out by R Godbehear of Bradbury Wilkinson, the company which had done all the preliminary engraving for the rejected designs. It had proved to be a very difficult task and every alteration had taken its toll of the timetable. One particular feature of Austin's design was the inclusion of 'Elizabeth R' in the medallion containing the portrait. The Court disliked it but O'Brien warned in April 1958 that Austin could well break his connection with the project if deletion was insisted upon, to the extent that he would disassociate himself from a modified version. Although misgivings continued to grow about the artistic concept of the designs, they were less easily forgeable than the 1928 designs and for this reason the project was allowed to proceed.

Neither the Prime Minister, Harold Macmillan, nor the Chancellor of the Exchequer, Derick Heathcoat Amory, criticised the design to any serious extent, however, and it was finally shown to the Queen herself in October 1958. In a personal letter of 22 October, her Private Secretary observed the 'Her one and only objection is that the drawing of her face does not show the line of her jaw at all. It remains as almost a plain white area... if this line could be indicated in any way, she thinks that it would be an improvement'. His official letter conveyed the Queen's admiration for Austin's 'skill in embodying the portrait in the intricate design of the note itself'. In the event the grave risk of spoiling the portrait altogether by strengthening the jaw line was not taken. Nevertheless, the result was not entirely satisfactory as the Queen appeared stiff-necked and leaning backwards.

Keesey had been refused permission to include his initials in the reverse designs for the 1928 issues. Some sharp-eyed observers believed that Austin had managed to secrete a personal element into his £1 note, pointing to what appears as an 'A' at the base of the neckline on the portrait. Those most closely involved in the project, including Lord O'Brien, could not recollect any such detail nor is reference made in any of the relevant files still extant to this point. It is simply a chance coincidence, not repeated on the smaller 10s note.

With the major hurdle cleared it was time to review the whole future of Series C. In 1958 it was the intention to manufacture all notes to the same dimensions (but in contrasting basic colourations). The popularity of the £5 Britannia encouraged the Bank in the belief that a £2 note would be an equally popular move and it was proposed to add it to Series C, which was already planned to incorporate the £10 denomination (last issued in 1943). Thoughts had also begun to crystallize around the concept that there should be a marked contrast in the designs of the 10s, £1 and £2 notes on the one hand and in those of the £5 and £10 notes on the other - particularly so if the sizes were to be uniform. A different approach to design suggested that a different artist ought to be recruited, preferably younger than Austin (then 63) but of distinction in his field. To try and avoid serious public criticism of designs, an informal committee of Directors was proposed, whom the Chief Cashier could consult on matters of taste and general design in the future. Fortunately, Austin reacted positively even to the extent of volunteering to go away and think of a suitable candidate as well as to continue to work on his 10s and £2 designs. By February 1959, however, he had failed to come up with a name. After due enquiry elsewhere the name of Reynolds Stone, a free-lance designer and engraver, was recommended although his forte was lettering and woodcuts. Stone

Austin's accepted but abandoned design for a £2 note (150mm x 72mm)

Front of Robert Austin's £1 note (Series C), issued in 1960, the first Bank of England note to bear the monarch's portrait (151 x 72mm)

was approached and after seeing the Chief Cashier and visiting the Printing Works on 15 May 1959, he expressed his willingness to be engaged and said he looked forward with keen interest to learning how to make use of such mechanical aids as geometrical lathes.

Unfortunately for the enthusiastic team at Debden who were working on Austin's £2 note, political considerations were beginning to overshadow the project: there were doubts about the wisdom of its introduction since the public would probably see it as an inevitable sign of inflationary trends (much as was to be argued in years to come when consideration was being given to the replacement of the £1 note by a £1 coin). In August 1959 the Chancellor of the Exchequer agreed that the Bank's proposal should be set aside for a few months, although he was personally in favour of the savings which would result from the decline in the demand for, and supply of, the £1 denomination. Further work was immediately suspended and it was finally abandoned when the Cabinet voted on 17 November against the issue. Later that month the Bank gave public notice of their plans for Series C, the intention to issue which had been briefly mentioned when the Series B £5 had been announced. Almost at once the organisations responsible for the welfare of blind and partially-sighted people voiced their objections for the Bank had informed the public that the 10s and £1 would be the same size as each other whilst the £5 and £10 would share common, larger dimensions. After due consultation and further consideration the Bank climbed down and agreed to differentiate the sizes throughout the series: this decision was announced in March 1960, just before Austin's £1 was released for the first time.

It is clear that the Bank as a whole did not feel that it had a winner in Austin's design but even so the extent of public criticism took them aback. The Queen's portrait took the brunt of the attack which focused quite simply on the point that it was a bad likeness. The overall design seemed to Harold Wilson (then MP for Huyton) more like 'a ticket on a detergent (gift) voucher' than a note. The press, who had for the first time been supplied with photographs[1], were nearly unanimous in their views. In the *Daily Express*, Osbert Lancaster severely criticised what 'one hesitates to call the design'. The back had a 'faint surrealists charm' like 'an illustration in an old-fashioned medical book of the stomach of a child who had recently swallowed a penny might be thought to possess', whilst the front was 'completely inexplicable'. One of the *Evening Standard's* regular cartoonists, Jak, drew a forgers' den with the caption 'Blimey, a portrait as

1 But only in black and white. These were accompanied by the request that they were returned with a letter confirming that 'all blocks, negatives, copy-prints and other working material' had been destroyed. 'The Bank of England don't trust us' observed the *Daily Sketch*.

well – who do you think I am, Annigoni!' a perhaps unconscious acknowledgement of the security value of the representation of the monarch. Another regular contributor, Vicky, suggested alternative designs of his own. In a leader on 22 March The *Daily Telegraph* commented 'It is an undistinguished design... severe without being stately this is not the Queen we know'. Their art critic, Terence Mullaly, probably expressed reactions best although he failed to appreciate the desirability of leaving the watermark panel unprinted since he was scathing of the blank space, use of which would have given balanced treatment to the heavy printing elsewhere. The Queen's portrait was bad; the lettering unclear and inelegant; Britannia was commonplace; the 'absurd network of ... lines ... on both sides of the note was unpardonable'. The *Guardian* saw it as a 'relapse into the worst of Victorian bad taste'. (If the Bank had been more informative at this time, some of the criticisms could have been averted.)

Within the banking industry the banking staff union, NUBE, complained to the Bank that, by placing the serial numbers at top left and bottom right, difficulties would be caused to tellers when counting the notes. The Union demanded that they should be consulted in future, a request which was firmly, but politely, declined.

Front of Robert Austin's 10s note (Series C), issued in 1961 (140 x 67mm)

Reverse of Austin's 10s note

Digesting this barrage, which included correspondence from such justifiably interested parties as the Council of Industrial Design, the Bank invited two experts to join the informal committee of Directors: they were Sir Gordon Russell, a former director of the Council, and Professor Anthony Blunt (later to be revealed as a Russian spy). Their first task was to consider Austin's design for the 10s note, which Russell promptly described as a 'curious assortment of unrelated shapes' (Blunt's opinion could not be taken as he was abroad at the time, convalescing). Some changes, particularly in the lettering, were made and the note released to the public on 12 October 1961. Godbehear's engraving of the Queen's portrait was again used. Wicks engraved the Britannia on the reverse side whilst Bert Cole of Bradbury Wilkinson cut the lettering. Shortly after, Austin ended his association, Stone's design for a £5 note having recently been preferred to Austin's. 'My period of usefulness at Debden is at an end', he wrote to the General Manager. 'The circumstances and conditions make it imperative that I should stop now.' A few weeks later, in a letter to O'Brien, he admitted both his enjoyment of the 'superb challenge' and the 'puzzling frustration' which he had often

Reverse of Austin's £1 note. The small letter R at the bottom indicates that the example was printed on a research machine; issued notes from these printings carried one of the cyphers A01N, A05N or A06N

found disruptive. Nevertheless, it had been an 'enormous honour' to work for the Bank in this field. Public reaction to the new 10s note was very muted; many, no doubt, had the same attitude towards it as a correspondent to The *Daily Telegraph* on 24 October: 'I think the design is rather attractive, but perhaps that is because I am used to the design of the pound note'. Only the sharpest eyes noticed the adoption of a lower case initial letter for the word 'promise'.

The new £1 notes were first produced in sheets of 24 but some experimental work was carried out in 1961 on a new reel–fed 'web' press which printed sheets of 21 notes. Three million of these experimental notes were issued to the public: they are identifiable by a minute letter R on the back (standing for Research). The same year, the Bank took steps to reduce the variety of their notes in the public's hands by calling in on 13 March the last issue of black and white £5 notes (ie. those dated 2 September 1944 to 20 September 1956, inclusive) – of which less than six million remained unpaid at that date. Plans were also advanced for the calling in of Series A £1 notes later that year but the natural reflux to the Bank tailed off at mid–year and the operation was postponed until 28 May 1962; some 250 million were outstanding. Six months later, on 29 October 1962, the Series A 10s note was also called in, an estimated 33 million only then remaining in circulation.

On 1 March 1962 O'Brien was appointed an Executive Director, his successor as Chief Cashier being J Q Hollom. Two important features in the history of the Bank of England note had occurred during the former's period in office: the issue of the first multi–coloured note (the Series B £5 Britannia) – serving 'as a bridge' between

£1 Series C, signed by J Q Hollom

Preliminary sketch by Austin for a £5 note in Series C

Preliminary sketch by Austin for a £10 note in Series C

the pre-war small denomination notes and a full-blown pictorial series - and the introduction of the Queen's portrait, which has remained a feature of Bank of England notes ever since.

As early as May 1960 the design by Reynolds Stone for a £5 (like Austin, he was retained as a consultant to the Bank) was much preferred to that of Austin and by November 1961 it was reported that his submission 'promised well'. He had also put forward a preliminary design for the £10 which was favourably received, too. (The Printing Works themselves were preparing an emergency £5 design, based on Britannia and capable of being printed by lithography.) At this stage the plan was to issue Stone's £5 in the Autumn of 1962. Bradbury Wilkinson were commissioned to engrave the Queen's portrait and used both Godbehear and a new, young engraver - Alan Dow. In the event, Dow's engravings were utilised for Stone's £5 and £10 and for all the Series D notes. In March 1962 a copy of the note was forwarded to the Queen's Private Secretary who passed on the comment that she found it a 'very agreeable design'. Although the timescale seemed to be holding well enough for the Clearing Banks to receive examples in July in confidence to show their Cash Centre managers it was soon realised that higher stocks of Series B £5 notes were going to be held than had been forecast. Since it was inadvisable to issue two different notes of the same value at the same time and uneconomic to waste these stocks by not releasing them, the issue date was postponed. The commercial banks' note-handling duties are at their most onerous for two months either side of Christmas so the postponement had to be in terms of months rather than weeks and it was not until 21 February 1963 that the public had the opportunity to pass judgment on a design which included a Britannia on the reverse which had been modelled by Stone's daughter, Phillida. The watermark was identical to that on the two lower denomination Austin notes since it was still the aim to produce these three denominations by the high-speed web machines on the successful completion of the lengthy trials, initially in sheets but later as 'single note delivery' (ie in a continuous process which would include guillotining into individual single bundles).

The official description of the new note was given with the press announcement of its release as follows:

'The main feature on the front of the note, which is predominantly blue, is an original portrait of Her Majesty The Queen; although wearing the diadem portrayed on the £1 and 10s notes, Her Majesty is pictured more nearly full-face on this occasion and wearing three rows of pearls. The portrait is on the right-hand side of the note and is framed by an oval of micro-lettering repeating many times the words 'Bank of England'.

At the top of the note the words 'Bank of England', separated by small engraved rosettes, appear in capitals; beneath them the words 'I Promise to pay the Bearer on Demand the Sum of' appear on a scroll, below which, in the centre of the note, the words 'Five Pounds' in white italic letters stand out boldly from a dark background. In the right-hand top corner is the figure '5' set in a machine engraved pattern, balanced by a similar figure '5' set in a different pattern in the left-hand bottom corner. The general background of the note consists of patterns in different shades of blue, mauve and brown formed by lines of varying thicknesses. The cipher and number of the note are in black at the top left-hand and the bottom right-hand corners. This is the first note to be issued bearing the signature of the present Chief Cashier, Mr J Q Hollom.

Preliminary sketch by Reynolds Stone of his £5 Series C note; and his original drawing of his daughter, Phillida, as the new Britannia

The watermark, the same as that on the £1 and 10s notes, appears on the left-hand side and is again repetitive, with a view to possible printing on continuous paper.

The back of the note incorporates a new variation of Britannia, perhaps younger in appearance, unhelmeted and in the traditional pose; she is surrounded by an oval design which incorporates the words 'Five Pounds' at the top and 'Bank of England' at the base. As on the front of the note, the figure '5' is inset in the right-hand and bottom left-hand corners. The colour of the reverse is again predominantly blue and the remaining design consists of geometrical patterns.'

As might be expected, most of the press comment centred on the new representation of Britannia. The *Daily Telegraph* thought her a 'likeable young lady ..... though not very regal'. They noted the absence of the £ sign. The *Daily Telegraph* thought the whole note 'clumsily designed' with Britannia now 'more like a bathing beauty'. The NBC broadcaster, Robert MacNeil, digesting all this commentary, observed that Britain now had 'a racy new Britannia thoroughly in tune with the times'. In more sober tones the March 1963 edition of The *Bankers' Magazine* reminded its readers that 'the design of any bank-note must be a compromise - it must look impressive

Front and reverse of Reynolds Stone's £5 note Series C, issued in 1963 (140 x 84mm)

and distinctive, while defeating the efforts of the counterfeiter' and 'one must not push aesthetic considerations very far ... After all, we can get used to anything'.

Within a week of the release of the new £5 note, supplies of Austin's £1 bearing Hollom's signature were available for issue. These included over 400 million which had been printed experimentally on the Goebel web press. They were distinguished by the insertion of the letter G on the reverse.

Front of Reynolds Stone's £10 note Series C, issued in 1964 (150 x 93mm)

Stone had submitted alternative designs for the last note planned in Series C and the basis of that for the note as finally issued was selected in May 1963. At this point a red thread was proposed in place of the normal 'silver' thread. Portals' view, however, was that a red thread was more easily visible in reflected light and therefore capable of being simulated by printing, with less difficulty than that presented by the usual coloured thread. The Chief Cashier heeded this warning and ruled against red. Governor Cromer criticised the figure 10 as appearing too like IO. By October progress was such that the Court could be shown a proof printing. Since the note was not intended to be web-printed a watermark of the Queen's head could be used (for the first time on a Bank of England note). The issue date was 21 February 1964, the following detailed description being released, with the now customary black and white photographs, the day before:

> 'The main feature on the front of the note, which is predominately dark brown, is the portrait of Her Majesty The Queen, which is the same as that appearing on the current issue of £5 notes. The portrait is on the right-hand side of the note and is set in an asymmetrical frame.
> At the top of the note the words 'Bank of England' appear in italic capitals, with beneath them the words 'I Promise to pay the Bearer on Demand the Sum of' in italic script. The word 'Ten' is shown in heavily outlined letters, while the word 'Pounds' stands out boldly in dark brown lettering. At the top right- and bottom

left-hand corners of the note there is a figure '10' set in a machine-engraved pattern; elsewhere the words 'Bank of England' are repeated many times in micro-lettering. The picture of Britannia is a smaller version of that which appears on the reverse of the £5 note.

The general background of the note is made up of multi-colour patterns in which mauve and reddish tints appear. The cypher and number of the note are in black at the top left- and bottom right-hand corners.

The watermark for the first time consists of a portrait of Her Majesty The Queen. It appears on the left-hand side of the note and, unlike the watermark on the other notes of this series, is not repetitive, since it is not intended at present that the new note should be printed on continuous paper. The paper also incorporates a metal thread to the right of centre of the note.

The back of the note, which is also predominately brown, has machine-engraved geometric patterns some of which have been incorporated in a design of a lion holding a key. The words 'Ten Pounds' in capitals appear in a scroll issuing from the lion's mouth. The words 'Bank of England' appear in another scroll at the top of the note; as on the front of the note the '10' appears at the top right- and bottom left-hand corners.'

Reverse of Stone's £10 Series C

The critics sharpened their pens. Thus The *Daily Telegraph*'s view:

'The study of the curate's little daughter as Britannia in the parish pageant has been removed to the front, and so reduced in size that at first glance it has been mercifully overlooked. In its place is set a quadruped which is neither the leopard of England nor the lion of Scotland, but an amiable hybrid of vaguely Assyrian aspect, its tresses coiffed in the style popularised in Ptolemaic Egypt by Miss Elizabeth Taylor. It grins like a dog and seems prepared to run about the City. Insecurely clasped in what heralds would blazon as the creature's dexter paw, an instrument between a skewer and a paper knife is no doubt a parable of some mystery rightly withheld from the impecunious multitude... the whole thing is an unrelated clutter.'

Once again Vicky (*Evening Standard*) preferred his own design which featured a portrait of the Prime Minister, Sir Alec Douglas-Home. Early snipers in The *Daily Telegraph*'s letters column were answered within the same column: 'I couldn't care less

CHAPTER 14 Conception and Perception

It will be obvious by now that designers of banknotes all face the same perennial problem: to make money uneconomic to produce unofficially, taking account of the availability of technical advances in paper-making and printing processes, yet producing a document which the public will find pleasing to look at even if they argue about specific details of the subject matter itself. Throughout 300 years, as has already been described, Bank of England notes have proved to be a tempting target for the counterfeiter. The better forgeries of recent years have all used a lithoprint process (one of the best in terms of deception required at least 11 plates), sometimes with a thread but more often with this feature and the watermark each being represented by a printing or tinting process. Very often the forger destroys all his equipment before distributing his product. Even so, it is often possible, by a careful study of examples seized when uttered, for the specialists at the Bank's Printing Works to estimate how many were originally produced and how many, allowing for spoilage, may have actually been released into general circulation. Clues are often left behind in the finished product which point to the type of machinery used for printing and the preparatory work such as colour separation. This is of considerable assistance to the police, particularly if the equipment used is likely not to be generally of service for genuine commercial work. The main problems facing the Bank's team were the increasingly sensitive photographic films and equipment now available; simplified techniques for colour separation and plate-making; the widespread availability of accurate, small offset presses for commercial and office work; and, perhaps most worrying of all, the threat of technical progress towards the capability for colour copiers to deal efficiently with multicolour work: all of which would be of help to the prospective forger.

Commissioned to submit designs for the successor Series D, Eccleston set himself the task of creating a recognisable 'family' of notes. In an interview reproduced in *Moneymakers international* he explained that his aim for each note was to create a single, integrated design, not a collection of different parts, yet make the whole series have the same look and balance. He first tackled the 10s denomination, which was designated 'T' (for temporary, since it was thought that it might eventually be phased out in favour of a coin if decimalisation came about; in fact, the 10s Series D note was never issued – in 1969 the denomination was replaced by the 50 new pence coin). It was to be printed by the offset process and featured Sir Walter Raleigh on the reverse: the denomination both in words and in figures was capable of being altered to the decimal equivalent of fifty pence. The Britannia included in the front design was based on a version used by the Bank in 1802. The Queen was depicted wearing the hat and robes of the Order of the Garter. The portrait was unframed, a decision made for the whole series so that it could be made larger and more part of the whole design rather than an independent vignette. The promissory clause was smaller so that it could in need be removed without affecting the balance of the design. The principal colours were brown and orange. Even a quick glance at this design shows that it would indeed have been the forerunner of the Series D 'family'.

Reverse of Eccleston's unissued 10s
Series D

By March 1967 it had been redesignated from 'T' to 'D'. The Design Committee liked what they saw although one non-executive Director, Cecil King, asked why Raleigh, who had been executed for treason, had been selected as the subject. Eccleston did not explain why but said that in his opinion the execution reflected more on the King (James I) who ordered the execution than on Raleigh's behaviour! At the same meeting Eccleston proposed either Henry Purcell or Isaac Newton as a suitable subject for the £1 note. Newton was chosen.

About this time the Bank was anxious to issue a new £50 denomination as a matter of priority over the £20 D but in their reply nearly three months later the Treasury asked for the £20 note to be dealt with first.

Eccleston had, of course, been working out possible subjects for the whole series and was well advanced on a Newton design for the £1, which the Committee saw in July 1967. At that time, Anthony Blunt was one of the two (original) outside expert advisers. He thought that Newton looked 'overwhelmed' by the Universe but then reflected that such a reaction might be appropriate!

On 11 August 1967 the Decimal Currency Board recommended that the Government should issue a 50 pence coin. By now preparations were finalised to print the 10s D so the Bank was not best pleased at the delay which then occurred in the Government's making up its mind on the matter. A letter written in October was not answered until December. Eventually, on 9 February 1968 it was announced that a coin for 50 pence would be issued and the Bank immediately abandoned plans for the dual purpose 10s/50p note which was now in full production. No more 10s notes were issued by the Bank after 13 October 1969, the date on which the (50p) coin was first released. The note was called in on 20 November 1970 as it was felt desirable to take this action before actual decimalisation. On that date there were 32 million outstanding.

It was time now for the Bank to let the public know its plans for the new series, particularly since the sizes of each of the denominations were to be reduced. On 15 February 1968 it was announced that

'(the new) notes, which will bear a portrait of Her Majesty the Queen, will be generally smaller in size that those at present in issue. The first of the new series will be a £20 note, which will be issued by 1970; work is proceeding on its design, but no details are available at this stage. The popularity of the higher denominations has continued to grow, thereby securing economies in production. It is felt that this trend will be further assisted by the introduction of a £20 note.

There will be no 10s note in the new series. The existing 10s will continue to be issued until it is replaced by a new coin. Owing to the similarity of their sizes, the £1 note in the new series will be introduced only after the 10s note has been withdrawn. The £5 and £10 denominations will follow later'.

The approximate sizes of the new notes followed.

A month later the Design Committee were shown Eccleston's proposals for the £20 note, now to be the first of Series D following the demise of the 10s denomination. The proposed subject was Shakespeare and the choices lay between using the Marshall portrait or the Kent statue in Westminster Abbey with a scene from Midsummer Night's Dream, Henry V or Romeo and Juliet. There was little debate, there being a clear preference for the Kent statue combined with the balcony scene from Romeo and Juliet. At the end of the year the Committee considered the subjects for the £5 and £10 denominations. Among the principal names were George Stephenson or Brunel, Marlborough, Charles Dickens, Constable, Disraeli or Pitt, Wren and Nelson as well as the favoured couple: Wellington and Florence Nightingale. (Wren was selected later for the £50 D whilst Stephenson and Dickens survived to be adopted for the £5 and £10 Series E.) It had originally been intended to plan on the basis of issuing the new £5 note during 1973 but the seizure by the police, before it could be marketed, of a dangerous Series C forgery of this denomination, albeit with no thread or watermark, alerted the Bank to the vulnerability of Stone's design and a decision was made to advance the appearance of a replacement to 1971. On 15 May 1969 the Design Committee selected the winged Victory vignette for the front, in preference to a mosaic representation of Henry VIII from the Boris Anrep coin and medal designs in the main corridors at Head Office, and a portrait of Wellington on the reverse, which was based on an 1814 painting by Sir Thomas Lawrence (a representation much favoured by the current Wellington family). As a matter of courtesy, the 7th Duke of Wellington was advised in confidence of the Bank's intention to portray his famous ancestor.

On 10 December 1969 a final proof of the £20 note was sent to Buckingham Palace because it showed the Queen in a new portrait. The cypher 'E II R' had been included in a lozenge at the left shoulder and attracted royal disfavour. The preferred representation was the cypher approved for official usage. This incorporated a crown above the lettering but as such would create disharmony in the design. A week later the proof was resubmitted with the official cypher used without the crown. This was acceptable but the alteration caused a delay of about 6 weeks in the programme. It also made the Bank realise that it must not presume that it could afford to wait until this late stage in the future. The print run began, with Fforde's signature as Chief Cashier. It was agreed that these products should be issued in due course even though he was appointed an Executive Director and was replaced by J B Page as Chief Cashier with effect from 1 March 1970. (When the Printing Works switched production of the £1 Series C note to print Page's signature in place of Fforde's they did so without an adequate supply of blocks bearing the new signature. So that production was not lost they used spare Fforde signature blocks and this series' £1 is therefore found with a mixture of signatures among the early cyphers.)

In preparing for the issue of £20 and £10 notes it was decided that the system hitherto in use whereby any spoiled note was replaced by a specially numbered, so-called 'star', note[1] (bearing a special prefix) should be dropped. The faulty note would simply be withdrawn and the numerical run continued after the break. In the days of the 'white' notes any spoils were replaced by a note, numbered on an individual machine, bearing the same number as the faulty note. The Bank's collection has examples (of £5 and £100 notes) where the replacement note was incorrectly numbered, resulting in pairs of genuine notes with the same cypher and number.

The provisional date for Series D to be launched in the shape of the £20 note was 4 June 1970 but the Chancellor of the Exchequer was concerned that political capital might be made out of it during the General Election - a new high denomination note, the first £20 available since 1943, could indicate the course of inflation - and the Bank agreed to postpone its appearance until 9 July. The customary release was made the day before in which a note to editors explained that as the £20 was designed and the printing had begun during Fforde's term of office 'it is for this reason that his signature appears on the first issue'.

Front of £20 note Series D, signed by J S Fforde although J B Page had succeeded him as Chief Cashier when the note was first issued in 1970 (160 x 90mm)

Reverse of £20 Series D

The main feature on the front of the note, which was predominantly purple, was a new portrait of the Queen, on the right-hand side of the note and set in an asymmetrical frame. Also prominent was a vignette depicting 'St George and the Dragon' which appeared in the centre of the note. At the top of the note, as usual, the words 'Bank of England' appeared; beneath them, but much smaller, were the words of the promissory clause. In addition to the denomination in words and figures, the latter set in a machine-engraved pattern, the phrases '£20/Twenty Pounds' and 'Bank of England' were repeated in micro-lettering, in combination, at the foot of the note and beneath the 'St George and the Dragon'. A small vignette of Britannia was positioned at the foot of the note, to the left of the Chief Cashier's signature, printed in black. The general background of the note comprised multi-colour patterns in which gold, blue and green tints predominated. The cypher and number of the note, also in black, were printed at the top left- and bottom right-hand corners. The watermark, on the left-hand side of the note, consisted of a portrait of the Queen, the same as that used in the Series C £10 note. The paper also incorporated a thread to the right of centre of the note.

£10 Series C, signed by J B Page

The back of the note was also predominantly purple; the dominant features, as already noted, were a reproduction of the statue of Shakespeare from the Kent memorial in Westminster Abbey and a vignette depicting the balcony scene from 'Romeo and Juliet'. In addition to the denomination, again in words and figures, there were areas of machine-engraved geometric patterns.

The St George and the Dragon vignette was based on a 1640 'Lesser George' Badge of the Order of the Garter in the Victoria and Albert Museum. The three heads at the base of Shakespeare's pedestal were Queen Elizabeth I, Henry V and Richard III. Eccleston estimated he had spent about six months working on the design initially, half in research and half in preparing the master drawings.

The Times observed that the new note appeared 'to be quite a breakthrough' having been designed by a member of the Bank's staff and portraying a figure other than Britannia or the Queen. A letter published two days later pointed out four distinctive features and asked if it was fair to associate the Queen's portrait with such an unfortunate package:

a) a promise by the Bank which was not worth the paper it was written on;

b) a Saint recently banished from the Canonical Calendar for lack of historical authenticity;

c) a heraldic female symbolic of a bygone naval and colonial supremacy;

d) a Shakespeare play about civil riots, juvenile delinquency and fornication with a girl below the legal age of consent.

A response was immediately forthcoming from E M Kelly, of the Bank's Archive Section but writing from home:

a) Payment of a Bank of England note had never been refused since 1694;

b) The Established Church had never repudiated St George;

c) The 'heraldic figure' had no such symbols of supremacy and as the badge of the note-issuing authority was a logical addition;

£1 Series C, signed by J B Page

d) The play was about the folly of factional conflict and illustrated the disastrous results of opposing civil and parental authority. What was the age of consent in Italy in the 16th Century and could intercourse in marriage really be described as fornication?

With the new note safely launched and only muted public reaction (mainly to journalists proferring £20 in payment of a 3d bus fare) it was time to review the future programme. The £5 looked likely to be ready for August 1971 (it was actually issued three months later), the £1 in 1972 or 1973 (but it took 5 more years) whilst the £10 had an agreed subject (Florence Nightingale) but no design work had been put in hand. Progress with the £5 went fairly smoothly following a meeting on 3 April 1970 when the Design Committee examined a colour transparency of the battle scene, commended the portrait and approved the watermark. Some problems arose at a late stage with ink chemistry as the first sheets came off the automatic presses. On 17 May 1971 a final proof was despatched to Buckingham Palace where it was seen with approval. First issues to the public were made on 11 November 1971.

The main feature on the front of the note, which was predominantly blue, was a portrait of the Queen on the right-hand side in an asymmetrical frame. Also featured on the front were a vignette depicting a Winged Victory and a medallion of Britannia.

As usual the words 'Bank of England' appeared at the top of the note with, beneath them, but much smaller, the promissory clause. The denomination was incorporated in words and figures whilst use was again made of micro-lettering to repeat 'Bank of England Five Pounds' in combination along two ribbons at the bottom of the note below the Chief Cashier's signature, printed in black. The general background of the note comprised multi-coloured patterns in which gold, blue and red tints predominated. The cypher and number of the note were also printed in black.

The back of the note was also predominantly blue, the main features being a portrait of the first Duke of Wellington and a vignette depicting a battle scene of the Peninsular War. The denomination was repeated in words and figures and use again made of multi-coloured, machine engraved geometric patterns in areas of the design.

The watermark, on the left-hand side of the note viewed from the front, consisted of a series of heads of the same portrait of the Duke of Wellington, and the paper incorporated the customary thread, to the right of the centre.

As an example of the thoroughness of Eccleston's research into his subjects, here is his brief for the Bank's Press Officer on some individual aspects of his design:

Front of the £5 note Series D, issued in 1971 (145 x 78mm)

Reverse of £5 Series D, part of the designed being engraved

'Wellington Portrait
This is a new portrait which is based on the painting (dated 1814) by Sir Thomas Lawrence PRA, in the Wellington Museum, Apsley House, and on the engraving of a portrait by Baron Francois Pascal Simon Gerard in the British Museum collection (also dated 1814). The Duke is shown facing in the opposite direction to the Lawrence portrait, although the pose is similar.

Orders
He is wearing a military uniform with the Riband and star of the Order of the Garter (conferred in 1813), the Badge of the Order of the Bath (conferred in 1804) and the Badge of the Spanish Order of the Golden Fleece (conferred in 1812). The Order of the Golden Fleece is depicted, as in the Lawrence portrait, with the Fleece hanging the wrong way round. According to my notes, Wellington was presented with this reversed Badge by the Emperor Charles V of Spain. He was also given the Badge which originally belonged to the Duke de Bourbon (by the Duke's widow?) on which the Fleece hangs in the correct position.

Uniform
As Wellington became a Field-Marshal in 1813 and the uniform is almost identical to his Field-Marshal's uniform dated 1843, which is displayed in the Military Museum, Camberley, it is almost certain that the uniform which appears in both the Lawrence and Gerard portraits is that of a Field-Marshal. It is an interesting point, that officers of the period had considerable latitude in designing their own uniforms.

Battle Vignette - Peninsula Campaign, Battle of Fuentes de Onoro, 3 - 5 May 1811
The vignette is based on an illustration from 'Campaigns of Field-Marshal His Grace, the Most Noble Arthur, Duke of Wellington,' published by Calignani, Paris. It depicts an episode in the battle fought in and around the village of Fuentes de Onoro, when the French under Massena tried to relieve the blockade of Almeida. On the second day of the battle, General Pakenham came to see Wellington and the British 74th and 88th regiments counter-attacked through the village. These two events appear to have been combined in the illustration to provide the required military and artistic impact.

As the research into the subject proceeded, it was found that a considerable amount of modification to the original would be required. The book from which the engraving was taken, although dedicated to the Glory of Wellington, was produced in France and proved to be not particularly accurate on British military detail. The modifications on the note include the substitution of a British six pounder gun for a French gun and adjustments to certain of the uniforms.

Uniforms
The normal convention in military painting of dressing the combatants in clean

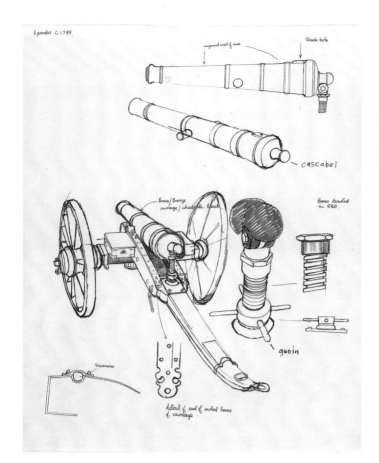

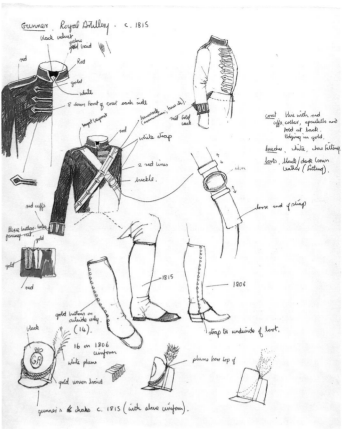

Preliminary sketches by H N Eccleston when researching background for the battle scene on the reverse of his £5 Series D note

uniforms has been followed, although it is known that by this stage in the campaign the uniforms were so tattered as to be scarcely identifiable. The colour of the uniforms is not accurate, because of the limitations of the printing process used.

Hats
Stove-pipe hats have been used in the note design. The Shako with the identifying plume on the side, introduced at Wellington's request to avoid confusion with the French, was not in use in 1811. Some authorities suggest that it never reached the Peninsula, although it was introduced in the last year of the war.

Winged Victory Vignette
The Winged Victory (Victoria Romana) was found to be the most common symbol of military prowess in use during the period. She appears, without the chariot, on the Waterloo medal, the Wellington Shield, the Portuguese Service and even as a small figure standing on the hand of the statue of Napoleon, by Canova - all in Apsley House.

The version with the chariot, although not so common, was also used. The vignette is based very loosely on one which decorates the base of a portrait engraving of the Duke by Thomas Martyn, (1815), in the British Museum collection, representing 'Victory in a car presenting the Laurel Crown to Wellington the Conqueror'.'

It is customary in distributing early numbers of new notes for the Prime Minister, ex-officio, to receive one. In acknowledging his, Edward Heath said he was 'glad to see one of my predecessors featuring on the back of the note, though I hope that our French friends will not misunderstand the depiction of what is clearly a major defeat for the French army'. Eccleston minuted internally that it was in fact a 'minor skirmish',

Reverse of £5 Series D, now lithoprinted (as indicated by the minute L). First issued in 1973

the defeat at Waterloo having been deliberately rejected. The *Scotsman* of 11 November 1971 best summarises Press comment. 'Why', it was asked, 'is the major part of the imagery on the note so belligerently militaristic ?... comes so appositely on the heels of our decision to join the Common Market ... looks as if the staid Old Lady of Threadneedle Street has been stirred to cock a snook at the Continentals'. *The Economist* suggested the design 'may not win prizes for artistic design but it is worth a blue ribbon for anti-counterfeit measures'.

Production pressures forced the Printing Works in March 1973 to propose that the back of the £5 should be printed wholly by offset processes, including a lithographic offset, instead of by direct plate printing. They were keen to distinguish such notes by an alteration to the design, for example replacing the coloured '£5' in the upper right corner on the reverse by an uncoloured value. Head Office were reluctant: the note had only been in issue for a short time and public criticism was feared. Reluctantly the resistance crumbled in the face of warnings that banknote printers internationally would support the line taken by Debden. In the end, the change was confined to the insertion of a minuscule 'L' in the lower left-hand corner of the reverse. The cyphers recommenced at 01A. The public had to be alerted and it was convenient that the time had come to call in Stone's Series C £5 since this would deflect too much attention from being given to the information about the change in the £5 D. The principal reason conveyed to the Press for the change was that it made it possible to bring other installed equipment into use to meet rising demand during the transition period in a continuing programme to re-equip the Printing Works with specialised machinery for web printing.

From the early 1960s those concerned in European central banks with banknote design and production had begun to discuss what helped the public to accept a note as genuine. A scientific approach to the problem of perception was still in its infancy. By the end of the decade some questions had been drawn up to provide a framework for further study:

1) What features did the public principally examine? was it the subject, the colour or shapes within the design?

2) What qualities were most clearly memorised? was it the general design, individual parts, the colour, the quality or feel of the paper?

3) When faced with a forgery was it easily perceived from memory of a genuine note or was comparison necessary?

Eccleston was closely associated with this work, helping to produce experimental designs such as a portrait head shown at different angles. Mis-registered and deliberately misprinted 'notes' were made and a total of 53 tests in all were subsequently evaluated. These included candid camera spying on cashiers in shops to learn their handling methods, films of sorting procedures and eye-cameras to record what parts of a note were actually looked at during the performance of various tasks.

Eccleston's artwork for part of the
hospital scene on the reverse of his £10
Series D note

Opposite page
Front of the £10 note Series D,
issued in 1975 (151 x 85mm).
Florence Nightingale's head was the
basis of the watermark
Reverse of £10 Series D

CHAPTER 15 Pounding the Pound

Although there was discussion at the end of 1973 on the possibility of printing the new £1 entirely by offset processes, the major effort was now centred on the £10 denomination. In August 1973 three trials of the reverse were examined, to one of which an Executive Director offered the observation that it looked more like a Turkish brothel than a Crimean War hospital scene. Finally, approval was given the following May when it was submitted to the Queen who reportedly found it 'very pleasing'. Production could now get under way, enabling the Design Committee to consider Eccleston's drawings for the reverse of the £1 Newton note. They gave the go-ahead for the dies to be cut for the front of this note. There was discussion, too, about transferring the £5 to web production and on the need to put in hand work on a reserve design for this denomination if web production for the £5 D proved not to be practical. The subject suggested was Christopher Wren or George Stephenson.

The £10 note was issued on 20 February 1975, preceded by the customary press release. The main design on the front, printed in brown, had the same portrait of the Queen in State Robes as was used on the £20 note. It also included a medallion of Britannia and the usual text together with the by now customary areas of machine-engraved work in which the denomination appeared. The remainder of the front of the note comprised multi-coloured patterns in predominantly orange and brown tints, including also a vignette derived from the Lily symbol used by Florence Nightingale.

The main feature on the back, also printed in brown, was a new portrait of Florence Nightingale, specially created for the note from photographs taken on her return from the Crimea. In addition, the back included a vignette printed in predominantly red and yellow tints and based on a lithograph of the time depicting her at the Barracks Hospital in Scutari. The remainder of the back consisted of areas of machine-engraved geometric patterns in various colours.

The Lily design on the front was derived from a water-colour, annotated 'Scutari'

and attributed to Florence Nightingale's sister Parthenope (Lady Verney). Although colour photographs would not have been of use to the Press at that time, for the first time specimen notes were made available by the Bank on loan for the use of television companies.

Yet again Eccleston's design brought praise from recipients of low numbered notes. The Prime Minister, Harold Wilson, thought it 'an elegant and attractive addition to the new range' whilst the Chancellor of the Exchequer, Denis Healey, spoke of it as 'a striking design which does credit to the Bank'. There was little public expression of opinion: perhaps they were unconsciously holding their ammunition back for the £1.

The success of the £20 note in being quickly adopted for transactional use by the public encouraged the Bank to raise again the question of a £50 denomination. In April 1975 the Treasury agreed that work could be put in hand and three months later the subject of the design and the size of the note were being discussed. The organisations involved most closely with the welfare of blind and near-blind people had, it may be recalled, indicated that no size difference was necessary between denominations of £20 and above. Consulted again, they changed their views and said that a £50 denomination ought really to be larger than the £20 note. By June 1976 the choice of subject lay between Wren, Elgar and J M W Turner. The then Governor's choice easily lay with Wren.

Front of Eccleston's £1 note Series D, issued in 1978 (135 x 67mm)

Reverse of £1 note Series D

Work on the Newton £1 was continuing on schedule. The decision to print only one number on each note was made in February 1977: the purpose was to enable space to be provided for encoding marks applied by bank note sorting machinery in the future. In July Buckingham Palace found the design entirely acceptable. Since many machines now accepted £1 notes (and therefore had to 'read' them) it was felt desirable to lend examples to manufacturers well in advance of the issue day. This meant earlier publicity than normal as evidenced by the release of a Press notice on 23 August 1977. The notice gave the size, predominant colour and printing method (offset-lithography); and also revealed the subject on the back as Newton and warned that only one serial number would be printed on each note. A more detailed description was released the day before the first notes were issued on 9 February 1978. The main design on the front, printed in green, showed the same portrait of the Queen as used on the £5 note. The usual text, a medallion of Britannia and areas of engraved work (in which the denomination appeared) were included. The remainder of the front of the note comprised multi-coloured patterns in predominantly yellow, green and blue, including a vignette of a design comprising a caduceus, cornucopia and an olive branch. This feature was based on a token commemorating Sir Isaac Newton, whose portrait appeared on the back of the note. Protective tints extended to all four edges of the front of the note.

The main feature on the back of the note was a new portrait in green of Newton, specially created for the note from a number of contemporary portraits. The remainder of the back consisted of multi-colour, machine-engraved patterns suggesting the solar system, overlaid by a geometric diagram from Newton's *Principia*.

The continuous watermark which ran down the note near the left hand side, seen from the front, was based on the same portrait head of Newton. The paper also incorporated the usual thread.

On this occasion Prime Minister James Callaghan repeated his predecessor's choice of 'elegant' to describe his reaction whilst conceding that the note was smaller than people were accustomed to using.

The Press had a field day (or two), almost every paper referring to the 'shrinking pound'. When the first announcement was made the *Daily Mirror's* view was that the 'only practical result of this meddling will be to unleash columns and columns of jocular letters to The Times and the Daily Telegraph about the price of apples and the force of gravity'. After issue date the *Daily Express* looked back to the days when 'Bank of England notes were magnificent sheets of finely watermarked paper large enough for wrapping up a small loaf ... The new currency is a gesture of humility tinged with masochism ... it sounds like a negotiable bus ticket with ideas above its station'. The *Evening News* reported a 'hostile reception from Londoners: toytown money'. Sir Hugh Casson, President of the Royal Academy, told the *Daily Mirror* 'it looks cheap, feels cheap and is cheap'. The inclusion of only one number soon had the press buzzing so loudly about the Bank's alleged error - suggesting that all the notes were to be called in and replaced by notes with two numbers - that an official denial had to be issued on 29 March, when the Press were given the reason for the appearance of only one number. There was much greater concern when £1 notes actually began to appear with the only number handwritten. It was then customary for notes which had missed being numbered to have the number written on them by checkers at the Printing Works, such notes normally being removed at a later stage of production. Several slipped the net, unfortunately. Already, however, the bell was beginning to toll for the £1 in note form. On 19 January 1978, Hollom (then Deputy Governor) had told a House of Commons Select Committee that the Bank hoped it would be possible eventually to move to a £1 coin.

Further discussions with representatives of the blind were initiated by the Printing Works early in 1979, although these were unlikely to affect the specification for the £50 D, the last of Eccleston's 'family'. Nevertheless, consideration needed to be given to the future development of the note issue and the successor series. Eccleston, appointed an OBE in 1979 and President of the Royal Society of Painter-Etchers and Engravers since 1975, already had the assistance of Roger Withington, who made the master drawing for the reverse of the £50 D (a task which took him over six months to

The original drawing prepared by
Roger Withington for the scene on the
reverse of the £50 Series D note

complete). Withington succeeded him as the Bank's designer in 1983. As focal point
for the meeting Debden suggested examination of

    i   a code contained in the intaglio print, similar to the devices used by the Belgian,
        Dutch and Swiss authorities;

   ii   coded dots in a varnish;

  iii the printing of bars in resin at intervals along the thread,

any of which might improve the ability of a blind or partially-sighted person to discriminate between values. The meeting was attended by representatives from the Royal National Institute for the Blind, St Dunstan's, the National Federation for the Blind in the United Kingdom and the National League of the Blind and Disabled. It was volunteered to them that an intaglio process was to be added to the existing £1 D in order to improve its feel. This revised £1 D was issued in 1981. At the meeting it was said that of 120,000 registered blind persons in this country 80% had 'guiding vision', ie some degree of peripheral vision but no reading ability. The most important indicator was variation in the height of notes, which could be measured against fixed marks on, for example, a till. Texture, in particular intaglio printing, was most valuable but not to everyone since a major cause of loss of vision - diabetes - also affected the sense of touch. Worn notes were a major problem and durability might benefit from further research. The representatives did not think that embossing would help, having handled examples of Dutch and Swiss currency which used a technique to raise features only .001/002 inches. Braille utilised a process which resulted in coding .016/018 inches high. An eventual result of this meeting was the inclusion in the Series E notes of a specific shape in each design to aid the partially-sighted - see Chapter 17.

Notes of the £1 and £10 denominations in Series C ceased to be legal tender on 31 May 1979. By June 1980 a new signature began to appear on £5 D notes, that of D H F Somerset who succeeded Page as Chief Cashier on 1 March 1980. His was also the first signature to be seen on a £50 note since Peppiatt's in 1943. Coincident with the release of this final denomination in Series D came the new version of the £1 incorporating an intaglio process on the front. Issue date was 20 March 1981 and the main points covered in the extensive Press notice the day before were as follows:

THE £50 NOTE

Design
Like the other denominations in the present series of Bank notes, the front of the new £50 note bears a portrait of Her Majesty The Queen and the back that of an historical figure; in this case, it is that of Sir Christopher Wren, whose design for St Paul's Cathedral has provided much additional subject matter for the note.

The portrait of Her Majesty in her State Robes is the same as that used on the present £20 and £10 notes. The portrait and the rest of the main front design (the lettering, a medallion of Britannia and areas of engraved work) are in multi-colour - olive green, brown and grey - instead of a single colour. The rest of the front of the note features a Phoenix based on a design by Sir Christopher Wren and also patterns derived from various design features of St Paul's. These backgrounds are printed mainly in orange, purple and ochre.

The main feature on the back of the note is the new portrait of Sir Christopher Wren, which was specially created for the note from contemporary portraits by J B Clostermann (1695) and Sir Godfrey Kneller (1711). The scene which forms a background to the portrait is based on a view of St Paul's from the River Thames as engraved by S & M Buck and published in 1749. St Paul's is also featured in the form of a floor plan and the design of the denomination guilloche which is developed from the wood carvings by Grinling Gibbons in the South Choir Aisle of the Cathedral. The rest of the back of the note is printed mainly in orange, blue and ochre. In the decorative sky, patterns from the Cathedral and a section from Flamsteed's 'Atlas Coelestis' of 1729 are combined to reflect Wren's interest in astronomy.

Front of Eccleston's £50 note Series D, issued in 1981   (169 x 95mm)

Reverse of £50 Series D. The original drawing of St Paul's and the London scene was done by Roger Withington

1 for slitting by a microprocessor-controlled laser.

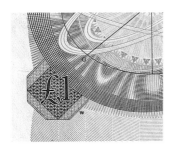

Apart from the engraving of the portraits, which was carried out by Mr Alan Dow of Bradbury Wilkinson and Company Limited of New Malden, all work on the preparation of the note has been carried out by staff of the Bank of England Printing Works.

Printing Processes and Security Features
The main front design including the portrait is printed by the intaglio process. The rest of the front of the note is printed by the offset process. On the back of the note the portrait of Sir Christopher Wren, the background scene and the features of St Paul's are printed in multi-coloured intaglio. The rest is printed by the offset process.

The watermark is a portrait of her Majesty the Queen and is the same as that used on the £20 note.

The note contains a new type of Security Thread. It is wider than the threads in the other denominations of Bank of England notes and has one edge contoured in a regular pattern. This contoured Security Thread is a Bank of England invention; the cutting of the thread was carried out on equipment[1] specially designed and manufactured for the Bank by the Culham Laboratory of the United Kingdom Atomic Energy Authority.

The note is slightly larger in both height and length than the £20 note. This is consistent with the Bank's policy of using differential note sizes as a means of assisting the blind to distinguish between denominations.

NEW VERSION OF THE £1 NOTE

Design

The overall appearance of the new version of the £1 note is little changed, but certain detailed features distinguish it from the existing note. On the front of the note, the portrait of Her Majesty is rather more sharply defined. On the back, the main print which includes the portrait of Sir Isaac Newton is rather more lively and is printed wholly in green. The general appearance is enhanced by the inclusion of additional background colours - mainly lilac, light green, yellow and pink. A small letter W (indicating Web printed) appears in the lower left-hand corner.

Printing Processes and Security Features
The new version of the note is being printed on Web presses similar to those used for production of £5 notes. These print the front main design by the intaglio process and the back by offset lithography.

Reverse of a web-printed £1 note Series D (indicated by the tiny letter W)

The serial numbers of the new £1 notes will commence with the cypher AN01 000001.

The intaglio printing (Her Majesty The Queen's portrait, the denomination guilloche and the lettering) is perceptible to the touch. It also gives the paper more of the traditional 'feel' of a Bank note.

Issue date coincided with a visit to the Printing Works by the Queen and the Duke of Edinburgh to celebrate the 25th Anniversary of the move out of St Luke's and the press showed photographs of them receiving the first two notes of each denomination from Governor Gordon Richardson. Within six months a shortage of supply of £50 notes was noticed. 'The Bank failed to anticipate its popularity' wrote *The Times*. The *Daily Telegraph* explained to its readers that it simply 'reflected the growth of the black economy'.

£20 note Series D, showing the improved 'stardust' or windowed thread; signed by D H F Somerset

Technical developments led to further changes in the Series D notes over the years, the first of which was to affect the appearance of the £20 Shakespeare from 15 November 1984. This had been the first note in this Series to appear and advantage needed to be taken of security features developed in the meantime for increasing resistance to counterfeiting. Although the predominant colour remained a purple shade, part of the intaglio design on the front and back was now printed in green and brown. Some re-drawing of the left-hand side of the front had also taken place to take advantage of improved printing techniques. The most significant change related to the security thread which, through a process called 'windowing', now appeared at intervals along the surface of the note. The process remains confidential and was developed by close co-operation between the Printing Works and Portals, the paper-makers. In

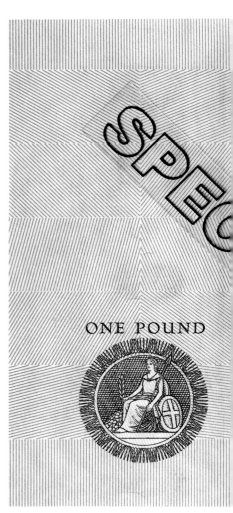

'Redundant': a sketch by Peter Brookes, published on 14 November 1984 in *The Times*, showing Sir Isaac Newton – no longer needed on the back of the £1 note – joining a Job Centre queue
© Peter Brookes/The Times, London

'One Pound': a sketch by Nicholas Garland, published on 13 November 1984 in The *Daily Telegraph* as a comment on the withdrawal of the £1 note. Chancellor of the Exchequer Nigel Lawson is depicted as an apple falling onto the head of Sir Isaac Newton
© The Telegraph PLC, 1984

normal handling the thread appears as an interrupted line on the surface but when held up to the light it appears as a continuous line. (A contoured thread, such as was included in the £50 note, was not available in sufficient quantity to be incorporated in other denominations.) Apart from the thread, the other main change was in the watermark where the head of Shakespeare replaced that of the Queen. The cyphers began at 01A.

New versions of the £5 and £10 notes were released to the public on 16 July 1987. On the former, the thread was doubled in width from 0.5 mm to 1.0 mm so as to make it more easily recognisable. On the latter there were minor changes to the background to the Queen's portrait and the thread was changed to a 'windowed' version as already introduced in the £20.

A pound coin was introduced by the Royal Mint in April 1983 and the Bank ceased to issue £1 notes at the end of the following year, when 600 million were outstanding. They were called in and ceased to be legal tender on 11 March 1988; some 70 million only remained outstanding when notice was finally given in December 1987.

BANK OF ENGLAND
PROMISE TO PAY THE BEARER ON DEMAND THE SUM OF

ONE POUND

£1

FOR THE GOV AND COMP OF THE BANK OF ENGLAND

CHIEF CASHIER

ER

DY21 999997

The last issued £1 note (the next two serial numbers were spoiled in production)

The last printing of the £1 had taken place on 30 November 1984 when the sole web press being used for this denomination was halted in a ceremony reminiscent of the 'banging out' procedure experienced by an apprentice completing his indentured time and attaining the status of journeyman. The scene was recorded in the Printing Works own house magazine, *Britannia Quarterly*. The machine was draped with the Union Flag. Black ties and armbands were worn by the crew as a sign of mourning and, in conformity with the traditional dress of yesteryear, the printers wore top hats. The female personnel made a black coffin and wreath. Shutdown was planned for 6 pm but 15 minutes earlier the web of paper broke. Fortunately the necessary repair was made just in time for the General Manager, G L Wheatley, to signal ceremonially for production to be officially halted. This order was accompanied by the cacophony of 'banging out'. The last ream was counted and placed in a black-draped cage, topped with the flag. One more 'bang out' and the cage was rolled away. Beneath the smiles and noisy ebullience there was considerable sadness both at the inevitable reduction in the workforce at Debden which would ensue but also at the fact that the national major unit of currency in the United Kingdom would no longer be produced by the Bank's printers after 56 years of continuous production (quite apart from the first efforts between 1797 and 1821).

Front of £50 Series D, signed by G M Gill and showing the windowed thread

Somerset retired at the end of February 1988, when he was replaced as Chief Cashier by G M Gill. In July of the same year the £50 note was altered, principally by the adoption of the windowed (or 'stardust' as it was sometimes called) thread but also by featuring new colours in various parts of the design such as the text, the Britannia symbol and the denomination numerals.

The design policy for Series D was aimed at the production of more colourful notes with greater visual impact on the public than the previous series had effected so that their attention was aroused to examine the notes more closely. In terms of protection against easy forgery, intaglio prints embodied the widest possible tonal range whilst the offset prints both protected the intaglio against photographic separation and gave areas of dominant multicolour patterns which diminished the success of monochrome forgeries. The potential forger was faced with the maximum amount of skilled handwork in stripping, retouching and redrawing.

It is worth pausing here and considering some of the detailed ideas incorporated in Eccleston's *magna opera*. In order of appearance, the £20 leads: here the use of machine rulings was made in order to frame the balcony scene with a coloured pattern suggestive of light coming up from the stage. On the £5, machine ruling has been utilised to form the flash of gunfire from the hand-engraved gun troop (dry-offset) in the distance beyond the hand-engraved, intaglio-printed Wellington. The £10 was a masterpiece of portraiture, contrived in such a way by the combined skills of Eccleston and Dow to draw attention to the face and, particularly, the eyes where imperfections were likely to appear in any counterfeit. Perspective was helped by the printing in flat colours of the hospital scene, leaving the impression that Florence Nightingale was standing in front of a stage. Machine ruled rays spread out from the lamp and illuminated the scene. The £1 note did not lend itself to this noble treatment but use was made of machine ruling to suggest the solar system and to represent geometric patterns which were part of Newton's work.

The £50 note is in a class of its own for the quality of the architectural drawing on the reverse side. For the river scene, Roger Withington (the Bank's Designer who produced the master drawing) had originally intended to copy an engraving of 1749 by S and M Buck which illustrated the River Thames and its waterfront, concentrating on the section covering the City of London houses and churches. By comparing this with modern photographs, he discovered many surviving buildings had been incorrectly sited by the Bucks. He then examined early prints etc to discover, for example, how ships were rigged. Finally he set himself upon the six month task of producing his master drawing which Dow translated onto metal (as he did Wren's

The first £1 million 'giant' note printed. Prepared in 1968 it bears the signature of J S Fforde. This is now the only denomination in use for solely internal reasons

portrait). An example of the detail in the design is the dog at the prow of the rowing-boat in the foreground. St Paul's Cathedral was engraved for offset printing by Wicks, the sky and the symbols of astronomy were machine-ruled by Brian Cruse whilst Alan Lye completed the remaining engraving. A notable feature is the way in which the intaglio foreground merges with the offset St Paul's and the machine-ruled sky.

One addition to the range of the Bank's notes which did *not* result from Eccleston's drawing board during the creation of Series D was that of £1 million. It had become necessary, through normal wear and tear, for existing 'Giant' notes to be replaced in July 1966 by a fresh printing of 2,000 @ £100,000 and also 500 @ £1,000. These were used for internal purposes, as described earlier (page 112), and bore Fforde's signature. In May 1968 a proposal was made to introduce £1 million notes in order to save space and time both of which had reflected inflationary trends in the Scottish and Northern Irish note issues. Because it was necessary to regard 'Giants' as having been issued within the meaning of the Currency and Bank Notes Act 1954, the Bank had to obtain the approval of the Treasury to the new denomination. This was forthcoming and an initial supply was printed with the date 1 August 1968 and, again, bearing Fforde's signature. The cypher was 01M. They carried the customary overprint which limited their use to internal Bank purposes only. The public first saw them – probably without noticing – in a scene showing them being checked in the Bank's Issue Office, as part of a publicity film. Further printings were ordered in 1975, 1977, 1982 and 1993. They currently bear the signature of G E A Kentfield but no longer carry the overprint[2]. The £1 million is now the only 'Giant' denomination available.

2 It was decided that the change of definition of 'banknotes' – from 'a note of the Bank of England' in the Currency and Bank Notes Act 1928 to 'notes of the Bank of England payable to the bearer on demand' in the Currency and Bank Notes Act 1954 – made this change desirable.

This lifting of the veil on matters hitherto regarded as secret was just one of a number of moves by the Bank to let the public know more about the note issue, in particular the creation of new designs. In 1982 the first detailed treatment appeared in Clive Goodacre's 'The Search for the Inimitable Note' which was an integral part of the *Penrose 1982* annual international review of the graphic arts. In 1987, in partnership with the British Museum, the Bank sponsored an exhibition 'As Good as Gold' on the subject of bank note design, and an accompanying illustrated book. The Printing Works, whose General Manager since 1987 has been Alex Jarvis, co-operated with seven other central bank or Government printers to produce *Moneymakers international* in 1989, lavishly illustrated with original artwork, printing techniques and finished products. When Series E began to appear, so did individual monographs of each of the new notes.

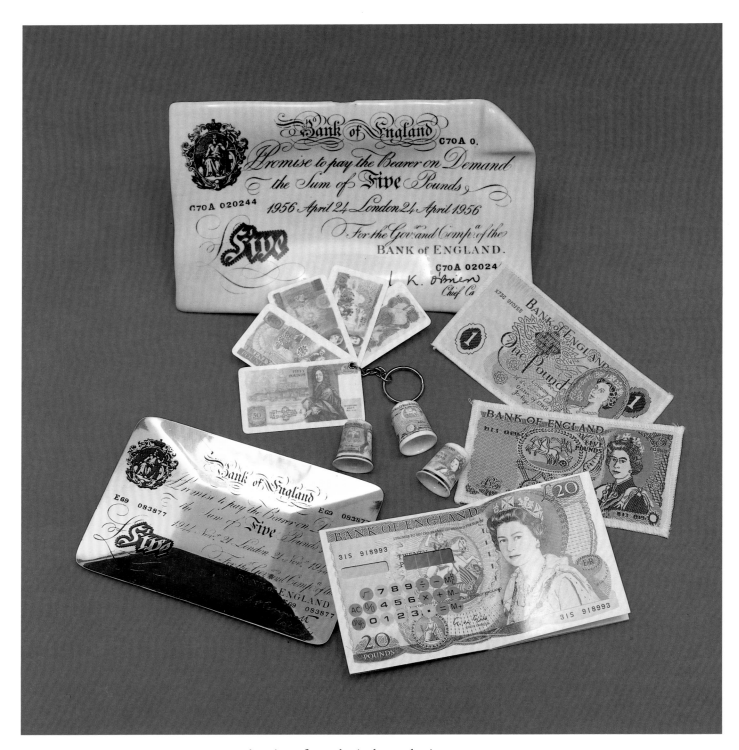

A variety of unauthorised reproductions
of Bank of England note designs on
modern commercial items: splash
patches, thimbles, key ring, ashtray,
copper tray and pocket calculator

CHAPTER 16　Facts of Life

In 1819, in a return to Parliament presented by Thomas Rippon but signed by Chief Cashier Hase, the Bank submitted calculations 'as far as it can be made out with a view to ascertain the number of days that a Bank Note of each denomination remained in circulation' in 1792 and 1818 - an early assessment of the life of a note. Not surprisingly, the lower sums circulated among the public far longer than did higher values which more quickly returned to the Bank's counters, being of limited general use. Hase's returns compare as follows

Life in days

Denomination	1792	1818
£1 and £2	N/A	147
£5	N/A	148
£10	236	137
£15	114	66
£20	209	121
£25	74	43
£30	95	55
£40	65	38
£50	124	72
£100	84	49
£200	31	18
£300	24	14
£500	24	14
£1,000	22	13

Although there was a shorter life expectancy for a note at the end of the 26-year period between the two dates, the proportion which each denomination above £5 bore to the total of the average days for those higher denominations was virtually unchanged. The Bank itself has very rarely reissued notes and when it did they were only of the lowest denomination of the black and white series. Some notes hardly had time to breathe, as it were: as recently as in the 1960's notes drawn by a customer at Head Office would not necessarily survive longer than it took a messenger to walk up two flights of stairs and purchase foreign currency notes from a special counter manned by the then Dealing and Accounts Office staff, where the sterling notes were promptly cancelled and joined others awaiting destruction.

As equally important as producing notes difficult to forge successfully is the method used to destroy them at the end of their useful life. Incineration was used for many years until the installation of a pulping machine in the Printing Department. The latter yielded to a guillotine with the special facility of shaving the paper automatically. In use at the beginning of the First World War, it could not cope with a large backlog of work, however, and this had to be burned at Peak Frean's biscuit factory in 1915. Outside facilities such as this demanded added security measures which required the highest co-operation from the company concerned; they were used, therefore, only as a last resort. No such problems attended the use of the Bank's Record Office at Roehampton for the same purpose.

The installation at St Luke's in the 1920s of 'Miracle Mills' enabled up to half a ton of notes to be converted each day into dry pulp for which there was only a limited commercial off-take (including the manufacture of toilet paper), but this expanded once a method of de-inking the pulp by using a caustic soda solution had been perfected. During the paper shortage after the Second World War various companies were persuaded to take the cancelled notes and manufacture their own pulp, although the Bank's stringent security requirements were always upsetting relations. When the paper situation eased in the mid-1950s these companies were quick to inform the Bank that they were no longer able to use the material economically. A useful source of revenue, which offset in a small way the costs of the note issue, was therefore shut off. In the autumn of 1957 the Treasury were advised that other methods of destruction would have to be developed. Until the completion of the construction of the necessary incinerators at Debden (from 1961) cremation took place primarily at Battersea and Fulham power stations. Partially burnt notes occasionally escaped the screening processes and were picked up by the public but never to any alarming extent. Today, all used notes are sent for granulation by an environmentally-friendly disintegrator.

By the mid-1960's the continued rise in the note circulation combined with a shorter life expectancy for notes (due to the velocity with which they passed from hand to hand) to put extreme pressure on the capacity of the Printing Works to satisfy demand. It was estimated that at this time a 10s note was surviving for only five months before it needed replacing, the £1 for a bare nine months, compared to 19 months nine years earlier, and the £5 for 15 months. In the Bank's view these lives could be lengthened if garbling (sorting) at the local branches of commercial banks was improved. The problem, the Bank felt, lay in the calibre of staff, the increasing use of counting machines (which demanded clean and crisp notes), the habit of some large customers to pre-pack their pay-ins to the banks - which were not then re-checked - and the insistence by some large, influential customers on having only new notes issued to them (particularly for making up wage packets). In comparison with other countries the public was being 'wildly extravagant' with banknotes. This was Hollom's view expressed at a meeting with the clearing banks early in 1966 when, as Chief Cashier, he sought solutions to the problem.

One possibility was for the banks to persuade their customers to accept used notes rather than new ones and to take the higher denominations - though it was recognised that the latter would required a change in the national habit. The banks could assist by themselves transferring surplus stocks to other note centres who were short, rather than pay surpluses in to the Bank of England or its branches. To assist the commercial banks, facilities would be reopened whereby they could pay in reissuable notes to a special store on which they could draw when needing further supplies. As a fall-back it might be necessary to ration the supply of new 10s and £1 notes. A suggestion which was in the event followed up was that the Bank should declare a 'moratorium' on the issue of new notes for certain periods of the year. To divert the sting from the banking system, it was further agreed that the Bank would publicise the measure itself and provide the commercial banks with posters to display each branch.

A useful opportunity to alert the public to the problem came with the publication of the March 1966 issue of the Bank's *Quarterly Bulletin* which carried an article on the soaring costs of the note issue following the rapid increase in demand. 'The Old Lady worries about her dirty notes' headed the City column of the *Daily Mail* on 6 March 1966: '... the Old Lady is very cross at the way we are no longer keeping banknotes in wallets and purses but squeezing, crushing and stuffing them into our pockets where they quickly get as grimy as our coins'. The Bank simultaneously gave notice that in the interests of economy it had become necessary to limit the issue of 10s and £1 notes and 'on occasion no new 10s and £1 notes will be available'. The notice ended with the request that customers be 'ready to accept used notes' and that they should 'ask for some £5 and £10 notes whenever possible.'

Shortly afterwards, the Bank again met the clearing banks and discussed the possibility of a short, experimental moratorium in early July 1966 with a two week follow-up two or three months later and perhaps a longer period after Christmas (when notes naturally flowed back from the public). It was agreed to fix the first period from 27 June to 9 July 1966 inclusive. In reviewing the event with the banks in September it was agreed that the first period had been an outstanding success. A very substantial decline in the number of new notes issued had occurred and the reduction in demand had in fact continued. From the front line position - branch counters - it was reported that few complaints had been received: most of these related to 10s notes in poor condition. Even so, the banks hoped that the Bank would continue its publicity campaign to make (or keep) the public aware of the reasons (and divert criticism away from them). The two further periods of moratoria were fixed for 24 October to 5 November 1966 and 9-28 January 1967. After the last of these three initial periods the Bank was able to report a 25% saving in new note issues (quantified as 425 million notes).

A sympathetic article by Margaret Reid appeared on the subject in the *Observer* on 4 June 1967. "The cashier winced 'Sorry, madam, old notes today. Bank of England orders' ''. She had spoken to a number of companies who were having to cope with making up wage packets during moratoria. The preference for new notes, aside from the aesthetic pleasure of handling a clean piece of money, had a more practical reason: consecutive numbering made checking easier. Perhaps the Bank should take a tougher line, the article continued, exercise its monopoly and restrict output and issue even further. 'But offered a choice between no new small denomination paper or old notes I think everyone ... would opt for the old notes which never reached the furnace'.

Another spectre, however, was to loom on the horizon: technical progress. In its Annual Report for 1984 the Bank noted that 'The clearing banks and other large users of notes have continued to co-operate in reducing the demand for new notes by drawing used notes when practicable. However, their increasing need for new notes to use in cash dispensing machines has had a marked effect on the drawings of such notes, particularly of £10 notes which doubled this year compared with last. In order to reduce the need to destroy notes which are still in good condition, the Bank is installing a number of high-speed note sorting machines; these will count and verify the notes and outsort those that are of sufficiently good quality to reissue to the general public through cash dispensing machines'. Two years later, the Annual Report was forced to admit that 'the continued growth of customers' drawings of notes from cash dispensers and automated teller machines, and the installation of new or enlarged networks of such machines by banks, building societies and other financial institutions, have led to an ever-increasing demand for good quality used notes (which) has been increasingly met by the automated sorting of used notes by the main note-handling banks and by the Bank of England'.

Some notes seem to live forever, by contrast: many held as curios and in collections will probably never be presented to the Bank for repayment of the face value, being regarded as worth more to collectors; others will have been destroyed in circumstances where no claim was possible. For example, many notes must have perished along with their owners during the bombing raids of the Second World War. Until 1968, the Bank included a table in its Annual Report which detailed the value of notes in circulation, by denomination up to £1,000. At the end of February 1968, according to the Bank's records, the approximate total number of unpresented black and white notes was as follows (the £5 and £10 totals by then included the Series B and C issues and are therefore omitted here)

£ 20	7,800
£ 50	5,540
£ 100	4,910
£ 500	78
£1,000	63

Since then, up to the end of September 1993, 480 £20 notes, 647 £50 notes, 441 £100 notes, 8 £500 notes and 2 £1,000 notes have been paid off. In addition, two of the £200 denomination (withdrawn in 1928) were paid, one in 1969 and another in 1973.

But it is not just fair wear and tear which normally take their toll of the lives of banknotes. Carelessness and dishonesty have a minor role, too. Examples of some of the claims made on the Bank in respect of notes mutilated or lost by the public have already been given in this brief history. Whilst there were registers of notes in existence, the process of stopping payment of a note was relatively straightforward to administer. Where only part of a note remained, the registers would reveal if a claim in respect of the rest had already been accepted by the Bank. No part payments were made on an individual note (which is the practice in some other countries: for example, half the face value will be paid out on half a note). The addition of a third number in 1903 had facilitated the procedure for dealing with claims. A refinement of public benefit, introduced in 1844, whereby the counterpart of lost notes of £100 and over was

CLEARER

£15 LONDON
£25 LONDON
£30 LONDON
£40 LONDON
£5 £10 £20 } DEFUNCT
£50 £100 } BRANCHES
£30 BRANCHES (INCL. DEFUNCT)
£40 BRANCHES (INCL. DEFUNCT)
£100 LONDON
£100 BRANCHES
£200 LONDON
£300 LONDON
£500 LONDON
£500 BRANCHES
£1000 LONDON

One of the last remaining volumes of Clearers, which are still occasionally used when old black and white notes are presented for payment to the Bank's Issue Office

invested and the interest paid to the claimant pending the expiry of a waiting period, was withdrawn by Order of the Court of Directors in 1910.

On rare occasions (only 19 instances between 1876 and 1928), an *ex gratia* payment of a claim was authorised by the Court or, later, the Governor where the lost or destroyed notes could not be identified (most claimants, if they could not produce any part of the note(s) concerned in their application, at least had a record of the serial numbers and could register a stop). Among the successful claimants were 'an Irish servant of humble means', 'a poor widow' and an unfortunate man whose life savings of £100 had been 'torn up and burnt by wife while temporarily insane': the Bank allowed him only £50 though!

Some banks must have believed that the Old Lady of Threadneedle Street was so isolated within her island site in London as to be unaware of the ways of the world outside, in spite of her great age. An applicant for payment of a mutilated £5 note explained that he had received it three months earlier on a bowling green during 'wet conditions'; he had placed it in a pocket with keys, which caused crushing. His branch bankers (at Farnworth) assured the Bank, when forwarding their customer's claim, that he was 'an eminently respectable man and quite trustworthy'. They found it necessary, however, to add that 'His business takes him on to the various Bowling Greens in all states of weather – in Lancashire these are one of the principal meeting places for the working classes and the matches are played irrespective of weather'. Any doubt which may have been harboured by the Bank was suitably washed away and their customer duly received payment.

By 1928, when the 10s and £1 notes were issued, without registers being established, the basic rules for the treatment of mutilated or destroyed notes of £5 and above were as follows:

1 Slightly mutilated: paid on presentation;

2 Severely mutilated but more than half remaining: usually paid under a bank or insurance company indemnity;

3 Half note presented, other half alleged lost or destroyed: paid after two months subject to a statutory declaration and indemnity being submitted.

4 Destroyed notes: with satisfactory evidence and subject to a statutory declaration and indemnity, paid after twelve months.

5 Missing, but no evidence of destruction: with a statutory declaration and an indemnity, payment made after five years.

The rules for the two smaller denominations, newly issued, required more complex specification:

1   Mutilated: paid forthwith where more than one half remained, on an

undivided portion of which the promissory clause appeared, together with at least one-third of the signature and one complete print of the series index (cypher) and serial number (not necessarily all in one corner together), with at least one other whole letter or figure from the other cypher/number.

2 Mutilated but without a complete print of the cypher/number: paid on presentation, subject to an indemnity given by the owner (and, of course, subject to the missing portion not having already been accepted and paid).

3 Other mutilated and identifiable: paid at discretion after a certain time had elapsed. Satisfactory evidence of destruction was required and an indemnity.

4 Unidentifiable: paid only when conclusive evidence of destruction was given with an indemnity.

5 No identifiable fragments: payment always refused.

The Bank's current practice is set out in an article in its *Quarterly Bulletin* for August 1989. Before the withdrawal from circulation of the 10s and £1 notes the total annual number of applications relating to mutilated notes had peaked in the early 1970s at about 180,000 shortly before the work was decentralised to the Bank's Newcastle Branch. The maximum staff involvement then was around 50, by 1989 it had been reduced to only six people, then processing about 27,000 claims covering some £800,000 each year. (They refer to themselves as the Bank's 'Mutilated Ladies'.) Authority has been delegated to banks and post offices to pay mutilated notes which broadly conform to

Nearly 40 years combined experience is brought to bear at the Bank's Newcastle-upon-Tyne Branch by Sylvia Straker (standing) and Maureen Howell in considering a mutilated note claim

Checking the thread of a damaged Series E £10 note

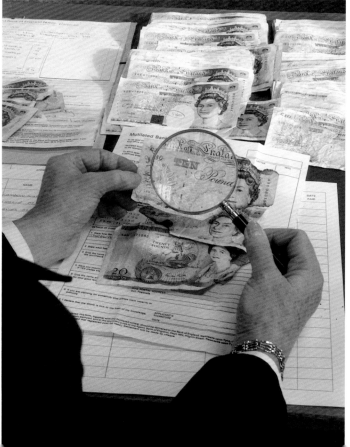

the first specification laid down in 1928: there must not be more than four fragments involved and *two* additional whole letter/numbers are now required, otherwise the conditions are the same as were originally applied by the Bank itself.

All other claims must be investigated by the 'Mutilated Ladies'. Decisions 'depend upon such factors as the fragments available, the evidence of the destruction of the remainder, the possibility of identifying the notes, the consistency of the account of the damage with the state of the fragments and, in the cases involving more than one note, the condition of the others'. Payment is sometimes made immediately, sometimes it is deferred for up to six months if there is the possibility of a second claim being received. If complementary parts are received from different persons each applicant is informed of the name and address of the other and the fragments, stamped 'valueless without other portion', are returned to the respective claimants. Hopefully they will agree that one will submit the claim and divide the proceeds or the other withdraw from contention, surrendering his or her fragments. The metal thread is not prima facie evidence of a destroyed banknote and sometimes it is necessary to seek expert examination by the Bank's Printing Works (where a special Mutilated Note Section was established many years ago) of the ash, or other remains, sent in, sometimes for forensic use. The rule that no identifiable remains means no payment is unchanged.

Claims over the years for notes damaged or lost through disasters are sadly not uncommon. Apart from the *Titanic* affair many instances have occurred where notes have been lost due to ships sinking in bad weather or through enemy action. Claims have related to material 'irretrievably lost' which has subsequently been recovered in more peaceful times or thanks to improved methods of salvage. Special arrangement existed for the disposal of notes discovered when the bodies of service personnel were being retrieved for burial during the Second World War. Great care needs to be exercised in dealing with notes contaminated by body fluids and noxious substances. The *Bulletin* article concluded with this description of accidental damage caused to the Bank's notes, some of which are reminiscent of the Bank's very early experiences:

'Other explanations for damage range from the bizarre to the mundane. The appetite of almost every conceivable household pet has been blamed when accidental damage has been caused. Some of the more unusual animals involved in eating notes have been camels and ferrets and many of the explanations of how the damage occurred are so strange that they seem unlikely to have been invented. Fire and water, however, account for damage to a large number of the notes which reach the Bank and the circumstances can be classified generally as accidental ('note fell from mantlepiece on to open fire') or as involving ill-judged attempts at storage or concealment – the remains of rotted notes which have been hidden under floorboards or buried in the garden are presented regularly. The number of people who choose to protect notes from burglars by hiding them in the oven – and these days, in the microwave – never fails to bring a smile to the faces of those whose job it is to sort out the ashes left after an unsuspecting person has attempted to cook the dinner. Flood damage, caused by adverse weather or leaking pipes, is also common and quite large quantities of soggy notes are retrieved from floor safes affected in this way. Many notes are discovered either when the washing machine breaks down (usually because of the amount of Bank note paper wedged in the pump!) or when the ironing is being done. It is as true today as in 1963[1] that some of the products of detergent manufacturers could claim, among their other characteristics, the ability to

1 the date of an earlier *Quarterly Bulletin* article on the subject

reduce a Bank note to a white sheet of paper.

Although the Bank's work in meeting claims for accidentally damaged notes has fallen over the last twenty years, the propensity of the public (and, in some cases today, machines) to do strange things to Bank notes remains undiminished. There is consequently every reason to believe that the need for this service will continue for a long time to come'.

The first limitation on the Bank of England's ability to issue notes which were secured on assets other than gold coin or gold and silver bullion (the portion now referred to as the Fiduciary Issue) was laid down in the Bank Charter Act of 1844. This was an acknowledged compromise between two conflicting schools of thought: the 'Currency' school theorised that the note issue should vary directly, and only, with movements of gold into and out of the country; the 'Banking' school's argument was that notes were just one form of credit instrument like deposits, bills of exchange and coins and that it would be without purpose to restrict the issue of notes because there would be an inevitable increase in the other categories to compensate. The 1844 Act laid down that the Fiduciary Issue was not to exceed £14 million, subject to the proviso that by Order in Council it might be increased by up to two-thirds of the amount of the authorised issue of any other bank in England and Wales which thereafter ceased to issue its own notes. Under this proviso the limit had been raised gradually to £18.45 million by the outbreak of the First World War and to £19.75 million when the last country bank withdrew.

It had, however, been prudent on three occasions – 1847, 1857 and 1866 – for the Government to release the Bank from the statutory limit in view of the development of extreme conditions of monetary stringency, although only in 1857 was it necessary actually to take advantage of the suspension of the limit. Under the Currency and Bank Notes Act of 1914 the Treasury were, as has already been described, authorised to issue 10s and £1 notes without limit of amount and without gold backing. They were also empowered to release the Bank from the statutory limit on the Fiduciary Issue. Nevertheless, the underlying idea of a link between the amount of the gold reserve and the size of the note issue was not abandoned but, rather, regarded as in abeyance. Governor Montagu Norman, in the much-changed economic climate of the post-war period, was anxious to re-establish the disciplines of the gold standard over monetary policy but was equally anxious to minimise public discussion which would arise whenever a change in the Fiduciary Issue was deemed necessary, even if only temporary. The Currency and Bank Notes Act of 1928 gave him his opportunity. Primarily designed to provide the legal basis for the Bank's assumption of responsibility for the issue of the 10s and £1 denominations, it set a new Fiduciary Issue limitation of £260 million (inevitably, in order to accommodate the transfer to the Bank of the Treasury's Currency Note responsibilities) but more importantly, in Norman's eyes, this limit was no longer rigidly fixed. The Treasury was given powers to increase the limit for periods not exceeding six months; such increases could be extended on the same authority for a total period of two years but any further extension required Parliamentary approval.

The link with gold was broken in 1931 when the Gold Standard (Amendment) Act entered the Statute Book and abrogated the public's right to demand gold from the

Bank at a fixed price. It was not until 1939, however, that all the gold in the Issue Department (save for a token amount of gold coinage, which continued to be held up to August 1970) was transferred to the Exchange Equalisation Account, thereby making the level of the Fiduciary Issue equal to that of the notes actually in circulation or held by the Banking Department. With the coming of war again in 1939, provision was made in the Defence Regulations for the suspension of the need for Parliamentary approval if the limit was increased for more than two years. A return to a statutory limit was made in the Currency and Bank Notes Act of 1954, which set the limit on the Fiduciary Issue at £1,575 million. The Act retained the flexibility of the 1928 Act by authorising the Treasury to direct an increase in the limit to such amount as was agreed between the Treasury and the Bank; such directions would follow from representations by the latter in the light of the current state of the note issue and forecasts of seasonal demands, particularly at Christmas. As before, Parliamentary approval was necessary if the increase over £1,575 million was required to extend beyond two years.

In practical day-to-day operations the Issue Department plays an essentially passive role in the supply of banknotes, as it has done for many years past, simply responding without question to public demand. Since the passing of the Currency Act 1983, the Bank has had sole responsibility for setting the daily level of the Fiduciary Issue, within the limit specified in that Act: '£13,500 million or such other amount as may from time to time be specified in a direction given by the Treasury'. Any increases must not exceed the previous limit by more than 25% ('previous limit' is defined as the limit in force two years earlier). A copy of the relevant Treasury Minute is laid before each House of Parliament.

The first increase became necessary during the run-up to the Christmas peak in 1984, the total being raised to £15,000 million (the actual maximum reached was £13,900 million). Subsequent increases for similar reasons were made just before Christmas in each of 1986 (to £16,500 million, actual £14,700 million), 1988 (to £18,750 million, peak £16,554 million) and 1990 (to £20,600 million, peak £18,400 million).

Since it is only the total of *issued* notes which is affected by the limitation of the 1983 Act it has no effect on the store of printed notes which it is necessary to maintain in order to replace soiled notes in circulation and to cope with seasonal, or unexpected, increases in demand. In other words, a store of printed security paper can be freely maintained by the Bank (subject only to constraints of space and of prudent budgeting, so as not to tie up the financing of printing costs) and only becomes banknotes when paid for to the Issue Department by the Banking Department.

The 1983 Act also made provision for a more rapid writing off of 'Dead Notes', that is, unpresented bank notes which have ceased to be legal tender. Under the Bank Act of 1892 writing off was authorised in respect of such notes which had been issued more than 40 years earlier. In the case of the old black and white notes, which carried dates, it was a simple matter to write off a note dated 1910 in 1950 but in the case of the first 10s and £1 notes writing off could not be effected until 40 years after the last note in the series had been issued, ie in 2001 and 2000 respectively. This delayed unnecessarily the transfer of the 'profit' to the Treasury (notes written off under this provision are credited to a profit account, the balance on which is absorbed by the Exchequer). Since payment of Bank of England (and Treasury) notes is not limited by time, the Bank recoups the cost of paying any dead note, which is subsequently presented for payment, by passing a debit to the profit account. The Currency Act 1983 reduced the waiting period to only 10 years.

The Bank has always been sensitive about the reproduction of its notes in any form and for many years was able to rely on the specific protection laid down in Acts of Parliament. Obviously, no one would challenge the concept of protecting the public against unofficial copies (forgeries, in other words) circulating as the genuine article but there is a recognisable difference between such criminal activity, where the copy is meant to look in all respects like the genuine article, and a highly enlarged or very small replica intended to assist in advertising a product or service. Until 1946 there was little flexibility in the Bank's attitude, even its own notes were launched in 1928 without any photographs being permitted. Certainly, no reproduction was sanctioned under the two governing acts, the Forgery Act 1913 and the Criminal Justice Act 1925. Nevertheless copies were made for innocent purposes which had subsequently been used to defraud and it was therefore the Bank's unwavering practice to take action whenever the law was breached, demanding destruction or surrender of the offending material. Unfortunately, the 1913 Act required an 'intent to defraud' and the later statute a calculation 'to deceive' before action in the Courts could be prosecuted successfully.

There was at the same time increasing pressure from advertisers to be allowed to use banknotes, or part of them, in certain campaigns. With the Treasury's agreement, therefore, the Bank let it be known that it would no longer object to reproductions which could not be passed off as genuine notes. The general guidelines given to the Advertising Association included the stipulation that the size must be larger or smaller than the real note, that it must be shown at an oblique angle, curled or partly overprinted and preferably in black and white. Needless to say all preparatory materials had to be destroyed after use. Permission was refused if the purpose was to make a purely commercial item (such as a black and white £5 design on a copper tray, a miniature Wellington £5 as a splash patch or a £1 note tea towel) or if the advertisement was demeaning to the currency, a feature of increased importance once the royal portrait was in use. As a later development, when it seemed reasonable to permit reproduction of notes for educational purposes, the Bank insisted on the copy being overprinted 'Specimen' even if the note concerned was no longer usable as money.

Film producers before the Second World War were supplied with dummy notes by St Luke's but this practice did not survive after the end of hostilities. As a result producers had to seek the Bank's permission to portray real notes on film or to get their agreement that the 'notes' which they had prepared were not so like real ones as to incur the Bank's wrath yet would fool the cinema audience.

The Bank allowed the production of a £1,000,000 note for a film of the same title, which starred Gregory Peck. Dimensions were approximately 9" x 7", much larger than any genuine Bank note of any age. Only a few copies were actually printed, one

The £1 million 'note' which the Bank allowed to be prepared and used for the film of that name

being in the Bank's Archive. Unfortunately for the J Arthur Rank Organisation, posters advertising the film also featured the note (in a smaller version), contrary to the Bank's ruling. As a result all the posters had to have the offending area covered over, a matter widely reported on in the press on 9 January 1954.

When the question of issuing official photographs of the new £1 note in 1960 was raised the Bank began to take a more relaxed attitude to the reproduction of its notes in books and magazines though sticking strictly to a ban on their use for political propaganda and, naturally, adhering also to the condition that the reproduction could not be removed and used fraudulently. The Bank authorities handling applications for permission to reproduce its notes found it at times embarrassing to be the arbiters of what was, or was not, permissible under the 1913 and 1925 Acts, and the Treasury were approached as to the possibility of drafting an appropriate section for inclusion in new legislation in 1967, but it was not until 1981 that new provisions came into force.

Section 19 (i) of the Forgery and Counterfeiting Act 1981 requires the prior consent of the Bank to be obtained in writing before its notes can be reproduced. (The Bank also owns the copyright in its notes.) In the current guidelines on its policy of allowing reproductions, the Bank explains that the basic philosophy is to ensure that they cannot be used to defraud the public; also, that they do not distort the Queen's portrait or display it in offensive surroundings. Advertisers etc are requested to get in touch at an early stage with the Bank's Issue Office to discuss their proposals and for their guidance the following criteria are set down:

1 No reproductions will be allowed for commercial sale (eg ashtrays).

2 Advertisements

    i   Reproduction of notes, whether in black and white or colour, must not be the same size as actual notes. If they are smaller, they can be up to half as long and half as wide. If they are to be larger, they must be at least twice as long and twice as wide. Reproductions of parts of notes must be in the same proportions.

    ii   As an additional protection against misuse, notes should be shown on the slant and not flat to camera. They should also form part of a larger pictorial design.

    iii Designs incorporating reproductions of notes for educational purposes (eg in educational books and training manuals), which must also be approved by the Bank, should satisfy the same size criteria as those for advertisements, but may be shown flat to camera provided that they have the word 'specimen' in solid black capitals across them.

    iv These criteria do not apply to reproductions of notes for educational purposes on film or television; such reproductions may be made without specific application being made to the Bank. If it is proposed to include reproductions in a film or television advertisement, the Bank must be consulted, as its permission is required.

CHAPTER 17

Houblon Revisited

Although it was not until 12 October 1988 that the Bank first revealed to the public its plans for Series E, comprising the four existing denominations of notes but in reduced sizes, preparatory work had been initiated by Roger Withington several months earlier when he drew up a list of possible subjects. He was looking for attractive illustrative material about persons who had helped to shape the nation's history in a substantial way and to this end he researched 72 names. Although no decision had at that time been made as to the possible areas of history which might be represented, it was obvious that each subject should stand alone in the 'family' of notes which would eventually circulate alongside one another; in other words, no subject should be drawn from the same science or art as another. The 72 names included Purcell, Elgar, Tennyson, Keats, Shelley, Gainsborough, Anne Boleyn, Grace Darling and Turner as well as the three eventually selected: George Stephenson, Faraday and Dickens.

Withington himself reduced the possibles to a new list of 15 probables but thereafter he would have little to do with the final selection, responsibility for which lay with the Governors and Directors. One name to be dismissed early on – in spite of the fact that Withington had taken a design to a late stage – was Charles Darwin, whose works might still be regarded as controversial: for that reason, said the Governor, 'He's out!'. By 1988 it had been decided to select Stephenson for the £5, Dickens for the £10, Faraday

The front and reverse designs of a projected 'family' of notes, £5 – £100 utilising side watermarks

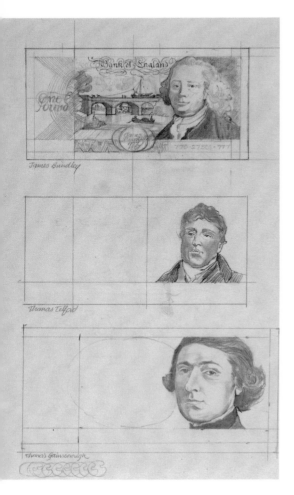

A selection of portraits for use with a possible £1 denomination.

for the £20 and Elgar for the £50. Within a year, however, Dickens had been replaced by Sir John Houblon, of insular rather than international fame. His choice was defended by Deputy Governor Sir George Blunden: 'We are looking at things that the UK had given to the world. To us as central bankers, central banking is a very important thing and most of the world's central banking... is modelled on the Bank of England and for most of the world the Bank of England is the mother central bank'. Nevertheless, he conceded that Houblon would be the odd one out in the series.

Supporters of Dickens as a subject moved fast and by the end of 1989 he had been reinstated on the £10 note, Houblon displacing Elgar on the £50, appropriately for a note destined at this stage for release in the Tercentenary year of the institution which had made note issuing functions its main contribution to European banking, as Clapham has already been quoted as observing.

The Bank continued to be persuaded of the need to maintain height and width differentials for each denomination for the particular assistance of the blind. The new sizes announced in 1988 (much more in advance than was customary because of the implications of the change for manufacturers of note handling, sorting and dispensing machinery), compared with the then existing sizes, were as follows:

Series E		Series D
£5	70 x 135 mm	78 x 145 mm
£10	75 x 142 mm	85 x 151 mm
£20	80 x 149 mm	90 x 160 mm
£50	85 x 156 mm	95 x 169 mm

Unwelcome publicity for the new £5 was received when a small news agency had brought to its attention in November 1989 that an error in printing the date of Stephenson's death had led to the destruction of notes with a face value totalling £30 mn. The story was released nationally, the *Daily Telegraph* estimating that it had cost the Printing Works about £180,000 in printing costs. The Bank confined its comments to confirmation that a mistake on a plate had been detected in the course of a test production run. Satisfactory products of 'test' runs are usually subsequently released into circulation.

Confirmation of the release of the first note in Series E came on 10 April 1990 with the announcement of the issue of the £5 denomination, featuring Stephenson, on 7 June 1990 (publicity was again advanced to assist machinery manufacturers). The customary details were released on 6 June. On the front of the note the lettering is based on a traditional form used frequently on earlier Bank note issues, for example, on the last 'white' £5. The Britannia figure is based on one which dates to about 1820 (roughly contemporary with the vignette on the reverse) and is surrounded by a border of oak and laurel leaves. The patterns which surround Britannia are an abstract representation of smoke, swirling gases and sparks. If examined through a magnifying glass, sparks suggestive of those which might emanate from a locomotive's chimney can be seen. It will also then be observed that the figure '£5' is a repetitive part of these patterns. To the left of Britannia is a pattern based on an hexagonal nut, blending into a pattern

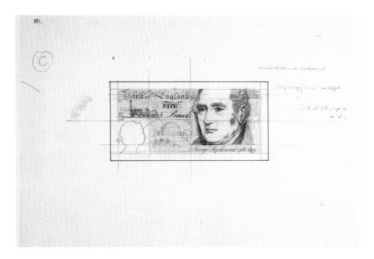

Tracings for the £5 note which featured George Stephenson.

The original version of the first denomination in Series E issued on 7 June 1990: Withington's £5 (135 x 70mm).

inspired by locomotive wheels. The design next to the Queen's portrait, at upper right, is composed of rows of engineer's dividers.

The portrait of George Stephenson on the reverse is identified by his name printed in a style similar to his signature. The *Rocket* locomotive is shown against a background of the *Locomotion* pulling a train across Skerne Bridge on the opening day in 1825 of the Stockton and Darlington Railway. The word 'LOCO-MOTION' is repeated in small lettering between the engine and the horse, on which a rider carries a flag to warn people of the approaching train. Under the arch of the bridge is a stationary engine-house. The circular pattern in the sky to the left of Stephenson's head represents a section through *Rocket's* boiler, showing the water and tubes inside. Part of the rim is like a toothed gear wheel. The yellow geometric pattern represents the sun, from which a ray of light hits the ground just behind *Rocket,* producing flames. This represents the focusing of the sun onto a piece of tarred rope in order to use the latter to light the fire in *Locomotion*. Informative posters and leaflets drew attention particularly to three entirely new features on a Bank of England note:

i) differently sized and coloured numbers

ii) a coloured denominational symbol (a turquoise circle) in order to aid the partially-sighted – a reminder of the angled Sum Block introduced for the £2 note in 1801 to help those who could see but not read

iii) the international copyright symbol (on both the front and the back of the note) explicitly to record the copyright which the Bank enjoys in all its note designs, completing the protection of that copyright in all countries party to the Universal Copyright Convention.

(A correspondent in *The Times* on 12 November 1991 missed the point of this symbol entirely: 'with the threat of civil action for breach of copyright' he wrote, 'even the most zealous of counterfeiters are sure to have second thoughts'.)

The number appears twice on the front: at top left, in multi-colour numerals of varying height, and at the right-hand edge, as single colour vertical numerals of constant height. Use was again made of the windowed thread in the paper.

The portrait of the Queen was printed from a new engraving approved by Buckingham Palace. Press reports on this aspect had appeared early in 1990. According to the *Independent on Sunday* of 4 February the Bank was 'bracing itself for trouble over the Queen's portrait ... the latest series should feature a likeness of the sovereign in the Nineties and not the fifties' (the headline ran 'Putting the wrinkle on the crinklies'). (A portrait of the Queen, without a tiara, appears in the watermark of each note in Series E.)

The Sun, on 4 April, claimed that one portrait was dropped as being too embarrassing to send to the Queen for approval. In fact, the engraving finally used is identical with the official photograph selected from a large number especially taken for this purpose and agreed by the Queen. Inevitably, the portrait aroused particular interest in the Press as a whole when the note finally appeared.

Today accused the Bank's artists of showing her as 'an ageing gran with a bulbous nose and double chin' supplementing this with a cartoon of the note by Gaskill on which an angry Queen is commenting 'we are not amused!!!'. *The Sun*, under the headline 'Does not one look old?!', appeared to report an interview with Withington: the Queen was 'shocked by her wrinkly looks ... It makes me look so old ... (sighing) I suppose I am old'. Correspondents in *The Times* thought the portrait 'only a slight resemblance' and asked why 'God could not save our Queen from the designer'. There was also a letter from Reynolds Stone's widow, harking back to the days of the 'large, white, well

The Series E £20 note, featuring Faraday, as originally issued on 5 June 1991 (149 x 80mm).

Below right
A modern 'curl-paper'? The third note, for £10, in the version issued on 29 April 1993 (142 x 75mm). Three bees hover above the hive.

Complaints from the public persuaded the Bank to improve the appearance of the £5 note in Series E by a strengthening of the denomination symbols in March 1993.

designed £5 note of long ago (which) ... it was a kind of agony' to her late husband to be asked to redesign in 1963 (in fact, Stone's £5 had replaced Gooden's 'Britannia' design, not the 'white' note).

Another *Times* correspondent drew attention to the fact that 'the new note emphasises 'five' (in letters), while banishing '£5' almost to vanishing point ... why does the Bank of England display such arrogant insularity?'. This virtual disappearance of '£5' had been raised at a meeting in the Bank during the preparatory stage: the experts' advice was that 'it's going to disappear under certain conditions when people try to replicate it'. A change had eventually to be made, although as late as November 1992 the Government Treasury spokesman in the House of Lords - Lord Henley - was justifying to a critical audience the hard-to-read figures on the grounds that this representation encouraged people to examine them closely and thus (helped to) combat forgery. The Bank, he concluded, had 'no plans' to highlight the numerals on the £5 and £20 note. Three months later, however, the Bank announced that a new version of the £5 note with stronger denomination symbols would be released on 1 March 1993. At the same time advance notice was given that similar changes would be made to the £20 and to the £10 Series E notes.

The reverse of the note also brought its critics, including the *Robert* Stephenson Trust who felt that *their* hero should have been depicted. One detailed criticism reported in *The Times* in September 1990 was from railway enthusiasts in the North of England who had closely examined the representation of the Skerne Bridge, ostensibly viewed from the south but containing two architectural features which are only visible from the north. The Bank's Press Office pleaded artistic licence.

Following the precedent set when announcing the issue of the new £5 note, the Bank gave longer notice than had been customary when the appearance of the second of the Series E issues, the £20 denomination, was brought to public attention. On 15 April 1991 it was revealed that issue date would be 5 June 1991 with Michael Faraday as the subject: 'Faraday upstages Bard' flashed *The Daily Telegraph*, 'Bard off the bill' punned the *Financial Times*. Nearer the date of the release, *The Times* cartoonist, Peter Brookes, drew a mock £20 reverse, depicting Faraday holding Shakespeare's head contemplatively, like Hamlet with the skull of Yorick.

On 4 June the usual information was provided to the public relative to the next day's initial release of the £20. The new features which had been detailed for the £5 were repeated, the special symbol to assist the partially-sighted being a purple square for the £20.

The figure of Britannia depicted on the front was designed by Daniel Maclise RA for use on the 'white' notes from 1855; it also appeared on the 1928 10s and £1 notes. The purple square was inspired by the hexagonal form of a benzene molecule, one of Faraday's most important discoveries in chemical compounds. Surrounding Britannia the patterns represent the lines of force demonstrated by magnets and iron filings. To the figure's right the arrows in opposing directions can be seen quite clearly and tiny figure 20's are incorporated. The outer part of the pattern above Britannia shows tiny

'Fe's' (the chemical symbol for iron), suggestive of iron filings falling on paper randomly before being brought into lines of force by the introduction of a magnet. To the left of Britannia the benzene molecule reappears, blending into a pattern running across the bottom edge of the note: this pattern represents bar magnets and lines of force produced by iron filings. The poles of the magnets, N and S, are marked. In the section below the Queen's portrait, the denomination 20 is repeated. In the top right-hand corner the pattern is based on a spherical condenser used by Faraday in comparing specific inductive capacities. Finally, the word 'TWENTY' contains patterns which recur throughout the design: the benzene molecule, arrows and 20's.

The portrait of Faraday on the reverse is supported by lettering in the style of his signature (cf the treatment of the name on the £5). To the left is a view of him lecturing at a Royal Institute Christmas Lecture. On the bench are various items which he might have used; there is a piece of paper with lines of force patterns produced by iron filings, held down by a spherical condenser. A small panel, slightly above and to the left of his raised arm lists new words which he introduced to the English language (eg 'ion'). The micro-lettering above this list of words reads vertically and horizontally ('TWENTY'). The area behind 'ENGLAND' and 'TWENTY POUNDS' includes white droplets, symbolising Faraday's work on the liquefaction of gases. Outward from that area, the pattern (like a sun) derives from a decorative plaster border of the central dome of the Royal Institute and from that, to the left, there begins a pattern based on the now familiar benzene molecule hexagon. In the foreground of the lecture scene is a magneto-electric spark apparatus. Finally it should be mentioned that the artist-designer seems to have used several familiar faces in his design team in order to humanise his audience for Faraday!

There was little press or public reaction; the £5 had drawn the fire on 'shrinking pounds'. *The Independent*, however, managed to uncover the history of Faraday's earlier association with the Bank when he was called in to advise on the safety of a method of heating the copper plates (see pages 80/1), including the fact that his account of £21 had taken the Bank three years to settle. 'It is a fair bet that the Bank is acting through a guilty conscience' in replacing Shakespeare by Faraday.

Both the £5 and the £20 were first issued with the signature of G M Gill as Chief Cashier. His retirement was announced by the Bank in July 1991. He was replaced with effect from 25 November 1991 by G E A Kentfield as Chief Cashier, the 28th to hold that office. The Press were given the opportunity to photograph him on 22 November and to receive an official photograph of his signature on a note, for reproduction in their editions, the following week.

Series D £5 notes ceased to be legal tender as from 29 November 1991, notice to that effect having been published the previous 29 August, when an estimated 58 million remained in circulation.

The choice of Charles Dickens as the subject of the third note in Series E - the £10 value - is perhaps not without the merit that he frequently referred to the Bank of England in a favourable way in his writings. He did not agree with capital punishment for forgery offences, observing in a *Tale of Two Cities* that it did not 'the least good in the way of prevention - it might almost have been worth remarking that the fact was exactly the reverse - but, it cleared off (as to this world) the trouble of each particular case'. In *Martin Chuzzlewit* he refers to the 'perfect respectability' of the Bank, one of whose notes he once described as 'a silver curl-paper (in) the shining locks of the ever-beautiful old lady of Threadneedle-Street' (*Doctor Marigold*). As a man of the world, Dickens was well aware of the facility of preventing a stolen banknote from being paid: he has Fagin in *Oliver Twist* commenting that £20 is not a lot of money 'when its's in a note you can't get rid of... Number and date taken, I suppose? Payment stopped at the Bank?'.

Advance notice was given in January 1993 of the release on 29 April of the new £10 Series E note, full details of which were given to the media the day before. Once again, attention was directed to the three new features introduced in the Series: differently sized and coloured serial numbers, the international copyright symbol and the special symbol designed to assist the partially-sighted - an orange diamond on this occasion.

In keeping with the approach used for the two previous notes in the Series, the figure of Britannia on the front is based on earlier representations used by the Bank: a late 19th century image combined with a border taken from an earlier figure. Above and to the right of Britannia there is a representation of flowers which form part of a sculptured relief on a fireplace surround in Dickens House in Doughty Street in London. The word 'TEN' which is superimposed on this feature incorporates quill pen images. Surrounding it are rows of microlettering wherein can be read the titles of some of Dickens' writings. To the left of Britannia a relief ruling is based on a motif from a goblet presented to the author by the *Morning Chronicle* staff in 1837. To the right of the Queen's portrait is a repeat pattern of pen nibs (size 10 to match the denomination!). In the top left corner, the pattern below the denominational figure is inspired by decorative marquetry work on a tea caddy which belonged to Dickens. Finally, there is a pattern within the orange diamond which is based on part of the decoration on the base of a clock in the Dickens House Museum.

On the reverse of the note, there appears a portarit of Dickens and a view illustrating the cricket match between Dingley Dell and All Muggleton, an episode in *The Pickwick Papers*. This view is based on the original illustration by R W Buss for the first edition of the novel in 1836. The scene is reversed for artistic reasons. The cricketing theme is continued in the decorative border, based on a cricket ball, surrounding the watermark. Sweeping up towards 'ENGLAND' and the star-like pattern are more pen nibs and copies of *David Copperfield*. The star is based on the decoration on a glass lampshade in the Dickens House Museum.

Many regretted the disappearance of Florence Nightingale from the notes in circulation, reflecting that Series E would be all male but forgetting that a female - Britannia - had appeared on every printed Bank of England note issued since 1694 and still does!

On 18 January 1993 the Bank gave formal notice of the withdrawal of legal tender status after 19 March from the Series D £20 note, which featured Shakespeare and which had first been issued in July 1970; some 43 million remained in circulation.

'In response to public comment on the clarity of the existing denomination symbols', the Bank announced on 22 September 1993 that a new version of the £20 E would be issued from 27 September. On the front, the symbol '£20' in the upper-left corner would be printed in dark purple and a similar but black symbol would replace the crown in the top-right corner. On the reverse, the upper-left symbol would be enlarged and an additional one would appear in the top-right corner.

A few weeks later there was a similar announcement relating to the £10 E. The crown in the top-right corner of the front would also be replaced, by a '£10' symbol, whilst an additional symbol would appear in the same corner on the reverse. The new version was issued from 22 November 1993.

Additional denomination symbols were inserted in a revised £20 note in Series E, released late in September 1993.

Above right
It was also necessary to insert extra denomination symbols in the £10 note in Series E to meet public criticism; the new version first appeared in November 1993.

The Bank of England is justifiably proud of its long history but eschewed the temptation to issue for one year any specifically commemorative note or to overprint appropriately an exisiting denomination; its note issue policy continues to be directed at supplying the general public with acceptable means of payment: it does not aim to produce collector's items. In terms of cost, a note available for one year only is hardly an economic project. (The Royal Mint, on the other hand, is continuing the tradition of striking commemorative coins by releasing during 1994 a £2 piece for the Tercentenary of the Bank.)

Nevertheless, as has already been mentioned, it was felt to be appropriate to use a portrait of the first Governor, Sir John Houblon, on the final note to be issued in Series E - the £50, little known as he is outside banking circles. His branch of the Houblon family were originally Huguenot dyestuff and fabric merchants who were forced by religious pressure to flee from Lille in France in 1567. Their later shipping interests brought them into contact with the diarist, Samuel Pepys, whom they bailed out when

The end of the 300-year story: the first Governor, Sir John Houblon, featured on Withington's final contribution to the Bank's note issues – the £50 in Series E, released on 20th April 1994 (156 x 85mm).

he was held in the Tower of London on suspicion of being a Papist. Our John Houblon was knighted in 1689 (the year he became Sheriff of London) and was Lord Mayor of London 1695-1696. He leased a house in Threadneedle Street on ground which now forms part of the Bank's site.

The £50 note continues the 'family likeness' of the Series, using on the front the same portrait of the Queen which appears on the three preceding values and echoing their layout, content and watermark, although it incorporates certain new features. The most important of these is the inclusion of a metallic silver foil feature which offers increased security against successful reproduction by colour-copying machines: the design is an oval surrounding the Royal cypher out of which a single Tudor rose projects.

The figure of Britannia is based on the official seal of 1694. The symbol to assist the partially-sighted is a red triangle resting on its base, produced by overprinting a dark red triangle by a deeper shade of red in a form of the figure '50'. Use has again been made of a windowed thread: this runs through the triangle, where it appears in a red colour as opposed to silver elsewhere.

The Queen's portrait is printed in neutral grey. The rest of the front of the note gives an overall image of red/orange. In an interview printed in the Printing Works' *Britannia News,* Roger Withington said that his 'original design ... was in green' which he found 'more aesthetically pleasing and which offers better security against colour copiers. However, having consulted opinion among certain groups the Banking Department decided that the note would be more easily distinguishable from the others in the Series if printed in red'.

To the left of Britannia is a pattern based on a motif incorporated into the dome of Sir Robert Taylor's Rotunda in the Bank of 1765. Above Britannia are two 2-guinea pieces, reproduced in two sizes, of 1694; between them is a pattern composed of '50' in a square. A hop plant is drawn to the left of the larger coin, a reference to the Houblons' canting arms ('houblon' is French for 'hop'). A common motif from early 19th century Bank of England buildings – similar to the Greek fret ornament – is utilised

The new security feature, metallic silver foil, incorporated in the £50 in Series E.

behind the £50 denominational figure in the top lefthand corner. The word 'FIFTY' under the Bank's title, contains an image similar to a Maltese Cross, the Huguenot emblem. Along the bottom edge is a pattern taken from the oldest item of furniture surviving in the Bank, the Great Iron Chest.

On the reverse of the note a portrait of Sir John Houblon, based by Withington on a copy of a Johann Closterman portrait, is shown in red next to a composite image in effectively neutral colours showing Sir John Houblon's house in Threadneedle Street and a Bank Gate Porter, William Banning, who held the position from 1763 to 1777. The bottom edge of the note contains a pattern based on a decoration frequently used by another Bank architect – Sir John Soane – when he rebuilt the Bank as it spread to occupy the whole of the present site. Other patterns incorporated in the design have no particular source or reason.

The £50 denomination forms about 10% of the total note circulation but its share is slowly increasing. The Series E version was first issued to the public on 20th April 1994, some three months after manufacturers of note recognition machinery had been loaned examples for trialling purposes.

On 15 February 1994 the Bank had announced that the Series D £10, featuring Florence Nightingale, would cease to be legal tender after 20 May 1994; some 80 million were outstanding.

This history has been able to touch only briefly on the many aspects of the Bank's note issues since 27 July 1694. Debate on a European currency which would replace national currencies continues from time to time, casting doubt on whether the Bank can look forward to another 10 years of note issue, let alone a fourth century. Be that as it may, thoughts have already turned to the next Series which will doubtless provide fertile ground for the future student or historian of the Bank of England's 'promises to pay'.

Selected Bibliography

Acres W M	The Bank of England from Within	1931
Burke Bryan	Nazi Counterfeiting of British Currency during World War II	1987
Clapham Sir John	The Bank of England: a history	1944
Coppieters Edmund	English Bank Note Circulation 1694-1954	1955
Craig Sir John	The Mint	1953
Cubbage M J S	The Further History of the Bank of England Printing Works (unpublished)	1989
de Fraine H G	Servant of this House	1960
Duggleby Vincent	English Paper Money (4th Edition)	1990
Goodacre Clive	The Search for the Inimitable Note	1982
Giuseppi J A	The Bank of England	1966
Hennessy Elizabeth	A Domestic History of the Bank of England	1992
Hewitt V H & Keyworth J M	As Good as Gold	1987
Kranister Willebald	The Moneymakers international	1989
Mackenzie A D	The Bank of England Note	1953
	The Later Years of St Luke's Printing Works	1961
Pirie Anthony	Operation Bernhard	1961
Sayers R S	The Bank of England 1891-1944	1976

APPENDIX A **Branch Issues**

Pre 1838 Since the Court of Directors resolved that each Branch should offer the same range of denominations, it must be presumed that they did, initially. Prior to 1838 this range was: £5, £10, £20, £30, £40, £50, £100 and £500 (the denominations of £200, £300 and – initially – £1,000 were reserved for London issues).

Unequivocal evidence is not available, however, as regards the denominations issued by Exeter during its short life (1827–1834). It is known that on 2 January 1835 that were outstanding issues from this Branch of the £5, £10, £20, £50 and £100. The Bank Museum's only example of an Exeter note is a paid £20 denomination. As the £30, £40 and £500 denominations were issued by other West Country branches it is improbable – for reasons of local prestige alone – that they were not also issued at Exeter.

1838–1938 The full range, as detailed above, was printed for each remaining country Branch at some time during the period, except for the following denominations:

£20 Liverpool Branch note 1934, £5 Gloucester Branch note (1838) and £10 Leeds Branch note (1936), the latter displaying a paper notch

Leicester (opened 1844)	£30, £40 and £500
Plymouth	£40 and £500
Portsmouth and Swansea	£500

Liverpool Branch half notes for £30 and £40 (1842), Newcastle Branch £100 note (1936) and Bristol Branch £50 note (1918)

For Hull, 4000 £1,000 notes were printed between 1882 and 1889 and issued to the public. This denomination, dated 1886, was also prepared for Liverpool during the period, but never delivered. The £20 was withdrawn surprisingly early from Bristol (1889), Plymouth (1861) and Portsmouth (1885).

As already stated in the main text of this book, the date printed on a note is not normally its date of manufacture or issue. Nevertheless, until the advent of notes bearing the printed signature of the Chief Cashier, it has become customary for collectors to attribute to each of them notes bearing dates during which they held office. All Branch issues were signed in London prior to the introduction of printed signatures, the use of which did not vary as between London and Branch issues.

1838-1864 – 'Marshall' notes

Notes bearing dates during Marshall's tenure of office were issued as detailed in the first paragraph of the preceding section. The £40 was generally withdrawn in 1851, the £30 in 1852.

The following final printings were made:

	£5	£10	£20	£30	£40	£50	£100	£500
Birmingham				1843	1843			
Bristol				1840	1840			
Gloucester (closed 1849)	1848	1848	1846	1838	1838	1848	1848	1840
Hull				1843	1842			
Leeds				1843	1842			
Liverpool				1843	1843			
Manchester				1844	1844			
Newcastle				1843	1843			1842
Norwich (closed 1852)	1851	1851	1843	1842	1842	1851	1851	1841
Plymouth			1861	1840				
Portsmouth				1840	1840			
Swansea (closed 1859)	1858	1858	1857	1835	1838	1858	1857	

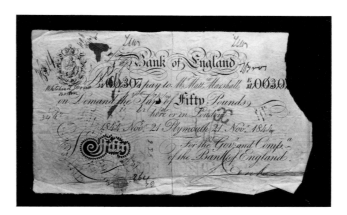

£10 Portsmouth Branch note of 17 October 1846, payable to Matthew Marshall (208 x 128mm)

1864-1866 – 'Miller' notes

The only full range (now £5, £10, £20, £50, £100 and £500) bearing dates within Miller's short term in office was printed for Manchester. Gaps in the other Branches' series were:

Birmingham, Hull, Leeds, Newcastle and Portsmouth	No £500
Bristol	No £20
Leicester	No £20, £50 or £500
Liverpool	No £50 or £100

whilst the only denomination printed for Plymouth was the £5.

Repaired £50 Plymouth Branch issue of 21 November 1844 (214 x 128mm)

1866-1873 – 'Forbes' notes	The range £5-£100 was issued by each Branch except Plymouth (no £20); and the £500 was additionally supplied to Bristol, Liverpool and Manchester.

Leicester was closed in 1872 and last printings for the Branch (£5-£100) were made in 1871.

1873-1893 – 'May' notes

The only Branch £1,000 notes were issued in May's time, by Hull, in addition to the normal range of £5-£500 which was also on offer at Birmingham, Bristol, Liverpool and Manchester. Leeds, Newcastle and Portsmouth issued £5-£100 and Plymouth the same but without the £20.

The last £20 was printed for Portsmouth in 1885 and for Bristol in 1889 although the latter had become an important note-issuing Branch by then. The final printing of the limited Hull £1,000 also took place in 1889.

1893-1902 – 'Bowen' notes

Birmingham, Hull, Leeds, Liverpool and Manchester	£5-£500
Bristol	£5-£500 except £20
Newcastle	£5-£100
Plymouth and Portsmouth	£5-£100 except £20

1902-1918 – 'Nairne' notes

As for Bowen above.

The final printings for the Portsmouth Branch (closed 1914) were made in 1912.

1918-1925 – 'Harvey' notes

Birmingham, Hull and Leeds, Liverpool and Manchester	£5-£500
Bristol	£5-£500 except £20
Newcastle	£5-£100
Plymouth	£5-£100 except £20

A final printing of Hull £20 notes was made in 1919 and of the Bristol £500 in 1920. (Stocks of these two denominations held in London and at the Branches were destroyed in 1929.)

1925-1929 – 'Mahon' notes

Birmingham, Leeds, Liverpool and Manchester	£5-£500
Hull	£5-£500 except £20
Newcastle	£5-£100
Bristol and Plymouth	£5-£100 except £20

The Hull £500 was last printed in 1926. (The London stock was destroyed in 1932 but the stock of 745 then held at the Branch remained available for issue.)

1929-1934 – 'Catterns' notes

Bristol, Liverpool and Manchester	£5-£500
Leeds	£5-£500 except £20
Newcastle	£5-£100
Bristol, Hull and Plymouth	£5-£100 except £20

1934–1938 'Peppiatt' notes

The final remaining denominations were printed as follows:

	£5	£10	£20	£50	£100	£500
Birmingham	1938	1938	1935	1937	1937	1937
Bristol	1937	1938		1937	1936	
Hull	1937	1937		1936	1936	
Leeds	1938	1937	1937	1936	1938	1936
Liverpool	1938	1938	1937	1938	1938	1937
Manchester	1938	1938	1937	1938	1938	1937
Newcastle	1937	1938	1937	1936	1937	
Plymouth	1937	1938		1936	1936	

The last Branch £5 note was issued at Liverpool, dated 25 July 1938 and prefixed $\frac{T}{310}$. However, Plymouth could boast the last date of all: the £10 denomination, dated 28 November 1938 and prefixed $\frac{V}{179}$.

APPENDIX B   # Private Marks

From at least the early years of the 19th Century the Bank's plate-printed black and white notes had secret, or private, marks incorporated in their designs as a protection against forgery. As will be seen, their appearance was such that anyone studying a note carefully would readily assume that what they were observing was simply a flaw in the printing process; there would be a natural tendency to correct the appearance when executing the forgery. Each denomination featured individual characteristics but three private marks were common to all and are to be found in the medallion of Britannia:

a) on the back of the Britannia's right hand, which holds the sprig, are one group of three dots and one group of two dots, both noticeably clear of the outline of the hand;

b) the inner, shading line running down the spear does not touch the horizontal at the base;

c) in the foliage surrounding the figure, at 2.30 o'clock, a hairline break runs across the lines of shading.

Another feature commonly missed by forgers was the tiny circle in Britannia's hair like a small pearl ear-ring in the figure's right ear.

The easiest individual private mark to locate is found in each Sum Block. In the issues current in the 1840's this comprised a whisker of black intruding into the second or third white letter of the denomination, such as might have simply been caused by an intrusive hair or thread on the plate. By the last printings this had become a small white nick into the black background at approximately the same place as the black 'whisker' had appeared some century earlier. Each plate was individual in other ways, making it impossible for the forger to avoid nearly complete duplication of his work if he wanted to produce more than one denomination. In particular, the first letters in 'Sum' and 'Pounds' were all designedly different (see illustration).

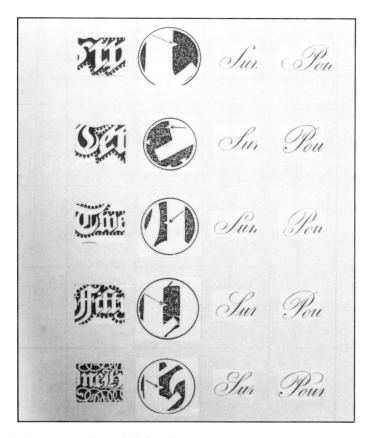

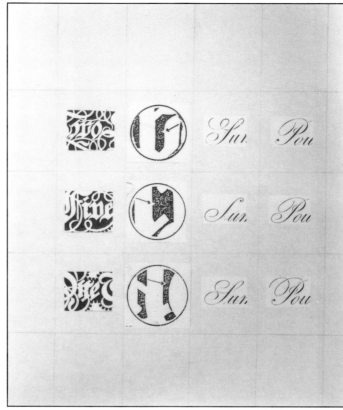

The secret marks included in the Sum Blocks of the £5, £10, £20, £50, £100, £200, £500 and £1,000 notes and comparisons of the decorative treatment applied to two capital letters in the body of each text

Other features to be noted in the medallion of a genuine Bank production of the last period are:

   a) the opening of the beehive at its base, its shading (by dots encircling it in parallel lines) and the absence of any definite outline;

   b) the two intensities of shading of the sea;

   c) the irregularity of the curve of the shield;

   d) the right thumb is slightly shaped and is long and not squat;

   e) the ermine in the crown is represented by uneven black marks;

   f) in the floral surround, at 5 o'clock, the right-hand edge of the projecting spur is extended up to the third line of shading.

Additionally, the principal points to study in other areas are:

   g) the registration of the upper right-hand number, which never entirely covers the 'd' in 'Demand';

   h) a triangular dot is placed after 'Compa' on the £5, £10 and £50 denomination whilst all other values additionally show a dot under the 'a';

i) in the title line, the chevrons on 'Bank of England' are joined by a line but there is a break before the tail line;

j) on the £5 denomination accurate registration of the plate means that the 'B' of 'BANK' always covers the last figure of the four in the watermark which relate to the week of manufacture of the paper;

k) normally, on the £5 denomination, the dots in the word 'Five' in the denomination line are not joined: however, those examples bearing dates in 1919, 1935 and 1936 are actually joined.

A further feature to be aware of is that between about 1810 and 1854 notes printed on the left-hand side of each sheet (i.e those with the deckle edge to the left) were distinguished by the inclusion, except for the £100 and £1,000 denominations, of a row of dots (varying in number) between the £ sign and the Sum Block. For the £100 notes the feature was a short horizontal line but no marking appeared on the £1,000. Notes with the deckle edge on the right side were not marked in any way. This distinction ceased with the introduction of the Maclise design in 1855: dots, or a line, appeared on *every* note save, as before, those at £1,000.

When examining suspected German forgeries of the Second World War, unless it is obvious that a note is not genuine (eg one where the date and the Chief Cashier's signature are not compatible) the medallion should be studied first, with particular attention to the private marks defined earlier and the 5 o'clock floral spur. It will very often be discovered that the 'ear-ring' is missing whilst the right thumb lacks the indentation of its joint; often, too, the beehive has been given a definite outline. The ermine in the crown shows up as dots whilst the dots on the back of the right hand often merge into the edge. Only one tone may be found in the sea. A comparison of the shading on Britannia's knee as depicted on a genuine note is often rewarding, too. Generally speaking, these guidelines should speedily establish the genuineness or otherwise of the document in question. Care must be exercised, however, since the Germans had noted the private marking in the Sum Blocks and incorporated these in the Sachsenhausen productions. An error which is occasionally met with was the use of a plain-tailed 'f' in 'of' in the signatory clause instead of the regular fish-tailed version. Another useful confirmatory feature would be a comparative bluntness in the black inset of the last letter in the £5 Sum Block.

Forgeries of Branch issues of £10 denomination are known to have been made with the V prefix as follows:

105	Birmingham	24 Dec 1926		C P Mahon
168	Bristol	10 Jun 1937		K O Peppiatt
138	Leeds	10 Jan 1933		B G Catterns
150	Leeds	27 Oct 1934	)	
165	Liverpool	28 Sep 1936	)	
170	Liverpool	10 Feb 1937	)	K O Peppiatt
153	Manchester	10 Jan 1935	)	
163	Manchester	28 Feb 1936	)	

With the exception of $\frac{138}{V}$, each cypher conformed to the usage for genuine issues both as regards Branch and date; $\frac{138}{V}$ had been allocated to Birmingham under date of 27 June 1932, the correct cypher for the Leeds issue on 10 January 1933 being $\frac{143}{V}$.

Allowing for the fact that only a comparatively small sample was examined, $\frac{150}{V}$ and $\frac{153}{V}$ appear to be the scarcest, only one of the former and four of the latter being discovered. The Manchester forgeries have a very narrow range of serial numbers which may indicate a part run only was achieved or distributed (or looted!).

It should be of no consolation in the United Kingdom to identify satisfactorily a German forgery since possession of a note, knowing it to be a forgery, is an offence against the Forgery and Counterfeiting Act 1981: it should therefore be surrendered to the Bank of England forthwith.

APPENDIX C   # The Numbering of Bank of England Black and White Notes 1838 – 1956

Details of the prefixes allocated to all of the Bank of England's black and white notes bearing dates from 1 January 1838 to the last printing of the £5 denomination issued to the public (20 September 1956) are contained in a series of 'cypher books' in the Bank's Archive. There are actually two sets, both of which are incomplete, but fortunately complementary. The principal record runs to 19 volumes, held under references C96/240-258 inclusive but it terminates with an entry for 1 February 1956 whereas printings are known to have continued for some months thereafter. These are listed in an incomplete set of the volumes previously used by the Printing Works (Archive reference PW 23/3-21). An extra record (C96/259) duplicates in calendar form information for 1838 – 1870 inclusive. In some entries the total number of notes printed with the specific prefix or cypher is given.

For the first few years London and Branch issues are intermixed although the principle was generally adhered to that the combination of denomination, allocated date, cypher and place of issue should be unique - eg a £30 note issued by Gloucester Branch with the date of 20 January 1838 will only be found with the prefix $\frac{C}{E}$. Furthermore each Branch was initially allocated one month of the year, eg all Gloucester notes with an 1838 date also bore the month of January; this dedication remained until the Branch was closed in 1849. As some Branches grew in importance it became necessary to allocate additional months, sometimes shared with smaller Branches.

By 1848 London issues were generally being differentiated from Branch issues: cyphers $\frac{A}{A}$ to $\frac{A}{Z}$ for example, were all devoted to London with the series $\frac{B}{A}$ to $\frac{B}{Z}$ being reserved for Branches, and so on. There were a number of exceptions to the principle of uniqueness. Manchester was issued with both £5 and £10 notes dated 16 February 1838. One unusual allocation concerned £5 notes printed for the Newcastle Branch and all bearing the date 28 August 1856: those numbered 1 - 80000 were prefixed $\frac{O}{W}$ whilst those numbered 80001 – 100000 were allocated $\frac{W}{O}$, which should have been allotted to a London issue. Examples of each are held in the Bank's Museum collection. No reason is offered by the bare records: possibly a mistake was made or else $\frac{W}{O}$ was due to be allocated coincidently with a requirement for more Newcastle £5 notes and it appealed to the responsible person in the Printing Department to marry the two. The date of 16 February 1855 was given to Birmingham and Liverpool £5 notes, but with different cyphers. The four printings of the rare Hull £1,000 denomination were serially numbered (1 - 1000, 1001 - 2000 etc) but each printing had a different prefix and date.

In 1853, seven months of the year were allocated haphazardly among the Branches. With the introduction of the Maclise medallion on notes dated after 1854, the Branches shared various January dates in 1855 and then shared the remaining months. From 1 January 1869 a number was introduced into the cypher or prefix; up to that point different typefaces had been utilised but it was felt essential - to avoid possible mistakes - that the style of the cypher should be changed. By introducing a number, a prefix letter would serve for more than the 26 cyphers permitted by a purely alphabetical system. At first the numbers only went up to 99.

Until 1859 Branch notes carried dates from the second half of the month only. So far as the £5 denomination was concerned, the dates were grouped – broadly speaking – in thirds of a month for London, the provincial issues using some of the remaining dates. Higher sums alternated similarly. By 1903 so many London notes were required that the month was now divided into two and the halves alternated year by year. For example, in even years London £5 notes used the first half of the month and in odd years dates in the second half. This pattern continued up to and including 1942, the last year in which notes of £10 and over were printed of this type.

1888 had seen the beginning of the practice of maintaining the same groups of prefixes year in, year out for London and the Branches respectively: Branches now had sole use of T – Z inclusive. The next major change was to occur in 1900 when the Branches' individual months were altered. Manchester had enjoyed January as its main month since the closure of Gloucester in 1849 but in 1900 its principal dedicated month was February, in 1901 March etc. In 1904 a third number was added near the signature, primarily to assist in the transmission of paid notes from the Branches to Head Office.

In 1917 and 1918 most cyphers were shared between Branches and many matching dates existed. Full details (including serial numbers) of all these issues are recorded in the cypher books. Cyphers using numbers larger than 99 first appear in 1921; the highest used was 499 in 1932 for a Manchester £5 issue.

To assist those responsible for the allocation of cyphers so-called 'Dating Scales' were printed and distributed to the offices closely concerned with the note issue. The earliest seen is for the Branches in 1855. The series is complete from 1869, bound into the cypher books.

Dating Scale applicable to notes dated 1895

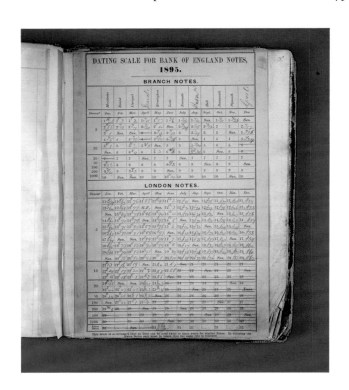

General Index

Denomination Index

see also Series A-E in General Index

General

notes under £20 not to be issued 14,23
notes under £50 not to be issued 16
notes under £1 statute barred 29
notes under £5 statute barred 29
notes over £5 discontinued 142

odd sums 12,23,30-1,69,89

1d (one penny) 89
6d 23
1s 139
2s 139
2s6d 139-40
5s 139-40
10s/50np 107,182,186
£1 35,39,41-2,69,72,107,197,202-3
£2 35,39,41-2,69,107,158,172-3,182
£2:10s 181-3
£3 158
£5 11,13,16,31,71,119-20,142-3,177
£10 11,13,16,29,71,119-20,172-3
£15 13,29
£20 11,13,16,21,29,71,181,186,188,210
£25 29,181-2
£30 13,21,29,71,97
£40 13,21,29,71,97
£50 11,13,21,29,71,182,186,196,201,210
£60,£70,£80 29,39
£90 16,29,39
£100 11,13,21,29,72,106,210
£200 29,72,76,106,118,210
£300 29,72,76,106
£400 29,39
£500 29,72,106,210
£700 29
£1,000 London 12,29,72,76,102,106,210
£1,000 Hull Branch 77,231

Illustrations